Table of Contents

Introduction

Rapid advances in data collection and storage technology have enabled organizations to accumulate vast amounts of data. However, extracting useful information has proven extremely challenging. Often, traditional data analysis tools and techniques cannot be used because of the massive size of a data set. Sometimes, the non-traditional nature of the data means that traditional approaches cannot be applied even if the data set is relatively small. In other situations, the questions that need to be answered cannot be addressed using existing data analysis techniques, and thus, new methods need to be developed.

Data mining is a technology that blends traditional data analysis methods with sophisticated algorithms for processing large volumes of data. It has also opened up exciting opportunities for exploring and analyzing new types of data and for analyzing old types of data in new ways. In this introductory chapter, we present an overview of data mining and outline the key topics to be covered in this book. We start with a description of some well-known applications that require new techniques for data analysis.

Business Point-of-sale data collection (bar code scanners, radio frequency identification (RFID), and smart card technology) have allowed retailers to collect up-to-the-minute data about customer purchases at the checkout counters of their stores. Retailers can utilize this information, along with other business-critical data such as Web logs from e-commerce Web sites and customer service records from call centers, to help them better understand the needs of their customers and make more informed business decisions.

Data mining techniques can be used to support a wide range of business intelligence applications such as customer profiling, targeted marketing, workflow management, store layout, and fraud detection. It can also help retailers answer important business questions such as "Who are the most profitable customers?" "What products can be cross-sold or up-sold?" and "What is the revenue outlook of the company for next year?" Some of these questions motivated the creation of association analysis (Chapters 6 and 7), a new data analysis technique.

Medicine, Science, and Engineering Researchers in medicine, science, and engineering are rapidly accumulating data that is key to important new discoveries. For example, as an important step toward improving our understanding of the Earth's climate system, NASA has deployed a series of Earth-orbiting satellites that continuously generate global observations of the land surface, oceans, and atmosphere. However, because of the size and spatio-temporal nature of the data, traditional methods are often not suitable for analyzing these data sets. Techniques developed in data mining can aid Earth scientists in answering questions such as "What is the relationship between the frequency and intensity of ecosystem disturbances such as droughts and hurricanes to global warming?" "How is land surface precipitation and temperature affected by ocean surface temperature?" and "How well can we predict the beginning and end of the growing season for a region?"

As another example, researchers in molecular biology hope to use the large amounts of genomic data currently being gathered to better understand the structure and function of genes. In the past, traditional methods in molecular biology allowed scientists to study only a few genes at a time in a given experiment. Recent breakthroughs in microarray technology have enabled scientists to compare the behavior of thousands of genes under various situations. Such comparisons can help determine the function of each gene and perhaps isolate the genes responsible for certain diseases. However, the noisy and high-dimensional nature of data requires new types of data analysis. In addition to analyzing gene array data, data mining can also be used to address other important biological challenges such as protein structure prediction, multiple sequence alignment, the modeling of biochemical pathways, and phylogenetics.

1.1 What Is Data Mining?

Data mining is the process of automatically discovering useful information in large data repositories. Data mining techniques are deployed to scour large databases in order to find novel and useful patterns that might otherwise remain unknown. They also provide capabilities to predict the outcome of a future observation, such as predicting whether a newly arrived customer will spend more than $100 at a department store.

Not all information discovery tasks are considered to be data mining. For example, looking up individual records using a database management system or finding particular Web pages via a query to an Internet search engine are tasks related to the area of **information retrieval**. Although such tasks are important and may involve the use of the sophisticated algorithms and data structures, they rely on traditional computer science techniques and obvious features of the data to create index structures for efficiently organizing and retrieving information. Nonetheless, data mining techniques have been used to enhance information retrieval systems.

Data Mining and Knowledge Discovery

Data mining is an integral part of **knowledge discovery in databases (KDD)**, which is the overall process of converting raw data into useful information, as shown in Figure 1.1. This process consists of a series of transformation steps, from data preprocessing to postprocessing of data mining results.

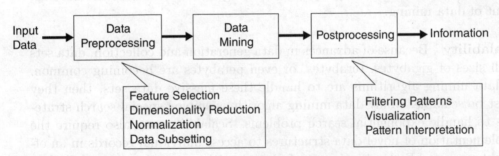

Figure 1.1. The process of knowledge discovery in databases (KDD).

The input data can be stored in a variety of formats (flat files, spreadsheets, or relational tables) and may reside in a centralized data repository or be distributed across multiple sites. The purpose of **preprocessing** is to transform the raw input data into an appropriate format for subsequent analysis. The steps involved in data preprocessing include fusing data from multiple sources, cleaning data to remove noise and duplicate observations, and selecting records and features that are relevant to the data mining task at hand. Because of the many ways data can be collected and stored, data preprocessing is perhaps the most laborious and time-consuming step in the overall knowledge discovery process.

"Closing the loop" is the phrase often used to refer to the process of integrating data mining results into decision support systems. For example, in business applications, the insights offered by data mining results can be integrated with campaign management tools so that effective marketing promotions can be conducted and tested. Such integration requires a **postprocessing** step that ensures that only valid and useful results are incorporated into the decision support system. An example of postprocessing is visualization (see Chapter 3), which allows analysts to explore the data and the data mining results from a variety of viewpoints. Statistical measures or hypothesis testing methods can also be applied during postprocessing to eliminate spurious data mining results.

1.2 Motivating Challenges

As mentioned earlier, traditional data analysis techniques have often encountered practical difficulties in meeting the challenges posed by new data sets. The following are some of the specific challenges that motivated the development of data mining.

Scalability Because of advances in data generation and collection, data sets with sizes of gigabytes, terabytes, or even petabytes are becoming common. If data mining algorithms are to handle these massive data sets, then they must be scalable. Many data mining algorithms employ special search strategies to handle exponential search problems. Scalability may also require the implementation of novel data structures to access individual records in an efficient manner. For instance, out-of-core algorithms may be necessary when processing data sets that cannot fit into main memory. Scalability can also be improved by using sampling or developing parallel and distributed algorithms.

High Dimensionality It is now common to encounter data sets with hundreds or thousands of attributes instead of the handful common a few decades ago. In bioinformatics, progress in microarray technology has produced gene expression data involving thousands of features. Data sets with temporal or spatial components also tend to have high dimensionality. For example, consider a data set that contains measurements of temperature at various locations. If the temperature measurements are taken repeatedly for an extended period, the number of dimensions (features) increases in proportion to the number of measurements taken. Traditional data analysis techniques that were developed for low-dimensional data often do not work well for such high-dimensional data. Also, for some data analysis algorithms, the computational complexity increases rapidly as the dimensionality (the number of features) increases.

Heterogeneous and Complex Data Traditional data analysis methods often deal with data sets containing attributes of the same type, either continuous or categorical. As the role of data mining in business, science, medicine, and other fields has grown, so has the need for techniques that can handle heterogeneous attributes. Recent years have also seen the emergence of more complex data objects. Examples of such non-traditional types of data include collections of Web pages containing semi-structured text and hyperlinks; DNA data with sequential and three-dimensional structure; and climate data that consists of time series measurements (temperature, pressure, etc.) at various locations on the Earth's surface. Techniques developed for mining such complex objects should take into consideration relationships in the data, such as temporal and spatial autocorrelation, graph connectivity, and parent-child relationships between the elements in semi-structured text and XML documents.

Data Ownership and Distribution Sometimes, the data needed for an analysis is not stored in one location or owned by one organization. Instead, the data is geographically distributed among resources belonging to multiple entities. This requires the development of distributed data mining techniques. Among the key challenges faced by distributed data mining algorithms include (1) how to reduce the amount of communication needed to perform the distributed computation, (2) how to effectively consolidate the data mining results obtained from multiple sources, and (3) how to address data security issues.

Non-traditional Analysis The traditional statistical approach is based on a hypothesize-and-test paradigm. In other words, a hypothesis is proposed, an experiment is designed to gather the data, and then the data is analyzed with respect to the hypothesis. Unfortunately, this process is extremely labor-intensive. Current data analysis tasks often require the generation and evaluation of thousands of hypotheses, and consequently, the development of some data mining techniques has been motivated by the desire to automate the process of hypothesis generation and evaluation. Furthermore, the data sets analyzed in data mining are typically not the result of a carefully designed experiment and often represent opportunistic samples of the data, rather than random samples. Also, the data sets frequently involve non-traditional types of data and data distributions.

1.3 The Origins of Data Mining

Brought together by the goal of meeting the challenges of the previous section, researchers from different disciplines began to focus on developing more efficient and scalable tools that could handle diverse types of data. This work, which culminated in the field of data mining, built upon the methodology and algorithms that researchers had previously used. In particular, data mining draws upon ideas, such as (1) sampling, estimation, and hypothesis testing from statistics and (2) search algorithms, modeling techniques, and learning theories from artificial intelligence, pattern recognition, and machine learning. Data mining has also been quick to adopt ideas from other areas, including optimization, evolutionary computing, information theory, signal processing, visualization, and information retrieval.

A number of other areas also play key supporting roles. In particular, database systems are needed to provide support for efficient storage, indexing, and query processing. Techniques from high performance (parallel) computing are often important in addressing the massive size of some data sets. Distributed techniques can also help address the issue of size and are essential when the data cannot be gathered in one location.

Figure 1.2 shows the relationship of data mining to other areas.

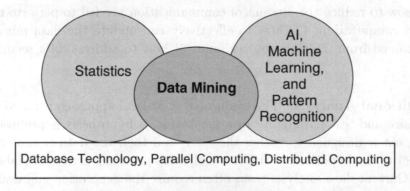

Figure 1.2. Data mining as a confluence of many disciplines.

1.4   Data Mining Tasks

Data mining tasks are generally divided into two major categories:

Predictive tasks. The objective of these tasks is to predict the value of a particular attribute based on the values of other attributes. The attribute to be predicted is commonly known as the **target** or **dependent variable**, while the attributes used for making the prediction are known as the **explanatory** or **independent variables**.

Descriptive tasks. Here, the objective is to derive patterns (correlations, trends, clusters, trajectories, and anomalies) that summarize the underlying relationships in data. Descriptive data mining tasks are often exploratory in nature and frequently require postprocessing techniques to validate and explain the results.

Figure 1.3 illustrates four of the core data mining tasks that are described in the remainder of this book.

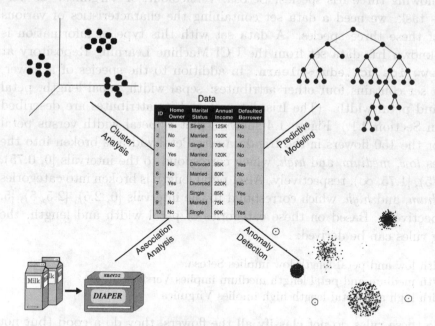

Figure 1.3. Four of the core data mining tasks.

Predictive modeling refers to the task of building a model for the target variable as a function of the explanatory variables. There are two types of predictive modeling tasks: **classification**, which is used for discrete target variables, and **regression**, which is used for continuous target variables. For example, predicting whether a Web user will make a purchase at an online bookstore is a classification task because the target variable is binary-valued. On the other hand, forecasting the future price of a stock is a regression task because price is a continuous-valued attribute. The goal of both tasks is to learn a model that minimizes the error between the predicted and true values of the target variable. Predictive modeling can be used to identify customers that will respond to a marketing campaign, predict disturbances in the Earth's ecosystem, or judge whether a patient has a particular disease based on the results of medical tests.

Example 1.1 (Predicting the Type of a Flower). Consider the task of predicting a species of flower based on the characteristics of the flower. In particular, consider classifying an Iris flower as to whether it belongs to one of the following three Iris species: Setosa, Versicolour, or Virginica. To perform this task, we need a data set containing the characteristics of various flowers of these three species. A data set with this type of information is the well-known Iris data set from the UCI Machine Learning Repository at `http://www.ics.uci.edu/~mlearn`. In addition to the species of a flower, this data set contains four other attributes: sepal width, sepal length, petal length, and petal width. (The Iris data set and its attributes are described further in Section 3.1.) Figure 1.4 shows a plot of petal width versus petal length for the 150 flowers in the Iris data set. Petal width is broken into the categories *low*, *medium*, and *high*, which correspond to the intervals [0, 0.75), [0.75, 1.75), [1.75, ∞), respectively. Also, petal length is broken into categories *low*, *medium*, and *high*, which correspond to the intervals [0, 2.5), [2.5, 5), [5, ∞), respectively. Based on these categories of petal width and length, the following rules can be derived:

Petal width low and petal length low implies Setosa.
Petal width medium and petal length medium implies Versicolour.
Petal width high and petal length high implies Virginica.

While these rules do not classify all the flowers, they do a good (but not perfect) job of classifying most of the flowers. Note that flowers from the Setosa species are well separated from the Versicolour and Virginica species with respect to petal width and length, but the latter two species overlap somewhat with respect to these attributes. ∎

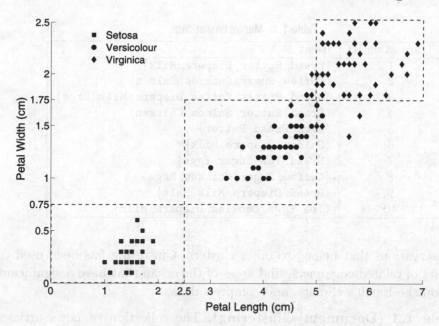

Figure 1.4. Petal width versus petal length for 150 Iris flowers.

Association analysis is used to discover patterns that describe strongly associated features in the data. The discovered patterns are typically represented in the form of implication rules or feature subsets. Because of the exponential size of its search space, the goal of association analysis is to extract the most interesting patterns in an efficient manner. Useful applications of association analysis include finding groups of genes that have related functionality, identifying Web pages that are accessed together, or understanding the relationships between different elements of Earth's climate system.

Example 1.2 (Market Basket Analysis). The transactions shown in Table 1.1 illustrate point-of-sale data collected at the checkout counters of a grocery store. Association analysis can be applied to find items that are frequently bought together by customers. For example, we may discover the rule {Diapers} ⟶ {Milk}, which suggests that customers who buy diapers also tend to buy milk. This type of rule can be used to identify potential cross-selling opportunities among related items. ∎

Cluster analysis seeks to find groups of closely related observations so that observations that belong to the same cluster are more similar to each other

Table 1.1. Market basket data.

Transaction ID	Items
1	{Bread, Butter, Diapers, Milk}
2	{Coffee, Sugar, Cookies, Salmon}
3	{Bread, Butter, Coffee, Diapers, Milk, Eggs}
4	{Bread, Butter, Salmon, Chicken}
5	{Eggs, Bread, Butter}
6	{Salmon, Diapers, Milk}
7	{Bread, Tea, Sugar, Eggs}
8	{Coffee, Sugar, Chicken, Eggs}
9	{Bread, Diapers, Milk, Salt}
10	{Tea, Eggs, Cookies, Diapers, Milk}

than observations that belong to other clusters. Clustering has been used to group sets of related customers, find areas of the ocean that have a significant impact on the Earth's climate, and compress data.

Example 1.3 (Document Clustering). The collection of news articles shown in Table 1.2 can be grouped based on their respective topics. Each article is represented as a set of word-frequency pairs (w, c), where w is a word and c is the number of times the word appears in the article. There are two natural clusters in the data set. The first cluster consists of the first four articles, which correspond to news about the economy, while the second cluster contains the last four articles, which correspond to news about health care. A good clustering algorithm should be able to identify these two clusters based on the similarity between words that appear in the articles.

Table 1.2. Collection of news articles.

Article	Words
1	dollar: 1, industry: 4, country: 2, loan: 3, deal: 2, government: 2
2	machinery: 2, labor: 3, market: 4, industry: 2, work: 3, country: 1
3	job: 5, inflation: 3, rise: 2, jobless: 2, market: 3, country: 2, index: 3
4	domestic: 3, forecast: 2, gain: 1, market: 2, sale: 3, price: 2
5	patient: 4, symptom: 2, drug: 3, health: 2, clinic: 2, doctor: 2
6	pharmaceutical: 2, company: 3, drug: 2, vaccine: 1, flu: 3
7	death: 2, cancer: 4, drug: 3, public: 4, health: 3, director: 2
8	medical: 2, cost: 3, increase: 2, patient: 2, health: 3, care: 1

Anomaly detection is the task of identifying observations whose characteristics are significantly different from the rest of the data. Such observations are known as **anomalies** or **outliers**. The goal of an anomaly detection algorithm is to discover the real anomalies and avoid falsely labeling normal objects as anomalous. In other words, a good anomaly detector must have a high detection rate and a low false alarm rate. Applications of anomaly detection include the detection of fraud, network intrusions, unusual patterns of disease, and ecosystem disturbances.

Example 1.4 (Credit Card Fraud Detection). A credit card company records the transactions made by every credit card holder, along with personal information such as credit limit, age, annual income, and address. Since the number of fraudulent cases is relatively small compared to the number of legitimate transactions, anomaly detection techniques can be applied to build a profile of legitimate transactions for the users. When a new transaction arrives, it is compared against the profile of the user. If the characteristics of the transaction are very different from the previously created profile, then the transaction is flagged as potentially fraudulent. ∎

1.5   Scope and Organization of the Book

This book introduces the major principles and techniques used in data mining from an algorithmic perspective. A study of these principles and techniques is essential for developing a better understanding of how data mining technology can be applied to various kinds of data. This book also serves as a starting point for readers who are interested in doing research in this field.

We begin the technical discussion of this book with a chapter on data (Chapter 2), which discusses the basic types of data, data quality, preprocessing techniques, and measures of similarity and dissimilarity. Although this material can be covered quickly, it provides an essential foundation for data analysis. Chapter 3, on data exploration, discusses summary statistics, visualization techniques, and On-Line Analytical Processing (OLAP). These techniques provide the means for quickly gaining insight into a data set.

Chapters 4 and 5 cover classification. Chapter 4 provides a foundation by discussing decision tree classifiers and several issues that are important to all classification: overfitting, performance evaluation, and the comparison of different classification models. Using this foundation, Chapter 5 describes a number of other important classification techniques: rule-based systems, nearest-neighbor classifiers, Bayesian classifiers, artificial neural networks, support vector machines, and ensemble classifiers, which are collections of classifiers. The multiclass and imbalanced class problems are also discussed. These topics can be covered independently.

Association analysis is explored in Chapters 6 and 7. Chapter 6 describes the basics of association analysis: frequent itemsets, association rules, and some of the algorithms used to generate them. Specific types of frequent itemsets—maximal, closed, and hyperclique—that are important for data mining are also discussed, and the chapter concludes with a discussion of evaluation measures for association analysis. Chapter 7 considers a variety of more advanced topics, including how association analysis can be applied to categorical and continuous data or to data that has a concept hierarchy. (A concept hierarchy is a hierarchical categorization of objects, e.g., store items, clothing, shoes, sneakers.) This chapter also describes how association analysis can be extended to find sequential patterns (patterns involving order), patterns in graphs, and negative relationships (if one item is present, then the other is not).

Cluster analysis is discussed in Chapters 8 and 9. Chapter 8 first describes the different types of clusters and then presents three specific clustering techniques: K-means, agglomerative hierarchical clustering, and DBSCAN. This is followed by a discussion of techniques for validating the results of a clustering algorithm. Additional clustering concepts and techniques are explored in Chapter 9, including fuzzy and probabilistic clustering, Self-Organizing Maps (SOM), graph-based clustering, and density-based clustering. There is also a discussion of scalability issues and factors to consider when selecting a clustering algorithm.

The last chapter, Chapter 10, is on anomaly detection. After some basic definitions, several different types of anomaly detection are considered: statistical, distance-based, density-based, and clustering-based. Appendices A through E give a brief review of important topics that are used in portions of the book: linear algebra, dimensionality reduction, statistics, regression, and optimization.

The subject of data mining, while relatively young compared to statistics or machine learning, is already too large to cover in a single book. Selected references to topics that are only briefly covered, such as data quality, are provided in the bibliographic notes of the appropriate chapter. References to topics not covered in this book, such as data mining for streams and privacy-preserving data mining, are provided in the bibliographic notes of this chapter.

1.6   Bibliographic Notes

The topic of data mining has inspired many textbooks. Introductory textbooks include those by Dunham [10], Han and Kamber [21], Hand et al. [23], and Roiger and Geatz [36]. Data mining books with a stronger emphasis on business applications include the works by Berry and Linoff [2], Pyle [34], and Parr Rud [33]. Books with an emphasis on statistical learning include those by Cherkassky and Mulier [6], and Hastie et al. [24]. Some books with an emphasis on machine learning or pattern recognition are those by Duda et al. [9], Kantardzic [25], Mitchell [31], Webb [41], and Witten and Frank [42]. There are also some more specialized books: Chakrabarti [4] (web mining), Fayyad et al. [13] (collection of early articles on data mining), Fayyad et al. [11] (visualization), Grossman et al. [18] (science and engineering), Kargupta and Chan [26] (distributed data mining), Wang et al. [40] (bioinformatics), and Zaki and Ho [44] (parallel data mining).

There are several conferences related to data mining. Some of the main conferences dedicated to this field include the ACM SIGKDD International Conference on Knowledge Discovery and Data Mining (KDD), the IEEE International Conference on Data Mining (ICDM), the SIAM International Conference on Data Mining (SDM), the European Conference on Principles and Practice of Knowledge Discovery in Databases (PKDD), and the Pacific-Asia Conference on Knowledge Discovery and Data Mining (PAKDD). Data mining papers can also be found in other major conferences such as the ACM SIGMOD/PODS conference, the International Conference on Very Large Data Bases (VLDB), the Conference on Information and Knowledge Management (CIKM), the International Conference on Data Engineering (ICDE), the International Conference on Machine Learning (ICML), and the National Conference on Artificial Intelligence (AAAI).

Journal publications on data mining include *IEEE Transactions on Knowledge and Data Engineering*, *Data Mining and Knowledge Discovery*, *Knowledge and Information Systems*, *Intelligent Data Analysis*, *Information Systems*, and the *Journal of Intelligent Information Systems*.

There have been a number of general articles on data mining that define the field or its relationship to other fields, particularly statistics. Fayyad et al. [12] describe data mining and how it fits into the total knowledge discovery process. Chen et al. [5] give a database perspective on data mining. Ramakrishnan and Grama [35] provide a general discussion of data mining and present several viewpoints. Hand [22] describes how data mining differs from statistics, as does Friedman [14]. Lambert [29] explores the use of statistics for large data sets and provides some comments on the respective roles of data mining and statistics.

Glymour et al. [16] consider the lessons that statistics may have for data mining. Smyth et al. [38] describe how the evolution of data mining is being driven by new types of data and applications, such as those involving streams, graphs, and text. Emerging applications in data mining are considered by Han et al. [20] and Smyth [37] describes some research challenges in data mining. A discussion of how developments in data mining research can be turned into practical tools is given by Wu et al. [43]. Data mining standards are the subject of a paper by Grossman et al. [17]. Bradley [3] discusses how data mining algorithms can be scaled to large data sets.

With the emergence of new data mining applications have come new challenges that need to be addressed. For instance, concerns about privacy breaches as a result of data mining have escalated in recent years, particularly in application domains such as Web commerce and health care. As a result, there is growing interest in developing data mining algorithms that maintain user privacy. Developing techniques for mining encrypted or randomized data is known as **privacy-preserving data mining**. Some general references in this area include papers by Agrawal and Srikant [1], Clifton et al. [7] and Kargupta et al. [27]. Vassilios et al. [39] provide a survey.

Recent years have witnessed a growing number of applications that rapidly generate continuous streams of data. Examples of stream data include network traffic, multimedia streams, and stock prices. Several issues must be considered when mining data streams, such as the limited amount of memory available, the need for online analysis, and the change of the data over time. Data mining for stream data has become an important area in data mining. Some selected publications are Domingos and Hulten [8] (classification), Giannella et al. [15] (association analysis), Guha et al. [19] (clustering), Kifer et al. [28] (change detection), Papadimitriou et al. [32] (time series), and Law et al. [30] (dimensionality reduction).

Bibliography

[1] R. Agrawal and R. Srikant. Privacy-preserving data mining. In *Proc. of 2000 ACM-SIGMOD Intl. Conf. on Management of Data*, pages 439–450, Dallas, Texas, 2000. ACM Press.

[2] M. J. A. Berry and G. Linoff. *Data Mining Techniques: For Marketing, Sales, and Customer Relationship Management*. Wiley Computer Publishing, 2nd edition, 2004.

[3] P. S. Bradley, J. Gehrke, R. Ramakrishnan, and R. Srikant. Scaling mining algorithms to large databases. *Communications of the ACM*, 45(8):38–43, 2002.

[4] S. Chakrabarti. *Mining the Web: Discovering Knowledge from Hypertext Data*. Morgan Kaufmann, San Francisco, CA, 2003.

[5] M.-S. Chen, J. Han, and P. S. Yu. Data Mining: An Overview from a Database Perspective. *IEEE Transactions on Knowledge abd Data Engineering*, 8(6):866–883, 1996.

[6] V. Cherkassky and F. Mulier. *Learning from Data: Concepts, Theory, and Methods.* Wiley Interscience, 1998.

[7] C. Clifton, M. Kantarcioglu, and J. Vaidya. Defining privacy for data mining. In *National Science Foundation Workshop on Next Generation Data Mining*, pages 126–133, Baltimore, MD, November 2002.

[8] P. Domingos and G. Hulten. Mining high-speed data streams. In *Proc. of the 6th Intl. Conf. on Knowledge Discovery and Data Mining*, pages 71–80, Boston, Massachusetts, 2000. ACM Press.

[9] R. O. Duda, P. E. Hart, and D. G. Stork. *Pattern Classification.* John Wiley & Sons, Inc., New York, 2nd edition, 2001.

[10] M. H. Dunham. *Data Mining: Introductory and Advanced Topics.* Prentice Hall, 2002.

[11] U. M. Fayyad, G. G. Grinstein, and A. Wierse, editors. *Information Visualization in Data Mining and Knowledge Discovery.* Morgan Kaufmann Publishers, San Francisco, CA, September 2001.

[12] U. M. Fayyad, G. Piatetsky-Shapiro, and P. Smyth. From Data Mining to Knowledge Discovery: An Overview. In *Advances in Knowledge Discovery and Data Mining*, pages 1–34. AAAI Press, 1996.

[13] U. M. Fayyad, G. Piatetsky-Shapiro, P. Smyth, and R. Uthurusamy, editors. *Advances in Knowledge Discovery and Data Mining.* AAAI/MIT Press, 1996.

[14] J. H. Friedman. Data Mining and Statistics: What's the Connection? Unpublished. www-stat.stanford.edu/~jhf/ftp/dm-stat.ps, 1997.

[15] C. Giannella, J. Han, J. Pei, X. Yan, and P. S. Yu. Mining Frequent Patterns in Data Streams at Multiple Time Granularities. In H. Kargupta, A. Joshi, K. Sivakumar, and Y. Yesha, editors, *Next Generation Data Mining*, pages 191–212. AAAI/MIT, 2003.

[16] C. Glymour, D. Madigan, D. Pregibon, and P. Smyth. Statistical Themes and Lessons for Data Mining. *Data Mining and Knowledge Discovery*, 1(1):11–28, 1997.

[17] R. L. Grossman, M. F. Hornick, and G. Meyer. Data mining standards initiatives. *Communications of the ACM*, 45(8):59–61, 2002.

[18] R. L. Grossman, C. Kamath, P. Kegelmeyer, V. Kumar, and R. Namburu, editors. *Data Mining for Scientific and Engineering Applications.* Kluwer Academic Publishers, 2001.

[19] S. Guha, A. Meyerson, N. Mishra, R. Motwani, and L. O'Callaghan. Clustering Data Streams: Theory and Practice. *IEEE Transactions on Knowledge and Data Engineering*, 15(3):515–528, May/June 2003.

[20] J. Han, R. B. Altman, V. Kumar, H. Mannila, and D. Pregibon. Emerging scientific applications in data mining. *Communications of the ACM*, 45(8):54–58, 2002.

[21] J. Han and M. Kamber. *Data Mining: Concepts and Techniques.* Morgan Kaufmann Publishers, San Francisco, 2001.

[22] D. J. Hand. Data Mining: Statistics and More? *The American Statistician*, 52(2): 112–118, 1998.

[23] D. J. Hand, H. Mannila, and P. Smyth. *Principles of Data Mining.* MIT Press, 2001.

[24] T. Hastie, R. Tibshirani, and J. H. Friedman. *The Elements of Statistical Learning: Data Mining, Inference, Prediction.* Springer, New York, 2001.

[25] M. Kantardzic. *Data Mining: Concepts, Models, Methods, and Algorithms.* Wiley-IEEE Press, Piscataway, NJ, 2003.

[26] H. Kargupta and P. K. Chan, editors. *Advances in Distributed and Parallel Knowledge Discovery.* AAAI Press, September 2002.

[27] H. Kargupta, S. Datta, Q. Wang, and K. Sivakumar. On the Privacy Preserving Properties of Random Data Perturbation Techniques. In *Proc. of the 2003 IEEE Intl. Conf. on Data Mining*, pages 99–106, Melbourne, Florida, December 2003. IEEE Computer Society.

[28] D. Kifer, S. Ben-David, and J. Gehrke. Detecting Change in Data Streams. In *Proc. of the 30th VLDB Conf.*, pages 180–191, Toronto, Canada, 2004. Morgan Kaufmann.

[29] D. Lambert. What Use is Statistics for Massive Data? In *ACM SIGMOD Workshop on Research Issues in Data Mining and Knowledge Discovery*, pages 54–62, 2000.

[30] M. H. C. Law, N. Zhang, and A. K. Jain. Nonlinear Manifold Learning for Data Streams. In *Proc. of the SIAM Intl. Conf. on Data Mining*, Lake Buena Vista, Florida, April 2004. SIAM.

[31] T. Mitchell. *Machine Learning.* McGraw-Hill, Boston, MA, 1997.

[32] S. Papadimitriou, A. Brockwell, and C. Faloutsos. Adaptive, unsupervised stream mining. *VLDB Journal*, 13(3):222–239, 2004.

[33] O. Parr Rud. *Data Mining Cookbook: Modeling Data for Marketing, Risk and Customer Relationship Management.* John Wiley & Sons, New York, NY, 2001.

[34] D. Pyle. *Business Modeling and Data Mining.* Morgan Kaufmann, San Francisco, CA, 2003.

[35] N. Ramakrishnan and A. Grama. Data Mining: From Serendipity to Science—Guest Editors' Introduction. *IEEE Computer*, 32(8):34–37, 1999.

[36] R. Roiger and M. Geatz. *Data Mining: A Tutorial Based Primer.* Addison-Wesley, 2002.

[37] P. Smyth. Breaking out of the Black-Box: Research Challenges in Data Mining. In *Proc. of the 2001 ACM SIGMOD Workshop on Research Issues in Data Mining and Knowledge Discovery*, 2001.

[38] P. Smyth, D. Pregibon, and C. Faloutsos. Data-driven evolution of data mining algorithms. *Communications of the ACM*, 45(8):33–37, 2002.

[39] V. S. Verykios, E. Bertino, I. N. Fovino, L. P. Provenza, Y. Saygin, and Y. Theodoridis. State-of-the-art in privacy preserving data mining. *SIGMOD Record*, 33(1):50–57, 2004.

[40] J. T. L. Wang, M. J. Zaki, H. Toivonen, and D. E. Shasha, editors. *Data Mining in Bioinformatics.* Springer, September 2004.

[41] A. R. Webb. *Statistical Pattern Recognition.* John Wiley & Sons, 2nd edition, 2002.

[42] I. H. Witten and E. Frank. *Data Mining: Practical Machine Learning Tools and Techniques with Java Implementations.* Morgan Kaufmann, 1999.

[43] X. Wu, P. S. Yu, and G. Piatetsky-Shapiro. Data Mining: How Research Meets Practical Development? *Knowledge and Information Systems*, 5(2):248–261, 2003.

[44] M. J. Zaki and C.-T. Ho, editors. *Large-Scale Parallel Data Mining.* Springer, September 2002.

1.7 Exercises

1. Discuss whether or not each of the following activities is a data mining task.

(a) Dividing the customers of a company according to their gender.

(b) Dividing the customers of a company according to their profitability.

(c) Computing the total sales of a company.

(d) Sorting a student database based on student identification numbers.

(e) Predicting the outcomes of tossing a (fair) pair of dice.

(f) Predicting the future stock price of a company using historical records.

(g) Monitoring the heart rate of a patient for abnormalities.

(h) Monitoring seismic waves for earthquake activities.

(i) Extracting the frequencies of a sound wave.

2. Suppose that you are employed as a data mining consultant for an Internet search engine company. Describe how data mining can help the company by giving specific examples of how techniques, such as clustering, classification, association rule mining, and anomaly detection can be applied.

3. For each of the following data sets, explain whether or not data privacy is an important issue.

(a) Census data collected from 1900–1950.

(b) IP addresses and visit times of Web users who visit your Website.

(c) Images from Earth-orbiting satellites.

(d) Names and addresses of people from the telephone book.

(e) Names and email addresses collected from the Web.

2

Data

This chapter discusses several data-related issues that are important for successful data mining:

The Type of Data Data sets differ in a number of ways. For example, the attributes used to describe data objects can be of different types—quantitative or qualitative—and data sets may have special characteristics; e.g., some data sets contain time series or objects with explicit relationships to one another. Not surprisingly, the type of data determines which tools and techniques can be used to analyze the data. Furthermore, new research in data mining is often driven by the need to accommodate new application areas and their new types of data.

The Quality of the Data Data is often far from perfect. While most data mining techniques can tolerate some level of imperfection in the data, a focus on understanding and improving data quality typically improves the quality of the resulting analysis. Data quality issues that often need to be addressed include the presence of noise and outliers; missing, inconsistent, or duplicate data; and data that is biased or, in some other way, unrepresentative of the phenomenon or population that the data is supposed to describe.

Preprocessing Steps to Make the Data More Suitable for Data Mining Often, the raw data must be processed in order to make it suitable for analysis. While one objective may be to improve data quality, other goals focus on modifying the data so that it better fits a specified data mining technique or tool. For example, a continuous attribute, e.g., length, may need to be transformed into an attribute with discrete categories, e.g., *short*, *medium*, or *long*, in order to apply a particular technique. As another example, the number of attributes in a data set is often reduced because many techniques are more effective when the data has a relatively small number of attributes.

Analyzing Data in Terms of Its Relationships One approach to data analysis is to find relationships among the data objects and then perform the remaining analysis using these relationships rather than the data objects themselves. For instance, we can compute the similarity or distance between pairs of objects and then perform the analysis—clustering, classification, or anomaly detection—based on these similarities or distances. There are many such similarity or distance measures, and the proper choice depends on the type of data and the particular application.

Example 2.1 (An Illustration of Data-Related Issues). To further illustrate the importance of these issues, consider the following hypothetical situation. You receive an email from a medical researcher concerning a project that you are eager to work on.

> Hi,
>
> I've attached the data file that I mentioned in my previous email.
> Each line contains the information for a single patient and consists
> of five fields. We want to predict the last field using the other fields.
> I don't have time to provide any more information about the data
> since I'm going out of town for a couple of days, but hopefully that
> won't slow you down too much. And if you don't mind, could we
> meet when I get back to discuss your preliminary results? I might
> invite a few other members of my team.
>
> Thanks and see you in a couple of days.

Despite some misgivings, you proceed to analyze the data. The first few rows of the file are as follows:

```
012   232   33.5   0    10.7
020   121   16.9   2   210.1
027   165   24.0   0   427.6
 ⋮
```

A brief look at the data reveals nothing strange. You put your doubts aside and start the analysis. There are only 1000 lines, a smaller data file than you had hoped for, but two days later, you feel that you have made some progress. You arrive for the meeting, and while waiting for others to arrive, you strike up a conversation with a statistician who is working on the project. When she learns that you have also been analyzing the data from the project, she asks if you would mind giving her a brief overview of your results.

Statistician: So, you got the data for all the patients?

Data Miner: Yes. I haven't had much time for analysis, but I do have a few interesting results.

Statistician: Amazing. There were so many data issues with this set of patients that I couldn't do much.

Data Miner: Oh? I didn't hear about any possible problems.

Statistician: Well, first there is field 5, the variable we want to predict. It's common knowledge among people who analyze this type of data that results are better if you work with the log of the values, but I didn't discover this until later. Was it mentioned to you?

Data Miner: No.

Statistician: But surely you heard about what happened to field 4? It's supposed to be measured on a scale from 1 to 10, with 0 indicating a missing value, but because of a data entry error, all 10's were changed into 0's. Unfortunately, since some of the patients have missing values for this field, it's impossible to say whether a 0 in this field is a real 0 or a 10. Quite a few of the records have that problem.

Data Miner: Interesting. Were there any other problems?

Statistician: Yes, fields 2 and 3 are basically the same, but I assume that you probably noticed that.

Data Miner: Yes, but these fields were only weak predictors of field 5.

Statistician: Anyway, given all those problems, I'm surprised you were able to accomplish anything.

Data Miner: True, but my results are really quite good. Field 1 is a very strong predictor of field 5. I'm surprised that this wasn't noticed before.

Statistician: What? Field 1 is just an identification number.

Data Miner: Nonetheless, my results speak for themselves.

Statistician: Oh, no! I just remembered. We assigned ID numbers after we sorted the records based on field 5. There is a strong connection, but it's meaningless. Sorry.

Although this scenario represents an extreme situation, it emphasizes the importance of "knowing your data." To that end, this chapter will address each of the four issues mentioned above, outlining some of the basic challenges and standard approaches.

2.1 Types of Data

A **data set** can often be viewed as a collection of **data objects**. Other names for a data object are *record*, *point*, *vector*, *pattern*, *event*, *case*, *sample*, *observation*, or *entity*. In turn, data objects are described by a number of **attributes** that capture the basic characteristics of an object, such as the mass of a physical object or the time at which an event occurred. Other names for an attribute are *variable*, *characteristic*, *field*, *feature*, or *dimension*.

Example 2.2 (Student Information). Often, a data set is a file, in which the objects are records (or rows) in the file and each field (or column) corresponds to an attribute. For example, Table 2.1 shows a data set that consists of student information. Each row corresponds to a student and each column is an attribute that describes some aspect of a student, such as grade point average (GPA) or identification number (ID).

Table 2.1. A sample data set containing student information.

Student ID	Year	Grade Point Average (GPA)	...
⋮			
1034262	Senior	3.24	...
1052663	Sophomore	3.51	...
1082246	Freshman	3.62	...
⋮			

Although record-based data sets are common, either in flat files or relational database systems, there are other important types of data sets and systems for storing data. In Section 2.1.2, we will discuss some of the types of data sets that are commonly encountered in data mining. However, we first consider attributes.

2.1.1 Attributes and Measurement

In this section we address the issue of describing data by considering what types of attributes are used to describe data objects. We first define an attribute, then consider what we mean by the type of an attribute, and finally describe the types of attributes that are commonly encountered.

What Is an attribute?

We start with a more detailed definition of an attribute.

Definition 2.1. An **attribute** is a property or characteristic of an object that may vary, either from one object to another or from one time to another.

For example, eye color varies from person to person, while the temperature of an object varies over time. Note that eye color is a symbolic attribute with a small number of possible values {*brown, black, blue, green, hazel, etc.*}, while temperature is a numerical attribute with a potentially unlimited number of values.

At the most basic level, attributes are not about numbers or symbols. However, to discuss and more precisely analyze the characteristics of objects, we assign numbers or symbols to them. To do this in a well-defined way, we need a measurement scale.

Definition 2.2. A **measurement scale** is a rule (function) that associates a numerical or symbolic value with an attribute of an object.

Formally, the process of **measurement** is the application of a measurement scale to associate a value with a particular attribute of a specific object. While this may seem a bit abstract, we engage in the process of measurement all the time. For instance, we step on a bathroom scale to determine our weight, we classify someone as male or female, or we count the number of chairs in a room to see if there will be enough to seat all the people coming to a meeting. In all these cases, the "physical value" of an attribute of an object is mapped to a numerical or symbolic value.

With this background, we can now discuss the type of an attribute, a concept that is important in determining if a particular data analysis technique is consistent with a specific type of attribute.

The Type of an Attribute

It should be apparent from the previous discussion that the properties of an attribute need not be the same as the properties of the values used to measure it. In other words, the values used to represent an attribute may have properties that are not properties of the attribute itself, and vice versa. This is illustrated with two examples.

Example 2.3 (Employee Age and ID Number). Two attributes that might be associated with an employee are *ID* and *age* (in years). Both of these attributes can be represented as integers. However, while it is reasonable to talk about the average age of an employee, it makes no sense to talk about the average employee ID. Indeed, the only aspect of employees that we want to capture with the ID attribute is that they are distinct. Consequently, the only valid operation for employee IDs is to test whether they are equal. There is no hint of this limitation, however, when integers are used to represent the employee ID attribute. For the age attribute, the properties of the integers used to represent age are very much the properties of the attribute. Even so, the correspondence is not complete since, for example, ages have a maximum, while integers do not. ∎

Example 2.4 (Length of Line Segments). Consider Figure 2.1, which shows some objects—line segments—and how the length attribute of these objects can be mapped to numbers in two different ways. Each successive line segment, going from the top to the bottom, is formed by appending the topmost line segment to itself. Thus, the second line segment from the top is formed by appending the topmost line segment to itself twice, the third line segment from the top is formed by appending the topmost line segment to itself three times, and so forth. In a very real (physical) sense, all the line segments are multiples of the first. This fact is captured by the measurements on the right-hand side of the figure, but not by those on the left hand-side. More specifically, the measurement scale on the left-hand side captures only the ordering of the length attribute, while the scale on the right-hand side captures both the ordering and additivity properties. Thus, an attribute can be measured in a way that does not capture all the properties of the attribute. ∎

The type of an attribute should tell us what properties of the attribute are reflected in the values used to measure it. Knowing the type of an attribute is important because it tells us which properties of the measured values are consistent with the underlying properties of the attribute, and therefore, it allows us to avoid foolish actions, such as computing the average employee ID. Note that it is common to refer to the type of an attribute as the **type of a measurement scale**.

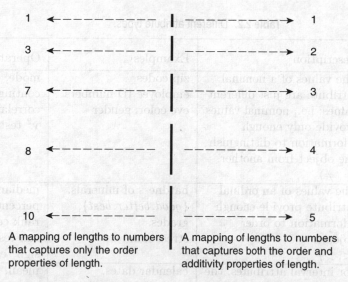

Figure 2.1. The measurement of the length of line segments on two different scales of measurement.

The Different Types of Attributes

A useful (and simple) way to specify the type of an attribute is to identify the properties of numbers that correspond to underlying properties of the attribute. For example, an attribute such as length has many of the properties of numbers. It makes sense to compare and order objects by length, as well as to talk about the differences and ratios of length. The following properties (operations) of numbers are typically used to describe attributes.

1. **Distinctness** $=$ and $\neq$

2. **Order** $<$, $\leq$, $>$, and $\geq$

3. **Addition** $+$ and $-$

4. **Multiplication** $*$ and $/$

Given these properties, we can define four types of attributes: **nominal**, **ordinal**, **interval**, and **ratio**. Table 2.2 gives the definitions of these types, along with information about the statistical operations that are valid for each type. Each attribute type possesses all of the properties and operations of the attribute types above it. Consequently, any property or operation that is valid for nominal, ordinal, and interval attributes is also valid for ratio attributes. In other words, the definition of the attribute types is cumulative. However,

Table 2.2. Different attribute types.

Attribute Type		Description	Examples	Operations
Categorical (Qualitative)	Nominal	The values of a nominal attribute are just different names; i.e., nominal values provide only enough information to distinguish one object from another. $(=, \neq)$	zip codes, employee ID numbers, eye color, gender	mode, entropy, contingency correlation, χ^2 test
	Ordinal	The values of an ordinal attribute provide enough information to order objects. $(<, >)$	hardness of minerals, $\{good, better, best\}$, grades, street numbers	median, percentiles, rank correlation, run tests, sign tests
Numeric (Quantitative)	Interval	For interval attributes, the differences between values are meaningful, i.e., a unit of measurement exists. $(+, -)$	calendar dates, temperature in Celsius or Fahrenheit	mean, standard deviation, Pearson's correlation, t and F tests
	Ratio	For ratio variables, both differences and ratios are meaningful. $(*, /)$	temperature in Kelvin, monetary quantities, counts, age, mass, length, electrical current	geometric mean, harmonic mean, percent variation

this does not mean that the operations appropriate for one attribute type are appropriate for the attribute types above it.

Nominal and ordinal attributes are collectively referred to as **categorical** or **qualitative** attributes. As the name suggests, qualitative attributes, such as employee ID, lack most of the properties of numbers. Even if they are represented by numbers, i.e., integers, they should be treated more like symbols. The remaining two types of attributes, interval and ratio, are collectively referred to as **quantitative** or **numeric** attributes. Quantitative attributes are represented by numbers and have most of the properties of numbers. Note that quantitative attributes can be integer-valued or continuous.

The types of attributes can also be described in terms of transformations that do not change the meaning of an attribute. Indeed, S. Smith Stevens, the psychologist who originally defined the types of attributes shown in Table 2.2, defined them in terms of these **permissible transformations**. For example,

Table 2.3. Transformations that define attribute levels.

Attribute Type		Transformation	Comment
Categorical (Qualitative)	Nominal	Any one-to-one mapping, e.g., a permutation of values	If all employee ID numbers are reassigned, it will not make any difference.
	Ordinal	An order-preserving change of values, i.e., $new\_value = f(old\_value)$, where f is a monotonic function.	An attribute encompassing the notion of good, better, best can be represented equally well by the values $\{1, 2, 3\}$ or by $\{0.5, 1, 10\}$.
Numeric (Quantitative)	Interval	$new\_value = a * old\_value + b$, a and b constants.	The Fahrenheit and Celsius temperature scales differ in the location of their zero value and the size of a degree (unit).
	Ratio	$new\_value = a * old\_value$	Length can be measured in meters or feet.

the meaning of a length attribute is unchanged if it is measured in meters instead of feet.

The statistical operations that make sense for a particular type of attribute are those that will yield the same results when the attribute is transformed using a transformation that preserves the attribute's meaning. To illustrate, the average length of a set of objects is different when measured in meters rather than in feet, but both averages represent the same length. Table 2.3 shows the permissible (meaning-preserving) transformations for the four attribute types of Table 2.2.

Example 2.5 (Temperature Scales). Temperature provides a good illustration of some of the concepts that have been described. First, temperature can be either an interval or a ratio attribute, depending on its measurement scale. When measured on the Kelvin scale, a temperature of 2° is, in a physically meaningful way, twice that of a temperature of 1°. This is not true when temperature is measured on either the Celsius or Fahrenheit scales, because, physically, a temperature of 1° Fahrenheit (Celsius) is not much different than a temperature of 2° Fahrenheit (Celsius). The problem is that the zero points of the Fahrenheit and Celsius scales are, in a physical sense, arbitrary, and therefore, the ratio of two Celsius or Fahrenheit temperatures is not physically meaningful. ∎

Describing Attributes by the Number of Values

An independent way of distinguishing between attributes is by the number of values they can take.

Discrete A discrete attribute has a finite or countably infinite set of values. Such attributes can be categorical, such as zip codes or ID numbers, or numeric, such as counts. Discrete attributes are often represented using integer variables. **Binary attributes** are a special case of discrete attributes and assume only two values, e.g., true/false, yes/no, male/female, or 0/1. Binary attributes are often represented as Boolean variables, or as integer variables that only take the values 0 or 1.

Continuous A continuous attribute is one whose values are real numbers. Examples include attributes such as temperature, height, or weight. Continuous attributes are typically represented as floating-point variables. Practically, real values can only be measured and represented with limited precision.

In theory, any of the measurement scale types—nominal, ordinal, interval, and ratio—could be combined with any of the types based on the number of attribute values—binary, discrete, and continuous. However, some combinations occur only infrequently or do not make much sense. For instance, it is difficult to think of a realistic data set that contains a continuous binary attribute. Typically, nominal and ordinal attributes are binary or discrete, while interval and ratio attributes are continuous. However, **count attributes**, which are discrete, are also ratio attributes.

Asymmetric Attributes

For asymmetric attributes, only presence—a non-zero attribute value—is regarded as important. Consider a data set where each object is a student and each attribute records whether or not a student took a particular course at a university. For a specific student, an attribute has a value of 1 if the student took the course associated with that attribute and a value of 0 otherwise. Because students take only a small fraction of all available courses, most of the values in such a data set would be 0. Therefore, it is more meaningful and more efficient to focus on the non-zero values. To illustrate, if students are compared on the basis of the courses they don't take, then most students would seem very similar, at least if the number of courses is large. Binary attributes where only non-zero values are important are called **asymmetric**

binary attributes. This type of attribute is particularly important for association analysis, which is discussed in Chapter 6. It is also possible to have discrete or continuous asymmetric features. For instance, if the number of credits associated with each course is recorded, then the resulting data set will consist of **asymmetric discrete** or **continuous attributes**.

2.1.2 Types of Data Sets

There are many types of data sets, and as the field of data mining develops and matures, a greater variety of data sets become available for analysis. In this section, we describe some of the most common types. For convenience, we have grouped the types of data sets into three groups: record data, graph-based data, and ordered data. These categories do not cover all possibilities and other groupings are certainly possible.

General Characteristics of Data Sets

Before providing details of specific kinds of data sets, we discuss three characteristics that apply to many data sets and have a significant impact on the data mining techniques that are used: dimensionality, sparsity, and resolution.

Dimensionality The dimensionality of a data set is the number of attributes that the objects in the data set possess. Data with a small number of dimensions tends to be qualitatively different than moderate or high-dimensional data. Indeed, the difficulties associated with analyzing high-dimensional data are sometimes referred to as the **curse of dimensionality**. Because of this, an important motivation in preprocessing the data is **dimensionality reduction**. These issues are discussed in more depth later in this chapter and in Appendix B.

Sparsity For some data sets, such as those with asymmetric features, most attributes of an object have values of 0; in many cases, fewer than 1% of the entries are non-zero. In practical terms, sparsity is an advantage because usually only the non-zero values need to be stored and manipulated. This results in significant savings with respect to computation time and storage. Furthermore, some data mining algorithms work well only for sparse data.

Resolution It is frequently possible to obtain data at different levels of resolution, and often the properties of the data are different at different resolutions. For instance, the surface of the Earth seems very uneven at a resolution of a few meters, but is relatively smooth at a resolution of tens of kilometers. The patterns in the data also depend on the level of resolution. If the resolution is too fine, a pattern may not be visible or may be buried in noise; if the resolution is too coarse, the pattern may disappear. For example, variations in atmospheric pressure on a scale of hours reflect the movement of storms and other weather systems. On a scale of months, such phenomena are not detectable.

Record Data

Much data mining work assumes that the data set is a collection of records (data objects), each of which consists of a fixed set of data fields (attributes). See Figure 2.2(a). For the most basic form of record data, there is no explicit relationship among records or data fields, and every record (object) has the same set of attributes. Record data is usually stored either in **flat** files or in relational databases. Relational databases are certainly more than a collection of records, but data mining often does not use any of the additional information available in a relational database. Rather, the database serves as a convenient place to find records. Different types of record data are described below and are illustrated in Figure 2.2.

Transaction or Market Basket Data Transaction data is a special type of record data, where each record (transaction) involves a set of items. Consider a grocery store. The set of products purchased by a customer during one shopping trip constitutes a transaction, while the individual products that were purchased are the items. This type of data is called **market basket data** because the items in each record are the products in a person's "market basket." Transaction data is a collection of sets of items, but it can be viewed as a set of records whose fields are asymmetric attributes. Most often, the attributes are binary, indicating whether or not an item was purchased, but more generally, the attributes can be discrete or continuous, such as the number of items purchased or the amount spent on those items. Figure 2.2(b) shows a sample transaction data set. Each row represents the purchases of a particular customer at a particular time.

The Data Matrix If the data objects in a collection of data all have the same fixed set of numeric attributes, then the data objects can be thought of as points (vectors) in a multidimensional space, where each dimension represents a distinct attribute describing the object. A set of such data objects can be interpreted as an m by n matrix, where there are m rows, one for each object,

Tid	Refund	Marital Status	Taxable Income	Defaulted Borrower
1	Yes	Single	125K	No
2	No	Married	100K	No
3	No	Single	70K	No
4	Yes	Married	120K	No
5	No	Divorced	95K	Yes
6	No	Married	60K	No
7	Yes	Divorced	220K	No
8	No	Single	85K	Yes
9	No	Married	75K	No
10	No	Single	90K	Yes

(a) Record data.

TID	ITEMS
1	Bread, Soda, Milk
2	Beer, Bread
3	Beer, Soda, Diaper, Milk
4	Beer, Bread, Diaper, Milk
5	Soda, Diaper, Milk

(b) Transaction data.

Projection of x Load	Projection of y Load	Distance	Load	Thickness
10.23	5.27	15.22	27	1.2
12.65	6.25	16.22	22	1.1
13.54	7.23	17.34	23	1.2
14.27	8.43	18.45	25	0.9

(c) Data matrix.

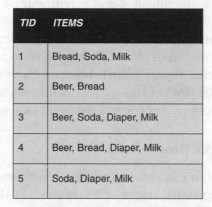

	team	coach	play	ball	score	game	win	lost	timeout	season
Document 1	3	0	5	0	2	6	0	2	0	2
Document 2	0	7	0	2	1	0	0	3	0	0
Document 3	0	1	0	0	1	2	2	0	3	0

(d) Document-term matrix.

Figure 2.2. Different variations of record data.

and n columns, one for each attribute. (A representation that has data objects as columns and attributes as rows is also fine.) This matrix is called a **data matrix** or a **pattern matrix**. A data matrix is a variation of record data, but because it consists of numeric attributes, standard matrix operation can be applied to transform and manipulate the data. Therefore, the data matrix is the standard data format for most statistical data. Figure 2.2(c) shows a sample data matrix.

The Sparse Data Matrix A sparse data matrix is a special case of a data matrix in which the attributes are of the same type and are asymmetric; i.e., only non-zero values are important. Transaction data is an example of a sparse data matrix that has only 0–1 entries. Another common example is document data. In particular, if the order of the terms (words) in a document is ignored, then a document can be represented as a term vector, where each term is a component (attribute) of the vector and the value of each component is the number of times the corresponding term occurs in the document. This representation of a collection of documents is often called a **document-term matrix**. Figure 2.2(d) shows a sample document-term matrix. The documents are the rows of this matrix, while the terms are the columns. In practice, only the non-zero entries of sparse data matrices are stored.

Graph-Based Data

A graph can sometimes be a convenient and powerful representation for data. We consider two specific cases: (1) the graph captures relationships among data objects and (2) the data objects themselves are represented as graphs.

Data with Relationships among Objects   The relationships among objects frequently convey important information. In such cases, the data is often represented as a graph. In particular, the data objects are mapped to nodes of the graph, while the relationships among objects are captured by the links between objects and link properties, such as direction and weight. Consider Web pages on the World Wide Web, which contain both text and links to other pages. In order to process search queries, Web search engines collect and process Web pages to extract their contents. It is well known, however, that the links to and from each page provide a great deal of information about the relevance of a Web page to a query, and thus, must also be taken into consideration. Figure 2.3(a) shows a set of linked Web pages.

Data with Objects That Are Graphs   If objects have structure, that is, the objects contain subobjects that have relationships, then such objects are frequently represented as graphs. For example, the structure of chemical compounds can be represented by a graph, where the nodes are atoms and the links between nodes are chemical bonds. Figure 2.3(b) shows a ball-and-stick diagram of the chemical compound benzene, which contains atoms of carbon (black) and hydrogen (gray). A graph representation makes it possible to determine which substructures occur frequently in a set of compounds and to ascertain whether the presence of any of these substructures is associated with the presence or absence of certain chemical properties, such as melting point or heat of formation. Substructure mining, which is a branch of data mining that analyzes such data, is considered in Section 7.5.

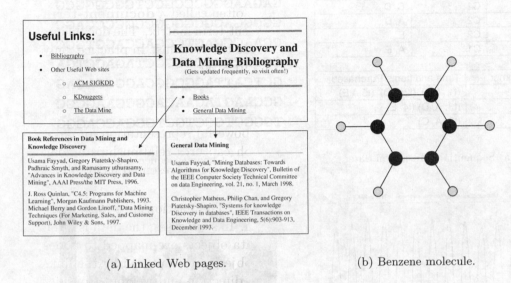

(a) Linked Web pages.   (b) Benzene molecule.

Figure 2.3. Different variations of graph data.

Ordered Data

For some types of data, the attributes have relationships that involve order in time or space. Different types of ordered data are described next and are shown in Figure 2.4.

Sequential Data   Sequential data, also referred to as **temporal data**, can be thought of as an extension of record data, where each record has a time associated with it. Consider a retail transaction data set that also stores the time at which the transaction took place. This time information makes it possible to find patterns such as "candy sales peak before Halloween." A time can also be associated with each attribute. For example, each record could be the purchase history of a customer, with a listing of items purchased at different times. Using this information, it is possible to find patterns such as "people who buy DVD players tend to buy DVDs in the period immediately following the purchase."

Figure 2.4(a) shows an example of sequential transaction data. There are five different times—*t1*, *t2*, *t3*, *t4*, and *t5*; three different customers—C1,

Time	Customer	Items Purchased
t1	C1	A, B
t2	C3	A, C
t2	C1	C, D
t3	C2	A, D
t4	C2	E
t5	C1	A, E

Customer	Time and Items Purchased
C1	(t1: A,B) (t2:C,D) (t5:A,E)
C2	(t3: A, D) (t4: E)
C3	(t2: A, C)

GGTTCCGCCTTCAGCCCCGCGCC
CGCAGGGCCCGCCCCGCGCCGTC
GAGAAGGGCCCGCCTGGCGGGCG
GGGGGAGGCGGGGCCGCCCGAGC
CCAACCGAGTCCGACCAGGTGCC
CCCTCTGCTCGGCCTAGACCTGA
GCTCATTAGGCGGCAGCGGACAG
GCCAAGTAGAACACGCGAAGCGC
TGGGCTGCCTGCTGCGACCAGGG

(a) Sequential transaction data.

(b) Genomic sequence data.

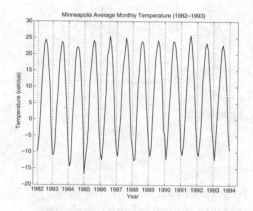

(c) Temperature time series.

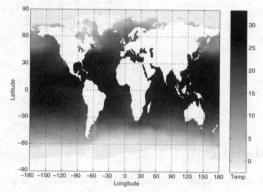

(d) Spatial temperature data.

Figure 2.4. Different variations of ordered data.

C2, and C3; and five different items—A, B, C, D, and E. In the top table, each row corresponds to the items purchased at a particular time by each customer. For instance, at time *t3*, customer C2 purchased items A and D. In the bottom table, the same information is displayed, but each row corresponds to a particular customer. Each row contains information on each transaction involving the customer, where a transaction is considered to be a set of items and the time at which those items were purchased. For example, customer C3 bought items A and C at time *t2*.

Sequence Data Sequence data consists of a data set that is a sequence of individual entities, such as a sequence of words or letters. It is quite similar to sequential data, except that there are no time stamps; instead, there are positions in an ordered sequence. For example, the genetic information of plants and animals can be represented in the form of sequences of nucleotides that are known as genes. Many of the problems associated with genetic sequence data involve predicting similarities in the structure and function of genes from similarities in nucleotide sequences. Figure 2.4(b) shows a section of the human genetic code expressed using the four nucleotides from which all DNA is constructed: A, T, G, and C.

Time Series Data Time series data is a special type of sequential data in which each record is a **time series**, i.e., a series of measurements taken over time. For example, a financial data set might contain objects that are time series of the daily prices of various stocks. As another example, consider Figure 2.4(c), which shows a time series of the average monthly temperature for Minneapolis during the years 1982 to 1994. When working with temporal data, it is important to consider **temporal autocorrelation**; i.e., if two measurements are close in time, then the values of those measurements are often very similar.

Spatial Data Some objects have spatial attributes, such as positions or areas, as well as other types of attributes. An example of spatial data is weather data (precipitation, temperature, pressure) that is collected for a variety of geographical locations. An important aspect of spatial data is **spatial autocorrelation**; i.e., objects that are physically close tend to be similar in other ways as well. Thus, two points on the Earth that are close to each other usually have similar values for temperature and rainfall.

Important examples of spatial data are the science and engineering data sets that are the result of measurements or model output taken at regularly or irregularly distributed points on a two- or three-dimensional grid or mesh. For instance, Earth science data sets record the temperature or pressure measured at points (grid cells) on latitude–longitude spherical grids of various resolutions, e.g., 1° by 1°. (See Figure 2.4(d).) As another example, in the simulation of the flow of a gas, the speed and direction of flow can be recorded for each grid point in the simulation.

Handling Non-Record Data

Most data mining algorithms are designed for record data or its variations, such as transaction data and data matrices. Record-oriented techniques can be applied to non-record data by extracting features from data objects and using these features to create a record corresponding to each object. Consider the chemical structure data that was described earlier. Given a set of common substructures, each compound can be represented as a record with binary attributes that indicate whether a compound contains a specific substructure. Such a representation is actually a transaction data set, where the transactions are the compounds and the items are the substructures.

In some cases, it is easy to represent the data in a record format, but this type of representation does not capture all the information in the data. Consider spatio-temporal data consisting of a time series from each point on a spatial grid. This data is often stored in a data matrix, where each row represents a location and each column represents a particular point in time. However, such a representation does not explicitly capture the time relationships that are present among attributes and the spatial relationships that exist among objects. This does not mean that such a representation is inappropriate, but rather that these relationships must be taken into consideration during the analysis. For example, it would not be a good idea to use a data mining technique that assumes the attributes are statistically independent of one another.

2.2 Data Quality

Data mining applications are often applied to data that was collected for another purpose, or for future, but unspecified applications. For that reason, data mining cannot usually take advantage of the significant benefits of "addressing quality issues at the source." In contrast, much of statistics deals with the design of experiments or surveys that achieve a prespecified level of data quality. Because preventing data quality problems is typically not an option, data mining focuses on (1) the detection and correction of data quality problems and (2) the use of algorithms that can tolerate poor data quality. The first step, detection and correction, is often called **data cleaning**.

The following sections discuss specific aspects of data quality. The focus is on measurement and data collection issues, although some application-related issues are also discussed.

2.2.1 Measurement and Data Collection Issues

It is unrealistic to expect that data will be perfect. There may be problems due to human error, limitations of measuring devices, or flaws in the data collection process. Values or even entire data objects may be missing. In other cases, there may be spurious or duplicate objects; i.e., multiple data objects that all correspond to a single "real" object. For example, there might be two different records for a person who has recently lived at two different addresses. Even if all the data is present and "looks fine," there may be inconsistencies—a person has a height of 2 meters, but weighs only 2 kilograms.

In the next few sections, we focus on aspects of data quality that are related to data measurement and collection. We begin with a definition of measurement and data collection errors and then consider a variety of problems that involve measurement error: noise, artifacts, bias, precision, and accuracy. We conclude by discussing data quality issues that may involve both measurement and data collection problems: outliers, missing and inconsistent values, and duplicate data.

Measurement and Data Collection Errors

The term **measurement error** refers to any problem resulting from the measurement process. A common problem is that the value recorded differs from the true value to some extent. For continuous attributes, the numerical difference of the measured and true value is called the **error**. The term **data collection error** refers to errors such as omitting data objects or attribute values, or inappropriately including a data object. For example, a study of animals of a certain species might include animals of a related species that are similar in appearance to the species of interest. Both measurement errors and data collection errors can be either systematic or random.

We will only consider general types of errors. Within particular domains, there are certain types of data errors that are commonplace, and there often exist well-developed techniques for detecting and/or correcting these errors. For example, keyboard errors are common when data is entered manually, and as a result, many data entry programs have techniques for detecting and, with human intervention, correcting such errors.

Noise and Artifacts

Noise is the random component of a measurement error. It may involve the distortion of a value or the addition of spurious objects. Figure 2.5 shows a time series before and after it has been disrupted by random noise. If a bit

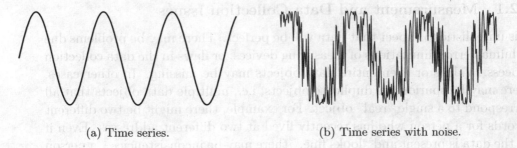

(a) Time series.   (b) Time series with noise.

Figure 2.5. Noise in a time series context.

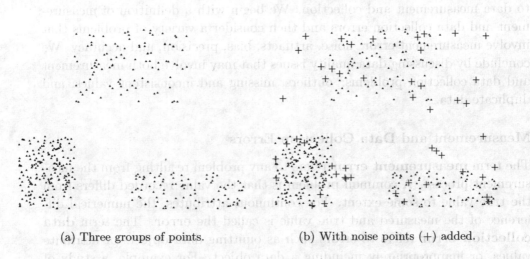

(a) Three groups of points.   (b) With noise points (+) added.

Figure 2.6. Noise in a spatial context.

more noise were added to the time series, its shape would be lost. Figure 2.6 shows a set of data points before and after some noise points (indicated by '+'s) have been added. Notice that some of the noise points are intermixed with the non-noise points.

The term noise is often used in connection with data that has a spatial or temporal component. In such cases, techniques from signal or image processing can frequently be used to reduce noise and thus, help to discover patterns (signals) that might be "lost in the noise." Nonetheless, the elimination of noise is frequently difficult, and much work in data mining focuses on devising **robust algorithms** that produce acceptable results even when noise is present.

Data errors may be the result of a more deterministic phenomenon, such as a streak in the same place on a set of photographs. Such deterministic distortions of the data are often referred to as **artifacts**.

Precision, Bias, and Accuracy

In statistics and experimental science, the quality of the measurement process and the resulting data are measured by precision and bias. We provide the standard definitions, followed by a brief discussion. For the following definitions, we assume that we make repeated measurements of the same underlying quantity and use this set of values to calculate a mean (average) value that serves as our estimate of the true value.

Definition 2.3 (Precision). The closeness of repeated measurements (of the same quantity) to one another.

Definition 2.4 (Bias). A systematic variation of measurements from the quantity being measured.

Precision is often measured by the standard deviation of a set of values, while bias is measured by taking the difference between the mean of the set of values and the known value of the quantity being measured. Bias can only be determined for objects whose measured quantity is known by means external to the current situation. Suppose that we have a standard laboratory weight with a mass of 1g and want to assess the precision and bias of our new laboratory scale. We weigh the mass five times, and obtain the following five values: $\{1.015, 0.990, 1.013, 1.001, 0.986\}$. The mean of these values is 1.001, and hence, the bias is 0.001. The precision, as measured by the standard deviation, is 0.013.

It is common to use the more general term, **accuracy**, to refer to the degree of measurement error in data.

Definition 2.5 (Accuracy). The closeness of measurements to the true value of the quantity being measured.

Accuracy depends on precision and bias, but since it is a general concept, there is no specific formula for accuracy in terms of these two quantities.

One important aspect of accuracy is the use of **significant digits**. The goal is to use only as many digits to represent the result of a measurement or calculation as are justified by the precision of the data. For example, if the length of an object is measured with a meter stick whose smallest markings are millimeters, then we should only record the length of data to the nearest millimeter. The precision of such a measurement would be $\pm$ 0.5mm. We do not review the details of working with significant digits, as most readers will have encountered them in previous courses, and they are covered in considerable depth in science, engineering, and statistics textbooks.

Issues such as significant digits, precision, bias, and accuracy are sometimes overlooked, but they are important for data mining as well as statistics and science. Many times, data sets do not come with information on the precision of the data, and furthermore, the programs used for analysis return results without any such information. Nonetheless, without some understanding of the accuracy of the data and the results, an analyst runs the risk of committing serious data analysis blunders.

Outliers

Outliers are either (1) data objects that, in some sense, have characteristics that are different from most of the other data objects in the data set, or (2) values of an attribute that are unusual with respect to the typical values for that attribute. Alternatively, we can speak of **anomalous** objects or values. There is considerable leeway in the definition of an outlier, and many different definitions have been proposed by the statistics and data mining communities. Furthermore, it is important to distinguish between the notions of noise and outliers. Outliers can be legitimate data objects or values. Thus, unlike noise, outliers may sometimes be of interest. In fraud and network intrusion detection, for example, the goal is to find unusual objects or events from among a large number of normal ones. Chapter 10 discusses anomaly detection in more detail.

Missing Values

It is not unusual for an object to be missing one or more attribute values. In some cases, the information was not collected; e.g., some people decline to give their age or weight. In other cases, some attributes are not applicable to all objects; e.g., often, forms have conditional parts that are filled out only when a person answers a previous question in a certain way, but for simplicity, all fields are stored. Regardless, missing values should be taken into account during the data analysis.

There are several strategies (and variations on these strategies) for dealing with missing data, each of which may be appropriate in certain circumstances. These strategies are listed next, along with an indication of their advantages and disadvantages.

Eliminate Data Objects or Attributes   A simple and effective strategy is to eliminate objects with missing values. However, even a partially specified data object contains some information, and if many objects have missing values, then a reliable analysis can be difficult or impossible. Nonetheless, if a data set has only a few objects that have missing values, then it may be expedient to omit them. A related strategy is to eliminate attributes that have missing values. This should be done with caution, however, since the eliminated attributes may be the ones that are critical to the analysis.

Estimate Missing Values   Sometimes missing data can be reliably estimated. For example, consider a time series that changes in a reasonably smooth fashion, but has a few, widely scattered missing values. In such cases, the missing values can be estimated (interpolated) by using the remaining values. As another example, consider a data set that has many similar data points. In this situation, the attribute values of the points closest to the point with the missing value are often used to estimate the missing value. If the attribute is continuous, then the average attribute value of the nearest neighbors is used; if the attribute is categorical, then the most commonly occurring attribute value can be taken. For a concrete illustration, consider precipitation measurements that are recorded by ground stations. For areas not containing a ground station, the precipitation can be estimated using values observed at nearby ground stations.

Ignore the Missing Value during Analysis   Many data mining approaches can be modified to ignore missing values. For example, suppose that objects are being clustered and the similarity between pairs of data objects needs to be calculated. If one or both objects of a pair have missing values for some attributes, then the similarity can be calculated by using only the attributes that do not have missing values. It is true that the similarity will only be approximate, but unless the total number of attributes is small or the number of missing values is high, this degree of inaccuracy may not matter much. Likewise, many classification schemes can be modified to work with missing values.

Inconsistent Values

Data can contain inconsistent values. Consider an address field, where both a zip code and city are listed, but the specified zip code area is not contained in that city. It may be that the individual entering this information transposed two digits, or perhaps a digit was misread when the information was scanned from a handwritten form. Regardless of the cause of the inconsistent values, it is important to detect and, if possible, correct such problems.

Some types of inconsistences are easy to detect. For instance, a person's height should not be negative. In other cases, it can be necessary to consult an external source of information. For example, when an insurance company processes claims for reimbursement, it checks the names and addresses on the reimbursement forms against a database of its customers.

Once an inconsistency has been detected, it is sometimes possible to correct the data. A product code may have "check" digits, or it may be possible to double-check a product code against a list of known product codes, and then correct the code if it is incorrect, but close to a known code. The correction of an inconsistency requires additional or redundant information.

Example 2.6 (Inconsistent Sea Surface Temperature). This example illustrates an inconsistency in actual time series data that measures the sea surface temperature (SST) at various points on the ocean. SST data was originally collected using ocean-based measurements from ships or buoys, but more recently, satellites have been used to gather the data. To create a long-term data set, both sources of data must be used. However, because the data comes from different sources, the two parts of the data are subtly different. This discrepancy is visually displayed in Figure 2.7, which shows the correlation of SST values between pairs of years. If a pair of years has a positive correlation, then the location corresponding to the pair of years is colored white; otherwise it is colored black. (Seasonal variations were removed from the data since, otherwise, all the years would be highly correlated.) There is a distinct change in behavior where the data has been put together in 1983. Years within each of the two groups, 1958–1982 and 1983–1999, tend to have a positive correlation with one another, but a negative correlation with years in the other group. This does not mean that this data should not be used, only that the analyst should consider the potential impact of such discrepancies on the data mining analysis.   ■

Duplicate Data

A data set may include data objects that are duplicates, or almost duplicates, of one another. Many people receive duplicate mailings because they appear in a database multiple times under slightly different names. To detect and eliminate such duplicates, two main issues must be addressed. First, if there are two objects that actually represent a single object, then the values of corresponding attributes may differ, and these inconsistent values must be

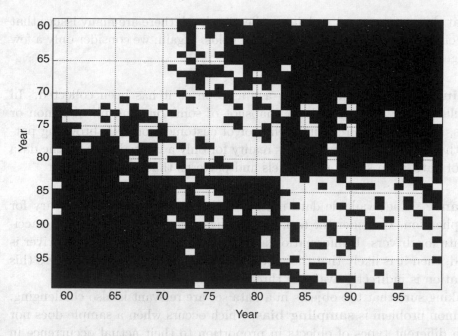

Figure 2.7. Correlation of SST data between pairs of years. White areas indicate positive correlation. Black areas indicate negative correlation.

resolved. Second, care needs to be taken to avoid accidentally combining data objects that are similar, but not duplicates, such as two distinct people with identical names. The term **deduplication** is often used to refer to the process of dealing with these issues.

In some cases, two or more objects are identical with respect to the attributes measured by the database, but they still represent different objects. Here, the duplicates are legitimate, but may still cause problems for some algorithms if the possibility of identical objects is not specifically accounted for in their design. An example of this is given in Exercise 13 on page 91.

2.2.2   Issues Related to Applications

Data quality issues can also be considered from an application viewpoint as expressed by the statement "data is of high quality if it is suitable for its intended use." This approach to data quality has proven quite useful, particularly in business and industry. A similar viewpoint is also present in statistics and the experimental sciences, with their emphasis on the careful design of experiments to collect the data relevant to a specific hypothesis. As with quality issues at the measurement and data collection level, there are many issues that are specific to particular applications and fields. Again, we consider only a few of the general issues.

Timeliness   Some data starts to age as soon as it has been collected. In particular, if the data provides a snapshot of some ongoing phenomenon or process, such as the purchasing behavior of customers or Web browsing patterns, then this snapshot represents reality for only a limited time. If the data is out of date, then so are the models and patterns that are based on it.

Relevance   The available data must contain the information necessary for the application. Consider the task of building a model that predicts the accident rate for drivers. If information about the age and gender of the driver is omitted, then it is likely that the model will have limited accuracy unless this information is indirectly available through other attributes.

Making sure that the objects in a data set are relevant is also challenging. A common problem is **sampling bias**, which occurs when a sample does not contain different types of objects in proportion to their actual occurrence in the population. For example, survey data describes only those who respond to the survey. (Other aspects of sampling are discussed further in Section 2.3.2.) Because the results of a data analysis can reflect only the data that is present, sampling bias will typically result in an erroneous analysis.

Knowledge about the Data   Ideally, data sets are accompanied by documentation that describes different aspects of the data; the quality of this documentation can either aid or hinder the subsequent analysis. For example, if the documentation identifies several attributes as being strongly related, these attributes are likely to provide highly redundant information, and we may decide to keep just one. (Consider sales tax and purchase price.) If the documentation is poor, however, and fails to tell us, for example, that the missing values for a particular field are indicated with a -9999, then our analysis of the data may be faulty. Other important characteristics are the precision of the data, the type of features (nominal, ordinal, interval, ratio), the scale of measurement (e.g., meters or feet for length), and the origin of the data.

2.3   Data Preprocessing

In this section, we address the issue of which preprocessing steps should be applied to make the data more suitable for data mining. Data preprocessing is a broad area and consists of a number of different strategies and techniques that are interrelated in complex ways. We will present some of the most important ideas and approaches, and try to point out the interrelationships among them. Specifically, we will discuss the following topics:

- Aggregation
- Sampling
- Dimensionality reduction
- Feature subset selection
- Feature creation
- Discretization and binarization
- Variable transformation

Roughly speaking, these items fall into two categories: selecting data objects and attributes for the analysis or creating/changing the attributes. In both cases the goal is to improve the data mining analysis with respect to time, cost, and quality. Details are provided in the following sections.

A quick note on terminology: In the following, we sometimes use synonyms for attribute, such as feature or variable, in order to follow common usage.

2.3.1 Aggregation

Sometimes "less is more" and this is the case with **aggregation**, the combining of two or more objects into a single object. Consider a data set consisting of transactions (data objects) recording the daily sales of products in various store locations (Minneapolis, Chicago, Paris, ...) for different days over the course of a year. See Table 2.4. One way to aggregate transactions for this data set is to replace all the transactions of a single store with a single storewide transaction. This reduces the hundreds or thousands of transactions that occur daily at a specific store to a single daily transaction, and the number of data objects is reduced to the number of stores.

An obvious issue is how an aggregate transaction is created; i.e., how the values of each attribute are combined across all the records corresponding to a particular location to create the aggregate transaction that represents the sales of a single store or date. Quantitative attributes, such as price, are typically aggregated by taking a sum or an average. A qualitative attribute, such as item, can either be omitted or summarized as the set of all the items that were sold at that location.

The data in Table 2.4 can also be viewed as a multidimensional array, where each attribute is a dimension. From this viewpoint, aggregation is the

Table 2.4. Data set containing information about customer purchases.

Transaction ID	Item	Store Location	Date	Price	...
⋮	⋮	⋮	⋮	⋮	
101123	Watch	Chicago	09/06/04	$25.99	...
101123	Battery	Chicago	09/06/04	$5.99	...
101124	Shoes	Minneapolis	09/06/04	$75.00	...
⋮	⋮	⋮	⋮	⋮	

process of eliminating attributes, such as the type of item, or reducing the number of values for a particular attribute; e.g., reducing the possible values for date from 365 days to 12 months. This type of aggregation is commonly used in Online Analytical Processing (OLAP), which is discussed further in Chapter 3.

There are several motivations for aggregation. First, the smaller data sets resulting from data reduction require less memory and processing time, and hence, aggregation may permit the use of more expensive data mining algorithms. Second, aggregation can act as a change of scope or scale by providing a high-level view of the data instead of a low-level view. In the previous example, aggregating over store locations and months gives us a monthly, per store view of the data instead of a daily, per item view. Finally, the behavior of groups of objects or attributes is often more stable than that of individual objects or attributes. This statement reflects the statistical fact that aggregate quantities, such as averages or totals, have less variability than the individual objects being aggregated. For totals, the actual amount of variation is larger than that of individual objects (on average), but the percentage of the variation is smaller, while for means, the actual amount of variation is less than that of individual objects (on average). A disadvantage of aggregation is the potential loss of interesting details. In the store example aggregating over months loses information about which day of the week has the highest sales.

Example 2.7 (Australian Precipitation). This example is based on precipitation in Australia from the period 1982 to 1993. Figure 2.8(a) shows a histogram for the standard deviation of average monthly precipitation for 3,030 0.5° by 0.5° grid cells in Australia, while Figure 2.8(b) shows a histogram for the standard deviation of the average yearly precipitation for the same locations. The average yearly precipitation has less variability than the average monthly precipitation. All precipitation measurements (and their standard deviations) are in centimeters.   ■

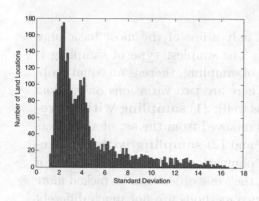

(a) Histogram of standard deviation of average monthly precipitation

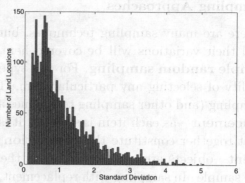

(b) Histogram of standard deviation of average yearly precipitation

Figure 2.8. Histograms of standard deviation for monthly and yearly precipitation in Australia for the period 1982 to 1993.

2.3.2 Sampling

Sampling is a commonly used approach for selecting a subset of the data objects to be analyzed. In statistics, it has long been used for both the preliminary investigation of the data and the final data analysis. Sampling can also be very useful in data mining. However, the motivations for sampling in statistics and data mining are often different. Statisticians use sampling because obtaining the entire set of data of interest is too expensive or time consuming, while data miners sample because it is too expensive or time consuming to process all the data. In some cases, using a sampling algorithm can reduce the data size to the point where a better, but more expensive algorithm can be used.

The key principle for effective sampling is the following: Using a sample will work almost as well as using the entire data set if the sample is representative. In turn, **a sample is representative** if it has approximately the same property (of interest) as the original set of data. If the mean (average) of the data objects is the property of interest, then a sample is representative if it has a mean that is close to that of the original data. Because sampling is a statistical process, the representativeness of any particular sample will vary, and the best that we can do is choose a sampling scheme that guarantees a high probability of getting a representative sample. As discussed next, this involves choosing the appropriate sample size and sampling techniques.

Sampling Approaches

There are many sampling techniques, but only a few of the most basic ones and their variations will be covered here. The simplest type of sampling is **simple random sampling**. For this type of sampling, there is an equal probability of selecting any particular item. There are two variations on random sampling (and other sampling techniques as well): (1) **sampling without replacement**—as each item is selected, it is removed from the set of all objects that together constitute the **population**, and (2) **sampling with replacement**—objects are not removed from the population as they are selected for the sample. In sampling with replacement, the same object can be picked more than once. The samples produced by the two methods are not much different when samples are relatively small compared to the data set size, but sampling with replacement is simpler to analyze since the probability of selecting any object remains constant during the sampling process.

When the population consists of different types of objects, with widely different numbers of objects, simple random sampling can fail to adequately represent those types of objects that are less frequent. This can cause problems when the analysis requires proper representation of all object types. For example, when building classification models for rare classes, it is critical that the rare classes be adequately represented in the sample. Hence, a sampling scheme that can accommodate differing frequencies for the items of interest is needed. **Stratified sampling**, which starts with prespecified groups of objects, is such an approach. In the simplest version, equal numbers of objects are drawn from each group even though the groups are of different sizes. In another variation, the number of objects drawn from each group is proportional to the size of that group.

Example 2.8 (Sampling and Loss of Information). Once a sampling technique has been selected, it is still necessary to choose the sample size. Larger sample sizes increase the probability that a sample will be representative, but they also eliminate much of the advantage of sampling. Conversely, with smaller sample sizes, patterns may be missed or erroneous patterns can be detected. Figure 2.9(a) shows a data set that contains 8000 two-dimensional points, while Figures 2.9(b) and 2.9(c) show samples from this data set of size 2000 and 500, respectively. Although most of the structure of this data set is present in the sample of 2000 points, much of the structure is missing in the sample of 500 points. ∎

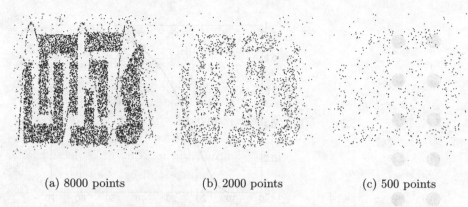

(a) 8000 points　　　　(b) 2000 points　　　　(c) 500 points

Figure 2.9. Example of the loss of structure with sampling.

Example 2.9 (Determining the Proper Sample Size). To illustrate that determining the proper sample size requires a methodical approach, consider the following task.

> Given a set of data that consists of a small number of almost equal-sized groups, find at least one representative point for each of the groups. Assume that the objects in each group are highly similar to each other, but not very similar to objects in different groups. Also assume that there are a relatively small number of groups, e.g., 10. Figure 2.10(a) shows an idealized set of clusters (groups) from which these points might be drawn.

This problem can be efficiently solved using sampling. One approach is to take a small sample of data points, compute the pairwise similarities between points, and then form groups of points that are highly similar. The desired set of representative points is then obtained by taking one point from each of these groups. To follow this approach, however, we need to determine a sample size that would guarantee, with a high probability, the desired outcome; that is, that at least one point will be obtained from each cluster. Figure 2.10(b) shows the probability of getting one object from each of the 10 groups as the sample size runs from 10 to 60. Interestingly, with a sample size of 20, there is little chance (20%) of getting a sample that includes all 10 clusters. Even with a sample size of 30, there is still a moderate chance (almost 40%) of getting a sample that doesn't contain objects from all 10 clusters. This issue is further explored in the context of clustering by Exercise 4 on page 559.

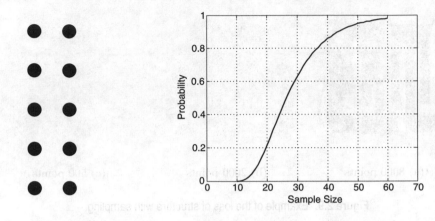

(a) Ten groups of points.   (b) Probability a sample contains points
                                       from each of 10 groups.

Figure 2.10. Finding representative points from 10 groups.

Progressive Sampling

The proper sample size can be difficult to determine, so **adaptive** or **progressive sampling** schemes are sometimes used. These approaches start with a small sample, and then increase the sample size until a sample of sufficient size has been obtained. While this technique eliminates the need to determine the correct sample size initially, it requires that there be a way to evaluate the sample to judge if it is large enough.

Suppose, for instance, that progressive sampling is used to learn a predictive model. Although the accuracy of predictive models increases as the sample size increases, at some point the increase in accuracy levels off. We want to stop increasing the sample size at this leveling-off point. By keeping track of the change in accuracy of the model as we take progressively larger samples, and by taking other samples close to the size of the current one, we can get an estimate as to how close we are to this leveling-off point, and thus, stop sampling.

2.3.3 Dimensionality Reduction

Data sets can have a large number of features. Consider a set of documents, where each document is represented by a vector whose components are the frequencies with which each word occurs in the document. In such cases, there are typically thousands or tens of thousands of attributes (components), one for each word in the vocabulary. As another example, consider a set of time series consisting of the daily closing price of various stocks over a period of 30 years. In this case, the attributes, which are the prices on specific days, again number in the thousands.

There are a variety of benefits to dimensionality reduction. A key benefit is that many data mining algorithms work better if the dimensionality—the number of attributes in the data—is lower. This is partly because dimensionality reduction can eliminate irrelevant features and reduce noise and partly because of the curse of dimensionality, which is explained below. Another benefit is that a reduction of dimensionality can lead to a more understandable model because the model may involve fewer attributes. Also, dimensionality reduction may allow the data to be more easily visualized. Even if dimensionality reduction doesn't reduce the data to two or three dimensions, data is often visualized by looking at pairs or triplets of attributes, and the number of such combinations is greatly reduced. Finally, the amount of time and memory required by the data mining algorithm is reduced with a reduction in dimensionality.

The term dimensionality reduction is often reserved for those techniques that reduce the dimensionality of a data set by creating new attributes that are a combination of the old attributes. The reduction of dimensionality by selecting new attributes that are a subset of the old is known as feature subset selection or feature selection. It will be discussed in Section 2.3.4.

In the remainder of this section, we briefly introduce two important topics: the curse of dimensionality and dimensionality reduction techniques based on linear algebra approaches such as principal components analysis (PCA). More details on dimensionality reduction can be found in Appendix B.

The Curse of Dimensionality

The curse of dimensionality refers to the phenomenon that many types of data analysis become significantly harder as the dimensionality of the data increases. Specifically, as dimensionality increases, the data becomes increasingly sparse in the space that it occupies. For classification, this can mean that there are not enough data objects to allow the creation of a model that reliably assigns a class to all possible objects. For clustering, the definitions of density and the distance between points, which are critical for clustering, become less meaningful. (This is discussed further in Sections 9.1.2, 9.4.5, and 9.4.7.) As a result, many clustering and classification algorithms (and other data analysis algorithms) have trouble with high-dimensional data—reduced classification accuracy and poor quality clusters.

Linear Algebra Techniques for Dimensionality Reduction

Some of the most common approaches for dimensionality reduction, particularly for continuous data, use techniques from linear algebra to project the data from a high-dimensional space into a lower-dimensional space. **Principal Components Analysis (PCA)** is a linear algebra technique for continuous attributes that finds new attributes (principal components) that (1) are linear combinations of the original attributes, (2) are **orthogonal** (perpendicular) to each other, and (3) capture the maximum amount of variation in the data. For example, the first two principal components capture as much of the variation in the data as is possible with two orthogonal attributes that are linear combinations of the original attributes. **Singular Value Decomposition (SVD)** is a linear algebra technique that is related to PCA and is also commonly used for dimensionality reduction. For additional details, see Appendices A and B.

2.3.4   Feature Subset Selection

Another way to reduce the dimensionality is to use only a subset of the features. While it might seem that such an approach would lose information, this is not the case if redundant and irrelevant features are present. **Redundant features** duplicate much or all of the information contained in one or more other attributes. For example, the purchase price of a product and the amount of sales tax paid contain much of the same information. **Irrelevant features** contain almost no useful information for the data mining task at hand. For instance, students' ID numbers are irrelevant to the task of predicting students' grade point averages. Redundant and irrelevant features can reduce classification accuracy and the quality of the clusters that are found.

While some irrelevant and redundant attributes can be eliminated immediately by using common sense or domain knowledge, selecting the best subset of features frequently requires a systematic approach. The ideal approach to feature selection is to try all possible subsets of features as input to the data mining algorithm of interest, and then take the subset that produces the best results. This method has the advantage of reflecting the objective and bias of the data mining algorithm that will eventually be used. Unfortunately, since the number of subsets involving n attributes is 2^n, such an approach is impractical in most situations and alternative strategies are needed. There are three standard approaches to feature selection: embedded, filter, and wrapper.

Embedded approaches Feature selection occurs naturally as part of the data mining algorithm. Specifically, during the operation of the data mining algorithm, the algorithm itself decides which attributes to use and which to ignore. Algorithms for building decision tree classifiers, which are discussed in Chapter 4, often operate in this manner.

Filter approaches Features are selected before the data mining algorithm is run, using some approach that is independent of the data mining task. For example, we might select sets of attributes whose pairwise correlation is as low as possible.

Wrapper approaches These methods use the target data mining algorithm as a black box to find the best subset of attributes, in a way similar to that of the ideal algorithm described above, but typically without enumerating all possible subsets.

Since the embedded approaches are algorithm-specific, only the filter and wrapper approaches will be discussed further here.

An Architecture for Feature Subset Selection

It is possible to encompass both the filter and wrapper approaches within a common architecture. The feature selection process is viewed as consisting of four parts: a measure for evaluating a subset, a search strategy that controls the generation of a new subset of features, a stopping criterion, and a validation procedure. Filter methods and wrapper methods differ only in the way in which they evaluate a subset of features. For a wrapper method, subset evaluation uses the target data mining algorithm, while for a filter approach, the evaluation technique is distinct from the target data mining algorithm. The following discussion provides some details of this approach, which is summarized in Figure 2.11.

Conceptually, feature subset selection is a search over all possible subsets of features. Many different types of search strategies can be used, but the search strategy should be computationally inexpensive and should find optimal or near optimal sets of features. It is usually not possible to satisfy both requirements, and thus, tradeoffs are necessary.

An integral part of the search is an evaluation step to judge how the current subset of features compares to others that have been considered. This requires an evaluation measure that attempts to determine the goodness of a subset of attributes with respect to a particular data mining task, such as classification

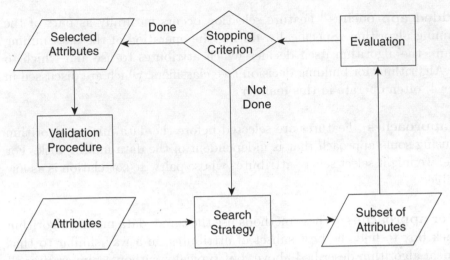

Figure 2.11. Flowchart of a feature subset selection process.

or clustering. For the filter approach, such measures attempt to predict how well the actual data mining algorithm will perform on a given set of attributes. For the wrapper approach, where evaluation consists of actually running the target data mining application, the subset evaluation function is simply the criterion normally used to measure the result of the data mining.

Because the number of subsets can be enormous and it is impractical to examine them all, some sort of stopping criterion is necessary. This strategy is usually based on one or more conditions involving the following: the number of iterations, whether the value of the subset evaluation measure is optimal or exceeds a certain threshold, whether a subset of a certain size has been obtained, whether simultaneous size and evaluation criteria have been achieved, and whether any improvement can be achieved by the options available to the search strategy.

Finally, once a subset of features has been selected, the results of the target data mining algorithm on the selected subset should be validated. A straightforward evaluation approach is to run the algorithm with the full set of features and compare the full results to results obtained using the subset of features. Hopefully, the subset of features will produce results that are better than or almost as good as those produced when using all features. Another validation approach is to use a number of different feature selection algorithms to obtain subsets of features and then compare the results of running the data mining algorithm on each subset.

Feature Weighting

Feature weighting is an alternative to keeping or eliminating features. More important features are assigned a higher weight, while less important features are given a lower weight. These weights are sometimes assigned based on domain knowledge about the relative importance of features. Alternatively, they may be determined automatically. For example, some classification schemes, such as support vector machines (Chapter 5), produce classification models in which each feature is given a weight. Features with larger weights play a more important role in the model. The normalization of objects that takes place when computing the cosine similarity (Section 2.4.5) can also be regarded as a type of feature weighting.

2.3.5 Feature Creation

It is frequently possible to create, from the original attributes, a new set of attributes that captures the important information in a data set much more effectively. Furthermore, the number of new attributes can be smaller than the number of original attributes, allowing us to reap all the previously described benefits of dimensionality reduction. Three related methodologies for creating new attributes are described next: feature extraction, mapping the data to a new space, and feature construction.

Feature Extraction

The creation of a new set of features from the original raw data is known as **feature extraction**. Consider a set of photographs, where each photograph is to be classified according to whether or not it contains a human face. The raw data is a set of pixels, and as such, is not suitable for many types of classification algorithms. However, if the data is processed to provide higher-level features, such as the presence or absence of certain types of edges and areas that are highly correlated with the presence of human faces, then a much broader set of classification techniques can be applied to this problem.

Unfortunately, in the sense in which it is most commonly used, feature extraction is highly domain-specific. For a particular field, such as image processing, various features and the techniques to extract them have been developed over a period of time, and often these techniques have limited applicability to other fields. Consequently, whenever data mining is applied to a relatively new area, a key task is the development of new features and feature extraction methods.

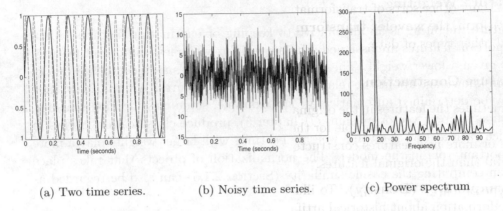

(a) Two time series.   (b) Noisy time series.   (c) Power spectrum

Figure 2.12. Application of the Fourier transform to identify the underlying frequencies in time series data.

Mapping the Data to a New Space

A totally different view of the data can reveal important and interesting features. Consider, for example, time series data, which often contains periodic patterns. If there is only a single periodic pattern and not much noise, then the pattern is easily detected. If, on the other hand, there are a number of periodic patterns and a significant amount of noise is present, then these patterns are hard to detect. Such patterns can, nonetheless, often be detected by applying a **Fourier transform** to the time series in order to change to a representation in which frequency information is explicit. In the example that follows, it will not be necessary to know the details of the Fourier transform. It is enough to know that, for each time series, the Fourier transform produces a new data object whose attributes are related to frequencies.

Example 2.10 (Fourier Analysis). The time series presented in Figure 2.12(b) is the sum of three other time series, two of which are shown in Figure 2.12(a) and have frequencies of 7 and 17 cycles per second, respectively. The third time series is random noise. Figure 2.12(c) shows the power spectrum that can be computed after applying a Fourier transform to the original time series. (Informally, the power spectrum is proportional to the square of each frequency attribute.) In spite of the noise, there are two peaks that correspond to the periods of the two original, non-noisy time series. Again, the main point is that better features can reveal important aspects of the data. ∎

Many other sorts of transformations are also possible. Besides the Fourier transform, the **wavelet transform** has also proven very useful for time series and other types of data.

Feature Construction

Sometimes the features in the original data sets have the necessary information, but it is not in a form suitable for the data mining algorithm. In this situation, one or more new features constructed out of the original features can be more useful than the original features.

Example 2.11 (Density). To illustrate this, consider a data set consisting of information about historical artifacts, which, along with other information, contains the volume and mass of each artifact. For simplicity, assume that these artifacts are made of a small number of materials (wood, clay, bronze, gold) and that we want to classify the artifacts with respect to the material of which they are made. In this case, a density feature constructed from the mass and volume features, i.e., $density = mass/volume$, would most directly yield an accurate classification. Although there have been some attempts to automatically perform feature construction by exploring simple mathematical combinations of existing attributes, the most common approach is to construct features using domain expertise. ∎

2.3.6 Discretization and Binarization

Some data mining algorithms, especially certain classification algorithms, require that the data be in the form of categorical attributes. Algorithms that find association patterns require that the data be in the form of binary attributes. Thus, it is often necessary to transform a continuous attribute into a categorical attribute (**discretization**), and both continuous and discrete attributes may need to be transformed into one or more binary attributes (**binarization**). Additionally, if a categorical attribute has a large number of values (categories), or some values occur infrequently, then it may be beneficial for certain data mining tasks to reduce the number of categories by combining some of the values.

As with feature selection, the best discretization and binarization approach is the one that "produces the best result for the data mining algorithm that will be used to analyze the data." It is typically not practical to apply such a criterion directly. Consequently, discretization or binarization is performed in

Table 2.5. Conversion of a categorical attribute to three binary attributes.

Categorical Value	Integer Value	x_1	x_2	x_3
awful	0	0	0	0
poor	1	0	0	1
OK	2	0	1	0
good	3	0	1	1
great	4	1	0	0

Table 2.6. Conversion of a categorical attribute to five asymmetric binary attributes.

Categorical Value	Integer Value	x_1	x_2	x_3	x_4	x_5
awful	0	1	0	0	0	0
poor	1	0	1	0	0	0
OK	2	0	0	1	0	0
good	3	0	0	0	1	0
great	4	0	0	0	0	1

a way that satisfies a criterion that is thought to have a relationship to good performance for the data mining task being considered.

Binarization

A simple technique to binarize a categorical attribute is the following: If there are m categorical values, then uniquely assign each original value to an integer in the interval $[0, m-1]$. If the attribute is ordinal, then order must be maintained by the assignment. (Note that even if the attribute is originally represented using integers, this process is necessary if the integers are not in the interval $[0, m-1]$.) Next, convert each of these m integers to a binary number. Since $n = \lceil \log_2(m) \rceil$ binary digits are required to represent these integers, represent these binary numbers using n binary attributes. To illustrate, a categorical variable with 5 values {*awful, poor, OK, good, great*} would require three binary variables x_1, x_2, and x_3. The conversion is shown in Table 2.5.

Such a transformation can cause complications, such as creating unintended relationships among the transformed attributes. For example, in Table 2.5, attributes x_2 and x_3 are correlated because information about the *good* value is encoded using both attributes. Furthermore, association analysis requires asymmetric binary attributes, where only the presence of the attribute (value = 1) is important. For association problems, it is therefore necessary to introduce one binary attribute for each categorical value, as in Table 2.6. If the number of resulting attributes is too large, then the techniques described below can be used to reduce the number of categorical values before binarization.

Likewise, for association problems, it may be necessary to replace a single binary attribute with two asymmetric binary attributes. Consider a binary attribute that records a person's gender, male or female. For traditional association rule algorithms, this information needs to be transformed into two asymmetric binary attributes, one that is a 1 only when the person is male and one that is a 1 only when the person is female. (For asymmetric binary attributes, the information representation is somewhat inefficient in that two bits of storage are required to represent each bit of information.)

Discretization of Continuous Attributes

Discretization is typically applied to attributes that are used in classification or association analysis. In general, the best discretization depends on the algorithm being used, as well as the other attributes being considered. Typically, however, the discretization of an attribute is considered in isolation.

Transformation of a continuous attribute to a categorical attribute involves two subtasks: deciding how many categories to have and determining how to map the values of the continuous attribute to these categories. In the first step, after the values of the continuous attribute are sorted, they are then divided into n intervals by specifying $n-1$ **split points**. In the second, rather trivial step, all the values in one interval are mapped to the same categorical value. Therefore, the problem of discretization is one of deciding how many split points to choose and where to place them. The result can be represented either as a set of intervals $\{(x_0, x_1], (x_1, x_2], \ldots, (x_{n-1}, x_n)\}$, where x_0 and x_n may be $+\infty$ or $-\infty$, respectively, or equivalently, as a series of inequalities $x_0 < x \leq x_1, \ldots, x_{n-1} < x < x_n$.

Unsupervised Discretization   A basic distinction between discretization methods for classification is whether class information is used (supervised) or not (unsupervised). If class information is not used, then relatively simple approaches are common. For instance, the **equal width** approach divides the range of the attribute into a user-specified number of intervals each having the same width. Such an approach can be badly affected by outliers, and for that reason, an **equal frequency (equal depth)** approach, which tries to put the same number of objects into each interval, is often preferred. As another example of unsupervised discretization, a clustering method, such as K-means (see Chapter 8), can also be used. Finally, visually inspecting the data can sometimes be an effective approach.

Example 2.12 (Discretization Techniques). This example demonstrates how these approaches work on an actual data set. Figure 2.13(a) shows data points belonging to four different groups, along with two outliers—the large dots on either end. The techniques of the previous paragraph were applied to discretize the x values of these data points into four categorical values. (Points in the data set have a random y component to make it easy to see how many points are in each group.) Visually inspecting the data works quite well, but is not automatic, and thus, we focus on the other three approaches. The split points produced by the techniques equal width, equal frequency, and K-means are shown in Figures 2.13(b), 2.13(c), and 2.13(d), respectively. The split points are represented as dashed lines. If we measure the performance of a discretization technique by the extent to which different objects in different groups are assigned the same categorical value, then K-means performs best, followed by equal frequency, and finally, equal width.   ∎

Supervised Discretization   The discretization methods described above are usually better than no discretization, but keeping the end purpose in mind and using additional information (class labels) often produces better results. This should not be surprising, since an interval constructed with no knowledge of class labels often contains a mixture of class labels. A conceptually simple approach is to place the splits in a way that maximizes the purity of the intervals. In practice, however, such an approach requires potentially arbitrary decisions about the purity of an interval and the minimum size of an interval. To overcome such concerns, some statistically based approaches start with each attribute value as a separate interval and create larger intervals by merging adjacent intervals that are similar according to a statistical test. Entropy-based approaches are one of the most promising approaches to discretization, and a simple approach based on entropy will be presented.

First, it is necessary to define **entropy**. Let k be the number of different class labels, m_i be the number of values in the ith interval of a partition, and m_{ij} be the number of values of class j in interval i. Then the entropy e_i of the ith interval is given by the equation

$$e_i = \sum_{i=1}^{k} p_{ij} \log_2 p_{ij},$$

where $p_{ij} = m_{ij}/m_i$ is the probability (fraction of values) of class j in the ith interval. The total entropy, e, of the partition is the weighted average of the individual interval entropies, i.e.,

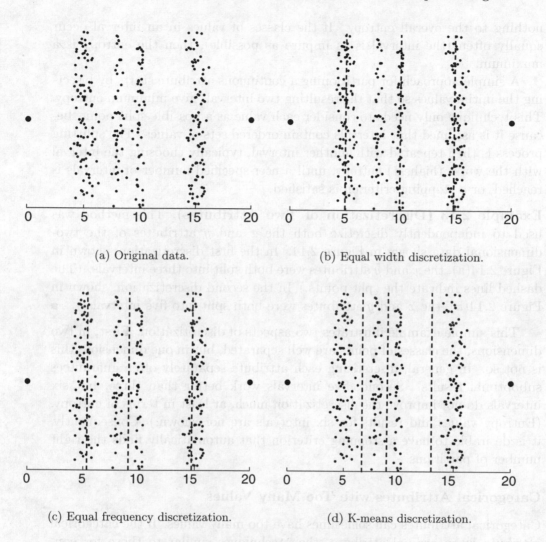

(a) Original data.

(b) Equal width discretization.

(c) Equal frequency discretization.

(d) K-means discretization.

Figure 2.13. Different discretization techniques.

$$e = \sum_{i=1}^{n} w_i e_i,$$

where m is the number of values, $w_i = m_i/m$ is the fraction of values in the ith interval, and n is the number of intervals. Intuitively, the entropy of an interval is a measure of the purity of an interval. If an interval contains only values of one class (is perfectly pure), then the entropy is 0 and it contributes nothing to the overall entropy. If the classes of values in an interval occur equally often (the interval is as impure as possible), then the entropy is a maximum.

A simple approach for partitioning a continuous attribute starts by bisecting the initial values so that the resulting two intervals give minimum entropy. This technique only needs to consider each value as a possible split point, because it is assumed that intervals contain ordered sets of values. The splitting process is then repeated with another interval, typically choosing the interval with the worst (highest) entropy, until a user-specified number of intervals is reached, or a stopping criterion is satisfied.

Example 2.13 (Discretization of Two Attributes). This method was used to independently discretize both the x and y attributes of the two-dimensional data shown in Figure 2.14. In the first discretization, shown in Figure 2.14(a), the x and y attributes were both split into three intervals. (The dashed lines indicate the split points.) In the second discretization, shown in Figure 2.14(b), the x and y attributes were both split into five intervals. ∎

This simple example illustrates two aspects of discretization. First, in two dimensions, the classes of points are well separated, but in one dimension, this is not so. In general, discretizing each attribute separately often guarantees suboptimal results. Second, five intervals work better than three, but six intervals do not improve the discretization much, at least in terms of entropy. (Entropy values and results for six intervals are not shown.) Consequently, it is desirable to have a stopping criterion that automatically finds the right number of partitions.

Categorical Attributes with Too Many Values

Categorical attributes can sometimes have too many values. If the categorical attribute is an ordinal attribute, then techniques similar to those for continuous attributes can be used to reduce the number of categories. If the categorical attribute is nominal, however, then other approaches are needed. Consider a university that has a large number of departments. Consequently, a *department name* attribute might have dozens of different values. In this situation, we could use our knowledge of the relationships among different departments to combine departments into larger groups, such as *engineering*, *social sciences*, or *biological sciences*. If domain knowledge does not serve as a useful guide or such an approach results in poor classification performance, then it is necessary to use a more empirical approach, such as grouping values

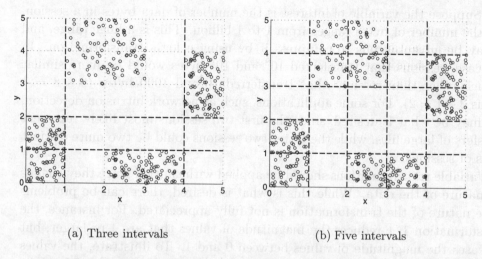

(a) Three intervals   (b) Five intervals

Figure 2.14. Discretizing x and y attributes for four groups (classes) of points.

together only if such a grouping results in improved classification accuracy or achieves some other data mining objective.

2.3.7 Variable Transformation

A **variable transformation** refers to a transformation that is applied to all the values of a variable. (We use the term variable instead of attribute to adhere to common usage, although we will also refer to attribute transformation on occasion.) In other words, for each object, the transformation is applied to the value of the variable for that object. For example, if only the magnitude of a variable is important, then the values of the variable can be transformed by taking the absolute value. In the following section, we discuss two important types of variable transformations: simple functional transformations and normalization.

Simple Functions

For this type of variable transformation, a simple mathematical function is applied to each value individually. If x is a variable, then examples of such transformations include x^k, $\log x$, e^x, $\sqrt{x}$, $1/x$, $\sin x$, or $|x|$. In statistics, variable transformations, especially *sqrt*, *log*, and $1/x$, are often used to transform data that does not have a Gaussian (normal) distribution into data that does. While this can be important, other reasons often take precedence in data mining. Suppose the variable of interest is the number of data bytes in a session, and the number of bytes ranges from 1 to 1 billion. This is a huge range, and it may be advantageous to compress it by using a $\log_{10}$ transformation. In this case, sessions that transferred 10^8 and 10^9 bytes would be more similar to each other than sessions that transferred 10 and 1000 bytes ($9 - 8 = 1$ versus $3 - 1 = 2$). For some applications, such as network intrusion detection, this may be what is desired, since the first two sessions most likely represent transfers of large files, while the latter two sessions could be two quite distinct types of sessions.

Variable transformations should be applied with caution since they change the nature of the data. While this is what is desired, there can be problems if the nature of the transformation is not fully appreciated. For instance, the transformation $1/x$ reduces the magnitude of values that are 1 or larger, but increases the magnitude of values between 0 and 1. To illustrate, the values $\{1, 2, 3\}$ go to $\{1, \frac{1}{2}, \frac{1}{3}\}$, but the values $\{1, \frac{1}{2}, \frac{1}{3}\}$ go to $\{1, 2, 3\}$. Thus, for all sets of values, the transformation $1/x$ reverses the order. To help clarify the effect of a transformation, it is important to ask questions such as the following: Does the order need to be maintained? Does the transformation apply to all values, especially negative values and 0? What is the effect of the transformation on the values between 0 and 1? Exercise 17 on page 92 explores other aspects of variable transformation.

Normalization or Standardization

Another common type of variable transformation is the **standardization** or **normalization** of a variable. (In the data mining community the terms are often used interchangeably. In statistics, however, the term normalization can be confused with the transformations used for making a variable **normal**, i.e., **Gaussian**.) The goal of standardization or normalization is to make an entire set of values have a particular property. A traditional example is that of "standardizing a variable" in statistics. If $\overline{x}$ is the mean (average) of the attribute values and s_x is their standard deviation, then the transformation $x' = (x - \overline{x})/s_x$ creates a new variable that has a mean of 0 and a standard deviation of 1. If different variables are to be combined in some way, then such a transformation is often necessary to avoid having a variable with large values dominate the results of the calculation. To illustrate, consider comparing people based on two variables: age and income. For any two people, the difference in income will likely be much higher in absolute terms (hundreds or thousands of dollars) than the difference in age (less than 150). If the differences in the range of values of age and income are not taken into account, then the comparison between people will be dominated by differences in income. In particular, if the similarity or dissimilarity of two people is calculated using the similarity or dissimilarity measures defined later in this chapter, then in many cases, such as that of Euclidean distance, the income values will dominate the calculation.

The mean and standard deviation are strongly affected by outliers, so the above transformation is often modified. First, the mean is replaced by the **median**, i.e., the middle value. Second, the standard deviation is replaced by the **absolute standard deviation**. Specifically, if x is a variable, then the absolute standard deviation of x is given by $\sigma_A = \sum_{i=1}^{m} |x_i - \mu|$, where x_i is the ith value of the variable, m is the number of objects, and μ is either the mean or median. Other approaches for computing estimates of the location (center) and spread of a set of values in the presence of outliers are described in Sections 3.2.3 and 3.2.4, respectively. These measures can also be used to define a standardization transformation.

2.4 Measures of Similarity and Dissimilarity

Similarity and dissimilarity are important because they are used by a number of data mining techniques, such as clustering, nearest neighbor classification, and anomaly detection. In many cases, the initial data set is not needed once these similarities or dissimilarities have been computed. Such approaches can be viewed as transforming the data to a similarity (dissimilarity) space and then performing the analysis.

We begin with a discussion of the basics: high-level definitions of similarity and dissimilarity, and a discussion of how they are related. For convenience, the term **proximity** is used to refer to either similarity or dissimilarity. Since the proximity between two objects is a function of the proximity between the corresponding attributes of the two objects, we first describe how to measure the proximity between objects having only one simple attribute, and then consider proximity measures for objects with multiple attributes. This includes measures such as correlation and Euclidean distance, which are useful for dense data such as time series or two-dimensional points, as well as the Jaccard and cosine similarity measures, which are useful for sparse data like documents. Next, we consider several important issues concerning proximity measures. The section concludes with a brief discussion of how to select the right proximity measure.

2.4.1   Basics

Definitions

Informally, the **similarity** between two objects is a numerical measure of the degree to which the two objects are alike. Consequently, similarities are *higher* for pairs of objects that are more alike. Similarities are usually non-negative and are often between 0 (no similarity) and 1 (complete similarity).

The **dissimilarity** between two objects is a numerical measure of the degree to which the two objects are different. Dissimilarities are *lower* for more similar pairs of objects. Frequently, the term **distance** is used as a synonym for dissimilarity, although, as we shall see, distance is often used to refer to a special class of dissimilarities. Dissimilarities sometimes fall in the interval $[0, 1]$, but it is also common for them to range from 0 to ∞.

Transformations

Transformations are often applied to convert a similarity to a dissimilarity, or vice versa, or to transform a proximity measure to fall within a particular range, such as [0,1]. For instance, we may have similarities that range from 1 to 10, but the particular algorithm or software package that we want to use may be designed to only work with dissimilarities, or it may only work with similarities in the interval [0,1]. We discuss these issues here because we will employ such transformations later in our discussion of proximity. In addition, these issues are relatively independent of the details of specific proximity measures.

Frequently, proximity measures, especially similarities, are defined or transformed to have values in the interval [0,1]. Informally, the motivation for this is to use a scale in which a proximity value indicates the fraction of similarity (or dissimilarity) between two objects. Such a transformation is often relatively straightforward. For example, if the similarities between objects range from 1 (not at all similar) to 10 (completely similar), we can make them fall within the range $[0, 1]$ by using the transformation $s' = (s - 1)/9$, where s and s' are the original and new similarity values, respectively. In the more general case, the transformation of similarities to the interval $[0, 1]$ is given by the expression $s' = (s - min\_s)/(max\_s - min\_s)$, where max_s and min_s are the maximum and minimum similarity values, respectively. Likewise, dissimilarity measures with a finite range can be mapped to the interval [0,1] by using the formula $d' = (d - min\_d)/(max\_d - min\_d)$.

There can be various complications in mapping proximity measures to the interval $[0, 1]$, however. If, for example, the proximity measure originally takes values in the interval $[0,\infty]$, then a non-linear transformation is needed and values will not have the same relationship to one another on the new scale. Consider the transformation $d' = d/(1 + d)$ for a dissimilarity measure that ranges from 0 to ∞. The dissimilarities 0, 0.5, 2, 10, 100, and 1000 will be transformed into the new dissimilarities 0, 0.33, 0.67, 0.90, 0.99, and 0.999, respectively. Larger values on the original dissimilarity scale are compressed into the range of values near 1, but whether or not this is desirable depends on the application. Another complication is that the meaning of the proximity measure may be changed. For example, correlation, which is discussed later, is a measure of similarity that takes values in the interval [-1,1]. Mapping these values to the interval [0,1] by taking the absolute value loses information about the sign, which can be important in some applications. See Exercise 22 on page 94.

Transforming similarities to dissimilarities and vice versa is also relatively straightforward, although we again face the issues of preserving meaning and changing a linear scale into a non-linear scale. If the similarity (or dissimilarity) falls in the interval [0,1], then the dissimilarity can be defined as $d = 1 - s$ ($s = 1 - d$). Another simple approach is to define similarity as the negative of the dissimilarity (or vice versa). To illustrate, the dissimilarities 0, 1, 10, and 100 can be transformed into the similarities 0, -1, -10, and -100, respectively.

The similarities resulting from the negation transformation are not restricted to the range $[0, 1]$, but if that is desired, then transformations such as $s = \frac{1}{d+1}$, $s = e^{-d}$, or $s = 1 - \frac{d-min\_d}{max\_d-min\_d}$ can be used. For the transformation $s = \frac{1}{d+1}$, the dissimilarities 0, 1, 10, 100 are transformed into 1, 0.5, 0.09, 0.01, respectively. For $s = e^{-d}$, they become 1.00, 0.37, 0.00, 0.00, respectively, while for $s = 1 - \frac{d-min\_d}{max\_d-min\_d}$ they become 1.00, 0.99, 0.00, 0.00, respectively. In this discussion, we have focused on converting dissimilarities to similarities. Conversion in the opposite direction is considered in Exercise 23 on page 94.

In general, any monotonic decreasing function can be used to convert dissimilarities to similarities, or vice versa. Of course, other factors also must be considered when transforming similarities to dissimilarities, or vice versa, or when transforming the values of a proximity measure to a new scale. We have mentioned issues related to preserving meaning, distortion of scale, and requirements of data analysis tools, but this list is certainly not exhaustive.

2.4.2   Similarity and Dissimilarity between Simple Attributes

The proximity of objects with a number of attributes is typically defined by combining the proximities of individual attributes, and thus, we first discuss proximity between objects having a single attribute. Consider objects described by one nominal attribute. What would it mean for two such objects to be similar? Since nominal attributes only convey information about the distinctness of objects, all we can say is that two objects either have the same value or they do not. Hence, in this case similarity is traditionally defined as 1 if attribute values match, and as 0 otherwise. A dissimilarity would be defined in the opposite way: 0 if the attribute values match, and 1 if they do not.

For objects with a single ordinal attribute, the situation is more complicated because information about order should be taken into account. Consider an attribute that measures the quality of a product, e.g., a candy bar, on the scale {*poor, fair, OK, good, wonderful*}. It would seem reasonable that a product, P1, which is rated *wonderful*, would be closer to a product P2, which is rated *good*, than it would be to a product P3, which is rated *OK*. To make this observation quantitative, the values of the ordinal attribute are often mapped to successive integers, beginning at 0 or 1, e.g., {*poor*=0, *fair*=1, *OK*=2, good=3, *wonderful*=4}. Then, $d(P1, P2) = 3 - 2 = 1$ or, if we want the dissimilarity to fall between 0 and 1, $d(P1, P2) = \frac{3-2}{4} = 0.25$. A similarity for ordinal attributes can then be defined as $s = 1 - d$.

This definition of similarity (dissimilarity) for an ordinal attribute should make the reader a bit uneasy since this assumes equal intervals, and this is not so. Otherwise, we would have an interval or ratio attribute. Is the difference between the values *fair* and *good* really the same as that between the values *OK* and *wonderful*? Probably not, but in practice, our options are limited, and in the absence of more information, this is the standard approach for defining proximity between ordinal attributes.

For interval or ratio attributes, the natural measure of dissimilarity between two objects is the absolute difference of their values. For example, we might compare our current weight and our weight a year ago by saying "I am ten pounds heavier." In cases such as these, the dissimilarities typically range from 0 to ∞, rather than from 0 to 1. The similarity of interval or ratio attributes is typically expressed by transforming a similarity into a dissimilarity, as previously described.

Table 2.7 summarizes this discussion. In this table, x and y are two objects that have one attribute of the indicated type. Also, $d(x, y)$ and $s(x, y)$ are the dissimilarity and similarity between x and y, respectively. Other approaches are possible; these are the most common ones.

The following two sections consider more complicated measures of proximity between objects that involve multiple attributes: (1) dissimilarities between data objects and (2) similarities between data objects. This division

Table 2.7. Similarity and dissimilarity for simple attributes

Attribute Type	Dissimilarity	Similarity
Nominal	$d = \begin{cases} 0 & \text{if } x = y \\ 1 & \text{if } x \neq y \end{cases}$	$s = \begin{cases} 1 & \text{if } x = y \\ 0 & \text{if } x \neq y \end{cases}$
Ordinal	$d = \lvert x - y \rvert / (n-1)$ (values mapped to integers 0 to $n-1$, where n is the number of values)	$s = 1 - d$
Interval or Ratio	$d = \lvert x - y \rvert$	$s = -d$, $s = \frac{1}{1+d}$, $s = e^{-d}$, $s = 1 - \frac{d - min\_d}{max\_d - min\_d}$

allows us to more naturally display the underlying motivations for employing various proximity measures. We emphasize, however, that similarities can be transformed into dissimilarities and vice versa using the approaches described earlier.

2.4.3 Dissimilarities between Data Objects

In this section, we discuss various kinds of dissimilarities. We begin with a discussion of distances, which are dissimilarities with certain properties, and then provide examples of more general kinds of dissimilarities.

Distances

We first present some examples, and then offer a more formal description of distances in terms of the properties common to all distances. The **Euclidean distance**, d, between two points, $\mathbf{x}$ and $\mathbf{y}$, in one-, two-, three-, or higher-dimensional space, is given by the following familiar formula:

$$d(\mathbf{x}, \mathbf{y}) = \sqrt{\sum_{k=1}^{n} (x_k - y_k)^2}, \tag{2.1}$$

where n is the number of dimensions and x_k and y_k are, respectively, the kth attributes (components) of x and y. We illustrate this formula with Figure 2.15 and Tables 2.8 and 2.9, which show a set of points, the x and y coordinates of these points, and the **distance matrix** containing the pairwise distances of these points.

Chapter 2   Data

The Euclidean distance measure given in Equation 2.1 is generalized by the **Minkowski** distance metric shown in Equation 2.2,

$$d(\mathbf{x}, \mathbf{y}) = \left(\sum_{k=1}^{n} |x_k - y_k|^r \right)^{1/r}, \tag{2.2}$$

where r is a parameter. The following are the three most common examples of Minkowski distances.

- $r = 1$. City block (Manhattan, taxicab, L_1 norm) distance. A common example is the **Hamming distance**, which is the number of bits that are different between two objects that have only binary attributes, i.e., between two binary vectors.

- $r = 2$. Euclidean distance (L_2 norm).

- $r = \infty$. Supremum (L_{max} or L_∞ norm) distance. This is the maximum difference between any attribute of the objects. More formally, the L_∞ distance is defined by Equation 2.3

$$d(\mathbf{x}, \mathbf{y}) = \lim_{r \to \infty} \left(\sum_{k=1}^{n} |x_k - y_k|^r \right)^{1/r}. \tag{2.3}$$

The r parameter should not be confused with the number of dimensions (attributes) n. The Euclidean, Manhattan, and supremum distances are defined for all values of n: $1, 2, 3, \ldots$, and specify different ways of combining the differences in each dimension (attribute) into an overall distance.

Tables 2.10 and 2.11, respectively, give the proximity matrices for the L_1 and L_∞ distances using data from Table 2.8. Notice that all these distance matrices are symmetric; i.e., the ij^{th} entry is the same as the ji^{th} entry. In Table 2.9, for instance, the fourth row of the first column and the fourth column of the first row both contain the value 5.1.

Distances, such as the Euclidean distance, have some well-known properties. If $d(\mathbf{x}, \mathbf{y})$ is the distance between two points, $\mathbf{x}$ and $\mathbf{y}$, then the following properties hold.

1. **Positivity**

    (a) $d(\mathbf{x}, \mathbf{x}) \geq 0$ for all $\mathbf{x}$ and $\mathbf{y}$,
    (b) $d(\mathbf{x}, \mathbf{y}) = 0$ only if $\mathbf{x} = \mathbf{y}$.

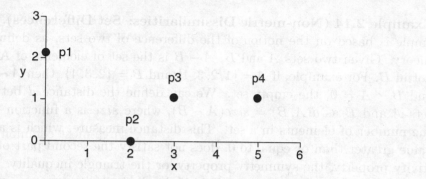

Figure 2.15. Four two-dimensional points.

Table 2.8. x and y coordinates of four points.

point	x coordinate	y coordinate
p1	0	2
p2	2	0
p3	3	1
p4	5	1

Table 2.9. Euclidean distance matrix for Table 2.8.

	p1	p2	p3	p4
p1	0.0	2.8	3.2	5.1
p2	2.8	0.0	1.4	3.2
p3	3.2	1.4	0.0	2.0
p4	5.1	3.2	2.0	0.0

Table 2.10. L_1 distance matrix for Table 2.8.

L_1	p1	p2	p3	p4
p1	0.0	4.0	4.0	6.0
p2	4.0	0.0	2.0	4.0
p3	4.0	2.0	0.0	2.0
p4	6.0	4.0	2.0	0.0

Table 2.11. L_∞ distance matrix for Table 2.8.

L_∞	p1	p2	p3	p4
p1	0.0	2.0	3.0	5.0
p2	2.0	0.0	1.0	3.0
p3	3.0	1.0	0.0	2.0
p4	5.0	3.0	2.0	0.0

2. **Symmetry**

$d(\mathbf{x}, \mathbf{y}) = d(\mathbf{y}, \mathbf{x})$ for all $\mathbf{x}$ and $\mathbf{y}$.

3. **Triangle Inequality**

$d(\mathbf{x}, \mathbf{z}) \leq d(\mathbf{x}, \mathbf{y}) + d(\mathbf{y}, \mathbf{z})$ for all points $\mathbf{x}$, $\mathbf{y}$, and $\mathbf{z}$.

Measures that satisfy all three properties are known as **metrics**. Some people only use the term distance for dissimilarity measures that satisfy these properties, but that practice is often violated. The three properties described here are useful, as well as mathematically pleasing. Also, if the triangle inequality holds, then this property can be used to increase the efficiency of techniques (including clustering) that depend on distances possessing this property. (See Exercise 25.) Nonetheless, many dissimilarities do not satisfy one or more of the metric properties. We give two examples of such measures.

Example 2.14 (Non-metric Dissimilarities: Set Differences). This example is based on the notion of the difference of two sets, as defined in set theory. Given two sets A and B, $A - B$ is the set of elements of A that are not in B. For example, if $A = \{1, 2, 3, 4\}$ and $B = \{2, 3, 4\}$, then $A - B = \{1\}$ and $B - A = \emptyset$, the empty set. We can define the distance d between two sets A and B as $d(A, B) = size(A - B)$, where $size$ is a function returning the number of elements in a set. This distance measure, which is an integer value greater than or equal to 0, does not satisfy the second part of the positivity property, the symmetry property, or the triangle inequality. However, these properties can be made to hold if the dissimilarity measure is modified as follows: $d(A, B) = size(A - B) + size(B - A)$. See Exercise 21 on page 94. ∎

Example 2.15 (Non-metric Dissimilarities: Time). This example gives a more everyday example of a dissimilarity measure that is not a metric, but that is still useful. Define a measure of the distance between times of the day as follows:

$$d(t_1, t_2) = \left\{ \begin{array}{ll} t_2 - t_1 & \text{if } t_1 \leq t_2 \\ 24 + (t_2 - t_1) & \text{if } t_1 \geq t_2 \end{array} \right\}. \tag{2.4}$$

To illustrate, $d(\text{1PM, 2PM}) = 1$ hour, while $d(\text{2PM, 1PM}) = 23$ hours. Such a definition would make sense, for example, when answering the question: "If an event occurs at 1PM every day, and it is now 2PM, how long do I have to wait for that event to occur again?" ∎

2.4.4 Similarities between Data Objects

For similarities, the triangle inequality (or the analogous property) typically does not hold, but symmetry and positivity typically do. To be explicit, if $s(\mathbf{x}, \mathbf{y})$ is the similarity between points $\mathbf{x}$ and $\mathbf{y}$, then the typical properties of similarities are the following:

1. $s(\mathbf{x}, \mathbf{y}) = 1$ only if $\mathbf{x} = \mathbf{y}$. $(0 \leq s \leq 1)$

2. $s(\mathbf{x}, \mathbf{y}) = s(\mathbf{y}, \mathbf{x})$ for all $\mathbf{x}$ and $\mathbf{y}$. (Symmetry)

There is no general analog of the triangle inequality for similarity measures. It is sometimes possible, however, to show that a similarity measure can easily be converted to a metric distance. The cosine and Jaccard similarity measures, which are discussed shortly, are two examples. Also, for specific similarity measures, it is possible to derive mathematical bounds on the similarity between two objects that are similar in spirit to the triangle inequality.

Example 2.16 (A Non-symmetric Similarity Measure). Consider an experiment in which people are asked to classify a small set of characters as they flash on a screen. The **confusion matrix** for this experiment records how often each character is classified as itself, and how often each is classified as another character. For instance, suppose that "0" appeared 200 times and was classified as a "0" 160 times, but as an "o" 40 times. Likewise, suppose that 'o' appeared 200 times and was classified as an "o" 170 times, but as "0" only 30 times. If we take these counts as a measure of the similarity between two characters, then we have a similarity measure, but one that is not symmetric. In such situations, the similarity measure is often made symmetric by setting $s'(\mathbf{x}, \mathbf{y}) = s'(\mathbf{y}, \mathbf{x}) = (s(\mathbf{x}, \mathbf{y}) + s(\mathbf{y}, \mathbf{x}))/2$, where s' indicates the new similarity measure. ∎

2.4.5 Examples of Proximity Measures

This section provides specific examples of some similarity and dissimilarity measures.

Similarity Measures for Binary Data

Similarity measures between objects that contain only binary attributes are called **similarity coefficients**, and typically have values between 0 and 1. A value of 1 indicates that the two objects are completely similar, while a value of 0 indicates that the objects are not at all similar. There are many rationales for why one coefficient is better than another in specific instances.

Let $\mathbf{x}$ and $\mathbf{y}$ be two objects that consist of n binary attributes. The comparison of two such objects, i.e., two binary vectors, leads to the following four quantities (frequencies):

f_{00} = the number of attributes where $\mathbf{x}$ is 0 and $\mathbf{y}$ is 0
f_{01} = the number of attributes where $\mathbf{x}$ is 0 and $\mathbf{y}$ is 1
f_{10} = the number of attributes where $\mathbf{x}$ is 1 and $\mathbf{y}$ is 0
f_{11} = the number of attributes where $\mathbf{x}$ is 1 and $\mathbf{y}$ is 1

Simple Matching Coefficient   One commonly used similarity coefficient is the **simple matching coefficient** (SMC), which is defined as

$$SMC = \frac{\text{number of matching attribute values}}{\text{number of attributes}} = \frac{f_{11} + f_{00}}{f_{01} + f_{10} + f_{11} + f_{00}}. \tag{2.5}$$

This measure counts both presences and absences equally. Consequently, the *SMC* could be used to find students who had answered questions similarly on a test that consisted only of true/false questions.

Jaccard Coefficient Suppose that **x** and **y** are data objects that represent two rows (two transactions) of a transaction matrix (see Section 2.1.2). If each asymmetric binary attribute corresponds to an item in a store, then a 1 indicates that the item was purchased, while a 0 indicates that the product was not purchased. Since the number of products not purchased by any customer far outnumbers the number of products that were purchased, a similarity measure such as *SMC* would say that all transactions are very similar. As a result, the Jaccard coefficient is frequently used to handle objects consisting of asymmetric binary attributes. The **Jaccard coefficient**, which is often symbolized by *J*, is given by the following equation:

$$J = \frac{\text{number of matching presences}}{\text{number of attributes not involved in 00 matches}} = \frac{f_{11}}{f_{01} + f_{10} + f_{11}}. \quad (2.6)$$

Example 2.17 (The SMC and Jaccard Similarity Coefficients). To illustrate the difference between these two similarity measures, we calculate *SMC* and *J* for the following two binary vectors.

$\mathbf{x} = (1, 0, 0, 0, 0, 0, 0, 0, 0, 0)$
$\mathbf{y} = (0, 0, 0, 0, 0, 0, 1, 0, 0, 1)$

$f_{01} = 2$ the number of attributes where **x** was 0 and **y** was 1
$f_{10} = 1$ the number of attributes where **x** was 1 and **y** was 0
$f_{00} = 7$ the number of attributes where **x** was 0 and **y** was 0
$f_{11} = 0$ the number of attributes where **x** was 1 and **y** was 1

$SMC = \frac{f_{11} + f_{00}}{f_{01} + f_{10} + f_{11} + f_{00}} = \frac{0 + 7}{2 + 1 + 0 + 7} = 0.7$

$J = \frac{f_{11}}{f_{01} + f_{10} + f_{11}} = \frac{0}{2 + 1 + 0} = 0$ ∎

Cosine Similarity

Documents are often represented as vectors, where each attribute represents the frequency with which a particular term (word) occurs in the document. It is more complicated than this, of course, since certain common words are ignored and various processing techniques are used to account for different forms of the same word, differing document lengths, and different word frequencies.

Even though documents have thousands or tens of thousands of attributes (terms), each document is sparse since it has relatively few non-zero attributes. (The normalizations used for documents do not create a non-zero entry where there was a zero entry; i.e., they preserve sparsity.) Thus, as with transaction data, similarity should not depend on the number of shared 0 values since any two documents are likely to "not contain" many of the same words, and therefore, if 0–0 matches are counted, most documents will be highly similar to most other documents. Therefore, a similarity measure for documents needs to ignores 0–0 matches like the Jaccard measure, but also must be able to handle non-binary vectors. The **cosine similarity**, defined next, is one of the most common measure of document similarity. If **x** and **y** are two document vectors, then

$$\cos(\mathbf{x}, \mathbf{y}) = \frac{\mathbf{x} \cdot \mathbf{y}}{\|\mathbf{x}\| \|\mathbf{y}\|}, \tag{2.7}$$

where $\cdot$ indicates the vector dot product, $\mathbf{x} \cdot \mathbf{y} = \sum_{k=1}^{n} x_k y_k$, and $\|\mathbf{x}\|$ is the length of vector **x**, $\|\mathbf{x}\| = \sqrt{\sum_{k=1}^{n} x_k^2} = \sqrt{\mathbf{x} \cdot \mathbf{x}}$.

Example 2.18 (Cosine Similarity of Two Document Vectors). This example calculates the cosine similarity for the following two data objects, which might represent document vectors:

$\mathbf{x} = (3, 2, 0, 5, 0, 0, 0, 2, 0, 0)$
$\mathbf{y} = (1, 0, 0, 0, 0, 0, 0, 1, 0, 2)$

$\mathbf{x} \cdot \mathbf{y} = 3*1 + 2*0 + 0*0 + 5*0 + 0*0 + 0*0 + 0*0 + 2*1 + 0*0 + 0*2 = 5$
$\|\mathbf{x}\| = \sqrt{3*3 + 2*2 + 0*0 + 5*5 + 0*0 + 0*0 + 0*0 + 2*2 + 0*0 + 0*0} = 6.48$
$\|\mathbf{y}\| = \sqrt{1*1 + 0*0 + 0*0 + 0*0 + 0*0 + 0*0 + 0*0 + 1*1 + 0*0 + 2*2} = 2.24$
$\cos(\mathbf{x}, \mathbf{y}) = \mathbf{0.31}$

∎

As indicated by Figure 2.16, cosine similarity really is a measure of the (cosine of the) angle between **x** and **y**. Thus, if the cosine similarity is 1, the angle between **x** and **y** is 0°, and **x** and **y** are the same except for magnitude (length). If the cosine similarity is 0, then the angle between **x** and **y** is 90°, and they do not share any terms (words).

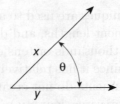

Figure 2.16. Geometric illustration of the cosine measure.

Equation 2.7 can be written as Equation 2.8.

$$\cos(\mathbf{x}, \mathbf{y}) = \frac{\mathbf{x}}{\|\mathbf{x}\|} \cdot \frac{\mathbf{y}}{\|\mathbf{y}\|} = \mathbf{x}' \cdot \mathbf{y}', \tag{2.8}$$

where $\mathbf{x}' = \mathbf{x}/\|\mathbf{x}\|$ and $\mathbf{y}' = \mathbf{y}/\|\mathbf{y}\|$. Dividing $\mathbf{x}$ and $\mathbf{y}$ by their lengths normalizes them to have a length of 1. This means that cosine similarity does not take the *magnitude* of the two data objects into account when computing similarity. (Euclidean distance might be a better choice when magnitude is important.) For vectors with a length of 1, the cosine measure can be calculated by taking a simple dot product. Consequently, when many cosine similarities between objects are being computed, normalizing the objects to have unit length can reduce the time required.

Extended Jaccard Coefficient (Tanimoto Coefficient)

The extended Jaccard coefficient can be used for document data and that reduces to the Jaccard coefficient in the case of binary attributes. The extended Jaccard coefficient is also known as the Tanimoto coefficient. (However, there is another coefficient that is also known as the Tanimoto coefficient.) This coefficient, which we shall represent as EJ, is defined by the following equation:

$$EJ(\mathbf{x}, \mathbf{y}) = \frac{\mathbf{x} \cdot \mathbf{y}}{\|\mathbf{x}\|^2 + \|\mathbf{y}\|^2 - \mathbf{x} \cdot \mathbf{y}}. \tag{2.9}$$

Correlation

The correlation between two data objects that have binary or continuous variables is a measure of the linear relationship between the attributes of the objects. (The calculation of correlation between attributes, which is more common, can be defined similarly.) More precisely, **Pearson's correlation** coefficient between two data objects, $\mathbf{x}$ and $\mathbf{y}$, is defined by the following equation:

$$\text{corr}(\mathbf{x}, \mathbf{y}) = \frac{\text{covariance}(\mathbf{x}, \mathbf{y})}{\text{standard\_deviation}(\mathbf{x}) * \text{standard\_deviation}(\mathbf{y})} = \frac{s_{xy}}{s_x \, s_y}, \quad (2.10)$$

where we are using the following standard statistical notation and definitions:

$$\text{covariance}(\mathbf{x}, \mathbf{y}) = s_{xy} = \frac{1}{n-1} \sum_{k=1}^{n} (x_k - \overline{x})(y_k - \overline{y}) \qquad (2.11)$$

$$\text{standard\_deviation}(\mathbf{x}) \;=\; s_x = \sqrt{\frac{1}{n-1} \sum_{k=1}^{n} (x_k - \overline{x})^2}$$

$$\text{standard\_deviation}(\mathbf{y}) \;=\; s_y = \sqrt{\frac{1}{n-1} \sum_{k=1}^{n} (y_k - \overline{y})^2}$$

$$\overline{x} \;=\; \frac{1}{n} \sum_{k=1}^{n} x_k \text{ is the mean of } \mathbf{x}$$

$$\overline{y} \;=\; \frac{1}{n} \sum_{k=1}^{n} y_k \text{ is the mean of } \mathbf{y}$$

Example 2.19 (Perfect Correlation). Correlation is always in the range -1 to 1. A correlation of 1 (-1) means that $\mathbf{x}$ and $\mathbf{y}$ have a perfect positive (negative) linear relationship; that is, $x_k = ay_k + b$, where a and b are constants. The following two sets of values for $\mathbf{x}$ and $\mathbf{y}$ indicate cases where the correlation is -1 and $+1$, respectively. In the first case, the means of $\mathbf{x}$ and $\mathbf{y}$ were chosen to be 0, for simplicity.

$\mathbf{x} = (-3, \; 6, \; 0, \; 3, -6)$
$\mathbf{y} = (\; 1, -2, \; 0, -1, \; 2)$

$\mathbf{x} = (3, 6, 0, 3, 6)$
$\mathbf{y} = (1, 2, 0, 1, 2)$

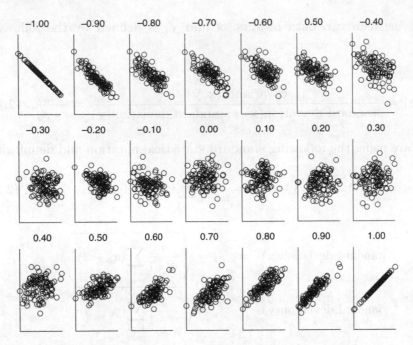

Figure 2.17. Scatter plots illustrating correlations from −1 to 1.

Example 2.20 (Non-linear Relationships). If the correlation is 0, then there is no linear relationship between the attributes of the two data objects. However, non-linear relationships may still exist. In the following example, $x_k = y_k^2$, but their correlation is 0.

$$\mathbf{x} = (-3, -2, -1, \ 0, \ 1, \ 2, \ 3)$$
$$\mathbf{y} = (\ 9, \quad 4, \quad 1, \ 0, \ 1, \ 4, \ 9)$$

■

Example 2.21 (Visualizing Correlation). It is also easy to judge the correlation between two data objects $\mathbf{x}$ and $\mathbf{y}$ by plotting pairs of corresponding attribute values. Figure 2.17 shows a number of these plots when $\mathbf{x}$ and $\mathbf{y}$ have 30 attributes and the values of these attributes are randomly generated (with a normal distribution) so that the correlation of $\mathbf{x}$ and $\mathbf{y}$ ranges from −1 to 1. Each circle in a plot represents one of the 30 attributes; its x coordinate is the value of one of the attributes for $\mathbf{x}$, while its y coordinate is the value of the same attribute for $\mathbf{y}$.

■

If we transform $\mathbf{x}$ and $\mathbf{y}$ by subtracting off their means and then normalizing them so that their lengths are 1, then their correlation can be calculated by taking the dot product. Notice that this is not the same as the standardization used in other contexts, where we make the transformations, $x'_k = (x_k - \overline{x})/s_x$ and $y'_k = (y_k - \overline{y})/s_y$.

Bregman Divergence* This section provides a brief description of Bregman divergences, which are a family of proximity functions that share some common properties. As a result, it is possible to construct general data mining algorithms, such as clustering algorithms, that work with any Bregman divergence. A concrete example is the K-means clustering algorithm (Section 8.2). Note that this section requires knowledge of vector calculus.

Bregman divergences are loss or distortion functions. To understand the idea of a loss function, consider the following. Let $\mathbf{x}$ and $\mathbf{y}$ be two points, where $\mathbf{y}$ is regarded as the original point and $\mathbf{x}$ is some distortion or approximation of it. For example, $\mathbf{x}$ may be a point that was generated, for example, by adding random noise to $\mathbf{y}$. The goal is to measure the resulting distortion or loss that results if $\mathbf{y}$ is approximated by $\mathbf{x}$. Of course, the more similar $\mathbf{x}$ and $\mathbf{y}$ are, the smaller the loss or distortion. Thus, Bregman divergences can be used as dissimilarity functions.

More formally, we have the following definition.

Definition 2.6 (Bregman Divergence). Given a strictly convex function ϕ (with a few modest restrictions that are generally satisfied), the Bregman divergence (loss function) $D(\mathbf{x}, \mathbf{y})$ generated by that function is given by the following equation:

$$D(\mathbf{x}, \mathbf{y}) = \phi(\mathbf{x}) - \phi(\mathbf{y}) - \langle \nabla\phi(\mathbf{y}), (\mathbf{x} - \mathbf{y}) \rangle \tag{2.12}$$

where $\nabla\phi(\mathbf{y})$ is the gradient of ϕ evaluated at $\mathbf{y}$, $\mathbf{x} - \mathbf{y}$, is the vector difference between $\mathbf{x}$ and $\mathbf{y}$, and $\langle \nabla\phi(\mathbf{y}), (\mathbf{x} - \mathbf{y}) \rangle$ is the inner product between $\nabla\phi(\mathbf{x})$ and $(\mathbf{x} - \mathbf{y})$. For points in Euclidean space, the inner product is just the dot product.

$D(\mathbf{x}, \mathbf{y})$ can be written as $D(\mathbf{x}, \mathbf{y}) = \phi(\mathbf{x}) - L(\mathbf{x})$, where $L(\mathbf{x}) = \phi(\mathbf{y}) + \langle \nabla\phi(\mathbf{y}), (\mathbf{x} - \mathbf{y}) \rangle$ and represents the equation of a plane that is tangent to the function ϕ at $\mathbf{y}$. Using calculus terminology, $L(\mathbf{x})$ is the linearization of ϕ around the point $\mathbf{y}$ and the Bregman divergence is just the difference between a function and a linear approximation to that function. Different Bregman divergences are obtained by using different choices for ϕ.

Example 2.22. We provide a concrete example using squared Euclidean distance, but restrict ourselves to one dimension to simplify the mathematics. Let

x and y be real numbers and $\phi(t)$ be the real valued function, $\phi(t) = t^2$. In that case, the gradient reduces to the derivative and the dot product reduces to multiplication. Specifically, Equation 2.12 becomes Equation 2.13.

$$D(x, y) = x^2 - y^2 - 2y(x - y) = (x - y)^2 \qquad (2.13)$$

The graph for this example, with $y = 1$, is shown in Figure 2.18. The Bregman divergence is shown for two values of x: $x = 2$ and $x = 3$. ∎

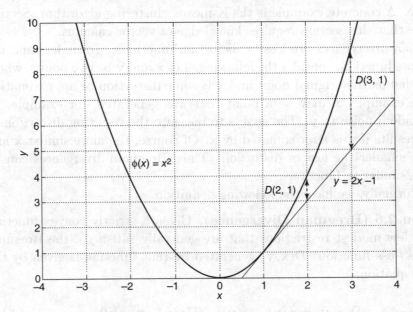

Figure 2.18. Illustration of Bregman divergence.

2.4.6   Issues in Proximity Calculation

This section discusses several important issues related to proximity measures: (1) how to handle the case in which attributes have different scales and/or are correlated, (2) how to calculate proximity between objects that are composed of different types of attributes, e.g., quantitative and qualitative, (3) and how to handle proximity calculation when attributes have different weights; i.e., when not all attributes contribute equally to the proximity of objects.

Standardization and Correlation for Distance Measures

An important issue with distance measures is how to handle the situation when attributes do not have the same range of values. (This situation is often described by saying that "the variables have different scales.") Earlier, Euclidean distance was used to measure the distance between people based on two attributes: age and income. Unless these two attributes are standardized, the distance between two people will be dominated by income.

A related issue is how to compute distance when there is correlation between some of the attributes, perhaps in addition to differences in the ranges of values. A generalization of Euclidean distance, the **Mahalanobis distance**, is useful when attributes are correlated, have different ranges of values (different variances), and the distribution of the data is approximately Gaussian (normal). Specifically, the Mahalanobis distance between two objects (vectors) $\mathbf{x}$ and $\mathbf{y}$ is defined as

$$\text{mahalanobis}(\mathbf{x}, \mathbf{y}) = (\mathbf{x} - \mathbf{y})\boldsymbol{\Sigma}^{-1}(\mathbf{x} - \mathbf{y})^T, \qquad (2.14)$$

where $\boldsymbol{\Sigma}^{-1}$ is the inverse of the covariance matrix of the data. Note that the covariance matrix $\boldsymbol{\Sigma}$ is the matrix whose ij^{th} entry is the covariance of the ith and j^{th} attributes as defined by Equation 2.11.

Example 2.23. In Figure 2.19, there are 1000 points, whose x and y attributes have a correlation of 0.6. The distance between the two large points at the opposite ends of the long axis of the ellipse is 14.7 in terms of Euclidean distance, but only 6 with respect to Mahalanobis distance. In practice, computing the Mahalanobis distance is expensive, but can be worthwhile for data whose attributes are correlated. If the attributes are relatively uncorrelated, but have different ranges, then standardizing the variables is sufficient. ∎

Combining Similarities for Heterogeneous Attributes

The previous definitions of similarity were based on approaches that assumed all the attributes were of the same type. A general approach is needed when the attributes are of different types. One straightforward approach is to compute the similarity between each attribute separately using Table 2.7, and then combine these similarities using a method that results in a similarity between 0 and 1. Typically, the overall similarity is defined as the average of all the individual attribute similarities.

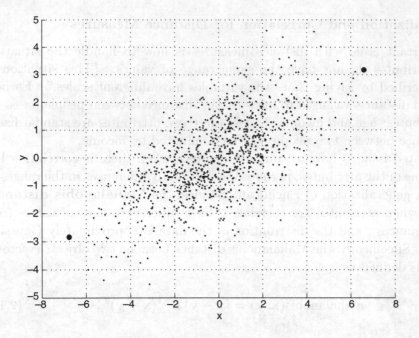

Figure 2.19. Set of two-dimensional points. The Mahalanobis distance between the two points represented by large dots is 6; their Euclidean distance is 14.7.

Unfortunately, this approach does not work well if some of the attributes are asymmetric attributes. For example, if all the attributes are asymmetric binary attributes, then the similarity measure suggested previously reduces to the simple matching coefficient, a measure that is not appropriate for asymmetric binary attributes. The easiest way to fix this problem is to omit asymmetric attributes from the similarity calculation when their values are 0 for both of the objects whose similarity is being computed. A similar approach also works well for handling missing values.

In summary, Algorithm 2.1 is effective for computing an overall similarity between two objects, **x** and **y**, with different types of attributes. This procedure can be easily modified to work with dissimilarities.

Using Weights

In much of the previous discussion, all attributes were treated equally when computing proximity. This is not desirable when some attributes are more important to the definition of proximity than others. To address these situations,

---

Algorithm 2.1 Similarities of heterogeneous objects.

1: For the kth attribute, compute a similarity, $s_k(\mathbf{x}, \mathbf{y})$, in the range $[0, 1]$.
2: Define an indicator variable, δ_k, for the kth attribute as follows:

$$\delta_k = \begin{cases} 0 & \text{if the } k^{th} \text{ attribute is an asymmetric attribute and} \\ & \text{both objects have a value of 0, or if one of the objects} \\ & \text{has a missing value for the } k^{th} \text{ attribute} \\ 1 & \text{otherwise} \end{cases}$$

3: Compute the overall similarity between the two objects using the following formula:

$$\text{similarity}(\mathbf{x}, \mathbf{y}) = \frac{\sum_{k=1}^{n} \delta_k s_k(\mathbf{x}, \mathbf{y})}{\sum_{k=1}^{n} \delta_k} \tag{2.15}$$

---

the formulas for proximity can be modified by weighting the contribution of each attribute.

If the weights w_k sum to 1, then (2.15) becomes

$$\text{similarity}(\mathbf{x}, \mathbf{y}) = \frac{\sum_{k=1}^{n} w_k \delta_k s_k(\mathbf{x}, \mathbf{y})}{\sum_{k=1}^{n} \delta_k}. \tag{2.16}$$

The definition of the Minkowski distance can also be modified as follows:

$$d(\mathbf{x}, \mathbf{y}) = \left(\sum_{k=1}^{n} w_k |x_k - y_k|^r \right)^{1/r}. \tag{2.17}$$

2.4.7 Selecting the Right Proximity Measure

The following are a few general observations that may be helpful. First, the type of proximity measure should fit the type of data. For many types of dense, continuous data, metric distance measures such as Euclidean distance are often used. Proximity between continuous attributes is most often expressed in terms of differences, and distance measures provide a well-defined way of combining these differences into an overall proximity measure. Although attributes can have different scales and be of differing importance, these issues can often be dealt with as described earlier.

For sparse data, which often consists of asymmetric attributes, we typically employ similarity measures that ignore 0–0 matches. Conceptually, this reflects the fact that, for a pair of complex objects, similarity depends on the number of characteristics they both share, rather than the number of characteristics they both lack. More specifically, for sparse, asymmetric data, most objects have only a few of the characteristics described by the attributes, and thus, are highly similar in terms of the characteristics they do not have. The cosine, Jaccard, and extended Jaccard measures are appropriate for such data.

There are other characteristics of data vectors that may need to be considered. Suppose, for example, that we are interested in comparing time series. If the magnitude of the time series is important (for example, each time series represent total sales of the same organization for a different year), then we could use Euclidean distance. If the time series represent different quantities (for example, blood pressure and oxygen consumption), then we usually want to determine if the time series have the same shape, not the same magnitude. Correlation, which uses a built-in normalization that accounts for differences in magnitude and level, would be more appropriate.

In some cases, transformation or normalization of the data is important for obtaining a proper similarity measure since such transformations are not always present in proximity measures. For instance, time series may have trends or periodic patterns that significantly impact similarity. Also, a proper computation of similarity may require that time lags be taken into account. Finally, two time series may only be similar over specific periods of time. For example, there is a strong relationship between temperature and the use of natural gas, but only during the heating season.

Practical consideration can also be important. Sometimes, a one or more proximity measures are already in use in a particular field, and thus, others will have answered the question of which proximity measures should be used. Other times, the software package or clustering algorithm being used may drastically limit the choices. If efficiency is a concern, then we may want to choose a proximity measure that has a property, such as the triangle inequality, that can be used to reduce the number of proximity calculations. (See Exercise 25.)

However, if common practice or practical restrictions do not dictate a choice, then the proper choice of a proximity measure can be a time-consuming task that requires careful consideration of both domain knowledge and the purpose for which the measure is being used. A number of different similarity measures may need to be evaluated to see which ones produce results that make the most sense.

2.5 Bibliographic Notes

It is essential to understand the nature of the data that is being analyzed, and at a fundamental level, this is the subject of measurement theory. In particular, one of the initial motivations for defining types of attributes was to be precise about which statistical operations were valid for what sorts of data. We have presented the view of measurement theory that was initially described in a classic paper by S. S. Stevens [79]. (Tables 2.2 and 2.3 are derived from those presented by Stevens [80].) While this is the most common view and is reasonably easy to understand and apply, there is, of course, much more to measurement theory. An authoritative discussion can be found in a three-volume series on the foundations of measurement theory [63, 69, 81]. Also of interest is a wide-ranging article by Hand [55], which discusses measurement theory and statistics, and is accompanied by comments from other researchers in the field. Finally, there are many books and articles that describe measurement issues for particular areas of science and engineering.

Data quality is a broad subject that spans every discipline that uses data. Discussions of precision, bias, accuracy, and significant figures can be found in many introductory science, engineering, and statistics textbooks. The view of data quality as "fitness for use" is explained in more detail in the book by Redman [76]. Those interested in data quality may also be interested in MIT's Total Data Quality Management program [70, 84]. However, the knowledge needed to deal with specific data quality issues in a particular domain is often best obtained by investigating the data quality practices of researchers in that field.

Aggregation is a less well-defined subject than many other preprocessing tasks. However, aggregation is one of the main techniques used by the database area of Online Analytical Processing (OLAP), which is discussed in Chapter 3. There has also been relevant work in the area of symbolic data analysis (Bock and Diday [47]). One of the goals in this area is to summarize traditional record data in terms of symbolic data objects whose attributes are more complex than traditional attributes. Specifically, these attributes can have values that are sets of values (categories), intervals, or sets of values with weights (histograms). Another goal of symbolic data analysis is to be able to perform clustering, classification, and other kinds of data analysis on data that consists of symbolic data objects.

Sampling is a subject that has been well studied in statistics and related fields. Many introductory statistics books, such as the one by Lindgren [65], have some discussion on sampling, and there are entire books devoted to the subject, such as the classic text by Cochran [49]. A survey of sampling for data mining is provided by Gu and Liu [54], while a survey of sampling for databases is provided by Olken and Rotem [72]. There are a number of other data mining and database-related sampling references that may be of interest, including papers by Palmer and Faloutsos [74], Provost et al. [75], Toivonen [82], and Zaki et al. [85].

In statistics, the traditional techniques that have been used for dimensionality reduction are multidimensional scaling (MDS) (Borg and Groenen [48], Kruskal and Uslaner [64]) and principal component analysis (PCA) (Jolliffe [58]), which is similar to singular value decomposition (SVD) (Demmel [50]). Dimensionality reduction is discussed in more detail in Appendix B.

Discretization is a topic that has been extensively investigated in data mining. Some classification algorithms only work with categorical data, and association analysis requires binary data, and thus, there is a significant motivation to investigate how to best binarize or discretize continuous attributes. For association analysis, we refer the reader to work by Srikant and Agrawal [78], while some useful references for discretization in the area of classification include work by Dougherty et al. [51], Elomaa and Rousu [52], Fayyad and Irani [53], and Hussain et al. [56].

Feature selection is another topic well investigated in data mining. A broad coverage of this topic is provided in a survey by Molina et al. [71] and two books by Liu and Motada [66, 67]. Other useful papers include those by Blum and Langley [46], Kohavi and John [62], and Liu et al. [68].

It is difficult to provide references for the subject of feature transformations because practices vary from one discipline to another. Many statistics books have a discussion of transformations, but typically the discussion is restricted to a particular purpose, such as ensuring the normality of a variable or making sure that variables have equal variance. We offer two references: Osborne [73] and Tukey [83].

While we have covered some of the most commonly used distance and similarity measures, there are hundreds of such measures and more are being created all the time. As with so many other topics in this chapter, many of these measures are specific to particular fields; e.g., in the area of time series see papers by Kalpakis et al. [59] and Keogh and Pazzani [61]. Clustering books provide the best general discussions. In particular, see the books by Anderberg [45], Jain and Dubes [57], Kaufman and Rousseeuw [60], and Sneath and Sokal [77].

Bibliography

[45] M. R. Anderberg. *Cluster Analysis for Applications*. Academic Press, New York, December 1973.

[46] A. Blum and P. Langley. Selection of Relevant Features and Examples in Machine Learning. *Artificial Intelligence*, 97(1–2):245–271, 1997.

Bibliography

[47] H. H. Bock and E. Diday. *Analysis of Symbolic Data: Exploratory Methods for Extracting Statistical Information from Complex Data (Studies in Classification, Data Analysis, and Knowledge Organization)*. Springer-Verlag Telos, January 2000.

[48] I. Borg and P. Groenen. *Modern Multidimensional Scaling—Theory and Applications*. Springer-Verlag, February 1997.

[49] W. G. Cochran. *Sampling Techniques*. John Wiley & Sons, 3rd edition, July 1977.

[50] J. W. Demmel. *Applied Numerical Linear Algebra*. Society for Industrial & Applied Mathematics, September 1997.

[51] J. Dougherty, R. Kohavi, and M. Sahami. Supervised and Unsupervised Discretization of Continuous Features. In *Proc. of the 12th Intl. Conf. on Machine Learning*, pages 194–202, 1995.

[52] T. Elomaa and J. Rousu. General and Efficient Multisplitting of Numerical Attributes. *Machine Learning*, 36(3):201–244, 1999.

[53] U. M. Fayyad and K. B. Irani. Multi-interval discretization of continuousvalued attributes for classification learning. In *Proc. 13th Int. Joint Conf. on Artificial Intelligence*, pages 1022–1027. Morgan Kaufman, 1993.

[54] F. H. Gaohua Gu and H. Liu. Sampling and Its Application in Data Mining: A Survey. Technical Report TRA6/00, National University of Singapore, Singapore, 2000.

[55] D. J. Hand. Statistics and the Theory of Measurement. *Journal of the Royal Statistical Society: Series A (Statistics in Society)*, 159(3):445–492, 1996.

[56] F. Hussain, H. Liu, C. L. Tan, and M. Dash. TRC6/99: Discretization: an enabling technique. Technical report, National University of Singapore, Singapore, 1999.

[57] A. K. Jain and R. C. Dubes. *Algorithms for Clustering Data*. Prentice Hall Advanced Reference Series. Prentice Hall, March 1988. Book available online at http://www.cse.msu.edu/~jain/Clustering_Jain_Dubes.pdf.

[58] I. T. Jolliffe. *Principal Component Analysis*. Springer Verlag, 2nd edition, October 2002.

[59] K. Kalpakis, D. Gada, and V. Puttagunta. Distance Measures for Effective Clustering of ARIMA Time-Series. In *Proc. of the 2001 IEEE Intl. Conf. on Data Mining*, pages 273–280. IEEE Computer Society, 2001.

[60] L. Kaufman and P. J. Rousseeuw. *Finding Groups in Data: An Introduction to Cluster Analysis*. Wiley Series in Probability and Statistics. John Wiley and Sons, New York, November 1990.

[61] E. J. Keogh and M. J. Pazzani. Scaling up dynamic time warping for datamining applications. In *KDD*, pages 285–289, 2000.

[62] R. Kohavi and G. H. John. Wrappers for Feature Subset Selection. *Artificial Intelligence*, 97(1–2):273–324, 1997.

[63] D. Krantz, R. D. Luce, P. Suppes, and A. Tversky. *Foundations of Measurements: Volume 1: Additive and polynomial representations*. Academic Press, New York, 1971.

[64] J. B. Kruskal and E. M. Uslaner. *Multidimensional Scaling*. Sage Publications, August 1978.

[65] B. W. Lindgren. *Statistical Theory*. CRC Press, January 1993.

[66] H. Liu and H. Motoda, editors. *Feature Extraction, Construction and Selection: A Data Mining Perspective*. Kluwer International Series in Engineering and Computer Science, 453. Kluwer Academic Publishers, July 1998.

[67] H. Liu and H. Motoda. *Feature Selection for Knowledge Discovery and Data Mining*. Kluwer International Series in Engineering and Computer Science, 454. Kluwer Academic Publishers, July 1998.

[68] H. Liu, H. Motoda, and L. Yu. Feature Extraction, Selection, and Construction. In N. Ye, editor, *The Handbook of Data Mining*, pages 22–41. Lawrence Erlbaum Associates, Inc., Mahwah, NJ, 2003.

[69] R. D. Luce, D. Krantz, P. Suppes, and A. Tversky. *Foundations of Measurements: Volume 3: Representation, Axiomatization, and Invariance*. Academic Press, New York, 1990.

[70] MIT Total Data Quality Management Program. web.mit.edu/tdqm/www/index.shtml, 2003.

[71] L. C. Molina, L. Belanche, and A. Nebot. Feature Selection Algorithms: A Survey and Experimental Evaluation. In *Proc. of the 2002 IEEE Intl. Conf. on Data Mining*, 2002.

[72] F. Olken and D. Rotem. Random Sampling from Databases—A Survey. *Statistics & Computing*, 5(1):25–42, March 1995.

[73] J. Osborne. Notes on the Use of Data Transformations. *Practical Assessment, Research & Evaluation*, 28(6), 2002.

[74] C. R. Palmer and C. Faloutsos. Density biased sampling: An improved method for data mining and clustering. *ACM SIGMOD Record*, 29(2):82–92, 2000.

[75] F. J. Provost, D. Jensen, and T. Oates. Efficient Progressive Sampling. In *Proc. of the 5th Intl. Conf. on Knowledge Discovery and Data Mining*, pages 23–32, 1999.

[76] T. C. Redman. *Data Quality: The Field Guide*. Digital Press, January 2001.

[77] P. H. A. Sneath and R. R. Sokal. *Numerical Taxonomy*. Freeman, San Francisco, 1971.

[78] R. Srikant and R. Agrawal. Mining Quantitative Association Rules in Large Relational Tables. In *Proc. of 1996 ACM-SIGMOD Intl. Conf. on Management of Data*, pages 1–12, Montreal, Quebec, Canada, August 1996.

[79] S. S. Stevens. On the Theory of Scales of Measurement. *Science*, 103(2684):677–680, June 1946.

[80] S. S. Stevens. Measurement. In G. M. Maranell, editor, *Scaling: A Sourcebook for Behavioral Scientists*, pages 22–41. Aldine Publishing Co., Chicago, 1974.

[81] P. Suppes, D. Krantz, R. D. Luce, and A. Tversky. *Foundations of Measurements: Volume 2: Geometrical, Threshold, and Probabilistic Representations*. Academic Press, New York, 1989.

[82] H. Toivonen. Sampling Large Databases for Association Rules. In *VLDB96*, pages 134–145. Morgan Kaufman, September 1996.

[83] J. W. Tukey. On the Comparative Anatomy of Transformations. *Annals of Mathematical Statistics*, 28(3):602–632, September 1957.

[84] R. Y. Wang, M. Ziad, Y. W. Lee, and Y. R. Wang. *Data Quality*. The Kluwer International Series on Advances in Database Systems, Volume 23. Kluwer Academic Publishers, January 2001.

[85] M. J. Zaki, S. Parthasarathy, W. Li, and M. Ogihara. Evaluation of Sampling for Data Mining of Association Rules. Technical Report TR617, Rensselaer Polytechnic Institute, 1996.

2.6 Exercises

1. In the initial example of Chapter 2, the statistician says, "Yes, fields 2 and 3 are basically the same." Can you tell from the three lines of sample data that are shown why she says that?

2. Classify the following attributes as binary, discrete, or continuous. Also classify them as qualitative (nominal or ordinal) or quantitative (interval or ratio). Some cases may have more than one interpretation, so briefly indicate your reasoning if you think there may be some ambiguity.

   Example: Age in years. **Answer:** Discrete, quantitative, ratio

   (a) Time in terms of AM or PM.

   (b) Brightness as measured by a light meter.

   (c) Brightness as measured by people's judgments.

   (d) Angles as measured in degrees between 0 and 360.

   (e) Bronze, Silver, and Gold medals as awarded at the Olympics.

   (f) Height above sea level.

   (g) Number of patients in a hospital.

   (h) ISBN numbers for books. (Look up the format on the Web.)

   (i) Ability to pass light in terms of the following values: opaque, translucent, transparent.

   (j) Military rank.

   (k) Distance from the center of campus.

   (l) Density of a substance in grams per cubic centimeter.

   (m) Coat check number. (When you attend an event, you can often give your coat to someone who, in turn, gives you a number that you can use to claim your coat when you leave.)

3. You are approached by the marketing director of a local company, who believes that he has devised a foolproof way to measure customer satisfaction. He explains his scheme as follows: "It's so simple that I can't believe that no one has thought of it before. I just keep track of the number of customer complaints for each product. I read in a data mining book that counts are ratio attributes, and so, my measure of product satisfaction must be a ratio attribute. But when I rated the products based on my new customer satisfaction measure and showed them to my boss, he told me that I had overlooked the obvious, and that my measure was worthless. I think that he was just mad because our best-selling product had the worst satisfaction since it had the most complaints. Could you help me set him straight?"

   (a) Who is right, the marketing director or his boss? If you answered, his boss, what would you do to fix the measure of satisfaction?

   (b) What can you say about the attribute type of the original product satisfaction attribute?

4. A few months later, you are again approached by the same marketing director as in Exercise 3. This time, he has devised a better approach to measure the extent to which a customer prefers one product over other, similar products. He explains, "When we develop new products, we typically create several variations and evaluate which one customers prefer. Our standard procedure is to give our test subjects all of the product variations at one time and then ask them to rank the product variations in order of preference. However, our test subjects are very indecisive, especially when there are more than two products. As a result, testing takes forever. I suggested that we perform the comparisons in pairs and then use these comparisons to get the rankings. Thus, if we have three product variations, we have the customers compare variations 1 and 2, then 2 and 3, and finally 3 and 1. Our testing time with my new procedure is a third of what it was for the old procedure, but the employees conducting the tests complain that they cannot come up with a consistent ranking from the results. And my boss wants the latest product evaluations, yesterday. I should also mention that he was the person who came up with the old product evaluation approach. Can you help me?"

(a) Is the marketing director in trouble? Will his approach work for generating an ordinal ranking of the product variations in terms of customer preference? Explain.

(b) Is there a way to fix the marketing director's approach? More generally, what can you say about trying to create an ordinal measurement scale based on pairwise comparisons?

(c) For the original product evaluation scheme, the overall rankings of each product variation are found by computing its average over all test subjects. Comment on whether you think that this is a reasonable approach. What other approaches might you take?

5. Can you think of a situation in which identification numbers would be useful for prediction?

6. An educational psychologist wants to use association analysis to analyze test results. The test consists of 100 questions with four possible answers each.

(a) How would you convert this data into a form suitable for association analysis?

(b) In particular, what type of attributes would you have and how many of them are there?

7. Which of the following quantities is likely to show more temporal autocorrelation: daily rainfall or daily temperature? Why?

8. Discuss why a document-term matrix is an example of a data set that has asymmetric discrete or asymmetric continuous features.

9. Many sciences rely on observation instead of (or in addition to) designed experiments. Compare the data quality issues involved in observational science with those of experimental science and data mining.

10. Discuss the difference between the precision of a measurement and the terms single and double precision, as they are used in computer science, typically to represent floating-point numbers that require 32 and 64 bits, respectively.

11. Give at least two advantages to working with data stored in text files instead of in a binary format.

12. Distinguish between noise and outliers. Be sure to consider the following questions.

    (a) Is noise ever interesting or desirable? Outliers?

    (b) Can noise objects be outliers?

    (c) Are noise objects always outliers?

    (d) Are outliers always noise objects?

    (e) Can noise make a typical value into an unusual one, or vice versa?

13. Consider the problem of finding the K nearest neighbors of a data object. A programmer designs Algorithm 2.2 for this task.

Algorithm 2.2 Algorithm for finding K nearest neighbors.

1: **for** $i = 1$ to *number of data objects* **do**
2:    Find the distances of the ith object to all other objects.
3:    Sort these distances in decreasing order.
      (Keep track of which object is associated with each distance.)
4:    **return** the objects associated with the first K distances of the sorted list
5: **end for**

    (a) Describe the potential problems with this algorithm if there are duplicate objects in the data set. Assume the distance function will only return a distance of 0 for objects that are the same.

    (b) How would you fix this problem?

14. The following attributes are measured for members of a herd of Asian elephants: *weight, height, tusk length, trunk length,* and *ear area*. Based on these measurements, what sort of similarity measure from Section 2.4 would you use to compare or group these elephants? Justify your answer and explain any special circumstances.

15. You are given a set of m objects that is divided into K groups, where the ith group is of size m_i. If the goal is to obtain a sample of size $n < m$, what is the difference between the following two sampling schemes? (Assume sampling with replacement.)

    (a) We randomly select $n * m_i/m$ elements from each group.

    (b) We randomly select n elements from the data set, without regard for the group to which an object belongs.

16. Consider a document-term matrix, where tf_{ij} is the frequency of the ith word (term) in the jth document and m is the number of documents. Consider the variable transformation that is defined by

$$tf'_{ij} = tf_{ij} * \log \frac{m}{df_i}, \qquad (2.18)$$

where df_i is the number of documents in which the ith term appears, which is known as the **document frequency** of the term. This transformation is known as the **inverse document frequency** transformation.

    (a) What is the effect of this transformation if a term occurs in one document? In every document?

    (b) What might be the purpose of this transformation?

17. Assume that we apply a square root transformation to a ratio attribute x to obtain the new attribute x^*. As part of your analysis, you identify an interval (a, b) in which x^* has a linear relationship to another attribute y.

    (a) What is the corresponding interval (a, b) in terms of x?

    (b) Give an equation that relates y to x.

18. This exercise compares and contrasts some similarity and distance measures.

    (a) For binary data, the L1 distance corresponds to the Hamming distance; that is, the number of bits that are different between two binary vectors. The Jaccard similarity is a measure of the similarity between two binary vectors. Compute the Hamming distance and the Jaccard similarity between the following two binary vectors.

    $\mathbf{x} = 0101010001$
    $\mathbf{y} = 0100011000$

    (b) Which approach, Jaccard or Hamming distance, is more similar to the Simple Matching Coefficient, and which approach is more similar to the cosine measure? Explain. (Note: The Hamming measure is a distance, while the other three measures are similarities, but don't let this confuse you.)

(c) Suppose that you are comparing how similar two organisms of different species are in terms of the number of genes they share. Describe which measure, Hamming or Jaccard, you think would be more appropriate for comparing the genetic makeup of two organisms. Explain. (Assume that each animal is represented as a binary vector, where each attribute is 1 if a particular gene is present in the organism and 0 otherwise.)

(d) If you wanted to compare the genetic makeup of two organisms of the same species, e.g., two human beings, would you use the Hamming distance, the Jaccard coefficient, or a different measure of similarity or distance? Explain. (Note that two human beings share > 99.9% of the same genes.)

19. For the following vectors, $\mathbf{x}$ and $\mathbf{y}$, calculate the indicated similarity or distance measures.

    (a) $\mathbf{x} = (1, 1, 1, 1)$, $\mathbf{y} = (2, 2, 2, 2)$ cosine, correlation, Euclidean

    (b) $\mathbf{x} = (0, 1, 0, 1)$, $\mathbf{y} = (1, 0, 1, 0)$ cosine, correlation, Euclidean, Jaccard

    (c) $\mathbf{x} = (0, -1, 0, 1)$, $\mathbf{y} = (1, 0, -1, 0)$ cosine, correlation, Euclidean

    (d) $\mathbf{x} = (1, 1, 0, 1, 0, 1)$, $\mathbf{y} = (1, 1, 1, 0, 0, 1)$ cosine, correlation, Jaccard

    (e) $\mathbf{x} = (2, -1, 0, 2, 0, -3)$, $\mathbf{y} = (-1, 1, -1, 0, 0, -1)$ cosine, correlation

20. Here, we further explore the cosine and correlation measures.

    (a) What is the range of values that are possible for the cosine measure?

    (b) If two objects have a cosine measure of 1, are they identical? Explain.

    (c) What is the relationship of the cosine measure to correlation, if any? (Hint: Look at statistical measures such as mean and standard deviation in cases where cosine and correlation are the same and different.)

    (d) Figure 2.20(a) shows the relationship of the cosine measure to Euclidean distance for 100,000 randomly generated points that have been normalized to have an L2 length of 1. What general observation can you make about the relationship between Euclidean distance and cosine similarity when vectors have an L2 norm of 1?

    (e) Figure 2.20(b) shows the relationship of correlation to Euclidean distance for 100,000 randomly generated points that have been standardized to have a mean of 0 and a standard deviation of 1. What general observation can you make about the relationship between Euclidean distance and correlation when the vectors have been standardized to have a mean of 0 and a standard deviation of 1?

    (f) Derive the mathematical relationship between cosine similarity and Euclidean distance when each data object has an L2 length of 1.

    (g) Derive the mathematical relationship between correlation and Euclidean distance when each data point has been been standardized by subtracting its mean and dividing by its standard deviation.

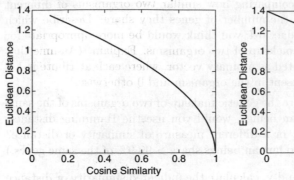

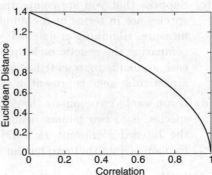

(a) Relationship between Euclidean distance and the cosine measure.

(b) Relationship between Euclidean distance and correlation.

Figure 2.20. Graphs for Exercise 20.

21. Show that the set difference metric given by

$$d(A, B) = size(A - B) + size(B - A) \tag{2.19}$$

satisfies the metric axioms given on page 70. A and B are sets and $A - B$ is the set difference.

22. Discuss how you might map correlation values from the interval $[-1,1]$ to the interval $[0,1]$. Note that the type of transformation that you use might depend on the application that you have in mind. Thus, consider two applications: clustering time series and predicting the behavior of one time series given another.

23. Given a similarity measure with values in the interval $[0,1]$ describe two ways to transform this similarity value into a dissimilarity value in the interval $[0,\infty]$.

24. Proximity is typically defined between a pair of objects.

    (a) Define two ways in which you might define the proximity among a group of objects.

    (b) How might you define the distance between two sets of points in Euclidean space?

    (c) How might you define the proximity between two sets of data objects? (Make no assumption about the data objects, except that a proximity measure is defined between any pair of objects.)

25. You are given a set of points S in Euclidean space, as well as the distance of each point in S to a point $\mathbf{x}$. (It does not matter if $\mathbf{x} \in S$.)

(a) If the goal is to find all points within a specified distance ε of point $\mathbf{y}$, $\mathbf{y} \neq \mathbf{x}$, explain how you could use the triangle inequality and the already calculated distances to $\mathbf{x}$ to potentially reduce the number of distance calculations necessary? Hint: The triangle inequality, $d(\mathbf{x}, \mathbf{z}) \leq d(\mathbf{x}, \mathbf{y}) + d(\mathbf{y}, \mathbf{x})$, can be rewritten as $d(\mathbf{x}, \mathbf{y}) \geq d(\mathbf{x}, \mathbf{z}) - d(\mathbf{y}, \mathbf{z})$.

(b) In general, how would the distance between $\mathbf{x}$ and $\mathbf{y}$ affect the number of distance calculations?

(c) Suppose that you can find a small subset of points S', from the original data set, such that every point in the data set is within a specified distance ε of at least one of the points in S', and that you also have the pairwise distance matrix for S'. Describe a technique that uses this information to compute, with a minimum of distance calculations, the set of all points within a distance of β of a specified point from the data set.

26. Show that 1 minus the Jaccard similarity is a distance measure between two data objects, $\mathbf{x}$ and $\mathbf{y}$, that satisfies the metric axioms given on page 70. Specifically, $d(\mathbf{x}, \mathbf{y}) = 1 - \text{J}(\mathbf{x}, \mathbf{y})$.

27. Show that the distance measure defined as the angle between two data vectors, $\mathbf{x}$ and $\mathbf{y}$, satisfies the metric axioms given on page 70. Specifically, $d(\mathbf{x}, \mathbf{y}) = \arccos(\cos(\mathbf{x}, \mathbf{y}))$.

28. Explain why computing the proximity between two attributes is often simpler than computing the similarity between two objects.

Exploring Data

The previous chapter addressed high-level data issues that are important in the knowledge discovery process. This chapter provides an introduction to **data exploration**, which is a preliminary investigation of the data in order to better understand its specific characteristics. Data exploration can aid in selecting the appropriate preprocessing and data analysis techniques. It can even address some of the questions typically answered by data mining. For example, patterns can sometimes be found by visually inspecting the data. Also, some of the techniques used in data exploration, such as visualization, can be used to understand and interpret data mining results.

This chapter covers three major topics: summary statistics, visualization, and On-Line Analytical Processing (OLAP). Summary statistics, such as the mean and standard deviation of a set of values, and visualization techniques, such as histograms and scatter plots, are standard methods that are widely employed for data exploration. OLAP, which is a more recent development, consists of a set of techniques for exploring multidimensional arrays of values. OLAP-related analysis functions focus on various ways to create summary data tables from a multidimensional data array. These techniques include aggregating data either across various dimensions or across various attribute values. For instance, if we are given sales information reported according to product, location, and date, OLAP techniques can be used to create a summary that describes the sales activity at a particular location by month and product category.

The topics covered in this chapter have considerable overlap with the area known as **Exploratory Data Analysis** (EDA), which was created in the 1970s by the prominent statistician, John Tukey. This chapter, like EDA, places a heavy emphasis on visualization. Unlike EDA, this chapter does not include topics such as cluster analysis or anomaly detection. There are two reasons for this. First, data mining views descriptive data analysis techniques as an end in themselves, whereas statistics, from which EDA originated, tends to view hypothesis-based testing as the final goal. Second, cluster analysis and anomaly detection are large areas and require full chapters for an in-depth discussion. Hence, cluster analysis is covered in Chapters 8 and 9, while anomaly detection is discussed in Chapter 10.

3.1   The Iris Data Set

In the following discussion, we will often refer to the Iris data set that is available from the University of California at Irvine (UCI) Machine Learning Repository. It consists of information on 150 Iris flowers, 50 each from one of three Iris species: Setosa, Versicolour, and Virginica. Each flower is characterized by five attributes:

1. sepal length in centimeters

2. sepal width in centimeters

3. petal length in centimeters

4. petal width in centimeters

5. class (Setosa, Versicolour, Virginica)

The sepals of a flower are the outer structures that protect the more fragile parts of the flower, such as the petals. In many flowers, the sepals are green, and only the petals are colorful. For Irises, however, the sepals are also colorful. As illustrated by the picture of a Virginica Iris in Figure 3.1, the sepals of an Iris are larger than the petals and are drooping, while the petals are upright.

3.2   Summary Statistics

Summary statistics are quantities, such as the mean and standard deviation, that capture various characteristics of a potentially large set of values with a single number or a small set of numbers. Everyday examples of summary statistics are the average household income or the fraction of college students who complete an undergraduate degree in four years. Indeed, for many people, summary statistics are the most visible manifestation of statistics. We will concentrate on summary statistics for the values of a single attribute, but will provide a brief description of some multivariate summary statistics.

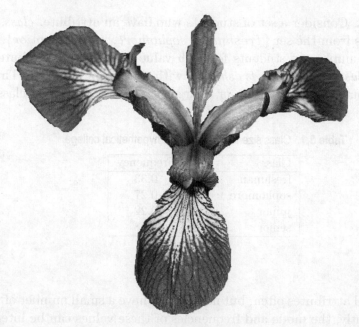

Figure 3.1. Picture of Iris Virginica. Robert H. Mohlenbrock @ USDA-NRCS PLANTS Database/ USDA NRCS. 1995. Northeast wetland flora: Field office guide to plant species. Northeast National Technical Center, Chester, PA. Background removed.

This section considers only the descriptive nature of summary statistics. However, as described in Appendix C, statistics views data as arising from an underlying statistical process that is characterized by various parameters, and some of the summary statistics discussed here can be viewed as estimates of statistical parameters of the underlying distribution that generated the data.

3.2.1 Frequencies and the Mode

Given a set of unordered categorical values, there is not much that can be done to further characterize the values except to compute the frequency with which each value occurs for a particular set of data. Given a categorical attribute x, which can take values $\{v_1, \ldots, v_i, \ldots v_k\}$ and a set of m objects, the frequency of a value v_i is defined as

$$\text{frequency}(v_i) = \frac{\text{number of objects with attribute value } v_i}{m}. \tag{3.1}$$

The **mode** of a categorical attribute is the value that has the highest frequency.

Example 3.1. Consider a set of students who have an attribute, *class*, which can take values from the set {*freshman, sophomore, junior, senior*}. Table 3.1 shows the number of students for each value of the *class* attribute. The mode of the *class* attribute is *freshman*, with a frequency of 0.33. This may indicate dropouts due to attrition or a larger than usual freshman class.

Table 3.1. Class size for students in a hypothetical college.

Class	Size	Frequency
freshman	140	0.33
sophomore	160	0.27
junior	130	0.22
senior	170	0.18

■

Categorical attributes often, but not always, have a small number of values, and consequently, the mode and frequencies of these values can be interesting and useful. Notice, though, that for the Iris data set and the *class* attribute, the three types of flower all have the same frequency, and therefore, the notion of a mode is not interesting.

For continuous data, the mode, as currently defined, is often not useful because a single value may not occur more than once. Nonetheless, in some cases, the mode may indicate important information about the nature of the values or the presence of missing values. For example, the heights of 20 people measured to the nearest millimeter will typically not repeat, but if the heights are measured to the nearest tenth of a meter, then some people may have the same height. Also, if a unique value is used to indicate a missing value, then this value will often show up as the mode.

3.2.2 Percentiles

For ordered data, it is more useful to consider the **percentiles** of a set of values. In particular, given an ordinal or continuous attribute x and a number p between 0 and 100, the pth percentile x_p is a value of x such that $p\%$ of the observed values of x are less than x_p. For instance, the 50th percentile is the value $x_{50\%}$ such that 50% of all values of x are less than $x_{50\%}$. Table 3.2 shows the percentiles for the four quantitative attributes of the Iris data set.

Table 3.2. Percentiles for sepal length, sepal width, petal length, and petal width. (All values are in centimeters.)

Percentile	Sepal Length	Sepal Width	Petal Length	Petal Width
0	4.3	2.0	1.0	0.1
10	4.8	2.5	1.4	0.2
20	5.0	2.7	1.5	0.2
30	5.2	2.8	1.7	0.4
40	5.6	3.0	3.9	1.2
50	5.8	3.0	4.4	1.3
60	6.1	3.1	4.6	1.5
70	6.3	3.2	5.0	1.8
80	6.6	3.4	5.4	1.9
90	6.9	3.6	5.8	2.2
100	7.9	4.4	6.9	2.5

Example 3.2. The percentiles, $x_{0\%}, x_{10\%}, \ldots, x_{90\%}, x_{100\%}$ of the integers from 1 to 10 are, in order, the following: 1.0, 1.5, 2.5, 3.5, 4.5, 5.5, 6.5, 7.5, 8.5, 9.5, 10.0. By tradition, $\min(x) = x_{0\%}$ and $\max(x) = x_{100\%}$. ∎

3.2.3 Measures of Location: Mean and Median

For continuous data, two of the most widely used summary statistics are the **mean** and **median**, which are measures of the *location* of a set of values. Consider a set of m objects and an attribute x. Let $\{x_1, \ldots, x_m\}$ be the attribute values of x for these m objects. As a concrete example, these values might be the heights of m children. Let $\{x_{(1)}, \ldots, x_{(m)}\}$ represent the values of x after they have been sorted in non-decreasing order. Thus, $x_{(1)} = \min(x)$ and $x_{(m)} = \max(x)$. Then, the mean and median are defined as follows:

$$\text{mean}(x) = \overline{x} = \frac{1}{m} \sum_{i=1}^{m} x_i \tag{3.2}$$

$$\text{median}(x) = \begin{cases} x_{(r+1)} & \text{if } m \text{ is odd, i.e., } m = 2r + 1 \\ \frac{1}{2}(x_{(r)} + x_{(r+1)}) & \text{if } m \text{ is even, i.e., } m = 2r \end{cases} \tag{3.3}$$

To summarize, the median is the middle value if there are an odd number of values, and the average of the two middle values if the number of values is even. Thus, for seven values, the median is $x_{(4)}$, while for ten values, the median is $\frac{1}{2}(x_{(5)} + x_{(6)})$.

Although the mean is sometimes interpreted as the middle of a set of values, this is only correct if the values are distributed in a symmetric manner. If the distribution of values is skewed, then the median is a better indicator of the middle. Also, the mean is sensitive to the presence of outliers. For data with outliers, the median again provides a more robust estimate of the middle of a set of values.

To overcome problems with the traditional definition of a mean, the notion of a **trimmed mean** is sometimes used. A percentage p between 0 and 100 is specified, the top and bottom $(p/2)\%$ of the data is thrown out, and the mean is then calculated in the normal way. The median is a trimmed mean with $p = 100\%$, while the standard mean corresponds to $p = 0\%$.

Example 3.3. Consider the set of values $\{1, 2, 3, 4, 5, 90\}$. The mean of these values is 17.5, while the median is 3.5. The trimmed mean with $p = 40\%$ is also 3.5. ∎

Example 3.4. The means, medians, and trimmed means ($p = 20\%$) of the four quantitative attributes of the Iris data are given in Table 3.3. The three measures of location have similar values except for the attribute *petal length*.

Table 3.3. Means and medians for sepal length, sepal width, petal length, and petal width. (All values are in centimeters.)

Measure	Sepal Length	Sepal Width	Petal Length	Petal Width
mean	5.84	3.05	3.76	1.20
median	5.80	3.00	4.35	1.30
trimmed mean (20%)	5.79	3.02	3.72	1.12

∎

3.2.4   Measures of Spread: Range and Variance

Another set of commonly used summary statistics for continuous data are those that measure the dispersion or spread of a set of values. Such measures indicate if the attribute values are widely spread out or if they are relatively concentrated around a single point such as the mean.

The simplest measure of spread is the **range**, which, given an attribute x with a set of m values $\{x_1, \ldots, x_m\}$, is defined as

$$\text{range}(x) = \max(x) - \min(x) = x_{(m)} - x_{(1)}. \tag{3.4}$$

Table 3.4. Range, standard deviation (std), absolute average difference (AAD), median absolute difference (MAD), and interquartile range (IQR) for sepal length, sepal width, petal length, and petal width. (All values are in centimeters.)

Measure	Sepal Length	Sepal Width	Petal Length	Petal Width
range	3.6	2.4	5.9	2.4
std	0.8	0.4	1.8	0.8
AAD	0.7	0.3	1.6	0.6
MAD	0.7	0.3	1.2	0.7
IQR	1.3	0.5	3.5	1.5

Although the range identifies the maximum spread, it can be misleading if most of the values are concentrated in a narrow band of values, but there are also a relatively small number of more extreme values. Hence, the **variance** is preferred as a measure of spread. The variance of the (observed) values of an attribute x is typically written as s_x^2 and is defined below. The **standard deviation**, which is the square root of the variance, is written as s_x and has the same units as x.

$$\text{variance}(x) = s_x^2 = \frac{1}{m-1} \sum_{i=1}^{m} (x_i - \overline{x})^2 \tag{3.5}$$

The mean can be distorted by outliers, and since the variance is computed using the mean, it is also sensitive to outliers. Indeed, the variance is particularly sensitive to outliers since it uses the squared difference between the mean and other values. As a result, more robust estimates of the spread of a set of values are often used. Following are the definitions of three such measures: the **absolute average deviation** (AAD), the **median absolute deviation** (MAD), and the **interquartile range**(IQR). Table 3.4 shows these measures for the Iris data set.

$$\text{AAD}(x) = \frac{1}{m} \sum_{i=1}^{m} |x_i - \overline{x}| \tag{3.6}$$

$$\text{MAD}(x) = median\left(\{|x_1 - \overline{x}|, \ldots, |x_m - \overline{x}|\} \right) \tag{3.7}$$

$$\text{interquartile range}(x) = x_{75\%} - x_{25\%} \tag{3.8}$$

3.2.5   Multivariate Summary Statistics

Measures of location for data that consists of several attributes (multivariate data) can be obtained by computing the mean or median separately for each attribute. Thus, given a data set the mean of the data objects, $\overline{\mathbf{x}}$, is given by

$$\overline{\mathbf{x}} = (\overline{x_1}, \ldots, \overline{x_n}), \tag{3.9}$$

where $\overline{x_i}$ is the mean of the ith attribute x_i.

For multivariate data, the spread of each attribute can be computed independently of the other attributes using any of the approaches described in Section 3.2.4. However, for data with continuous variables, the spread of the data is most commonly captured by the **covariance matrix S**, whose ij^{th} entry s_{ij} is the covariance of the ith and j^{th} attributes of the data. Thus, if x_i and x_j are the ith and j^{th} attributes, then

$$s_{ij} = \text{covariance}(x_i, x_j). \tag{3.10}$$

In turn, $covariance(x_i, x_j)$ is given by

$$\text{covariance}(x_i, x_j) = \frac{1}{m-1} \sum_{k=1}^{m} (x_{ki} - \overline{x_i})(x_{kj} - \overline{x_j}), \tag{3.11}$$

where x_{ki} and x_{kj} are the values of the ith and j^{th} attributes for the kth object. Notice that covariance(x_i, x_i) = variance(x_i). Thus, the covariance matrix has the variances of the attributes along the diagonal.

The covariance of two attributes is a measure of the degree to which two attributes vary together and depends on the magnitudes of the variables. A value near 0 indicates that two attributes do not have a (linear) relationship, but it is not possible to judge the degree of relationship between two variables by looking only at the value of the covariance. Because the correlation of two attributes immediately gives an indication of how strongly two attributes are (linearly) related, correlation is preferred to covariance for data exploration. (Also see the discussion of correlation in Section 2.4.5.) The ij^{th} entry of the **correlation matrix R**, is the correlation between the ith and j^{th} attributes of the data. If x_i and x_j are the ith and j^{th} attributes, then

$$r_{ij} = \text{correlation}(x_i, x_j) = \frac{\text{covariance}(x_i, x_j)}{s_i s_j}, \tag{3.12}$$

where s_i and s_j are the variances of x_i and x_j, respectively. The diagonal entries of $\mathbf{R}$ are correlation$(x_i, x_i) = 1$, while the other entries are between -1 and 1. It is also useful to consider correlation matrices that contain the pairwise correlations of objects instead of attributes.

3.2.6 Other Ways to Summarize the Data

There are, of course, other types of summary statistics. For instance, the **skewness** of a set of values measures the degree to which the values are symmetrically distributed around the mean. There are also other characteristics of the data that are not easy to measure quantitatively, such as whether the distribution of values is multimodal; i.e., the data has multiple "bumps" where most of the values are concentrated. In many cases, however, the most effective approach to understanding the more complicated or subtle aspects of how the values of an attribute are distributed, is to view the values graphically in the form of a histogram. (Histograms are discussed in the next section.)

3.3 Visualization

Data visualization is the display of information in a graphic or tabular format. Successful visualization requires that the data (information) be converted into a visual format so that the characteristics of the data and the relationships among data items or attributes can be analyzed or reported. The goal of visualization is the interpretation of the visualized information by a person and the formation of a mental model of the information.

In everyday life, visual techniques such as graphs and tables are often the preferred approach used to explain the weather, the economy, and the results of political elections. Likewise, while algorithmic or mathematical approaches are often emphasized in most technical disciplines—data mining included— visual techniques can play a key role in data analysis. In fact, sometimes the use of visualization techniques in data mining is referred to as **visual data mining**.

3.3.1 Motivations for Visualization

The overriding motivation for using visualization is that people can quickly absorb large amounts of visual information and find patterns in it. Consider Figure 3.2, which shows the Sea Surface Temperature (SST) in degrees Celsius for July, 1982. This picture summarizes the information from approximately 250,000 numbers and is readily interpreted in a few seconds. For example, it

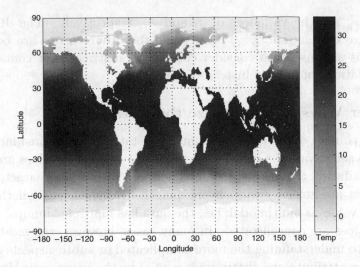

Figure 3.2. Sea Surface Temperature (SST) for July, 1982.

is easy to see that the ocean temperature is highest at the equator and lowest at the poles.

Another general motivation for visualization is to make use of the domain knowledge that is "locked up in people's heads." While the use of domain knowledge is an important task in data mining, it is often difficult or impossible to fully utilize such knowledge in statistical or algorithmic tools. In some cases, an analysis can be performed using non-visual tools, and then the results presented visually for evaluation by the domain expert. In other cases, having a domain specialist examine visualizations of the data may be the best way of finding patterns of interest since, by using domain knowledge, a person can often quickly eliminate many uninteresting patterns and direct the focus to the patterns that are important.

3.3.2   General Concepts

This section explores some of the general concepts related to visualization, in particular, general approaches for visualizing the data and its attributes. A number of visualization techniques are mentioned briefly and will be described in more detail when we discuss specific approaches later on. We assume that the reader is familiar with line graphs, bar charts, and scatter plots.

Representation: Mapping Data to Graphical Elements

The first step in visualization is the mapping of information to a visual format; i.e., mapping the objects, attributes, and relationships in a set of information to visual objects, attributes, and relationships. That is, data objects, their attributes, and the relationships among data objects are translated into graphical elements such as points, lines, shapes, and colors.

Objects are usually represented in one of three ways. First, if only a single categorical attribute of the object is being considered, then objects are often lumped into categories based on the value of that attribute, and these categories are displayed as an entry in a table or an area on a screen. (Examples shown later in this chapter are a cross-tabulation table and a bar chart.) Second, if an object has multiple attributes, then the object can be displayed as a row (or column) of a table or as a line on a graph. Finally, an object is often interpreted as a point in two- or three-dimensional space, where graphically, the point might be represented by a geometric figure, such as a circle, cross, or box.

For attributes, the representation depends on the type of attribute, i.e., nominal, ordinal, or continuous (interval or ratio). Ordinal and continuous attributes can be mapped to continuous, ordered graphical features such as location along the x, y, or z axes; intensity; color; or size (diameter, width, height, etc.). For categorical attributes, each category can be mapped to a distinct position, color, shape, orientation, embellishment, or column in a table. However, for nominal attributes, whose values are unordered, care should be taken when using graphical features, such as color and position that have an inherent ordering associated with their values. In other words, the graphical elements used to represent the ordinal values often have an order, but ordinal values do not.

The representation of relationships via graphical elements occurs either explicitly or implicitly. For graph data, the standard graph representation— a set of nodes with links between the nodes—is normally used. If the nodes (data objects) or links (relationships) have attributes or characteristics of their own, then this is represented graphically. To illustrate, if the nodes are cities and the links are highways, then the diameter of the nodes might represent population, while the width of the links might represent the volume of traffic.

In most cases, though, mapping objects and attributes to graphical elements implicitly maps the relationships in the data to relationships among graphical elements. To illustrate, if the data object represents a physical object that has a location, such as a city, then the relative positions of the graphical objects corresponding to the data objects tend to naturally preserve the actual relative positions of the objects. Likewise, if there are two or three continuous attributes that are taken as the coordinates of the data points, then the resulting plot often gives considerable insight into the relationships of the attributes and the data points because data points that are visually close to each other have similar values for their attributes.

In general, it is difficult to ensure that a mapping of objects and attributes will result in the relationships being mapped to easily observed relationships among graphical elements. Indeed, this is one of the most challenging aspects of visualization. In any given set of data, there are many implicit relationships, and hence, a key challenge of visualization is to choose a technique that makes the relationships of interest easily observable.

Arrangement

As discussed earlier, the proper choice of visual representation of objects and attributes is essential for good visualization. The arrangement of items within the visual display is also crucial. We illustrate this with two examples.

Example 3.5. This example illustrates the importance of rearranging a table of data. In Table 3.5, which shows nine objects with six binary attributes, there is no clear relationship between objects and attributes, at least at first glance. If the rows and columns of this table are permuted, however, as shown in Table 3.6, then it is clear that there are really only two types of objects in the table—one that has all ones for the first three attributes and one that has only ones for the last three attributes. ∎

Table 3.5. A table of nine objects (rows) with six binary attributes (columns).

	1	2	3	4	5	6
1	0	1	0	1	1	0
2	1	0	1	0	0	1
3	0	1	0	1	1	0
4	1	0	1	0	0	1
5	0	1	0	1	1	0
6	1	0	1	0	0	1
7	0	1	0	1	1	0
8	1	0	1	0	0	1
9	0	1	0	1	1	0

Table 3.6. A table of nine objects (rows) with six binary attributes (columns) permuted so that the relationships of the rows and columns are clear.

	6	1	3	2	5	4
4	1	1	1	0	0	0
2	1	1	1	0	0	0
6	1	1	1	0	0	0
8	1	1	1	0	0	0
5	0	0	0	1	1	1
3	0	0	0	1	1	1
9	0	0	0	1	1	1
1	0	0	0	1	1	1
7	0	0	0	1	1	1

Example 3.6. Consider Figure 3.3(a), which shows a visualization of a graph. If the connected components of the graph are separated, as in Figure 3.3(b), then the relationships between nodes and graphs become much simpler to understand. ∎

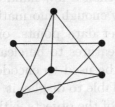 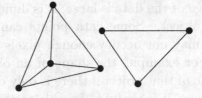

(a) Original view of a graph.   (b) Uncoupled view of connected components of the graph.

Figure 3.3. Two visualizations of a graph.

Selection

Another key concept in visualization is **selection**, which is the elimination or the de-emphasis of certain objects and attributes. Specifically, while data objects that only have a few dimensions can often be mapped to a two- or three-dimensional graphical representation in a straightforward way, there is no completely satisfactory and general approach to represent data with many attributes. Likewise, if there are many data objects, then visualizing all the objects can result in a display that is too crowded. If there are many attributes and many objects, then the situation is even more challenging.

The most common approach to handling many attributes is to choose a subset of attributes—usually two—for display. If the dimensionality is not too high, a matrix of bivariate (two-attribute) plots can be constructed for simultaneous viewing. (Figure 3.16 shows a matrix of scatter plots for the pairs of attributes of the Iris data set.) Alternatively, a visualization program can automatically show a series of two-dimensional plots, in which the sequence is user directed or based on some predefined strategy. The hope is that visualizing a collection of two-dimensional plots will provide a more complete view of the data.

The technique of selecting a pair (or small number) of attributes is a type of dimensionality reduction, and there are many more sophisticated dimensionality reduction techniques that can be employed, e.g., principal components analysis (PCA). Consult Appendices A (Linear Algebra) and B (Dimensionality Reduction) for more information.

When the number of data points is high, e.g., more than a few hundred, or if the range of the data is large, it is difficult to display enough information about each object. Some data points can obscure other data points, or a data object may not occupy enough pixels to allow its features to be clearly displayed. For example, the shape of an object cannot be used to encode a characteristic of that object if there is only one pixel available to display it. In these situations, it is useful to be able to eliminate some of the objects, either by zooming in on a particular region of the data or by taking a sample of the data points.

3.3.3   Techniques

Visualization techniques are often specialized to the type of data being analyzed. Indeed, new visualization techniques and approaches, as well as specialized variations of existing approaches, are being continuously created, typically in response to new kinds of data and visualization tasks.

Despite this specialization and the ad hoc nature of visualization, there are some generic ways to classify visualization techniques. One such classification is based on the number of attributes involved (1, 2, 3, or many) or whether the data has some special characteristic, such as a hierarchical or graph structure. Visualization methods can also be classified according to the type of attributes involved. Yet another classification is based on the type of application: scientific, statistical, or information visualization. The following discussion will use three categories: visualization of a small number of attributes, visualization of data with spatial and/or temporal attributes, and visualization of data with many attributes.

Most of the visualization techniques discussed here can be found in a wide variety of mathematical and statistical packages, some of which are freely available. There are also a number of data sets that are freely available on the World Wide Web. Readers are encouraged to try these visualization techniques as they proceed through the following sections.

Visualizing Small Numbers of Attributes

This section examines techniques for visualizing data with respect to a small number of attributes. Some of these techniques, such as histograms, give insight into the distribution of the observed values for a single attribute. Other techniques, such as scatter plots, are intended to display the relationships between the values of two attributes.

Stem and Leaf Plots Stem and leaf plots can be used to provide insight into the distribution of one-dimensional integer or continuous data. (We will assume integer data initially, and then explain how stem and leaf plots can be applied to continuous data.) For the simplest type of stem and leaf plot, we split the values into groups, where each group contains those values that are the same except for the last digit. Each group becomes a stem, while the last digits of a group are the leaves. Hence, if the values are two-digit integers, e.g., 35, 36, 42, and 51, then the stems will be the high-order digits, e.g., 3, 4, and 5, while the leaves are the low-order digits, e.g., 1, 2, 5, and 6. By plotting the stems vertically and leaves horizontally, we can provide a visual representation of the distribution of the data.

Example 3.7. The set of integers shown in Figure 3.4 is the sepal length in centimeters (multiplied by 10 to make the values integers) taken from the Iris data set. For convenience, the values have also been sorted.

The stem and leaf plot for this data is shown in Figure 3.5. Each number in Figure 3.4 is first put into one of the vertical groups—4, 5, 6, or 7—according to its ten's digit. Its last digit is then placed to the right of the colon. Often, especially if the amount of data is larger, it is desirable to split the stems. For example, instead of placing all values whose ten's digit is 4 in the same "bucket," the stem 4 is repeated twice; all values 40–44 are put in the bucket corresponding to the first stem and all values 45–49 are put in the bucket corresponding to the second stem. This approach is shown in the stem and leaf plot of Figure 3.6. Other variations are also possible. ∎

Histograms Stem and leaf plots are a type of **histogram**, a plot that displays the distribution of values for attributes by dividing the possible values into bins and showing the number of objects that fall into each bin. For categorical data, each value is a bin. If this results in too many values, then values are combined in some way. For continuous attributes, the range of values is divided into bins—typically, but not necessarily, of equal width—and the values in each bin are counted.

```
43 44 44 44 45 46 46 46 46 47 47 48 48 48 48 48 49 49 49 49 49 49 50
50 50 50 50 50 50 50 50 50 51 51 51 51 51 51 51 51 51 52 52 52 52 53
54 54 54 54 54 54 55 55 55 55 55 55 55 56 56 56 56 56 56 57 57 57 57
57 57 57 57 58 58 58 58 58 58 58 59 59 59 60 60 60 60 60 60 61 61 61
61 61 61 62 62 62 62 63 63 63 63 63 63 63 63 63 64 64 64 64 64 64 64
65 65 65 65 65 66 66 67 67 67 67 67 67 67 67 68 68 68 69 69 69 69 70
71 72 72 72 73 74 76 77 77 77 77 79
```

Figure 3.4. Sepal length data from the Iris data set.

```
4 :   34444566667788888999999
5 :   00000000000111111111122223444444455555555666666777777778888888999
6 :   000000111111222233333333334444444455555566777777778889999
7 :   0122234677779
```

Figure 3.5. Stem and leaf plot for the sepal length from the Iris data set.

```
4 :   3444
4 :   566667788888999999
5 :   00000000000111111111122223444444
5 :   555555556666667777777778888888999
6 :   00000011111122223333333333334444444
6 :   5555566777777778889999
7 :   0122234
7 :   677779
```

Figure 3.6. Stem and leaf plot for the sepal length from the Iris data set when buckets corresponding to digits are split.

Once the counts are available for each bin, a **bar plot** is constructed such that each bin is represented by one bar and the area of each bar is proportional to the number of values (objects) that fall into the corresponding range. If all intervals are of equal width, then all bars are the same width and the height of a bar is proportional to the number of values in the corresponding bin.

Example 3.8. Figure 3.7 shows histograms (with 10 bins) for sepal length, sepal width, petal length, and petal width. Since the shape of a histogram can depend on the number of bins, histograms for the same data, but with 20 bins, are shown in Figure 3.8.   ∎

There are variations of the histogram plot. A **relative (frequency) histogram** replaces the count by the relative frequency. However, this is just a

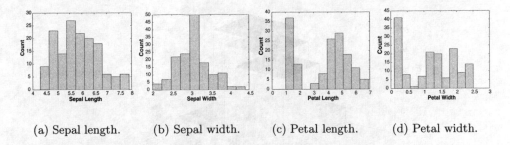

(a) Sepal length.   (b) Sepal width.   (c) Petal length.   (d) Petal width.

Figure 3.7. Histograms of four Iris attributes (10 bins).

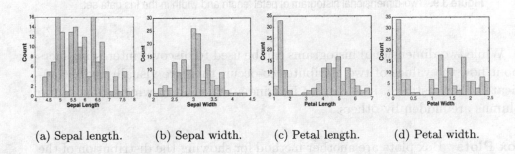

(a) Sepal length.   (b) Sepal width.   (c) Petal length.   (d) Petal width.

Figure 3.8. Histograms of four Iris attributes (20 bins).

change in scale of the y axis, and the shape of the histogram does not change. Another common variation, especially for unordered categorical data, is the **Pareto histogram**, which is the same as a normal histogram except that the categories are sorted by count so that the count is decreasing from left to right.

Two-Dimensional Histograms   Two-dimensional histograms are also possible. Each attribute is divided into intervals and the two sets of intervals define two-dimensional rectangles of values.

Example 3.9. Figure 3.9 shows a two-dimensional histogram of petal length and petal width. Because each attribute is split into three bins, there are nine rectangular two-dimensional bins. The height of each rectangular bar indicates the number of objects (flowers in this case) that fall into each bin. Most of the flowers fall into only three of the bins—those along the diagonal. It is not possible to see this by looking at the one-dimensional distributions.   ∎

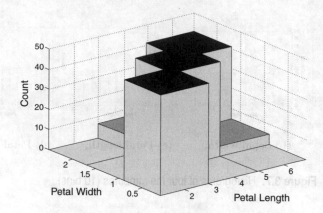

Figure 3.9. Two-dimensional histogram of petal length and width in the Iris data set.

While two-dimensional histograms can be used to discover interesting facts about how the values of two attributes co-occur, they are visually more complicated. For instance, it is easy to imagine a situation in which some of the columns are hidden by others.

Box Plots Box plots are another method for showing the distribution of the values of a single numerical attribute. Figure 3.10 shows a labeled box plot for sepal length. The lower and upper ends of the box indicate the 25th and 75th percentiles, respectively, while the line inside the box indicates the value of the 50th percentile. The top and bottom lines of the **tails** indicate the 10th and 90th percentiles. Outliers are shown by "+" marks. Box plots are relatively compact, and thus, many of them can be shown on the same plot. Simplified versions of the box plot, which take less space, can also be used.

Example 3.10. The box plots for the first four attributes of the Iris data set are shown in Figure 3.11. Box plots can also be used to compare how attributes vary between different classes of objects, as shown in Figure 3.12. ∎

Pie Chart A pie chart is similar to a histogram, but is typically used with categorical attributes that have a relatively small number of values. Instead of showing the relative frequency of different values with the area or height of a bar, as in a histogram, a pie chart uses the relative area of a circle to indicate relative frequency. Although pie charts are common in popular articles, they

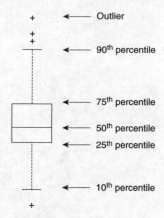

Figure 3.10. Description of box plot for sepal length.

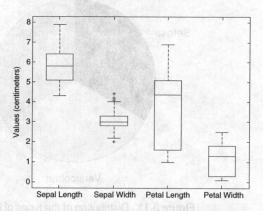

Figure 3.11. Box plot for Iris attributes.

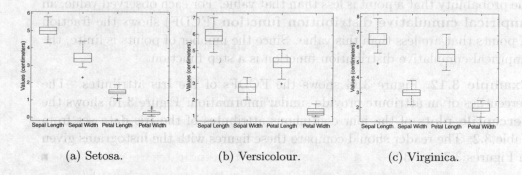

(a) Setosa.   (b) Versicolour.   (c) Virginica.

Figure 3.12. Box plots of attributes by Iris species.

are used less frequently in technical publications because the size of relative areas can be hard to judge. Histograms are preferred for technical work.

Example 3.11. Figure 3.13 displays a pie chart that shows the distribution of Iris species in the Iris data set. In this case, all three flower types have the same frequency. ∎

Percentile Plots and Empirical Cumulative Distribution Functions

A type of diagram that shows the distribution of the data more quantitatively is the plot of an empirical cumulative distribution function. While this type of plot may sound complicated, the concept is straightforward. For each value of a statistical distribution, a **cumulative distribution function** (CDF) shows

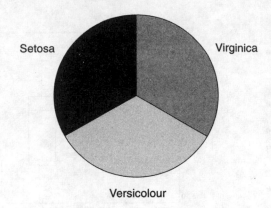

Figure 3.13. Distribution of the types of Iris flowers.

the probability that a point is less than that value. For each observed value, an **empirical cumulative distribution function** (ECDF) shows the fraction of points that are less than this value. Since the number of points is finite, the empirical cumulative distribution function is a step function.

Example 3.12. Figure 3.14 shows the ECDFs of the Iris attributes. The percentiles of an attribute provide similar information. Figure 3.15 shows the **percentile plots** of the four continuous attributes of the Iris data set from Table 3.2. The reader should compare these figures with the histograms given in Figures 3.7 and 3.8.   ∎

Scatter Plots   Most people are familiar with scatter plots to some extent, and they were used in Section 2.4.5 to illustrate linear correlation. Each data object is plotted as a point in the plane using the values of the two attributes as x and y coordinates. It is assumed that the attributes are either integer- or real-valued.

Example 3.13. Figure 3.16 shows a scatter plot for each pair of attributes of the Iris data set. The different species of Iris are indicated by different markers. The arrangement of the scatter plots of pairs of attributes in this type of tabular format, which is known as a **scatter plot matrix**, provides an organized way to examine a number of scatter plots simultaneously.   ∎

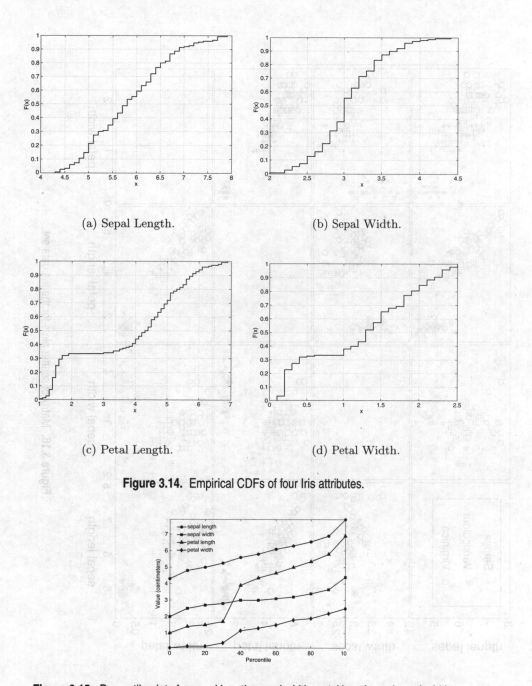

(a) Sepal Length.

(b) Sepal Width.

(c) Petal Length.

(d) Petal Width.

Figure 3.14. Empirical CDFs of four Iris attributes.

Figure 3.15. Percentile plots for sepal length, sepal width, petal length, and petal width.

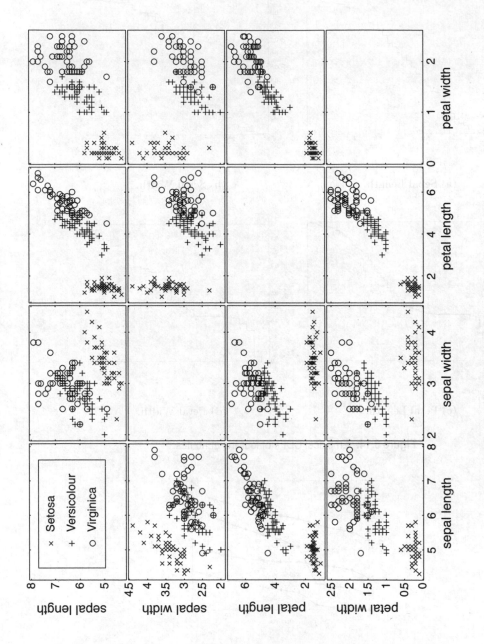

Figure 3.16. Matrix of scatter plots for the Iris data set.

There are two main uses for scatter plots. First, they graphically show the relationship between two attributes. In Section 2.4.5, we saw how scatter plots could be used to judge the degree of linear correlation. (See Figure 2.17.) Scatter plots can also be used to detect non-linear relationships, either directly or by using a scatter plot of the transformed attributes.

Second, when class labels are available, they can be used to investigate the degree to which two attributes separate the classes. If is possible to draw a line (or a more complicated curve) that divides the plane defined by the two attributes into separate regions that contain mostly objects of one class, then it is possible to construct an accurate classifier based on the specified pair of attributes. If not, then more attributes or more sophisticated methods are needed to build a classifier. In Figure 3.16, many of the pairs of attributes (for example, petal width and petal length) provide a moderate separation of the Iris species.

Example 3.14. There are two separate approaches for displaying three attributes of a data set with a scatter plot. First, each object can be displayed according to the values of three, instead of two attributes. Figure 3.17 shows a three-dimensional scatter plot for three attributes in the Iris data set. Second, one of the attributes can be associated with some characteristic of the marker, such as its size, color, or shape. Figure 3.18 shows a plot of three attributes of the Iris data set, where one of the attributes, sepal width, is mapped to the size of the marker. ∎

Extending Two- and Three-Dimensional Plots As illustrated by Figure 3.18, two- or three-dimensional plots can be extended to represent a few additional attributes. For example, scatter plots can display up to three additional attributes using color or shading, size, and shape, allowing five or six dimensions to be represented. There is a need for caution, however. As the complexity of a visual representation of the data increases, it becomes harder for the intended audience to interpret the information. There is no benefit in packing six dimensions' worth of information into a two- or three-dimensional plot, if doing so makes it impossible to understand.

Visualizing Spatio-temporal Data

Data often has spatial or temporal attributes. For instance, the data may consist of a set of observations on a spatial grid, such as observations of pressure on the surface of the Earth or the modeled temperature at various grid points in the simulation of a physical object. These observations can also be

The first two uses for scatter plots. First, they typically show
the relationship between two attributes. In Section 2.4.5, we saw how scatter
plots could be used to judge the degree of linear correlation. (See Figure 2.17.)
Scatter plots can also be used to detect non-linear relationships, either directly
or by seeing if a transformation of the data result a linear relationship.

Second, when class labels are available, they can be used to investigate the
degree to which two attributes separate the classes. As a positive conclusive
sign for a more complicated data set, let a pair of the attributes define a pair of
attributes into separate classes, so a pair of attributes separating the classes, then
only that pair of attributes are useful in based on the type of class, but if
attributes that separate the classes very much as well, the attributes are
useful to help classify. In Figure 3.17, plots of the pairs of attributes using
a single petal width and petal width) provide a good separation of the of the
three species.

Example 3.13. There are two separate approaches for displaying three attributes of a data set with a scatter plot. First, each object can be displayed
according to the three attributes — i.e., sepal width, sepal length, and petal width.
The resulting scatter plot for three attributes in the iris data set. Second,
one of the attributes can be associated with some characteristic of the marker,
such as size, color, or shape. Figure 3.18 shows a plot of three attributes
of the iris data set where the attributes, sepal, are mapped to the
size of the marker.

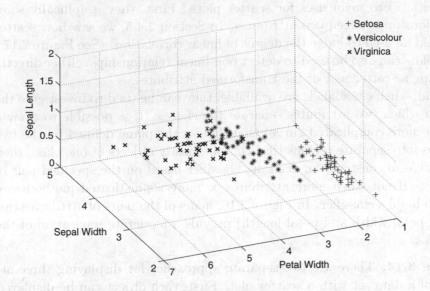

Figure 3.17. Three-dimensional scatter plot of sepal width, sepal length, and petal width.

Extending Two and Three-Dimensional Plots As illustrated by
the earlier two-dimensional displays can be extended to represent a few
additional attributes. For example, scatter plots can display up to an additional attribute using color, size, shape, and slope. Also, there are a
different ways to represent. There is a limit, for certain, however. As the
complexity of a visual representation of the data increases, it becomes harder
for the reader/audience to interpret the information. There is no benefit in
packing six dimensions' worth of information into a two- or three-dimensional
plot, if it makes it impossible to understand.

Visualizing Spatio-Temporal Data

Data often has spatial or temporal attributes. For instance, the data may
consist of a set of observations on the surface of the Earth or the applied temperature at various grid
points on the Earth, or the temperature at various grid
points in the simulation of a physical object. These observations can also be

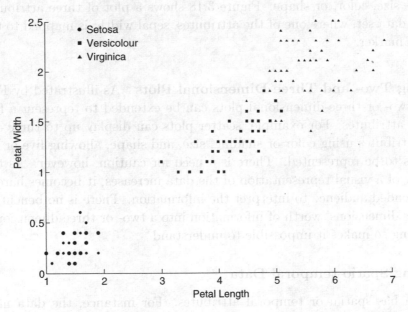

Figure 3.18. Scatter plot of petal length versus petal width, with the size of the marker indicating sepal width.

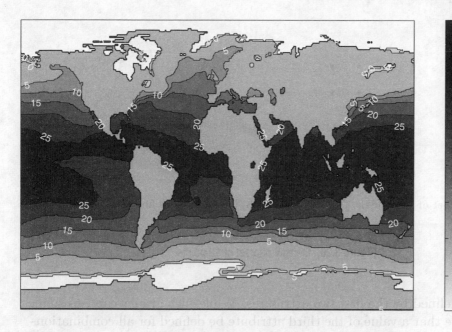

Figure 3.19. Contour plot of SST for December 1998.

made at various points in time. In addition, data may have only a temporal component, such as time series data that gives the daily prices of stocks.

Contour Plots For some three-dimensional data, two attributes specify a position in a plane, while the third has a continuous value, such as temperature or elevation. A useful visualization for such data is a **contour plot**, which breaks the plane into separate regions where the values of the third attribute (temperature, elevation) are roughly the same. A common example of a contour plot is a contour map that shows the elevation of land locations.

Example 3.15. Figure 3.19 shows a contour plot of the average sea surface temperature (SST) for December 1998. The land is arbitrarily set to have a temperature of 0°C. In many contour maps, such as that of Figure 3.19, the **contour lines** that separate two regions are labeled with the value used to separate the regions. For clarity, some of these labels have been deleted. ∎

Surface Plots Like contour plots, **surface plots** use two attributes for the x and y coordinates. The third attribute is used to indicate the height above

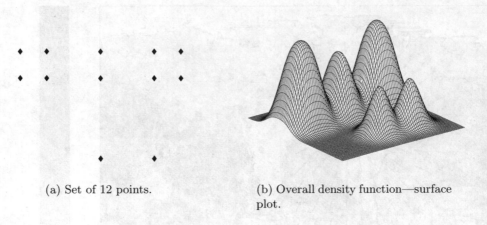

(a) Set of 12 points.

(b) Overall density function—surface plot.

Figure 3.20. Density of a set of 12 points.

the plane defined by the first two attributes. While such graphs can be useful, they require that a value of the third attribute be defined for all combinations of values for the first two attributes, at least over some range. Also, if the surface is too irregular, then it can be difficult to see all the information, unless the plot is viewed interactively. Thus, surface plots are often used to describe mathematical functions or physical surfaces that vary in a relatively smooth manner.

Example 3.16. Figure 3.20 shows a surface plot of the density around a set of 12 points. This example is further discussed in Section 9.3.3. ∎

Vector Field Plots In some data, a characteristic may have both a magnitude and a direction associated with it. For example, consider the flow of a substance or the change of density with location. In these situations, it can be useful to have a plot that displays both direction and magnitude. This type of plot is known as a **vector plot**.

Example 3.17. Figure 3.21 shows a contour plot of the density of the two smaller density peaks from Figure 3.20(b), annotated with the density gradient vectors. ∎

Lower-Dimensional Slices Consider a spatio-temporal data set that records some quantity, such as temperature or pressure, at various locations over time. Such a data set has four dimensions and cannot be easily displayed by the types

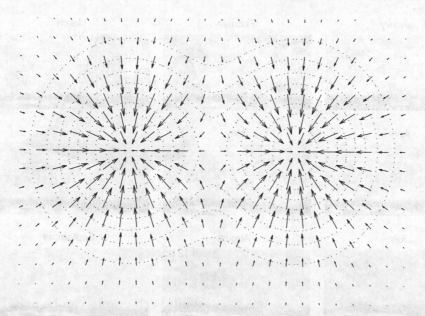

Figure 3.21. Vector plot of the gradient (change) in density for the bottom two density peaks of Figure 3.20.

of plots that we have described so far. However, separate "slices" of the data can be displayed by showing a set of plots, one for each month. By examining the change in a particular area from one month to another, it is possible to notice changes that occur, including those that may be due to seasonal factors.

Example 3.18. The underlying data set for this example consists of the average monthly sea level pressure (SLP) from 1982 to 1999 on a 2.5° by 2.5° latitude-longitude grid. The twelve monthly plots of pressure for one year are shown in Figure 3.22. In this example, we are interested in slices for a particular month in the year 1982. More generally, we can consider slices of the data along any arbitrary dimension. ∎

Animation   Another approach to dealing with slices of data, whether or not time is involved, is to employ animation. The idea is to display successive two-dimensional slices of the data. The human visual system is well suited to detecting visual changes and can often notice changes that might be difficult to detect in another manner. Despite the visual appeal of animation, a set of still plots, such as those of Figure 3.22, can be more useful since this type of visualization allows the information to be studied in arbitrary order and for arbitrary amounts of time.

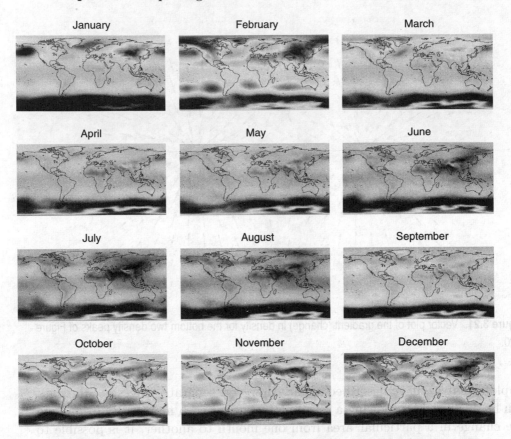

Figure 3.22. Monthly plots of sea level pressure over the 12 months of 1982.

3.3.4   Visualizing Higher-Dimensional Data

This section considers visualization techniques that can display more than the handful of dimensions that can be observed with the techniques just discussed. However, even these techniques are somewhat limited in that they only show some aspects of the data.

Matrices   An image can be regarded as a rectangular array of pixels, where each pixel is characterized by its color and brightness. A data matrix is a rectangular array of values. Thus, a data matrix can be visualized as an image by associating each entry of the data matrix with a pixel in the image. The brightness or color of the pixel is determined by the value of the corresponding entry of the matrix.

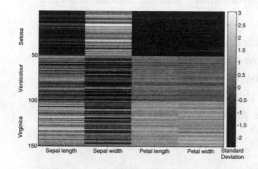

Figure 3.23. Plot of the Iris data matrix where columns have been standardized to have a mean of 0 and standard deviation of 1.

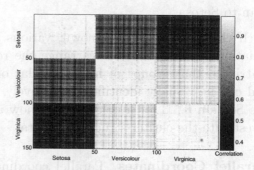

Figure 3.24. Plot of the Iris correlation matrix.

There are some important practical considerations when visualizing a data matrix. If class labels are known, then it is useful to reorder the data matrix so that all objects of a class are together. This makes it easier, for example, to detect if all objects in a class have similar attribute values for some attributes. If different attributes have different ranges, then the attributes are often standardized to have a mean of zero and a standard deviation of 1. This prevents the attribute with the largest magnitude values from visually dominating the plot.

Example 3.19. Figure 3.23 shows the standardized data matrix for the Iris data set. The first 50 rows represent Iris flowers of the species Setosa, the next 50 Versicolour, and the last 50 Virginica. The Setosa flowers have petal width and length well below the average, while the Versicolour flowers have petal width and length around average. The Virginica flowers have petal width and length above average. ∎

It can also be useful to look for structure in the plot of a proximity matrix for a set of data objects. Again, it is useful to sort the rows and columns of the similarity matrix (when class labels are known) so that all the objects of a class are together. This allows a visual evaluation of the cohesiveness of each class and its separation from other classes.

Example 3.20. Figure 3.24 shows the correlation matrix for the Iris data set. Again, the rows and columns are organized so that all the flowers of a particular species are together. The flowers in each group are most similar to each other, but Versicolour and Virginica are more similar to one another than to Setosa.   ■

If class labels are not known, various techniques (matrix reordering and seriation) can be used to rearrange the rows and columns of the similarity matrix so that groups of highly similar objects and attributes are together and can be visually identified. Effectively, this is a simple kind of clustering. See Section 8.5.3 for a discussion of how a proximity matrix can be used to investigate the cluster structure of data.

Parallel Coordinates   Parallel coordinates have one coordinate axis for each attribute, but the different axes are parallel to one other instead of perpendicular, as is traditional. Furthermore, an object is represented as a line instead of as a point. Specifically, the value of each attribute of an object is mapped to a point on the coordinate axis associated with that attribute, and these points are then connected to form the line that represents the object.

It might be feared that this would yield quite a mess. However, in many cases, objects tend to fall into a small number of groups, where the points in each group have similar values for their attributes. If so, and if the number of data objects is not too large, then the resulting parallel coordinates plot can reveal interesting patterns.

Example 3.21. Figure 3.25 shows a parallel coordinates plot of the four numerical attributes of the Iris data set. The lines representing objects of different classes are distinguished by their shading and the use of three different line styles—solid, dotted, and dashed. The parallel coordinates plot shows that the classes are reasonably well separated for petal width and petal length, but less well separated for sepal length and sepal width. Figure 3.25 is another parallel coordinates plot of the same data, but with a different ordering of the axes.   ■

One of the drawbacks of parallel coordinates is that the detection of patterns in such a plot may depend on the order. For instance, if lines cross a lot, the picture can become confusing, and thus, it can be desirable to order the coordinate axes to obtain sequences of axes with less crossover. Compare Figure 3.26, where sepal width (the attribute that is most mixed) is at the left of the figure, to Figure 3.25, where this attribute is in the middle.

Star Coordinates and Chernoff Faces

Another approach to displaying multidimensional data is to encode objects as **glyphs** or **icons**—symbols that impart information non-verbally. More

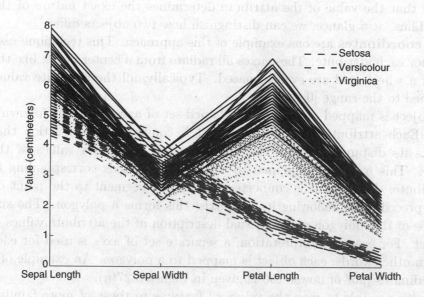

Figure 3.25. A parallel coordinates plot of the four Iris attributes.

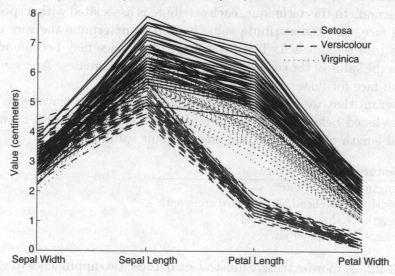

Figure 3.26. A parallel coordinates plot of the four Iris attributes with the attributes reordered to emphasize similarities and dissimilarities of groups.

specifically, each attribute of an object is mapped to a particular feature of a glyph, so that the value of the attribute determines the exact nature of the feature. Thus, at a glance, we can distinguish how two objects differ.

Star coordinates are one example of this approach. This technique uses one axis for each attribute. These axes all radiate from a center point, like the spokes of a wheel, and are evenly spaced. Typically, all the attribute values are mapped to the range [0,1].

An object is mapped onto this star-shaped set of axes using the following process: Each attribute value of the object is converted to a fraction that represents its distance between the minimum and maximum values of the attribute. This fraction is mapped to a point on the axis corresponding to this attribute. Each point is connected with a line segment to the point on the axis preceding or following its own axis; this forms a polygon. The size and shape of this polygon gives a visual description of the attribute values of the object. For ease of interpretation, a separate set of axes is used for each object. In other words, each object is mapped to a polygon. An example of a star coordinates plot of flower 150 is given in Figure 3.27(a).

It is also possible to map the values of features to those of more familiar objects, such as faces. This technique is named **Chernoff faces** for its creator, Herman Chernoff. In this technique, each attribute is associated with a specific feature of a face, and the attribute value is used to determine the way that the facial feature is expressed. Thus, the shape of the face may become more elongated as the value of the corresponding data feature increases. An example of a Chernoff face for flower 150 is given in Figure 3.27(b).

The program that we used to make this face mapped the features to the four features listed below. Other features of the face, such as width between the eyes and length of the mouth, are given default values.

Data Feature	Facial Feature
sepal length	size of face
sepal width	forehead/jaw relative arc length
petal length	shape of forehead
petal width	shape of jaw

Example 3.22. A more extensive illustration of these two approaches to viewing multidimensional data is provided by Figures 3.28 and 3.29, which shows the star and face plots, respectively, of 15 flowers from the Iris data set. The first 5 flowers are of species Setosa, the second 5 are Versicolour, and the last 5 are Virginica. ∎

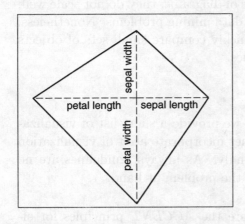

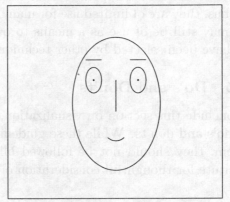

(a) Star graph of Iris 150.

(b) Chernoff face of Iris 150.

Figure 3.27. Star coordinates graph and Chernoff face of the 150th flower of the Iris data set.

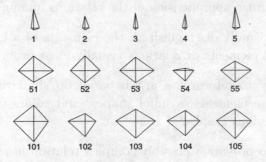

Figure 3.28. Plot of 15 Iris flowers using star coordinates.

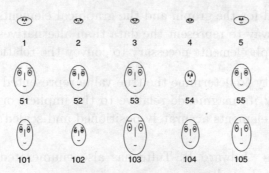

Figure 3.29. A plot of 15 Iris flowers using Chernoff faces.

Despite the visual appeal of these sorts of diagrams, they do not scale well, and thus, they are of limited use for many data mining problems. Nonetheless, they may still be of use as a means to quickly compare small sets of objects that have been selected by other techniques.

3.3.5 Do's and Don'ts

To conclude this section on visualization, we provide a short list of visualization do's and don'ts. While these guidelines incorporate a lot of visualization wisdom, they should not be followed blindly. As always, guidelines are no substitute for thoughtful consideration of the problem at hand.

ACCENT Principles The following are the *ACCENT* principles for effective graphical display put forth by D. A. Burn (as adapted by Michael Friendly):

Apprehension Ability to correctly perceive relations among variables. Does the graph maximize apprehension of the relations among variables?

Clarity Ability to visually distinguish all the elements of a graph. Are the most important elements or relations visually most prominent?

Consistency Ability to interpret a graph based on similarity to previous graphs. Are the elements, symbol shapes, and colors consistent with their use in previous graphs?

Efficiency Ability to portray a possibly complex relation in as simple a way as possible. Are the elements of the graph economically used? Is the graph easy to interpret?

Necessity The need for the graph, and the graphical elements. Is the graph a more useful way to represent the data than alternatives (table, text)? Are all the graph elements necessary to convey the relations?

Truthfulness Ability to determine the true value represented by any graphical element by its magnitude relative to the implicit or explicit scale. Are the graph elements accurately positioned and scaled?

Tufte's Guidelines Edward R. Tufte has also enumerated the following principles for graphical excellence:

- Graphical excellence is the well-designed presentation of interesting data—a matter of *substance*, of *statistics*, and of *design*.

- Graphical excellence consists of complex ideas communicated with clarity, precision, and efficiency.

- Graphical excellence is that which gives to the viewer the greatest number of ideas in the shortest time with the least ink in the smallest space.

- Graphical excellence is nearly always multivariate.

- And graphical excellence requires telling the truth about the data.

3.4 OLAP and Multidimensional Data Analysis

In this section, we investigate the techniques and insights that come from viewing data sets as multidimensional arrays. A number of database systems support such a viewpoint, most notably, On-Line Analytical Processing (OLAP) systems. Indeed, some of the terminology and capabilities of OLAP systems have made their way into spreadsheet programs that are used by millions of people. OLAP systems also have a strong focus on the interactive analysis of data and typically provide extensive capabilities for visualizing the data and generating summary statistics. For these reasons, our approach to multidimensional data analysis will be based on the terminology and concepts common to OLAP systems.

3.4.1 Representing Iris Data as a Multidimensional Array

Most data sets can be represented as a table, where each row is an object and each column is an attribute. In many cases, it is also possible to view the data as a multidimensional array. We illustrate this approach by representing the Iris data set as a multidimensional array.

Table 3.7 was created by discretizing the petal length and petal width attributes to have values of *low*, *medium*, and *high* and then counting the number of flowers from the Iris data set that have particular combinations of petal width, petal length, and species type. (For petal width, the categories *low*, *medium*, and *high* correspond to the intervals [0, 0.75], [0.75, 1.75], [1.75, ∞), respectively. For petal length, the categories *low*, *medium*, and *high* correspond to the intervals [0, 2.5), [2.5, 5), [5, ∞), respectively.)

Table 3.7. Number of flowers having a particular combination of petal width, petal length, and species type.

Petal Length	Petal Width	Species Type	Count
low	low	Setosa	46
low	medium	Setosa	2
medium	low	Setosa	2
medium	medium	Versicolour	43
medium	high	Versicolour	3
medium	high	Virginica	3
high	medium	Versicolour	2
high	medium	Virginica	3
high	high	Versicolour	2
high	high	Virginica	44

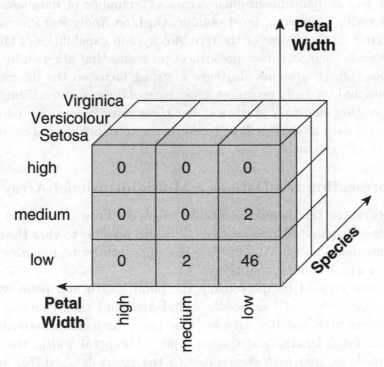

Figure 3.30. A multidimensional data representation for the Iris data set.

Table 3.8. Cross-tabulation of flowers according to petal length and width for flowers of the Setosa species.

		Width		
		low	medium	high
Length	low	46	2	0
	medium	2	0	0
	high	0	0	0

Table 3.9. Cross-tabulation of flowers according to petal length and width for flowers of the Versicolour species.

		Width		
		low	medium	high
Length	low	0	0	0
	medium	0	43	3
	high	0	2	2

Table 3.10. Cross-tabulation of flowers according to petal length and width for flowers of the Virginica species.

		Width		
		low	medium	high
Length	low	0	0	0
	medium	0	0	3
	high	0	3	44

Empty combinations—those combinations that do not correspond to at least one flower—are not shown.

The data can be organized as a multidimensional array with three dimensions corresponding to petal width, petal length, and species type, as illustrated in Figure 3.30. For clarity, slices of this array are shown as a set of three two-dimensional tables, one for each species—see Tables 3.8, 3.9, and 3.10. The information contained in both Table 3.7 and Figure 3.30 is the same. However, in the multidimensional representation shown in Figure 3.30 (and Tables 3.8, 3.9, and 3.10), the values of the attributes—petal width, petal length, and species type—are array indices.

What is important are the insights can be gained by looking at data from a multidimensional viewpoint. Tables 3.8, 3.9, and 3.10 show that each species of Iris is characterized by a different combination of values of petal length and width. Setosa flowers have low width and length, Versicolour flowers have medium width and length, and Virginica flowers have high width and length.

3.4.2   Multidimensional Data: The General Case

The previous section gave a specific example of using a multidimensional approach to represent and analyze a familiar data set. Here we describe the general approach in more detail.

The starting point is usually a tabular representation of the data, such as that of Table 3.7, which is called a **fact table**. Two steps are necessary in order to represent data as a multidimensional array: identification of the dimensions and identification of an attribute that is the focus of the analysis. The dimensions are categorical attributes or, as in the previous example, continuous attributes that have been converted to categorical attributes. The values of an attribute serve as indices into the array for the dimension corresponding to the attribute, and the number of attribute values is the size of that dimension. In the previous example, each attribute had three possible values, and thus, each dimension was of size three and could be indexed by three values. This produced a $3 \times 3 \times 3$ multidimensional array.

Each combination of attribute values (one value for each different attribute) defines a cell of the multidimensional array. To illustrate using the previous example, if petal length = *low*, petal width = *medium*, and species = Setosa, a specific cell containing the value 2 is identified. That is, there are only two flowers in the data set that have the specified attribute values. Notice that each row (object) of the data set in Table 3.7 corresponds to a cell in the multidimensional array.

The contents of each cell represents the value of a **target quantity** (target variable or attribute) that we are interested in analyzing. In the Iris example, the target quantity is the *number of flowers* whose petal width and length fall within certain limits. The target attribute is quantitative because a key goal of multidimensional data analysis is to look aggregate quantities, such as totals or averages.

The following summarizes the procedure for creating a multidimensional data representation from a data set represented in tabular form. First, identify the categorical attributes to be used as the dimensions and a quantitative attribute to be used as the target of the analysis. Each row (object) in the table is mapped to a cell of the multidimensional array. The indices of the cell are specified by the values of the attributes that were selected as dimensions, while the value of the cell is the value of the target attribute. Cells not defined by the data are assumed to have a value of 0.

Example 3.23. To further illustrate the ideas just discussed, we present a more traditional example involving the sale of products.The fact table for this example is given by Table 3.11. The dimensions of the multidimensional representation are the *product ID*, *location*, and *date* attributes, while the target attribute is the *revenue*. Figure 3.31 shows the multidimensional representation of this data set. This larger and more complicated data set will be used to illustrate additional concepts of multidimensional data analysis. ∎

3.4.3   Analyzing Multidimensional Data

In this section, we describe different multidimensional analysis techniques. In particular, we discuss the creation of data cubes, and related operations, such as slicing, dicing, dimensionality reduction, roll-up, and drill down.

Data Cubes: Computing Aggregate Quantities

A key motivation for taking a multidimensional viewpoint of data is the importance of aggregating data in various ways. In the sales example, we might wish to find the total sales revenue for a specific year and a specific product. Or we might wish to see the yearly sales revenue for each location across all products. Computing aggregate totals involves fixing specific values for some of the attributes that are being used as dimensions and then summing over all possible values for the attributes that make up the remaining dimensions. There are other types of aggregate quantities that are also of interest, but for simplicity, this discussion will use totals (sums).

Table 3.12 shows the result of summing over all locations for various combinations of date and product. For simplicity, assume that all the dates are within one year. If there are 365 days in a year and 1000 products, then Table 3.12 has 365,000 entries (totals), one for each product-data pair. We could also specify the store location and date and sum over products, or specify the location and product and sum over all dates.

Table 3.13 shows the **marginal totals** of Table 3.12. These totals are the result of further summing over either dates or products. In Table 3.13, the total sales revenue due to product 1, which is obtained by summing across row 1 (over all dates), is $370,000. The total sales revenue on January 1, 2004, which is obtained by summing down column 1 (over all products), is $527,362. The total sales revenue, which is obtained by summing over all rows and columns (all times and products) is $227,352,127. All of these totals are for all locations because the entries of Table 3.13 include all locations.

A key point of this example is that there are a number of different totals (aggregates) that can be computed for a multidimensional array, depending on how many attributes we sum over. Assume that there are n dimensions and that the ith dimension (attribute) has s_i possible values. There are n different ways to sum only over a single attribute. If we sum over dimension j, then we obtain $s_1 * \cdots * s_{j-1} * s_{j+1} * \cdots * s_n$ totals, one for each possible combination of attribute values of the $n-1$ other attributes (dimensions). The totals that result from summing over one attribute form a multidimensional array of $n-1$ dimensions and there are n such arrays of totals. In the sales example, there

Table 3.11. Sales revenue of products (in dollars) for various locations and times.

Product ID	Location	Date	Revenue
⋮	⋮	⋮	
1	Minneapolis	Oct. 18, 2004	$250
1	Chicago	Oct. 18, 2004	$79
⋮	⋮	⋮	
1	Paris	Oct. 18, 2004	301
⋮	⋮	⋮	
27	Minneapolis	Oct. 18, 2004	$2,321
27	Chicago	Oct. 18, 2004	$3,278
⋮	⋮	⋮	
27	Paris	Oct. 18, 2004	$1,325
⋮	⋮	⋮	

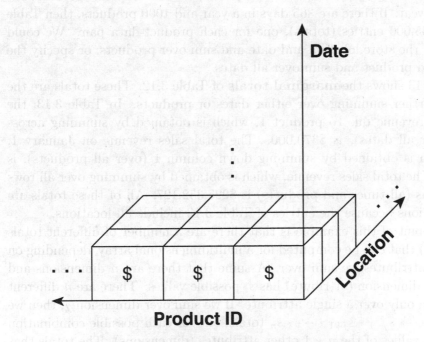

Figure 3.31. Multidimensional data representation for sales data.

Table 3.12. Totals that result from summing over all locations for a fixed time and product.

product ID	date			
	Jan 1, 2004	Jan 2, 2004	...	Dec 31, 2004
1	$1,001	$987	...	$891
⋮				⋮
27	$10,265	$10,225	...	$9,325
⋮				

Table 3.13. Table 3.12 with marginal totals.

product ID	date				
	Jan 1, 2004	Jan 2, 2004	...	Dec 31, 2004	total
1	$1,001	$987	...	$891	$370,000
⋮	⋮			⋮	⋮
27	$10,265	$10,225	...	$9,325	$3,800,020
⋮				⋮	
total	$527,362	$532,953	...	$631,221	$227,352,127

are three sets of totals that result from summing over only one dimension and each set of totals can be displayed as a two-dimensional table.

If we sum over two dimensions (perhaps starting with one of the arrays of totals obtained by summing over one dimension), then we will obtain a multidimensional array of totals with $n - 2$ dimensions. There will be $\binom{n}{2}$ distinct arrays of such totals. For the sales examples, there will be $\binom{3}{2} = 3$ arrays of totals that result from summing over location and product, location and time, or product and time. In general, summing over k dimensions yields $\binom{n}{k}$ arrays of totals, each with dimension $n - k$.

A multidimensional representation of the data, together with all possible totals (aggregates), is known as a **data cube**. Despite the name, the size of each dimension—the number of attribute values—does not need to be equal. Also, a data cube may have either more or fewer than three dimensions. More importantly, a data cube is a generalization of what is known in statistical terminology as a **cross-tabulation**. If marginal totals were added, Tables 3.8, 3.9, or 3.10 would be typical examples of cross tabulations.

Dimensionality Reduction and Pivoting

The aggregation described in the last section can be viewed as a form of **dimensionality reduction**. Specifically, the jth dimension is eliminated by summing over it. Conceptually, this collapses each "column" of cells in the jth dimension into a single cell. For both the sales and Iris examples, aggregating over one dimension reduces the dimensionality of the data from 3 to 2. If s_j is the number of possible values of the jth dimension, the number of cells is reduced by a factor of s_j. Exercise 17 on page 143 asks the reader to explore the difference between this type of dimensionality reduction and that of PCA.

Pivoting refers to aggregating over all dimensions except two. The result is a two-dimensional cross tabulation with the two specified dimensions as the only remaining dimensions. Table 3.13 is an example of pivoting on date and product.

Slicing and Dicing

These two colorful names refer to rather straightforward operations. **Slicing** is selecting a group of cells from the entire multidimensional array by specifying a specific value for one or more dimensions. Tables 3.8, 3.9, and 3.10 are three slices from the Iris set that were obtained by specifying three separate values for the species dimension. **Dicing** involves selecting a subset of cells by specifying a range of attribute values. This is equivalent to defining a subarray from the complete array. In practice, both operations can also be accompanied by aggregation over some dimensions.

Roll-Up and Drill-Down

In Chapter 2, attribute values were regarded as being "atomic" in some sense. However, this is not always the case. In particular, each date has a number of properties associated with it such as the year, month, and week. The data can also be identified as belonging to a particular business quarter, or if the application relates to education, a school quarter or semester. A location also has various properties: continent, country, state (province, etc.), and city. Products can also be divided into various categories, such as clothing, electronics, and furniture.

Often these categories can be organized as a hierarchical tree or lattice. For instance, years consist of months or weeks, both of which consist of days. Locations can be divided into nations, which contain states (or other units of local government), which in turn contain cities. Likewise, any category of products can be further subdivided. For example, the product category, furniture, can be subdivided into the subcategories, chairs, tables, sofas, etc.

This hierarchical structure gives rise to the roll-up and drill-down operations. To illustrate, starting with the original sales data, which is a multidimensional array with entries for each date, we can aggregate (**roll up**) the sales across all the dates in a month. Conversely, given a representation of the data where the time dimension is broken into months, we might want to split the monthly sales totals (**drill down**) into daily sales totals. Of course, this requires that the underlying sales data be available at a daily granularity.

Thus, roll-up and drill-down operations are related to aggregation. Notice, however, that they differ from the aggregation operations discussed until now in that they aggregate cells within a dimension, not across the entire dimension.

3.4.4 Final Comments on Multidimensional Data Analysis

Multidimensional data analysis, in the sense implied by OLAP and related systems, consists of viewing the data as a multidimensional array and aggregating data in order to better analyze the structure of the data. For the Iris data, the differences in petal width and length are clearly shown by such an analysis. The analysis of business data, such as sales data, can also reveal many interesting patterns, such as profitable (or unprofitable) stores or products.

As mentioned, there are various types of database systems that support the analysis of multidimensional data. Some of these systems are based on relational databases and are known as ROLAP systems. More specialized database systems that specifically employ a multidimensional data representation as their fundamental data model have also been designed. Such systems are known as MOLAP systems. In addition to these types of systems, statistical databases (SDBs) have been developed to store and analyze various types of statistical data, e.g., census and public health data, that are collected by governments or other large organizations. References to OLAP and SDBs are provided in the bibliographic notes.

3.5 Bibliographic Notes

Summary statistics are discussed in detail in most introductory statistics books, such as [92]. References for exploratory data analysis are the classic text by Tukey [104] and the book by Velleman and Hoaglin [105].

The basic visualization techniques are readily available, being an integral part of most spreadsheets (Microsoft EXCEL [95]), statistics programs (SAS

[99], SPSS [102], R [96], and S-PLUS [98]), and mathematics software (MAT-LAB [94] and Mathematica [93]). Most of the graphics in this chapter were generated using MATLAB. The statistics package R is freely available as an open source software package from the R project.

The literature on visualization is extensive, covering many fields and many decades. One of the classics of the field is the book by Tufte [103]. The book by Spence [101], which strongly influenced the visualization portion of this chapter, is a useful reference for information visualization—both principles and techniques. This book also provides a thorough discussion of many dynamic visualization techniques that were not covered in this chapter. Two other books on visualization that may also be of interest are those by Card et al. [87] and Fayyad et al. [89].

Finally, there is a great deal of information available about data visualization on the World Wide Web. Since Web sites come and go frequently, the best strategy is a search using "information visualization," "data visualization," or "statistical graphics." However, we do want to single out for attention "The Gallery of Data Visualization," by Friendly [90]. The ACCENT Principles for effective graphical display as stated in this chapter can be found there, or as originally presented in the article by Burn [86].

There are a variety of graphical techniques that can be used to explore whether the distribution of the data is Gaussian or some other specified distribution. Also, there are plots that display whether the observed values are statistically significant in some sense. We have not covered any of these techniques here and refer the reader to the previously mentioned statistical and mathematical packages.

Multidimensional analysis has been around in a variety of forms for some time. One of the original papers was a white paper by Codd [88], the father of relational databases. The data cube was introduced by Gray et al. [91], who described various operations for creating and manipulating data cubes within a relational database framework. A comparison of statistical databases and OLAP is given by Shoshani [100]. Specific information on OLAP can be found in documentation from database vendors and many popular books. Many database textbooks also have general discussions of OLAP, often in the context of data warehousing. For example, see the text by Ramakrishnan and Gehrke [97].

Bibliography

[86] D. A. Burn. Designing Effective Statistical Graphs. In C. R. Rao, editor, *Handbook of Statistics 9*. Elsevier/North-Holland, Amsterdam, The Netherlands, September 1993.

[87] S. K. Card, J. D. MacKinlay, and B. Shneiderman, editors. *Readings in Information Visualization: Using Vision to Think*. Morgan Kaufmann Publishers, San Francisco, CA, January 1999.

[88] E. F. Codd, S. B. Codd, and C. T. Smalley. Providing OLAP (On-line Analytical Processing) to User- Analysts: An IT Mandate. White Paper, E.F. Codd and Associates, 1993.

[89] U. M. Fayyad, G. G. Grinstein, and A. Wierse, editors. *Information Visualization in Data Mining and Knowledge Discovery*. Morgan Kaufmann Publishers, San Francisco, CA, September 2001.

[90] M. Friendly. Gallery of Data Visualization. http://www.math.yorku.ca/SCS/Gallery/, 2005.

[91] J. Gray, S. Chaudhuri, A. Bosworth, A. Layman, D. Reichart, M. Venkatrao, F. Pellow, and H. Pirahesh. Data Cube: A Relational Aggregation Operator Generalizing Group-By, Cross-Tab, and Sub-Totals. *Journal Data Mining and Knowledge Discovery*, 1(1): 29–53, 1997.

[92] B. W. Lindgren. *Statistical Theory*. CRC Press, January 1993.

[93] Mathematica 5.1. Wolfram Research, Inc. http://www.wolfram.com/, 2005.

[94] MATLAB 7.0. The MathWorks, Inc. http://www.mathworks.com, 2005.

[95] Microsoft Excel 2003. Microsoft, Inc. http://www.microsoft.com/, 2003.

[96] R: A language and environment for statistical computing and graphics. The R Project for Statistical Computing. http://www.r-project.org/, 2005.

[97] R. Ramakrishnan and J. Gehrke. *Database Management Systems*. McGraw-Hill, 3rd edition, August 2002.

[98] S-PLUS. Insightful Corporation. http://www.insightful.com, 2005.

[99] SAS: Statistical Analysis System. SAS Institute Inc. http://www.sas.com/, 2005.

[100] A. Shoshani. OLAP and statistical databases: similarities and differences. In *Proc. of the Sixteenth ACM SIGACT-SIGMOD-SIGART Symp. on Principles of Database Systems*, pages 185–196. ACM Press, 1997.

[101] R. Spence. *Information Visualization*. ACM Press, New York, December 2000.

[102] SPSS: Statistical Package for the Social Sciences. SPSS, Inc. http://www.spss.com/, 2005.

[103] E. R. Tufte. *The Visual Display of Quantitative Information*. Graphics Press, Cheshire, CT, March 1986.

[104] J. W. Tukey. *Exploratory data analysis*. Addison-Wesley, 1977.

[105] P. Velleman and D. Hoaglin. *The ABC's of EDA: Applications, Basics, and Computing of Exploratory Data Analysis*. Duxbury, 1981.

3.6 Exercises

1. Obtain one of the data sets available at the UCI Machine Learning Repository and apply as many of the different visualization techniques described in the chapter as possible. The bibliographic notes and book Web site provide pointers to visualization software.

2. Identify at least two advantages and two disadvantages of using color to visually represent information.

3. What are the arrangement issues that arise with respect to three-dimensional plots?

4. Discuss the advantages and disadvantages of using sampling to reduce the number of data objects that need to be displayed. Would simple random sampling (without replacement) be a good approach to sampling? Why or why not?

5. Describe how you would create visualizations to display information that describes the following types of systems.

   (a) Computer networks. Be sure to include both the static aspects of the network, such as connectivity, and the dynamic aspects, such as traffic.

   (b) The distribution of specific plant and animal species around the world for a specific moment in time.

   (c) The use of computer resources, such as processor time, main memory, and disk, for a set of benchmark database programs.

   (d) The change in occupation of workers in a particular country over the last thirty years. Assume that you have yearly information about each person that also includes gender and level of education.

   Be sure to address the following issues:

   - **Representation.** How will you map objects, attributes, and relationships to visual elements?
   - **Arrangement.** Are there any special considerations that need to be taken into account with respect to how visual elements are displayed? Specific examples might be the choice of viewpoint, the use of transparency, or the separation of certain groups of objects.
   - **Selection.** How will you handle a large number of attributes and data objects?

6. Describe one advantage and one disadvantage of a stem and leaf plot with respect to a standard histogram.

7. How might you address the problem that a histogram depends on the number and location of the bins?

8. Describe how a box plot can give information about whether the value of an attribute is symmetrically distributed. What can you say about the symmetry of the distributions of the attributes shown in Figure 3.11?

9. Compare sepal length, sepal width, petal length, and petal width, using Figure 3.12.

10. Comment on the use of a box plot to explore a data set with four attributes: age, weight, height, and income.

11. Give a possible explanation as to why most of the values of petal length and width fall in the buckets along the diagonal in Figure 3.9.

12. Use Figures 3.14 and 3.15 to identify a characteristic shared by the petal width and petal length attributes.

13. Simple line plots, such as that displayed in Figure 2.12 on page 56, which shows two time series, can be used to effectively display high-dimensional data. For example, in Figure 2.12 it is easy to tell that the frequencies of the two time series are different. What characteristic of time series allows the effective visualization of high-dimensional data?

14. Describe the types of situations that produce sparse or dense data cubes. Illustrate with examples other than those used in the book.

15. How might you extend the notion of multidimensional data analysis so that the target variable is a qualitative variable? In other words, what sorts of summary statistics or data visualizations would be of interest?

16. Construct a data cube from Table 3.14. Is this a dense or sparse data cube? If it is sparse, identify the cells that empty.

Table 3.14. Fact table for Exercise 16.

Product ID	Location ID	Number Sold
1	1	10
1	3	6
2	1	5
2	2	22

17. Discuss the differences between dimensionality reduction based on aggregation and dimensionality reduction based on techniques such as PCA and SVD.

Classification: Basic Concepts, Decision Trees, and Model Evaluation

Classification, which is the task of assigning objects to one of several predefined categories, is a pervasive problem that encompasses many diverse applications. Examples include detecting spam email messages based upon the message header and content, categorizing cells as malignant or benign based upon the results of MRI scans, and classifying galaxies based upon their shapes (see Figure 4.1).

(a) A spiral galaxy.   (b) An elliptical galaxy.

Figure 4.1. Classification of galaxies. The images are from the NASA website.

From Chapter 4 of *Introduction to Data Mining*, First Edition. Pang-Ning Tan, Michael Steinbach, Vipin Kumar. Copyright © 2006 by Pearson Education, Inc. All rights reserved.

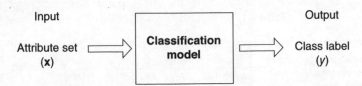

Figure 4.2. Classification as the task of mapping an input attribute set x into its class label y.

This chapter introduces the basic concepts of classification, describes some of the key issues such as model overfitting, and presents methods for evaluating and comparing the performance of a classification technique. While it focuses mainly on a technique known as decision tree induction, most of the discussion in this chapter is also applicable to other classification techniques, many of which are covered in Chapter 5.

4.1   Preliminaries

The input data for a classification task is a collection of records. Each record, also known as an instance or example, is characterized by a tuple $(\mathbf{x}, y)$, where $\mathbf{x}$ is the attribute set and y is a special attribute, designated as the class label (also known as category or target attribute). Table 4.1 shows a sample data set used for classifying vertebrates into one of the following categories: mammal, bird, fish, reptile, or amphibian. The attribute set includes properties of a vertebrate such as its body temperature, skin cover, method of reproduction, ability to fly, and ability to live in water. Although the attributes presented in Table 4.1 are mostly discrete, the attribute set can also contain continuous features. The class label, on the other hand, must be a discrete attribute. This is a key characteristic that distinguishes classification from **regression**, a predictive modeling task in which y is a continuous attribute. Regression techniques are covered in Appendix D.

Definition 4.1 (Classification). Classification is the task of learning a **target function** f that maps each attribute set $\mathbf{x}$ to one of the predefined class labels y.

The target function is also known informally as a **classification model**. A classification model is useful for the following purposes.

Descriptive Modeling   A classification model can serve as an explanatory tool to distinguish between objects of different classes. For example, it would be useful—for both biologists and others—to have a descriptive model that

Table 4.1. The vertebrate data set.

Name	Body Temperature	Skin Cover	Gives Birth	Aquatic Creature	Aerial Creature	Has Legs	Hiber- nates	Class Label
human	warm-blooded	hair	yes	no	no	yes	no	mammal
python	cold-blooded	scales	no	no	no	no	yes	reptile
salmon	cold-blooded	scales	no	yes	no	no	no	fish
whale	warm-blooded	hair	yes	yes	no	no	no	mammal
frog	cold-blooded	none	no	semi	no	yes	yes	amphibian
komodo dragon	cold-blooded	scales	no	no	no	yes	no	reptile
bat	warm-blooded	hair	yes	no	yes	yes	yes	mammal
pigeon	warm-blooded	feathers	no	no	yes	yes	no	bird
cat	warm-blooded	fur	yes	no	no	yes	no	mammal
leopard shark	cold-blooded	scales	yes	yes	no	no	no	fish
turtle	cold-blooded	scales	no	semi	no	yes	no	reptile
penguin	warm-blooded	feathers	no	semi	no	yes	no	bird
porcupine	warm-blooded	quills	yes	no	no	yes	yes	mammal
eel	cold-blooded	scales	no	yes	no	no	no	fish
salamander	cold-blooded	none	no	semi	no	yes	yes	amphibian

summarizes the data shown in Table 4.1 and explains what features define a vertebrate as a mammal, reptile, bird, fish, or amphibian.

Predictive Modeling A classification model can also be used to predict the class label of unknown records. As shown in Figure 4.2, a classification model can be treated as a black box that automatically assigns a class label when presented with the attribute set of an unknown record. Suppose we are given the following characteristics of a creature known as a gila monster:

Name	Body Temperature	Skin Cover	Gives Birth	Aquatic Creature	Aerial Creature	Has Legs	Hiber- nates	Class Label
gila monster	cold-blooded	scales	no	no	no	yes	yes	?

We can use a classification model built from the data set shown in Table 4.1 to determine the class to which the creature belongs.

Classification techniques are most suited for predicting or describing data sets with binary or nominal categories. They are less effective for ordinal categories (e.g., to classify a person as a member of high-, medium-, or low-income group) because they do not consider the implicit order among the categories. Other forms of relationships, such as the subclass–superclass relationships among categories (e.g., humans and apes are primates, which in turn, is a subclass of mammals) are also ignored. The remainder of this chapter focuses only on binary or nominal class labels.

4.2   General Approach to Solving a Classification Problem

A classification technique (or classifier) is a systematic approach to building classification models from an input data set. Examples include decision tree classifiers, rule-based classifiers, neural networks, support vector machines, and naïve Bayes classifiers. Each technique employs a **learning algorithm** to identify a model that best fits the relationship between the attribute set and class label of the input data. The model generated by a learning algorithm should both fit the input data well and correctly predict the class labels of records it has never seen before. Therefore, a key objective of the learning algorithm is to build models with good generalization capability; i.e., models that accurately predict the class labels of previously unknown records.

Figure 4.3 shows a general approach for solving classification problems. First, a **training set** consisting of records whose class labels are known must

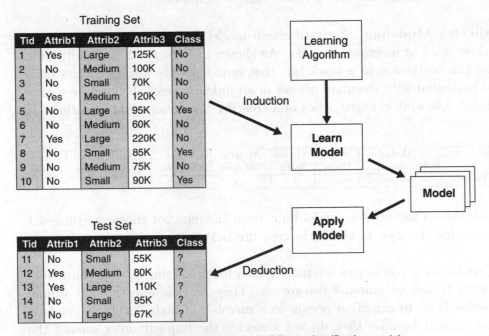

Figure 4.3. General approach for building a classification model.

4.2 General Approach to Solving a Classification Problem

Table 4.2. Confusion matrix for a 2-class problem.

		Predicted Class	
		$Class = 1$	$Class = 0$
Actual	$Class = 1$	f_{11}	f_{10}
Class	$Class = 0$	f_{01}	f_{00}

be provided. The training set is used to build a classification model, which is subsequently applied to the **test set**, which consists of records with unknown class labels.

Evaluation of the performance of a classification model is based on the counts of test records correctly and incorrectly predicted by the model. These counts are tabulated in a table known as a **confusion matrix**. Table 4.2 depicts the confusion matrix for a binary classification problem. Each entry f_{ij} in this table denotes the number of records from class i predicted to be of class j. For instance, f_{01} is the number of records from class 0 incorrectly predicted as class 1. Based on the entries in the confusion matrix, the total number of correct predictions made by the model is $(f_{11} + f_{00})$ and the total number of incorrect predictions is $(f_{10} + f_{01})$.

Although a confusion matrix provides the information needed to determine how well a classification model performs, summarizing this information with a single number would make it more convenient to compare the performance of different models. This can be done using a **performance metric** such as **accuracy**, which is defined as follows:

$$\text{Accuracy} = \frac{\text{Number of correct predictions}}{\text{Total number of predictions}} = \frac{f_{11} + f_{00}}{f_{11} + f_{10} + f_{01} + f_{00}}. \quad (4.1)$$

Equivalently, the performance of a model can be expressed in terms of its **error rate**, which is given by the following equation:

$$\text{Error rate} = \frac{\text{Number of wrong predictions}}{\text{Total number of predictions}} = \frac{f_{10} + f_{01}}{f_{11} + f_{10} + f_{01} + f_{00}}. \quad (4.2)$$

Most classification algorithms seek models that attain the highest accuracy, or equivalently, the lowest error rate when applied to the test set. We will revisit the topic of model evaluation in Section 4.5.

4.3   Decision Tree Induction

This section introduces a **decision tree** classifier, which is a simple yet widely used classification technique.

4.3.1   How a Decision Tree Works

To illustrate how classification with a decision tree works, consider a simpler version of the vertebrate classification problem described in the previous section. Instead of classifying the vertebrates into five distinct groups of species, we assign them to two categories: mammals and non-mammals.

Suppose a new species is discovered by scientists. How can we tell whether it is a mammal or a non-mammal? One approach is to pose a series of questions about the characteristics of the species. The first question we may ask is whether the species is cold- or warm-blooded. If it is cold-blooded, then it is definitely not a mammal. Otherwise, it is either a bird or a mammal. In the latter case, we need to ask a follow-up question: Do the females of the species give birth to their young? Those that do give birth are definitely mammals, while those that do not are likely to be non-mammals (with the exception of egg-laying mammals such as the platypus and spiny anteater).

The previous example illustrates how we can solve a classification problem by asking a series of carefully crafted questions about the attributes of the test record. Each time we receive an answer, a follow-up question is asked until we reach a conclusion about the class label of the record. The series of questions and their possible answers can be organized in the form of a decision tree, which is a hierarchical structure consisting of nodes and directed edges. Figure 4.4 shows the decision tree for the mammal classification problem. The tree has three types of nodes:

- A **root node** that has no incoming edges and zero or more outgoing edges.

- **Internal nodes**, each of which has exactly one incoming edge and two or more outgoing edges.

- **Leaf** or **terminal** nodes, each of which has exactly one incoming edge and no outgoing edges.

In a decision tree, each leaf node is assigned a class label. The **non-terminal** nodes, which include the root and other internal nodes, contain attribute test conditions to separate records that have different characteristics. For example, the root node shown in Figure 4.4 uses the attribute Body

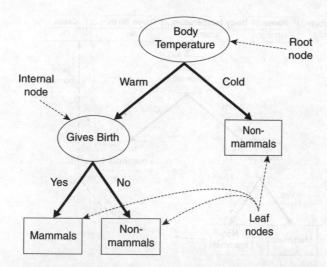

Figure 4.4. A decision tree for the mammal classification problem.

Temperature to separate warm-blooded from cold-blooded vertebrates. Since all cold-blooded vertebrates are non-mammals, a leaf node labeled `Non-mammals` is created as the right child of the root node. If the vertebrate is warm-blooded, a subsequent attribute, `Gives Birth`, is used to distinguish mammals from other warm-blooded creatures, which are mostly birds.

Classifying a test record is straightforward once a decision tree has been constructed. Starting from the root node, we apply the test condition to the record and follow the appropriate branch based on the outcome of the test. This will lead us either to another internal node, for which a new test condition is applied, or to a leaf node. The class label associated with the leaf node is then assigned to the record. As an illustration, Figure 4.5 traces the path in the decision tree that is used to predict the class label of a flamingo. The path terminates at a leaf node labeled `Non-mammals`.

4.3.2   How to Build a Decision Tree

In principle, there are exponentially many decision trees that can be constructed from a given set of attributes. While some of the trees are more accurate than others, finding the optimal tree is computationally infeasible because of the exponential size of the search space. Nevertheless, efficient algorithms have been developed to induce a reasonably accurate, albeit suboptimal, decision tree in a reasonable amount of time. These algorithms usually employ a greedy strategy that grows a decision tree by making a series of locally op-

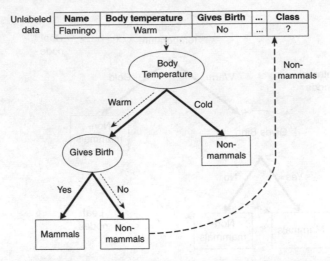

Figure 4.5. Classifying an unlabeled vertebrate. The dashed lines represent the outcomes of applying various attribute test conditions on the unlabeled vertebrate. The vertebrate is eventually assigned to the Non-mammal class.

timum decisions about which attribute to use for partitioning the data. One such algorithm is **Hunt's algorithm**, which is the basis of many existing decision tree induction algorithms, including ID3, C4.5, and CART. This section presents a high-level discussion of Hunt's algorithm and illustrates some of its design issues.

Hunt's Algorithm

In Hunt's algorithm, a decision tree is grown in a recursive fashion by partitioning the training records into successively purer subsets. Let D_t be the set of training records that are associated with node t and $y = \{y_1, y_2, \ldots, y_c\}$ be the class labels. The following is a recursive definition of Hunt's algorithm.

Step 1: If all the records in D_t belong to the same class y_t, then t is a leaf node labeled as y_t.

Step 2: If D_t contains records that belong to more than one class, an **attribute test condition** is selected to partition the records into smaller subsets. A child node is created for each outcome of the test condition and the records in D_t are distributed to the children based on the outcomes. The algorithm is then recursively applied to each child node.

		binary		categorical		continuous		class

Tid	Home Owner	Marital Status	Annual Income	Defaulted Borrower
1	Yes	Single	125K	No
2	No	Married	100K	No
3	No	Single	70K	No
4	Yes	Married	120K	No
5	No	Divorced	95K	Yes
6	No	Married	60K	No
7	Yes	Divorced	220K	No
8	No	Single	85K	Yes
9	No	Married	75K	No
10	No	Single	90K	Yes

Figure 4.6. Training set for predicting borrowers who will default on loan payments.

To illustrate how the algorithm works, consider the problem of predicting whether a loan applicant will repay her loan obligations or become delinquent, subsequently defaulting on her loan. A training set for this problem can be constructed by examining the records of previous borrowers. In the example shown in Figure 4.6, each record contains the personal information of a borrower along with a class label indicating whether the borrower has defaulted on loan payments.

The initial tree for the classification problem contains a single node with class label `Defaulted = No` (see Figure 4.7(a)), which means that most of the borrowers successfully repaid their loans. The tree, however, needs to be refined since the root node contains records from both classes. The records are subsequently divided into smaller subsets based on the outcomes of the `Home Owner` test condition, as shown in Figure 4.7(b). The justification for choosing this attribute test condition will be discussed later. For now, we will assume that this is the best criterion for splitting the data at this point. Hunt's algorithm is then applied recursively to each child of the root node. From the training set given in Figure 4.6, notice that all borrowers who are home owners successfully repaid their loans. The left child of the root is therefore a leaf node labeled `Defaulted = No` (see Figure 4.7(b)). For the right child, we need to continue applying the recursive step of Hunt's algorithm until all the records belong to the same class. The trees resulting from each recursive step are shown in Figures 4.7(c) and (d).

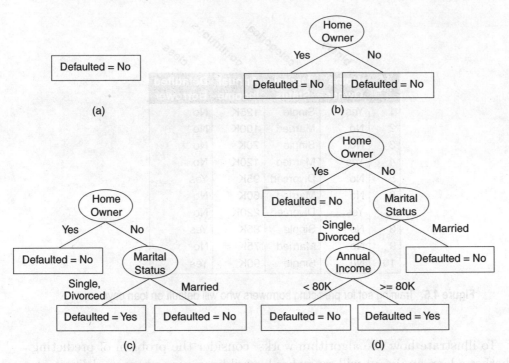

Figure 4.7. Hunt's algorithm for inducing decision trees.

Hunt's algorithm will work if every combination of attribute values is present in the training data and each combination has a unique class label. These assumptions are too stringent for use in most practical situations. Additional conditions are needed to handle the following cases:

1. It is possible for some of the child nodes created in Step 2 to be empty; i.e., there are no records associated with these nodes. This can happen if none of the training records have the combination of attribute values associated with such nodes. In this case the node is declared a leaf node with the same class label as the majority class of training records associated with its parent node.

2. In Step 2, if all the records associated with D_t have identical attribute values (except for the class label), then it is not possible to split these records any further. In this case, the node is declared a leaf node with the same class label as the majority class of training records associated with this node.

Design Issues of Decision Tree Induction

A learning algorithm for inducing decision trees must address the following two issues.

1. **How should the training records be split?** Each recursive step of the tree-growing process must select an attribute test condition to divide the records into smaller subsets. To implement this step, the algorithm must provide a method for specifying the test condition for different attribute types as well as an objective measure for evaluating the goodness of each test condition.

2. **How should the splitting procedure stop?** A stopping condition is needed to terminate the tree-growing process. A possible strategy is to continue expanding a node until either all the records belong to the same class or all the records have identical attribute values. Although both conditions are sufficient to stop any decision tree induction algorithm, other criteria can be imposed to allow the tree-growing procedure to terminate earlier. The advantages of early termination will be discussed later in Section 4.4.5.

4.3.3 Methods for Expressing Attribute Test Conditions

Decision tree induction algorithms must provide a method for expressing an attribute test condition and its corresponding outcomes for different attribute types.

Binary Attributes The test condition for a binary attribute generates two potential outcomes, as shown in Figure 4.8.

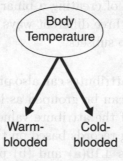

Figure 4.8. Test condition for binary attributes.

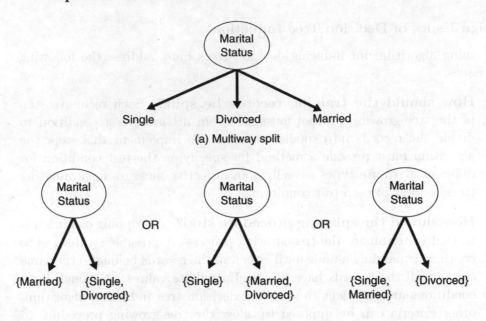

Figure 4.9. Test conditions for nominal attributes.

Nominal Attributes   Since a nominal attribute can have many values, its test condition can be expressed in two ways, as shown in Figure 4.9. For a multiway split (Figure 4.9(a)), the number of outcomes depends on the number of distinct values for the corresponding attribute. For example, if an attribute such as marital status has three distinct values—single, married, or divorced—its test condition will produce a three-way split. On the other hand, some decision tree algorithms, such as CART, produce only binary splits by considering all $2^{k-1} - 1$ ways of creating a binary partition of k attribute values. Figure 4.9(b) illustrates three different ways of grouping the attribute values for marital status into two subsets.

Ordinal Attributes   Ordinal attributes can also produce binary or multiway splits. Ordinal attribute values can be grouped as long as the grouping does not violate the order property of the attribute values. Figure 4.10 illustrates various ways of splitting training records based on the Shirt Size attribute. The groupings shown in Figures 4.10(a) and (b) preserve the order among the attribute values, whereas the grouping shown in Figure 4.10(c) violates this property because it combines the attribute values Small and Large into

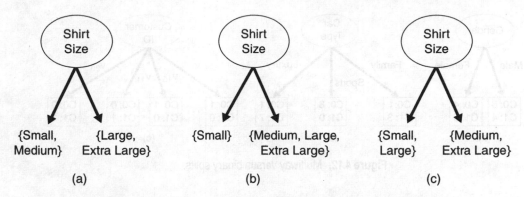

Figure 4.10. Different ways of grouping ordinal attribute values.

the same partition while `Medium` and `Extra Large` are combined into another partition.

Continuous Attributes   For continuous attributes, the test condition can be expressed as a comparison test $(A < v)$ or $(A \geq v)$ with binary outcomes, or a range query with outcomes of the form $v_i \leq A < v_{i+1}$, for $i = 1, \ldots, k$. The difference between these approaches is shown in Figure 4.11. For the binary case, the decision tree algorithm must consider all possible split positions v, and it selects the one that produces the best partition. For the multiway split, the algorithm must consider all possible ranges of continuous values. One approach is to apply the discretization strategies described in Section 2.3.6 on page 57. After discretization, a new ordinal value will be assigned to each discretized interval. Adjacent intervals can also be aggregated into wider ranges as long as the order property is preserved.

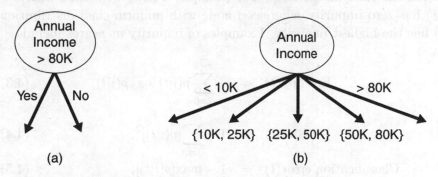

Figure 4.11. Test condition for continuous attributes.

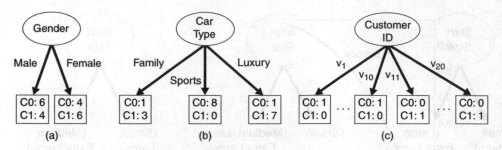

Figure 4.12. Multiway versus binary splits.

4.3.4 Measures for Selecting the Best Split

There are many measures that can be used to determine the best way to split the records. These measures are defined in terms of the class distribution of the records before and after splitting.

Let $p(i|t)$ denote the fraction of records belonging to class i at a given node t. We sometimes omit the reference to node t and express the fraction as p_i. In a two-class problem, the class distribution at any node can be written as (p_0, p_1), where $p_1 = 1 - p_0$. To illustrate, consider the test conditions shown in Figure 4.12. The class distribution before splitting is $(0.5, 0.5)$ because there are an equal number of records from each class. If we split the data using the **Gender** attribute, then the class distributions of the child nodes are $(0.6, 0.4)$ and $(0.4, 0.6)$, respectively. Although the classes are no longer evenly distributed, the child nodes still contain records from both classes. Splitting on the second attribute, **Car Type**, will result in purer partitions.

The measures developed for selecting the best split are often based on the degree of impurity of the child nodes. The smaller the degree of impurity, the more skewed the class distribution. For example, a node with class distribution $(0, 1)$ has zero impurity, whereas a node with uniform class distribution $(0.5, 0.5)$ has the highest impurity. Examples of impurity measures include

$$\text{Entropy}(t) = -\sum_{i=0}^{c-1} p(i|t) \log_2 p(i|t), \qquad (4.3)$$

$$\text{Gini}(t) = 1 - \sum_{i=0}^{c-1} [p(i|t)]^2, \qquad (4.4)$$

$$\text{Classification error}(t) = 1 - \max_i [p(i|t)], \qquad (4.5)$$

where c is the number of classes and $0 \log_2 0 = 0$ in entropy calculations.

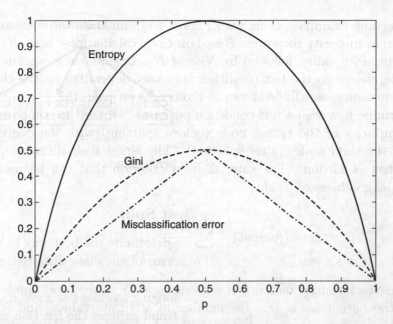

Figure 4.13. Comparison among the impurity measures for binary classification problems.

Figure 4.13 compares the values of the impurity measures for binary classification problems. p refers to the fraction of records that belong to one of the two classes. Observe that all three measures attain their maximum value when the class distribution is uniform (i.e., when $p = 0.5$). The minimum values for the measures are attained when all the records belong to the same class (i.e., when p equals 0 or 1). We next provide several examples of computing the different impurity measures.

Node N_1	Count
Class=0	0
Class=1	6

Gini = $1 - (0/6)^2 - (6/6)^2 = 0$
Entropy = $-(0/6)\log_2(0/6) - (6/6)\log_2(6/6) = 0$
Error = $1 - \max[0/6, 6/6] = 0$

Node N_2	Count
Class=0	1
Class=1	5

Gini = $1 - (1/6)^2 - (5/6)^2 = 0.278$
Entropy = $-(1/6)\log_2(1/6) - (5/6)\log_2(5/6) = 0.650$
Error = $1 - \max[1/6, 5/6] = 0.167$

Node N_3	Count
Class=0	3
Class=1	3

Gini = $1 - (3/6)^2 - (3/6)^2 = 0.5$
Entropy = $-(3/6)\log_2(3/6) - (3/6)\log_2(3/6) = 1$
Error = $1 - \max[3/6, 3/6] = 0.5$

The preceding examples, along with Figure 4.13, illustrate the consistency among different impurity measures. Based on these calculations, node N_1 has the lowest impurity value, followed by N_2 and N_3. Despite their consistency, the attribute chosen as the test condition may vary depending on the choice of impurity measure, as will be shown in Exercise 3 on page 198.

To determine how well a test condition performs, we need to compare the degree of impurity of the parent node (before splitting) with the degree of impurity of the child nodes (after splitting). The larger their difference, the better the test condition. The gain, Δ, is a criterion that can be used to determine the goodness of a split:

$$\Delta = I(\text{parent}) - \sum_{j=1}^{k} \frac{N(v_j)}{N} I(v_j), \tag{4.6}$$

where $I(\cdot)$ is the impurity measure of a given node, N is the total number of records at the parent node, k is the number of attribute values, and $N(v_j)$ is the number of records associated with the child node, v_j. Decision tree induction algorithms often choose a test condition that maximizes the gain Δ. Since $I(\text{parent})$ is the same for all test conditions, maximizing the gain is equivalent to minimizing the weighted average impurity measures of the child nodes. Finally, when entropy is used as the impurity measure in Equation 4.6, the difference in entropy is known as the **information gain**, Δ_{info}.

Splitting of Binary Attributes

Consider the diagram shown in Figure 4.14. Suppose there are two ways to split the data into smaller subsets. Before splitting, the Gini index is 0.5 since there are an equal number of records from both classes. If attribute A is chosen to split the data, the Gini index for node N1 is 0.4898, and for node N2, it is 0.480. The weighted average of the Gini index for the descendent nodes is $(7/12) \times 0.4898 + (5/12) \times 0.480 = 0.486$. Similarly, we can show that the weighted average of the Gini index for attribute B is 0.375. Since the subsets for attribute B have a smaller Gini index, it is preferred over attribute A.

Splitting of Nominal Attributes

As previously noted, a nominal attribute can produce either binary or multi-way splits, as shown in Figure 4.15. The computation of the Gini index for a binary split is similar to that shown for determining binary attributes. For the first binary grouping of the **Car Type** attribute, the Gini index of {Sports,

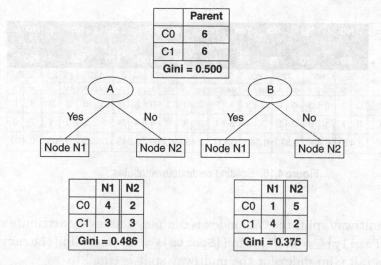

Figure 4.14. Splitting binary attributes.

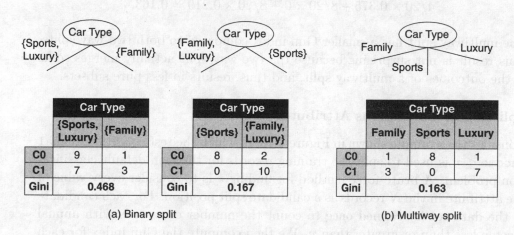

(a) Binary split   (b) Multiway split

Figure 4.15. Splitting nominal attributes.

Luxury} is 0.4922 and the Gini index of {Family} is 0.3750. The weighted average Gini index for the grouping is equal to

$$16/20 \times 0.4922 + 4/20 \times 0.3750 = 0.468.$$

Similarly, for the second binary grouping of {Sports} and {Family, Luxury}, the weighted average Gini index is 0.167. The second grouping has a lower Gini index because its corresponding subsets are much purer.

Class	No		No		No		Yes		Yes		Yes		No		No		No		No	
									Annual Income											
Sorted Values →	60		70		75		85		90		95		100		120		125		220	
Split Positions →	55		65		72		80		87		92		97		110		122		172		230
	<=	>	<=	>	<=	>	<=	>	<=	>	<=	>	<=	>	<=	>	<=	>	<=	>
Yes	0	3	0	3	0	3	0	3	1	2	2	1	3	0	3	0	3	0	3	0
No	0	7	1	6	2	5	3	4	3	4	3	4	3	4	4	3	5	2	6	1	7	0
Gini	0.420		0.400		0.375		0.343		0.417		0.400		*0.300*		0.343		0.375		0.400		0.420	

Figure 4.16. Splitting continuous attributes.

For the multiway split, the Gini index is computed for every attribute value. Since Gini({Family}) = 0.375, Gini({Sports}) = 0, and Gini({Luxury}) = 0.219, the overall Gini index for the multiway split is equal to

$$4/20 \times 0.375 + 8/20 \times 0 + 8/20 \times 0.219 = 0.163.$$

The multiway split has a smaller Gini index compared to both two-way splits. This result is not surprising because the two-way split actually merges some of the outcomes of a multiway split, and thus, results in less pure subsets.

Splitting of Continuous Attributes

Consider the example shown in Figure 4.16, in which the test condition Annual Income $\leq v$ is used to split the training records for the loan default classification problem. A brute-force method for finding v is to consider every value of the attribute in the N records as a candidate split position. For each candidate v, the data set is scanned once to count the number of records with annual income less than or greater than v. We then compute the Gini index for each candidate and choose the one that gives the lowest value. This approach is computationally expensive because it requires $O(N)$ operations to compute the Gini index at each candidate split position. Since there are N candidates, the overall complexity of this task is $O(N^2)$. To reduce the complexity, the training records are sorted based on their annual income, a computation that requires $O(N \log N)$ time. Candidate split positions are identified by taking the midpoints between two adjacent sorted values: 55, 65, 72, and so on. However, unlike the brute-force approach, we do not have to examine all N records when evaluating the Gini index of a candidate split position.

For the first candidate, $v = 55$, none of the records has annual income less than $55K. As a result, the Gini index for the descendent node with Annual

`Income` < $55K is zero. On the other hand, the number of records with annual income greater than or equal to $55K is 3 (for class `Yes`) and 7 (for class `No`), respectively. Thus, the Gini index for this node is 0.420. The overall Gini index for this candidate split position is equal to $0 \times 0 + 1 \times 0.420 = 0.420$.

For the second candidate, $v = 65$, we can determine its class distribution by updating the distribution of the previous candidate. More specifically, the new distribution is obtained by examining the class label of the record with the lowest annual income (i.e., $60K). Since the class label for this record is `No`, the count for class `No` is increased from 0 to 1 (for `Annual Income` $\leq$ $65K) and is decreased from 7 to 6 (for `Annual Income` > $65K). The distribution for class `Yes` remains unchanged. The new weighted-average Gini index for this candidate split position is 0.400.

This procedure is repeated until the Gini index values for all candidates are computed, as shown in Figure 4.16. The best split position corresponds to the one that produces the smallest Gini index, i.e., $v = 97$. This procedure is less expensive because it requires a constant amount of time to update the class distribution at each candidate split position. It can be further optimized by considering only candidate split positions located between two adjacent records with different class labels. For example, because the first three sorted records (with annual incomes $60K, $70K, and $75K) have identical class labels, the best split position should not reside between $60K and $75K. Therefore, the candidate split positions at $v = $55K, $65K, $72K, $87K, $92K, $110K, $122K, $172K, and $230K are ignored because they are located between two adjacent records with the same class labels. This approach allows us to reduce the number of candidate split positions from 11 to 2.

Gain Ratio

Impurity measures such as entropy and Gini index tend to favor attributes that have a large number of distinct values. Figure 4.12 shows three alternative test conditions for partitioning the data set given in Exercise 2 on page 198. Comparing the first test condition, `Gender`, with the second, `Car Type`, it is easy to see that `Car Type` seems to provide a better way of splitting the data since it produces purer descendent nodes. However, if we compare both conditions with `Customer ID`, the latter appears to produce purer partitions. Yet `Customer ID` is not a predictive attribute because its value is unique for each record. Even in a less extreme situation, a test condition that results in a large number of outcomes may not be desirable because the number of records associated with each partition is too small to enable us to make any reliable predictions.

There are two strategies for overcoming this problem. The first strategy is to restrict the test conditions to binary splits only. This strategy is employed by decision tree algorithms such as CART. Another strategy is to modify the splitting criterion to take into account the number of outcomes produced by the attribute test condition. For example, in the C4.5 decision tree algorithm, a splitting criterion known as **gain ratio** is used to determine the goodness of a split. This criterion is defined as follows:

$$\text{Gain ratio} = \frac{\Delta_{\text{info}}}{\text{Split Info}}. \tag{4.7}$$

Here, Split Info $= -\sum_{i=1}^{k} P(v_i) \log_2 P(v_i)$ and k is the total number of splits. For example, if each attribute value has the same number of records, then $\forall i : P(v_i) = 1/k$ and the split information would be equal to $\log_2 k$. This example suggests that if an attribute produces a large number of splits, its split information will also be large, which in turn reduces its gain ratio.

4.3.5   Algorithm for Decision Tree Induction

A skeleton decision tree induction algorithm called `TreeGrowth` is shown in Algorithm 4.1. The input to this algorithm consists of the training records E and the attribute set F. The algorithm works by recursively selecting the best attribute to split the data (Step 7) and expanding the leaf nodes of the

---

Algorithm 4.1 A skeleton decision tree induction algorithm.

`TreeGrowth` (E, F)
1: **if** stopping_cond$(E,F) = true$ **then**
2:    $leaf = $ createNode$()$.
3:    $leaf.label = $ Classify(E).
4:    **return** $leaf$.
5: **else**
6:    $root = $ createNode$()$.
7:    $root.test_cond = $ find_best_split(E, F).
8:    let $V = \{v | v$ is a possible outcome of $root.test\_cond$ $\}$.
9:    **for** each $v \in V$ **do**
10:      $E_v = \{e \mid root.test\_cond(e) = v$ and $e \in E\}$.
11:      $child = $ `TreeGrowth`(E_v, F).
12:      add $child$ as descendent of $root$ and label the edge $(root \rightarrow child)$ as v.
13:    **end for**
14: **end if**
15: **return** $root$.

---

tree (Steps 11 and 12) until the stopping criterion is met (Step 1). The details of this algorithm are explained below:

1. The `createNode()` function extends the decision tree by creating a new node. A node in the decision tree has either a test condition, denoted as *node.test_cond*, or a class label, denoted as *node.label*.

2. The `find_best_split()` function determines which attribute should be selected as the test condition for splitting the training records. As previously noted, the choice of test condition depends on which impurity measure is used to determine the goodness of a split. Some widely used measures include entropy, the Gini index, and the χ^2 statistic.

3. The `Classify()` function determines the class label to be assigned to a leaf node. For each leaf node t, let $p(i|t)$ denote the fraction of training records from class i associated with the node t. In most cases, the leaf node is assigned to the class that has the majority number of training records:

$$leaf.label = \underset{i}{\operatorname{argmax}}\ p(i|t), \qquad (4.8)$$

where the argmax operator returns the argument i that maximizes the expression $p(i|t)$. Besides providing the information needed to determine the class label of a leaf node, the fraction $p(i|t)$ can also be used to estimate the probability that a record assigned to the leaf node t belongs to class i. Sections 5.7.2 and 5.7.3 describe how such probability estimates can be used to determine the performance of a decision tree under different cost functions.

4. The `stopping_cond()` function is used to terminate the tree-growing process by testing whether all the records have either the same class label or the same attribute values. Another way to terminate the recursive function is to test whether the number of records have fallen below some minimum threshold.

After building the decision tree, a **tree-pruning** step can be performed to reduce the size of the decision tree. Decision trees that are too large are susceptible to a phenomenon known as **overfitting**. Pruning helps by trimming the branches of the initial tree in a way that improves the generalization capability of the decision tree. The issues of overfitting and tree pruning are discussed in more detail in Section 4.4.

Session	IP Address	Timestamp	Request Method	Requested Web Page	Protocol	Status	Number of Bytes	Referrer	User Agent
1	160.11.11.11	08/Aug/2004 10:15:21	GET	http://www.cs.umn.edu/~kumar	HTTP/1.1	200	6424		Mozilla/4.0 (compatible; MSIE 6.0; Windows NT 5.0)
1	160.11.11.11	08/Aug/2004 10:15:34	GET	http://www.cs.umn.edu/~kumar/MINDS	HTTP/1.1	200	41378	http://www.cs.umn.edu/~kumar	Mozilla/4.0 (compatible; MSIE 6.0; Windows NT 5.0)
1	160.11.11.11	08/Aug/2004 10:15:41	GET	http://www.cs.umn.edu/~kumar/MINDS/MINDS _papers.htm	HTTP/1.1	200	1018516	http://www.cs.umn.edu/~kumar/MINDS	Mozilla/4.0 (compatible; MSIE 6.0; Windows NT 5.0)
1	160.11.11.11	08/Aug/2004 10:16:11	GET	http://www.cs.umn.edu/~kumar/papers/papers.html	HTTP/1.1	200	7463	http://www.cs.umn.edu/~kumar	Mozilla/4.0 (compatible; MSIE 6.0; Windows NT 5.0)
2	35.9.2.2	08/Aug/2004 10:16:15	GET	http://www.cs.umn.edu/~steinbac	HTTP/1.0	200	3149		Mozilla/5.0 (Windows; U; Windows NT 5.1; en-US; rv:1.7) Gecko/20040616

(a) Example of a Web server log.

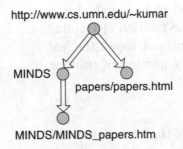

(b) Graph of a Web session.

Attribute Name	Description
totalPages	Total number of pages retrieved in a Web session
ImagePages	Total number of image pages retrieved in a Web session
TotalTime	Total amount of time spent by Web site visitor
RepeatedAccess	The same page requested more than once in a Web session
ErrorRequest	Errors in requesting for Web pages
GET	Percentage of requests made using GET method
POST	Percentage of requests made using POST method
HEAD	Percentage of requests made using HEAD method
Breadth	Breadth of Web traversal
Depth	Depth of Web traversal
MultiIP	Session with multiple IP addresses
MultiAgent	Session with multiple user agents

(c) Derived attributes for Web robot detection.

Figure 4.17. Input data for Web robot detection.

4.3.6 An Example: Web Robot Detection

Web usage mining is the task of applying data mining techniques to extract useful patterns from Web access logs. These patterns can reveal interesting characteristics of site visitors; e.g., people who repeatedly visit a Web site and view the same product description page are more likely to buy the product if certain incentives such as rebates or free shipping are offered.

In Web usage mining, it is important to distinguish accesses made by human users from those due to Web robots. A Web robot (also known as a Web crawler) is a software program that automatically locates and retrieves information from the Internet by following the hyperlinks embedded in Web pages. These programs are deployed by search engine portals to gather the documents necessary for indexing the Web. Web robot accesses must be discarded before applying Web mining techniques to analyze human browsing behavior.

This section describes how a decision tree classifier can be used to distinguish between accesses by human users and those by Web robots. The input data was obtained from a Web server log, a sample of which is shown in Figure 4.17(a). Each line corresponds to a single page request made by a Web client (a user or a Web robot). The fields recorded in the Web log include the IP address of the client, timestamp of the request, Web address of the requested document, size of the document, and the client's identity (via the user agent field). A Web session is a sequence of requests made by a client during a single visit to a Web site. Each Web session can be modeled as a directed graph, in which the nodes correspond to Web pages and the edges correspond to hyperlinks connecting one Web page to another. Figure 4.17(b) shows a graphical representation of the first Web session given in the Web server log.

To classify the Web sessions, features are constructed to describe the characteristics of each session. Figure 4.17(c) shows some of the features used for the Web robot detection task. Among the notable features include the `depth` and `breadth` of the traversal. `Depth` determines the maximum distance of a requested page, where distance is measured in terms of the number of hyperlinks away from the entry point of the Web site. For example, the home page `http://www.cs.umn.edu/~kumar` is assumed to be at depth 0, whereas `http://www.cs.umn.edu/kumar/MINDS/MINDS_papers.htm` is located at depth 2. Based on the Web graph shown in Figure 4.17(b), the `depth` attribute for the first session is equal to two. The `breadth` attribute measures the width of the corresponding Web graph. For example, the `breadth` of the Web session shown in Figure 4.17(b) is equal to two.

The data set for classification contains 2916 records, with equal numbers of sessions due to Web robots (class 1) and human users (class 0). 10% of the data were reserved for training while the remaining 90% were used for testing. The induced decision tree model is shown in Figure 4.18. The tree has an error rate equal to 3.8% on the training set and 5.3% on the test set.

The model suggests that Web robots can be distinguished from human users in the following way:

1. Accesses by Web robots tend to be broad but shallow, whereas accesses by human users tend to be more focused (narrow but deep).

2. Unlike human users, Web robots seldom retrieve the image pages associated with a Web document.

3. Sessions due to Web robots tend to be long and contain a large number of requested pages.

```
Decision Tree:
depth = 1:
| breadth> 7 :  class 1
| breadth<= 7:
| | breadth <= 3:
| | | ImagePages> 0.375:  class 0
| | | ImagePages<= 0.375:
| | | | totalPages<= 6:  class 1
| | | | totalPages> 6:
| | | | | breadth <= 1:  class 1
| | | | | breadth > 1:  class 0
| | width > 3:
| | | MultiIP = 0:
| | | | ImagePages<= 0.1333:  class 1
| | | | ImagePages> 0.1333:
| | | | breadth <= 6:  class 0
| | | | breadth > 6:  class 1
| | | MultiIP = 1:
| | | | TotalTime <= 361:  class 0
| | | | TotalTime > 361:  class 1
depth> 1:
| MultiAgent = 0:
| | depth > 2:  class 0
| | depth < 2:
| | | MultiIP = 1:  class 0
| | | MultiIP = 0:
| | | | breadth <= 6:  class 0
| | | | breadth > 6:
| | | | | RepeatedAccess <= 0.322:  class 0
| | | | | RepeatedAccess > 0.322:  class 1
| MultiAgent = 1:
| | totalPages <= 81:  class 0
| | totalPages > 81:  class 1
```

Figure 4.18. Decision tree model for Web robot detection.

4. Web robots are more likely to make repeated requests for the same document since the Web pages retrieved by human users are often cached by the browser.

4.3.7   Characteristics of Decision Tree Induction

The following is a summary of the important characteristics of decision tree induction algorithms.

1. Decision tree induction is a nonparametric approach for building classification models. In other words, it does not require any prior assumptions regarding the type of probability distributions satisfied by the class and other attributes (unlike some of the techniques described in Chapter 5).

2. Finding an optimal decision tree is an NP-complete problem. Many decision tree algorithms employ a heuristic-based approach to guide their search in the vast hypothesis space. For example, the algorithm presented in Section 4.3.5 uses a greedy, top-down, recursive partitioning strategy for growing a decision tree.

3. Techniques developed for constructing decision trees are computationally inexpensive, making it possible to quickly construct models even when the training set size is very large. Furthermore, once a decision tree has been built, classifying a test record is extremely fast, with a worst-case complexity of $O(w)$, where w is the maximum depth of the tree.

4. Decision trees, especially smaller-sized trees, are relatively easy to interpret. The accuracies of the trees are also comparable to other classification techniques for many simple data sets.

5. Decision trees provide an expressive representation for learning discrete-valued functions. However, they do not generalize well to certain types of Boolean problems. One notable example is the parity function, whose value is 0 (1) when there is an odd (even) number of Boolean attributes with the value $True$. Accurate modeling of such a function requires a full decision tree with 2^d nodes, where d is the number of Boolean attributes (see Exercise 1 on page 198).

6. Decision tree algorithms are quite robust to the presence of noise, especially when methods for avoiding overfitting, as described in Section 4.4, are employed.

7. The presence of redundant attributes does not adversely affect the accuracy of decision trees. An attribute is redundant if it is strongly correlated with another attribute in the data. One of the two redundant attributes will not be used for splitting once the other attribute has been chosen. However, if the data set contains many irrelevant attributes, i.e., attributes that are not useful for the classification task, then some of the irrelevant attributes may be accidently chosen during the tree-growing process, which results in a decision tree that is larger than necessary. Feature selection techniques can help to improve the accuracy of decision trees by eliminating the irrelevant attributes during preprocessing. We will investigate the issue of too many irrelevant attributes in Section 4.4.3.

8. Since most decision tree algorithms employ a top-down, recursive partitioning approach, the number of records becomes smaller as we traverse down the tree. At the leaf nodes, the number of records may be too small to make a statistically significant decision about the class representation of the nodes. This is known as the **data fragmentation** problem. One possible solution is to disallow further splitting when the number of records falls below a certain threshold.

9. A subtree can be replicated multiple times in a decision tree, as illustrated in Figure 4.19. This makes the decision tree more complex than necessary and perhaps more difficult to interpret. Such a situation can arise from decision tree implementations that rely on a single attribute test condition at each internal node. Since most of the decision tree algorithms use a divide-and-conquer partitioning strategy, the same test condition can be applied to different parts of the attribute space, thus leading to the subtree replication problem.

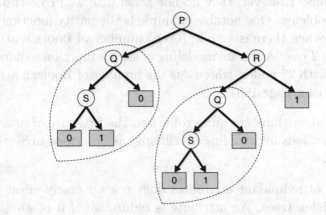

Figure 4.19. Tree replication problem. The same subtree can appear at different branches.

10. The test conditions described so far in this chapter involve using only a single attribute at a time. As a consequence, the tree-growing procedure can be viewed as the process of partitioning the attribute space into disjoint regions until each region contains records of the same class (see Figure 4.20). The border between two neighboring regions of different classes is known as a **decision boundary**. Since the test condition involves only a single attribute, the decision boundaries are rectilinear; i.e., parallel to the "coordinate axes." This limits the expressiveness of the

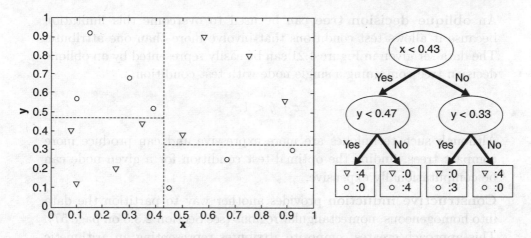

Figure 4.20. Example of a decision tree and its decision boundaries for a two-dimensional data set.

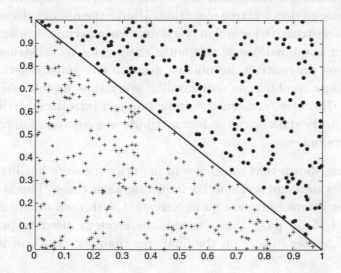

Figure 4.21. Example of data set that cannot be partitioned optimally using test conditions involving single attributes.

decision tree representation for modeling complex relationships among continuous attributes. Figure 4.21 illustrates a data set that cannot be classified effectively by a decision tree algorithm that uses test conditions involving only a single attribute at a time.

An **oblique decision tree** can be used to overcome this limitation because it allows test conditions that involve more than one attribute. The data set given in Figure 4.21 can be easily represented by an oblique decision tree containing a single node with test condition

$$x + y < 1.$$

Although such techniques are more expressive and can produce more compact trees, finding the optimal test condition for a given node can be computationally expensive.

Constructive induction provides another way to partition the data into homogeneous, nonrectangular regions (see Section 2.3.5 on page 57). This approach creates composite attributes representing an arithmetic or logical combination of the existing attributes. The new attributes provide a better discrimination of the classes and are augmented to the data set prior to decision tree induction. Unlike the oblique decision tree approach, constructive induction is less expensive because it identifies all the relevant combinations of attributes once, prior to constructing the decision tree. In contrast, an oblique decision tree must determine the right attribute combination dynamically, every time an internal node is expanded. However, constructive induction can introduce attribute redundancy in the data since the new attribute is a combination of several existing attributes.

11. Studies have shown that the choice of impurity measure has little effect on the performance of decision tree induction algorithms. This is because many impurity measures are quite consistent with each other, as shown in Figure 4.13 on page 159. Indeed, the strategy used to prune the tree has a greater impact on the final tree than the choice of impurity measure.

4.4   Model Overfitting

The errors committed by a classification model are generally divided into two types: **training errors** and **generalization errors**. Training error, also known as **resubstitution error** or **apparent error**, is the number of misclassification errors committed on training records, whereas generalization error is the expected error of the model on previously unseen records.

Recall from Section 4.2 that a good classification model must not only fit the training data well, it must also accurately classify records it has never

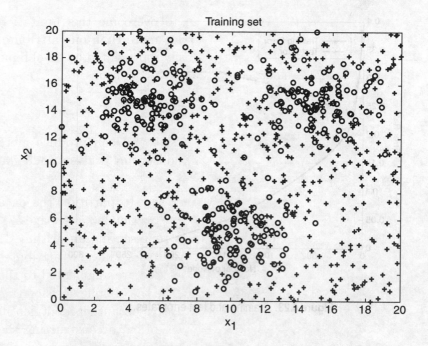

Figure 4.22. Example of a data set with binary classes.

seen before. In other words, a good model must have low training error as well as low generalization error. This is important because a model that fits the training data too well can have a poorer generalization error than a model with a higher training error. Such a situation is known as model overfitting.

Overfitting Example in Two-Dimensional Data For a more concrete example of the overfitting problem, consider the two-dimensional data set shown in Figure 4.22. The data set contains data points that belong to two different classes, denoted as class o and class +, respectively. The data points for the o class are generated from a mixture of three Gaussian distributions, while a uniform distribution is used to generate the data points for the + class. There are altogether 1200 points belonging to the o class and 1800 points belonging to the + class. 30% of the points are chosen for training, while the remaining 70% are used for testing. A decision tree classifier that uses the Gini index as its impurity measure is then applied to the training set. To investigate the effect of overfitting, different levels of pruning are applied to the initial, fully-grown tree. Figure 4.23(b) shows the training and test error rates of the decision tree.

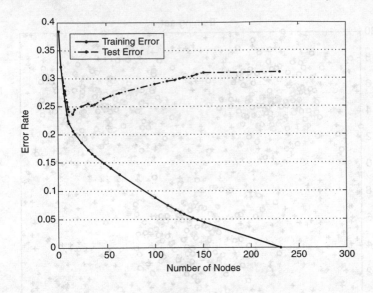

Figure 4.23. Training and test error rates.

Notice that the training and test error rates of the model are large when the size of the tree is very small. This situation is known as **model underfitting**. Underfitting occurs because the model has yet to learn the true structure of the data. As a result, it performs poorly on both the training and the test sets. As the number of nodes in the decision tree increases, the tree will have fewer training and test errors. However, once the tree becomes too large, its test error rate begins to increase even though its training error rate continues to decrease. This phenomenon is known as **model overfitting**.

To understand the overfitting phenomenon, note that the training error of a model can be reduced by increasing the model complexity. For example, the leaf nodes of the tree can be expanded until it perfectly fits the training data. Although the training error for such a complex tree is zero, the test error can be large because the tree may contain nodes that accidently fit some of the noise points in the training data. Such nodes can degrade the performance of the tree because they do not generalize well to the test examples. Figure 4.24 shows the structure of two decision trees with different number of nodes. The tree that contains the smaller number of nodes has a higher training error rate, but a lower test error rate compared to the more complex tree.

Overfitting and underfitting are two pathologies that are related to the model complexity. The remainder of this section examines some of the potential causes of model overfitting.

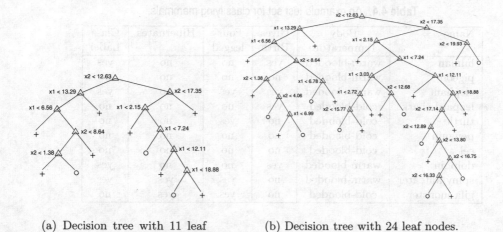

(a) Decision tree with 11 leaf nodes.

(b) Decision tree with 24 leaf nodes.

Figure 4.24. Decision trees with different model complexities.

4.4.1   Overfitting Due to Presence of Noise

Consider the training and test sets shown in Tables 4.3 and 4.4 for the mammal classification problem. Two of the ten training records are mislabeled: bats and whales are classified as non-mammals instead of mammals.

A decision tree that perfectly fits the training data is shown in Figure 4.25(a). Although the training error for the tree is zero, its error rate on

Table 4.3. An example training set for classifying mammals. Class labels with asterisk symbols represent mislabeled records.

Name	Body Temperature	Gives Birth	Four-legged	Hibernates	Class Label
porcupine	warm-blooded	yes	yes	yes	yes
cat	warm-blooded	yes	yes	no	yes
bat	warm-blooded	yes	no	yes	no*
whale	warm-blooded	yes	no	no	no*
salamander	cold-blooded	no	yes	yes	no
komodo dragon	cold-blooded	no	yes	no	no
python	cold-blooded	no	no	yes	no
salmon	cold-blooded	no	no	no	no
eagle	warm-blooded	no	no	no	no
guppy	cold-blooded	yes	no	no	no

Table 4.4. An example test set for classifying mammals.

Name	Body Temperature	Gives Birth	Four-legged	Hibernates	Class Label
human	warm-blooded	yes	no	no	yes
pigeon	warm-blooded	no	no	no	no
elephant	warm-blooded	yes	yes	no	yes
leopard shark	cold-blooded	yes	no	no	no
turtle	cold-blooded	no	yes	no	no
penguin	cold-blooded	no	no	no	no
eel	cold-blooded	no	no	no	no
dolphin	warm-blooded	yes	no	no	yes
spiny anteater	warm-blooded	no	yes	yes	yes
gila monster	cold-blooded	no	yes	yes	no

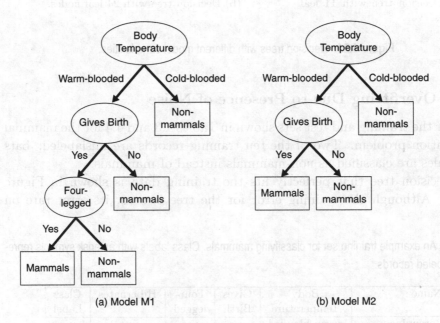

Figure 4.25. Decision tree induced from the data set shown in Table 4.3.

the test set is 30%. Both humans and dolphins were misclassified as non-mammals because their attribute values for Body Temperature, Gives Birth, and Four-legged are identical to the mislabeled records in the training set. Spiny anteaters, on the other hand, represent an exceptional case in which the class label of a test record contradicts the class labels of other similar records in the training set. Errors due to exceptional cases are often unavoidable and establish the minimum error rate achievable by any classifier.

In contrast, the decision tree $M2$ shown in Figure 4.25(b) has a lower test error rate (10%) even though its training error rate is somewhat higher (20%). It is evident that the first decision tree, $M1$, has overfitted the training data because there is a simpler model with lower error rate on the test set. The **Four-legged** attribute test condition in model $M1$ is spurious because it fits the mislabeled training records, which leads to the misclassification of records in the test set.

4.4.2 Overfitting Due to Lack of Representative Samples

Models that make their classification decisions based on a small number of training records are also susceptible to overfitting. Such models can be generated because of lack of representative samples in the training data and learning algorithms that continue to refine their models even when few training records are available. We illustrate these effects in the example below.

Consider the five training records shown in Table 4.5. All of these training records are labeled correctly and the corresponding decision tree is depicted in Figure 4.26. Although its training error is zero, its error rate on the test set is 30%.

Table 4.5. An example training set for classifying mammals.

Name	Body Temperature	Gives Birth	Four-legged	Hibernates	Class Label
salamander	cold-blooded	no	yes	yes	no
guppy	cold-blooded	yes	no	no	no
eagle	warm-blooded	no	no	no	no
poorwill	warm-blooded	no	no	yes	no
platypus	warm-blooded	no	yes	yes	yes

Humans, elephants, and dolphins are misclassified because the decision tree classifies all warm-blooded vertebrates that do not hibernate as non-mammals. The tree arrives at this classification decision because there is only one training record, which is an eagle, with such characteristics. This example clearly demonstrates the danger of making wrong predictions when there are not enough representative examples at the leaf nodes of a decision tree.

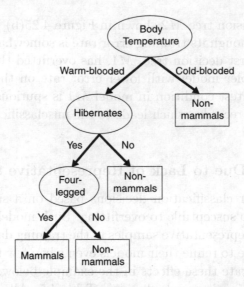

Figure 4.26. Decision tree induced from the data set shown in Table 4.5.

4.4.3   Overfitting and the Multiple Comparison Procedure

Model overfitting may arise in learning algorithms that employ a methodology known as multiple comparison procedure. To understand multiple comparison procedure, consider the task of predicting whether the stock market will rise or fall in the next ten trading days. If a stock analyst simply makes random guesses, the probability that her prediction is correct on any trading day is 0.5. However, the probability that she will predict correctly at least eight out of the ten times is

$$\frac{\binom{10}{8} + \binom{10}{9} + \binom{10}{10}}{2^{10}} = 0.0547,$$

which seems quite unlikely.

Suppose we are interested in choosing an investment advisor from a pool of fifty stock analysts. Our strategy is to select the analyst who makes the most correct predictions in the next ten trading days. The flaw in this strategy is that even if all the analysts had made their predictions in a random fashion, the probability that at least one of them makes at least eight correct predictions is

$$1 - (1 - 0.0547)^{50} = 0.9399,$$

which is very high. Although each analyst has a low probability of predicting at least eight times correctly, putting them together, we have a high probability of finding an analyst who can do so. Furthermore, there is no guarantee in the future that such an analyst will continue to make accurate predictions through random guessing.

How does the multiple comparison procedure relate to model overfitting? Many learning algorithms explore a set of independent alternatives, $\{\gamma_i\}$, and then choose an alternative, γ_{max}, that maximizes a given criterion function. The algorithm will add γ_{max} to the current model in order to improve its overall performance. This procedure is repeated until no further improvement is observed. As an example, during decision tree growing, multiple tests are performed to determine which attribute can best split the training data. The attribute that leads to the best split is chosen to extend the tree as long as the observed improvement is statistically significant.

Let T_0 be the initial decision tree and T_x be the new tree after inserting an internal node for attribute x. In principle, x can be added to the tree if the observed gain, $\Delta(T_0, T_x)$, is greater than some predefined threshold α. If there is only one attribute test condition to be evaluated, then we can avoid inserting spurious nodes by choosing a large enough value of α. However, in practice, more than one test condition is available and the decision tree algorithm must choose the best attribute x_{max} from a set of candidates, $\{x_1, x_2, \ldots, x_k\}$, to partition the data. In this situation, the algorithm is actually using a multiple comparison procedure to decide whether a decision tree should be extended. More specifically, it is testing for $\Delta(T_0, T_{x_{max}}) > \alpha$ instead of $\Delta(T_0, T_x) > \alpha$. As the number of alternatives, k, increases, so does our chance of finding $\Delta(T_0, T_{x_{max}}) > \alpha$. Unless the gain function Δ or threshold α is modified to account for k, the algorithm may inadvertently add spurious nodes to the model, which leads to model overfitting.

This effect becomes more pronounced when the number of training records from which x_{max} is chosen is small, because the variance of $\Delta(T_0, T_{x_{max}})$ is high when fewer examples are available for training. As a result, the probability of finding $\Delta(T_0, T_{x_{max}}) > \alpha$ increases when there are very few training records. This often happens when the decision tree grows deeper, which in turn reduces the number of records covered by the nodes and increases the likelihood of adding unnecessary nodes into the tree. Failure to compensate for the large number of alternatives or the small number of training records will therefore lead to model overfitting.

4.4.4 Estimation of Generalization Errors

Although the primary reason for overfitting is still a subject of debate, it is generally agreed that the complexity of a model has an impact on model overfitting, as was illustrated in Figure 4.23. The question is, how do we determine the right model complexity? The ideal complexity is that of a model that produces the lowest generalization error. The problem is that the learning algorithm has access only to the training set during model building (see Figure 4.3). It has no knowledge of the test set, and thus, does not know how well the tree will perform on records it has never seen before. The best it can do is to estimate the generalization error of the induced tree. This section presents several methods for doing the estimation.

Using Resubstitution Estimate

The resubstitution estimate approach assumes that the training set is a good representation of the overall data. Consequently, the training error, otherwise known as resubstitution error, can be used to provide an optimistic estimate for the generalization error. Under this assumption, a decision tree induction algorithm simply selects the model that produces the lowest training error rate as its final model. However, the training error is usually a poor estimate of generalization error.

Example 4.1. Consider the binary decision trees shown in Figure 4.27. Assume that both trees are generated from the same training data and both make their classification decisions at each leaf node according to the majority class. Note that the left tree, T_L, is more complex because it expands some of the leaf nodes in the right tree, T_R. The training error rate for the left tree is $e(T_L) = 4/24 = 0.167$, while the training error rate for the right tree is

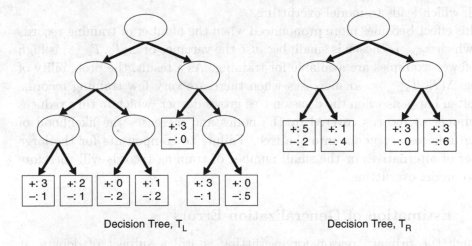

Decision Tree, T_L Decision Tree, T_R

Figure 4.27. Example of two decision trees generated from the same training data.

$e(T_R) = 6/24 = 0.25$. Based on their resubstitution estimate, the left tree is considered better than the right tree. ∎

Incorporating Model Complexity

As previously noted, the chance for model overfitting increases as the model becomes more complex. For this reason, we should prefer simpler models, a strategy that agrees with a well-known principle known as **Occam's razor** or the **principle of parsimony**:

Definition 4.2. Occam's Razor: Given two models with the same generalization errors, the simpler model is preferred over the more complex model.

Occam's razor is intuitive because the additional components in a complex model stand a greater chance of being fitted purely by chance. In the words of Einstein, "Everything should be made as simple as possible, but not simpler." Next, we present two methods for incorporating model complexity into the evaluation of classification models.

Pessimistic Error Estimate   The first approach explicitly computes generalization error as the sum of training error and a penalty term for model complexity. The resulting generalization error can be considered its pessimistic error estimate. For instance, let $n(t)$ be the number of training records classified by node t and $e(t)$ be the number of misclassified records. The pessimistic error estimate of a decision tree T, $e_g(T)$, can be computed as follows:

$$e_g(T) = \frac{\sum_{i=1}^{k}[e(t_i) + \Omega(t_i)]}{\sum_{i=1}^{k} n(t_i)} = \frac{e(T) + \Omega(T)}{N_t},$$

where k is the number of leaf nodes, $e(T)$ is the overall training error of the decision tree, N_t is the number of training records, and $\Omega(t_i)$ is the penalty term associated with each node t_i.

Example 4.2. Consider the binary decision trees shown in Figure 4.27. If the penalty term is equal to 0.5, then the pessimistic error estimate for the left tree is

$$e_g(T_L) = \frac{4 + 7 \times 0.5}{24} = \frac{7.5}{24} = 0.3125$$

and the pessimistic error estimate for the right tree is

$$e_g(T_R) = \frac{6 + 4 \times 0.5}{24} = \frac{8}{24} = 0.3333.$$

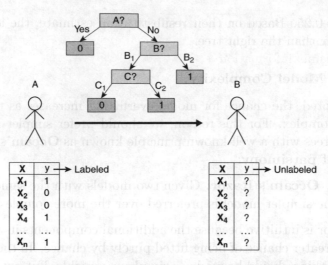

Figure 4.28. The minimum description length (MDL) principle.

Thus, the left tree has a better pessimistic error rate than the right tree. For binary trees, a penalty term of 0.5 means a node should always be expanded into its two child nodes as long as it improves the classification of at least one training record because expanding a node, which is equivalent to adding 0.5 to the overall error, is less costly than committing one training error.

If $\Omega(t) = 1$ for all the nodes t, the pessimistic error estimate for the left tree is $e_g(T_L) = 11/24 = 0.458$, while the pessimistic error estimate for the right tree is $e_g(T_R) = 10/24 = 0.417$. The right tree therefore has a better pessimistic error rate than the left tree. Thus, a node should not be expanded into its child nodes unless it reduces the misclassification error for more than one training record. ∎

Minimum Description Length Principle   Another way to incorporate model complexity is based on an information-theoretic approach known as the minimum description length or MDL principle. To illustrate this principle, consider the example shown in Figure 4.28. In this example, both A and B are given a set of records with known attribute values **x**. In addition, person A knows the exact class label for each record, while person B knows none of this information. B can obtain the classification of each record by requesting that A transmits the class labels sequentially. Such a message would require $\Theta(n)$ bits of information, where n is the total number of records.

Alternatively, A may decide to build a classification model that summarizes the relationship between **x** and y. The model can be encoded in a compact form before being transmitted to B. If the model is 100% accurate, then the cost of transmission is equivalent to the cost of encoding the model. Otherwise, A must also transmit information about which record is classified incorrectly by the model. Thus, the overall cost of transmission is

$$Cost(model, data) = Cost(model) + Cost(data|model), \qquad (4.9)$$

where the first term on the right-hand side is the cost of encoding the model, while the second term represents the cost of encoding the mislabeled records. According to the MDL principle, we should seek a model that minimizes the overall cost function. An example showing how to compute the total description length of a decision tree is given by Exercise 9 on page 202.

Estimating Statistical Bounds

The generalization error can also be estimated as a statistical correction to the training error. Since generalization error tends to be larger than training error, the statistical correction is usually computed as an upper bound to the training error, taking into account the number of training records that reach a particular leaf node. For instance, in the C4.5 decision tree algorithm, the number of errors committed by each leaf node is assumed to follow a binomial distribution. To compute its generalization error, we must determine the upper bound limit to the observed training error, as illustrated in the next example.

Example 4.3. Consider the left-most branch of the binary decision trees shown in Figure 4.27. Observe that the left-most leaf node of T_R has been expanded into two child nodes in T_L. Before splitting, the error rate of the node is $2/7 = 0.286$. By approximating a binomial distribution with a normal distribution, the following upper bound of the error rate e can be derived:

$$e_{upper}(N, e, \alpha) = \frac{e + \frac{z_{\alpha/2}^2}{2N} + z_{\alpha/2}\sqrt{\frac{e(1-e)}{N} + \frac{z_{\alpha/2}^2}{4N^2}}}{1 + \frac{z_{\alpha/2}^2}{N}}, \qquad (4.10)$$

where α is the confidence level, $z_{\alpha/2}$ is the standardized value from a standard normal distribution, and N is the total number of training records used to compute e. By replacing $\alpha = 25\%$, $N = 7$, and $e = 2/7$, the upper bound for the error rate is $e_{upper}(7, 2/7, 0.25) = 0.503$, which corresponds to $7 \times 0.503 = 3.521$ errors. If we expand the node into its child nodes as shown in T_L, the training error rates for the child nodes are $1/4 = 0.250$ and $1/3 = 0.333$, respectively. Using Equation 4.10, the upper bounds of these error rates are $e_{upper}(4, 1/4, 0.25) = 0.537$ and $e_{upper}(3, 1/3, 0.25) = 0.650$, respectively. The overall training error of the child nodes is $4 \times 0.537 + 3 \times 0.650 = 4.098$, which is larger than the estimated error for the corresponding node in T_R. ∎

Using a Validation Set

In this approach, instead of using the training set to estimate the generalization error, the original training data is divided into two smaller subsets. One of the subsets is used for training, while the other, known as the validation set, is used for estimating the generalization error. Typically, two-thirds of the training set is reserved for model building, while the remaining one-third is used for error estimation.

This approach is typically used with classification techniques that can be parameterized to obtain models with different levels of complexity. The complexity of the best model can be estimated by adjusting the parameter of the learning algorithm (e.g., the pruning level of a decision tree) until the empirical model produced by the learning algorithm attains the lowest error rate on the validation set. Although this approach provides a better way for estimating how well the model performs on previously unseen records, less data is available for training.

4.4.5 Handling Overfitting in Decision Tree Induction

In the previous section, we described several methods for estimating the generalization error of a classification model. Having a reliable estimate of generalization error allows the learning algorithm to search for an accurate model without overfitting the training data. This section presents two strategies for avoiding model overfitting in the context of decision tree induction.

Prepruning (Early Stopping Rule) In this approach, the tree-growing algorithm is halted before generating a fully grown tree that perfectly fits the entire training data. To do this, a more restrictive stopping condition must be used; e.g., stop expanding a leaf node when the observed gain in impurity measure (or improvement in the estimated generalization error) falls below a certain threshold. The advantage of this approach is that it avoids generating overly complex subtrees that overfit the training data. Nevertheless, it is difficult to choose the right threshold for early termination. Too high of a threshold will result in underfitted models, while a threshold that is set too low may not be sufficient to overcome the model overfitting problem. Furthermore,

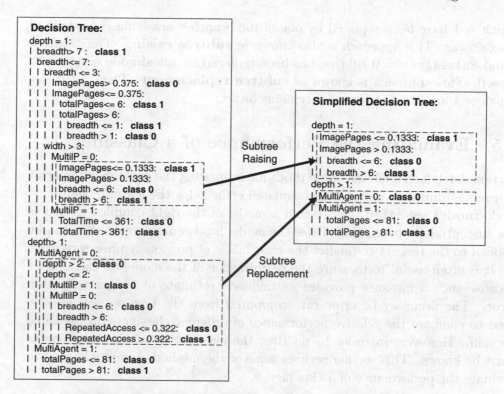

```
Decision Tree:
depth = 1:
| breadth> 7 :  class 1
| breadth<= 7:
| | breadth <= 3:
| | | ImagePages> 0.375:  class 0
| | | ImagePages<= 0.375:
| | | | totalPages<= 6:  class 1
| | | | totalPages> 6:
| | | | | breadth <= 1:  class 1
| | | | | breadth > 1:  class 0
| | width > 3:
| | | MultiIP = 0:
| | | | ImagePages<= 0.1333:  class 1
| | | | ImagePages> 0.1333:
| | | | breadth <= 6:  class 0
| | | | breadth > 6:  class 1
| | | MultiIP = 1:
| | | | TotalTime <= 361:  class 0
| | | | TotalTime > 361:  class 1
depth> 1:
| MultiAgent = 0:
| | depth > 2:  class 0
| | depth <= 2:
| | | MultiIP = 1:  class 0
| | | MultiIP = 0:
| | | | breadth <= 6:  class 0
| | | | breadth > 6:
| | | | | RepeatedAccess <= 0.322:  class 0
| | | | | RepeatedAccess > 0.322:  class 1
| MultiAgent = 1:
| | totalPages <= 81:  class 0
| | totalPages > 81:  class 1
```

```
Simplified Decision Tree:
depth = 1:
| | ImagePages <= 0.1333:  class 1
| | ImagePages > 0.1333:
| | breadth <= 6:  class 0
| | breadth > 6:  class 1
depth > 1:
| MultiAgent = 0:  class 0
| MultiAgent = 1:
| | totalPages <= 81:  class 0
| | totalPages > 81:  class 1
```

Subtree
Raising

Subtree
Replacement

Figure 4.29. Post-pruning of the decision tree for Web robot detection.

even if no significant gain is obtained using one of the existing attribute test conditions, subsequent splitting may result in better subtrees.

Post-pruning   In this approach, the decision tree is initially grown to its maximum size. This is followed by a tree-pruning step, which proceeds to trim the fully grown tree in a bottom-up fashion. Trimming can be done by replacing a subtree with (1) a new leaf node whose class label is determined from the majority class of records affiliated with the subtree, or (2) the most frequently used branch of the subtree. The tree-pruning step terminates when no further improvement is observed. Post-pruning tends to give better results than prepruning because it makes pruning decisions based on a fully grown tree, unlike prepruning, which can suffer from premature termination of the tree-growing process. However, for post-pruning, the additional computations needed to grow the full tree may be wasted when the subtree is pruned.

Figure 4.29 illustrates the simplified decision tree model for the Web robot detection example given in Section 4.3.6. Notice that the subtrees rooted at depth $= 1$ have been replaced by one of the branches involving the attribute ImagePages. This approach is also known as **subtree raising**. The depth $>$ 1 and MultiAgent $= 0$ subtree has been replaced by a leaf node assigned to class 0. This approach is known as **subtree replacement**. The subtree for depth > 1 and MultiAgent $= 1$ remains intact.

4.5 Evaluating the Performance of a Classifier

Section 4.4.4 described several methods for estimating the generalization error of a model during training. The estimated error helps the learning algorithm to do **model selection**; i.e., to find a model of the right complexity that is not susceptible to overfitting. Once the model has been constructed, it can be applied to the test set to predict the class labels of previously unseen records.

It is often useful to measure the performance of the model on the test set because such a measure provides an unbiased estimate of its generalization error. The accuracy or error rate computed from the test set can also be used to compare the relative performance of different classifiers on the same domain. However, in order to do this, the class labels of the test records must be known. This section reviews some of the methods commonly used to evaluate the performance of a classifier.

4.5.1 Holdout Method

In the holdout method, the original data with labeled examples is partitioned into two disjoint sets, called the training and the test sets, respectively. A classification model is then induced from the training set and its performance is evaluated on the test set. The proportion of data reserved for training and for testing is typically at the discretion of the analysts (e.g., 50-50 or two-thirds for training and one-third for testing). The accuracy of the classifier can be estimated based on the accuracy of the induced model on the test set.

The holdout method has several well-known limitations. First, fewer labeled examples are available for training because some of the records are withheld for testing. As a result, the induced model may not be as good as when all the labeled examples are used for training. Second, the model may be highly dependent on the composition of the training and test sets. The smaller the training set size, the larger the variance of the model. On the other hand, if the training set is too large, then the estimated accuracy computed from the smaller test set is less reliable. Such an estimate is said to have a wide confidence interval. Finally, the training and test sets are no longer independent of each other. Because the training and test sets are subsets of the original data, a class that is overrepresented in one subset will be underrepresented in the other, and vice versa.

4.5.2 Random Subsampling

The holdout method can be repeated several times to improve the estimation of a classifier's performance. This approach is known as random subsampling. Let acc_i be the model accuracy during the ith iteration. The overall accuracy is given by $acc_{sub} = \sum_{i=1}^{k} acc_i/k$. Random subsampling still encounters some of the problems associated with the holdout method because it does not utilize as much data as possible for training. It also has no control over the number of times each record is used for testing and training. Consequently, some records might be used for training more often than others.

4.5.3 Cross-Validation

An alternative to random subsampling is cross-validation. In this approach, each record is used the same number of times for training and exactly once for testing. To illustrate this method, suppose we partition the data into two equal-sized subsets. First, we choose one of the subsets for training and the other for testing. We then swap the roles of the subsets so that the previous training set becomes the test set and vice versa. This approach is called a two-fold cross-validation. The total error is obtained by summing up the errors for both runs. In this example, each record is used exactly once for training and once for testing. The k-fold cross-validation method generalizes this approach by segmenting the data into k equal-sized partitions. During each run, one of the partitions is chosen for testing, while the rest of them are used for training. This procedure is repeated k times so that each partition is used for testing exactly once. Again, the total error is found by summing up the errors for all k runs. A special case of the k-fold cross-validation method sets $k = N$, the size of the data set. In this so-called **leave-one-out** approach, each test set contains only one record. This approach has the advantage of utilizing as much data as possible for training. In addition, the test sets are mutually exclusive and they effectively cover the entire data set. The drawback of this approach is that it is computationally expensive to repeat the procedure N times. Furthermore, since each test set contains only one record, the variance of the estimated performance metric tends to be high.

4.5.4   Bootstrap

The methods presented so far assume that the training records are sampled without replacement. As a result, there are no duplicate records in the training and test sets. In the bootstrap approach, the training records are sampled with replacement; i.e., a record already chosen for training is put back into the original pool of records so that it is equally likely to be redrawn. If the original data has N records, it can be shown that, on average, a bootstrap sample of size N contains about 63.2% of the records in the original data. This approximation follows from the fact that the probability a record is chosen by a bootstrap sample is $1 - (1 - 1/N)^N$. When N is sufficiently large, the probability asymptotically approaches $1 - e^{-1} = 0.632$. Records that are not included in the bootstrap sample become part of the test set. The model induced from the training set is then applied to the test set to obtain an estimate of the accuracy of the bootstrap sample, ϵ_i. The sampling procedure is then repeated b times to generate b bootstrap samples.

There are several variations to the bootstrap sampling approach in terms of how the overall accuracy of the classifier is computed. One of the more widely used approaches is the **.632 bootstrap**, which computes the overall accuracy by combining the accuracies of each bootstrap sample (ϵ_i) with the accuracy computed from a training set that contains all the labeled examples in the original data (acc_s):

$$\text{Accuracy, } acc_{boot} = \frac{1}{b} \sum_{i=1}^{b} (0.632 \times \epsilon_i + 0.368 \times acc_s). \qquad (4.11)$$

4.6   Methods for Comparing Classifiers

It is often useful to compare the performance of different classifiers to determine which classifier works better on a given data set. However, depending on the size of the data, the observed difference in accuracy between two classifiers may not be statistically significant. This section examines some of the statistical tests available to compare the performance of different models and classifiers.

For illustrative purposes, consider a pair of classification models, M_A and M_B. Suppose M_A achieves 85% accuracy when evaluated on a test set containing 30 records, while M_B achieves 75% accuracy on a different test set containing 5000 records. Based on this information, is M_A a better model than M_B?

The preceding example raises two key questions regarding the statistical significance of the performance metrics:

1. Although M_A has a higher accuracy than M_B, it was tested on a smaller test set. How much confidence can we place on the accuracy for M_A?

2. Is it possible to explain the difference in accuracy as a result of variations in the composition of the test sets?

The first question relates to the issue of estimating the confidence interval of a given model accuracy. The second question relates to the issue of testing the statistical significance of the observed deviation. These issues are investigated in the remainder of this section.

4.6.1   Estimating a Confidence Interval for Accuracy

To determine the confidence interval, we need to establish the probability distribution that governs the accuracy measure. This section describes an approach for deriving the confidence interval by modeling the classification task as a binomial experiment. Following is a list of characteristics of a binomial experiment:

1. The experiment consists of N independent trials, where each trial has two possible outcomes: success or failure.

2. The probability of success, p, in each trial is constant.

An example of a binomial experiment is counting the number of heads that turn up when a coin is flipped N times. If X is the number of successes observed in N trials, then the probability that X takes a particular value is given by a binomial distribution with mean Np and variance $Np(1-p)$:

$$P(X = v) = \binom{N}{p}p^v(1-p)^{N-v}.$$

For example, if the coin is fair ($p = 0.5$) and is flipped fifty times, then the probability that the head shows up 20 times is

$$P(X = 20) = \binom{50}{20}0.5^{20}(1-0.5)^{30} = 0.0419.$$

If the experiment is repeated many times, then the average number of heads expected to show up is $50 \times 0.5 = 25$, while its variance is $50 \times 0.5 \times 0.5 = 12.5$.

The task of predicting the class labels of test records can also be considered as a binomial experiment. Given a test set that contains N records, let X be the number of records correctly predicted by a model and p be the true accuracy of the model. By modeling the prediction task as a binomial experiment, X has a binomial distribution with mean Np and variance $Np(1-p)$. It can be shown that the empirical accuracy, $acc = X/N$, also has a binomial distribution with mean p and variance $p(1-p)/N$ (see Exercise 12). Although the binomial distribution can be used to estimate the confidence interval for acc, it is often approximated by a normal distribution when N is sufficiently large. Based on the normal distribution, the following confidence interval for acc can be derived:

$$P\left(- Z_{\alpha/2} \leq \frac{acc - p}{\sqrt{p(1-p)/N}} \leq Z_{1-\alpha/2} \right) = 1 - \alpha, \qquad (4.12)$$

where $Z_{\alpha/2}$ and $Z_{1-\alpha/2}$ are the upper and lower bounds obtained from a standard normal distribution at confidence level $(1 - \alpha)$. Since a standard normal distribution is symmetric around $Z = 0$, it follows that $Z_{\alpha/2} = Z_{1-\alpha/2}$. Rearranging this inequality leads to the following confidence interval for p:

$$\frac{2 \times N \times acc + Z_{\alpha/2}^2 \pm Z_{\alpha/2}\sqrt{Z_{\alpha/2}^2 + 4Nacc - 4Nacc^2}}{2(N + Z_{\alpha/2}^2)}. \qquad (4.13)$$

The following table shows the values of $Z_{\alpha/2}$ at different confidence levels:

$1 - \alpha$	0.99	0.98	0.95	0.9	0.8	0.7	0.5
$Z_{\alpha/2}$	2.58	2.33	1.96	1.65	1.28	1.04	0.67

Example 4.4. Consider a model that has an accuracy of 80% when evaluated on 100 test records. What is the confidence interval for its true accuracy at a 95% confidence level? The confidence level of 95% corresponds to $Z_{\alpha/2} = 1.96$ according to the table given above. Inserting this term into Equation 4.13 yields a confidence interval between 71.1% and 86.7%. The following table shows the confidence interval when the number of records, N, increases:

N	20	50	100	500	1000	5000
Confidence	0.584	0.670	0.711	0.763	0.774	0.789
Interval	− 0.919	− 0.888	− 0.867	− 0.833	− 0.824	− 0.811

Note that the confidence interval becomes tighter when N increases.   ■

4.6.2 Comparing the Performance of Two Models

Consider a pair of models, M_1 and M_2, that are evaluated on two independent test sets, D_1 and D_2. Let n_1 denote the number of records in D_1 and n_2 denote the number of records in D_2. In addition, suppose the error rate for M_1 on D_1 is e_1 and the error rate for M_2 on D_2 is e_2. Our goal is to test whether the observed difference between e_1 and e_2 is statistically significant.

Assuming that n_1 and n_2 are sufficiently large, the error rates e_1 and e_2 can be approximated using normal distributions. If the observed difference in the error rate is denoted as $d = e_1 - e_2$, then d is also normally distributed with mean d_t, its true difference, and variance, σ_d^2. The variance of d can be computed as follows:

$$\sigma_d^2 \simeq \widehat{\sigma}_d^2 = \frac{e_1(1 - e_1)}{n_1} + \frac{e_2(1 - e_2)}{n_2}, \tag{4.14}$$

where $e_1(1 - e_1)/n_1$ and $e_2(1 - e_2)/n_2$ are the variances of the error rates. Finally, at the $(1 - \alpha)\%$ confidence level, it can be shown that the confidence interval for the true difference d_t is given by the following equation:

$$d_t = d \pm z_{\alpha/2}\widehat{\sigma}_d. \tag{4.15}$$

Example 4.5. Consider the problem described at the beginning of this section. Model M_A has an error rate of $e_1 = 0.15$ when applied to $N_1 = 30$ test records, while model M_B has an error rate of $e_2 = 0.25$ when applied to $N_2 = 5000$ test records. The observed difference in their error rates is $d = |0.15 - 0.25| = 0.1$. In this example, we are performing a two-sided test to check whether $d_t = 0$ or $d_t \neq 0$. The estimated variance of the observed difference in error rates can be computed as follows:

$$\widehat{\sigma}_d^2 = \frac{0.15(1 - 0.15)}{30} + \frac{0.25(1 - 0.25)}{5000} = 0.0043$$

or $\widehat{\sigma}_d = 0.0655$. Inserting this value into Equation 4.15, we obtain the following confidence interval for d_t at 95% confidence level:

$$d_t = 0.1 \pm 1.96 \times 0.0655 = 0.1 \pm 0.128.$$

As the interval spans the value zero, we can conclude that the observed difference is not statistically significant at a 95% confidence level. ∎

At what confidence level can we reject the hypothesis that $d_t = 0$? To do this, we need to determine the value of $Z_{\alpha/2}$ such that the confidence interval for d_t does not span the value zero. We can reverse the preceding computation and look for the value $Z_{\alpha/2}$ such that $d > Z_{\alpha/2}\widehat{\sigma}_d$. Replacing the values of d and $\widehat{\sigma}_d$ gives $Z_{\alpha/2} < 1.527$. This value first occurs when $(1-\alpha) \lesssim 0.936$ (for a two-sided test). The result suggests that the null hypothesis can be rejected at confidence level of 93.6% or lower.

4.6.3   Comparing the Performance of Two Classifiers

Suppose we want to compare the performance of two classifiers using the k-fold cross-validation approach. Initially, the data set D is divided into k equal-sized partitions. We then apply each classifier to construct a model from $k-1$ of the partitions and test it on the remaining partition. This step is repeated k times, each time using a different partition as the test set.

Let M_{ij} denote the model induced by classification technique L_i during the jth iteration. Note that each pair of models M_{1j} and M_{2j} are tested on the same partition j. Let e_{1j} and e_{2j} be their respective error rates. The difference between their error rates during the jth fold can be written as $d_j = e_{1j} - e_{2j}$. If k is sufficiently large, then d_j is normally distributed with mean d_t^{cv}, which is the true difference in their error rates, and variance σ^{cv}. Unlike the previous approach, the overall variance in the observed differences is estimated using the following formula:

$$\widehat{\sigma}_{d^{cv}}^2 = \frac{\sum_{j=1}^{k}(d_j - \overline{d})^2}{k(k-1)}, \tag{4.16}$$

where $\overline{d}$ is the average difference. For this approach, we need to use a t-distribution to compute the confidence interval for d_t^{cv}:

$$d_t^{cv} = \overline{d} \pm t_{(1-\alpha),k-1}\widehat{\sigma}_{d^{cv}}.$$

The coefficient $t_{(1-\alpha),k-1}$ is obtained from a probability table with two input parameters, its confidence level $(1-\alpha)$ and the number of degrees of freedom, $k-1$. The probability table for the t-distribution is shown in Table 4.6.

Example 4.6. Suppose the estimated difference in the accuracy of models generated by two classification techniques has a mean equal to 0.05 and a standard deviation equal to 0.002. If the accuracy is estimated using a 30-fold cross-validation approach, then at a 95% confidence level, the true accuracy difference is

$$d_t^{cv} = 0.05 \pm 2.04 \times 0.002. \tag{4.17}$$

Table 4.6. Probability table for *t*-distribution.

$k-1$	\(1 - \alpha\)				
	0.99	0.98	0.95	0.9	0.8
1	3.08	6.31	12.7	31.8	63.7
2	1.89	2.92	4.30	6.96	9.92
4	1.53	2.13	2.78	3.75	4.60
9	1.38	1.83	2.26	2.82	3.25
14	1.34	1.76	2.14	2.62	2.98
19	1.33	1.73	2.09	2.54	2.86
24	1.32	1.71	2.06	2.49	2.80
29	1.31	1.70	2.04	2.46	2.76

Since the confidence interval does not span the value zero, the observed difference between the techniques is statistically significant. ∎

4.7 Bibliographic Notes

Early classification systems were developed to organize a large collection of objects. For example, the Dewey Decimal and Library of Congress classification systems were designed to catalog and index the vast number of library books. The categories are typically identified in a manual fashion, with the help of domain experts.

Automated classification has been a subject of intensive research for many years. The study of classification in classical statistics is sometimes known as **discriminant analysis**, where the objective is to predict the group membership of an object based on a set of predictor variables. A well-known classical method is Fisher's linear discriminant analysis [117], which seeks to find a linear projection of the data that produces the greatest discrimination between objects that belong to different classes.

Many pattern recognition problems also require the discrimination of objects from different classes. Examples include speech recognition, handwritten character identification, and image classification. Readers who are interested in the application of classification techniques for pattern recognition can refer to the survey articles by Jain et al. [122] and Kulkarni et al. [128] or classic pattern recognition books by Bishop [107], Duda et al. [114], and Fukunaga [118]. The subject of classification is also a major research topic in the fields of neural networks, statistical learning, and machine learning. An in-depth treatment of various classification techniques is given in the books by Cherkassky and Mulier [112], Hastie et al. [120], Michie et al. [133], and Mitchell [136].

An overview of decision tree induction algorithms can be found in the survey articles by Buntine [110], Moret [137], Murthy [138], and Safavian et al. [147]. Examples of some well-known decision tree algorithms include CART [108], ID3 [143], C4.5 [145], and CHAID [125]. Both ID3 and C4.5 employ the entropy measure as their splitting function. An in-depth discussion of the C4.5 decision tree algorithm is given by Quinlan [145]. Besides explaining the methodology for decision tree growing and tree pruning, Quinlan [145] also described how the algorithm can be modified to handle data sets with missing values. The CART algorithm was developed by Breiman et al. [108] and uses the Gini index as its splitting function. CHAID [125] uses the statistical χ^2 test to determine the best split during the tree-growing process.

The decision tree algorithm presented in this chapter assumes that the splitting condition is specified one attribute at a time. An oblique decision tree can use multiple attributes to form the attribute test condition in the internal nodes [121, 152]. Breiman et al. [108] provide an option for using linear combinations of attributes in their CART implementation. Other approaches for inducing oblique decision trees were proposed by Heath et al. [121], Murthy et al. [139], Cantú-Paz and Kamath [111], and Utgoff and Brodley [152]. Although oblique decision trees help to improve the expressiveness of a decision tree representation, learning the appropriate test condition at each node is computationally challenging. Another way to improve the expressiveness of a decision tree without using oblique decision trees is to apply a method known as **constructive induction** [132]. This method simplifies the task of learning complex splitting functions by creating compound features from the original attributes.

Besides the top-down approach, other strategies for growing a decision tree include the bottom-up approach by Landeweerd et al. [130] and Pattipati and Alexandridis [142], as well as the bidirectional approach by Kim and Landgrebe [126]. Schuermann and Doster [150] and Wang and Suen [154] proposed using a **soft splitting criterion** to address the data fragmentation problem. In this approach, each record is assigned to different branches of the decision tree with different probabilities.

Model overfitting is an important issue that must be addressed to ensure that a decision tree classifier performs equally well on previously unknown records. The model overfitting problem has been investigated by many authors including Breiman et al. [108], Schaffer [148], Mingers [135], and Jensen and Cohen [123]. While the presence of noise is often regarded as one of the primary reasons for overfitting [135, 140], Jensen and Cohen [123] argued that overfitting is the result of using incorrect hypothesis tests in a multiple comparison procedure.

Schapire [149] defined generalization error as "the probability of misclassifying a new example" and test error as "the fraction of mistakes on a newly sampled test set." Generalization error can therefore be considered as the expected test error of a classifier. Generalization error may sometimes refer to the true error [136] of a model, i.e., its expected error for randomly drawn data points from the same population distribution where the training set is sampled. These definitions are in fact equivalent if both the training and test sets are gathered from the same population distribution, which is often the case in many data mining and machine learning applications.

The Occam's razor principle is often attributed to the philosopher William of Occam. Domingos [113] cautioned against the pitfall of misinterpreting Occam's razor as comparing models with similar training errors, instead of generalization errors. A survey on decision tree-pruning methods to avoid overfitting is given by Breslow and Aha [109] and Esposito et al. [116]. Some of the typical pruning methods include reduced error pruning [144], pessimistic error pruning [144], minimum error pruning [141], critical value pruning [134], cost-complexity pruning [108], and error-based pruning [145]. Quinlan and Rivest proposed using the minimum description length principle for decision tree pruning in [146].

Kohavi [127] had performed an extensive empirical study to compare the performance metrics obtained using different estimation methods such as random subsampling, bootstrapping, and k-fold cross-validation. Their results suggest that the best estimation method is based on the ten-fold stratified cross-validation. Efron and Tibshirani [115] provided a theoretical and empirical comparison between cross-validation and a bootstrap method known as the 632+ rule.

Current techniques such as C4.5 require that the entire training data set fit into main memory. There has been considerable effort to develop parallel and scalable versions of decision tree induction algorithms. Some of the proposed algorithms include SLIQ by Mehta et al. [131], SPRINT by Shafer et al. [151], CMP by Wang and Zaniolo [153], CLOUDS by Alsabti et al. [106], RainForest by Gehrke et al. [119], and ScalParC by Joshi et al. [124]. A general survey of parallel algorithms for data mining is available in [129].

Bibliography

[106] K. Alsabti, S. Ranka, and V. Singh. CLOUDS: A Decision Tree Classifier for Large Datasets. In *Proc. of the 4th Intl. Conf. on Knowledge Discovery and Data Mining*, pages 2–8, New York, NY, August 1998.

[107] C. M. Bishop. *Neural Networks for Pattern Recognition*. Oxford University Press, Oxford, U.K., 1995.

[108] L. Breiman, J. H. Friedman, R. Olshen, and C. J. Stone. *Classification and Regression Trees*. Chapman & Hall, New York, 1984.

[109] L. A. Breslow and D. W. Aha. Simplifying Decision Trees: A Survey. *Knowledge Engineering Review*, 12(1):1–40, 1997.

[110] W. Buntine. Learning classification trees. In *Artificial Intelligence Frontiers in Statistics*, pages 182–201. Chapman & Hall, London, 1993.

[111] E. Cantú-Paz and C. Kamath. Using evolutionary algorithms to induce oblique decision trees. In *Proc. of the Genetic and Evolutionary Computation Conf.*, pages 1053–1060, San Francisco, CA, 2000.

[112] V. Cherkassky and F. Mulier. *Learning from Data: Concepts, Theory, and Methods*. Wiley Interscience, 1998.

[113] P. Domingos. The Role of Occam's Razor in Knowledge Discovery. *Data Mining and Knowledge Discovery*, 3(4):409–425, 1999.

[114] R. O. Duda, P. E. Hart, and D. G. Stork. *Pattern Classification*. John Wiley & Sons, Inc., New York, 2nd edition, 2001.

[115] B. Efron and R. Tibshirani. Cross-validation and the Bootstrap: Estimating the Error Rate of a Prediction Rule. Technical report, Stanford University, 1995.

[116] F. Esposito, D. Malerba, and G. Semeraro. A Comparative Analysis of Methods for Pruning Decision Trees. *IEEE Trans. Pattern Analysis and Machine Intelligence*, 19 (5):476–491, May 1997.

[117] R. A. Fisher. The use of multiple measurements in taxonomic problems. *Annals of Eugenics*, 7:179–188, 1936.

[118] K. Fukunaga. *Introduction to Statistical Pattern Recognition*. Academic Press, New York, 1990.

[119] J. Gehrke, R. Ramakrishnan, and V. Ganti. RainForest—A Framework for Fast Decision Tree Construction of Large Datasets. *Data Mining and Knowledge Discovery*, 4 (2/3):127–162, 2000.

[120] T. Hastie, R. Tibshirani, and J. H. Friedman. *The Elements of Statistical Learning: Data Mining, Inference, Prediction*. Springer, New York, 2001.

[121] D. Heath, S. Kasif, and S. Salzberg. Induction of Oblique Decision Trees. In *Proc. of the 13th Intl. Joint Conf. on Artificial Intelligence*, pages 1002–1007, Chambery, France, August 1993.

[122] A. K. Jain, R. P. W. Duin, and J. Mao. Statistical Pattern Recognition: A Review. *IEEE Tran. Patt. Anal. and Mach. Intellig.*, 22(1):4–37, 2000.

[123] D. Jensen and P. R. Cohen. Multiple Comparisons in Induction Algorithms. *Machine Learning*, 38(3):309–338, March 2000.

[124] M. V. Joshi, G. Karypis, and V. Kumar. ScalParC: A New Scalable and Efficient Parallel Classification Algorithm for Mining Large Datasets. In *Proc. of 12th Intl. Parallel Processing Symp. (IPPS/SPDP)*, pages 573–579, Orlando, FL, April 1998.

[125] G. V. Kass. An Exploratory Technique for Investigating Large Quantities of Categorical Data. *Applied Statistics*, 29:119–127, 1980.

[126] B. Kim and D. Landgrebe. Hierarchical decision classifiers in high-dimensional and large class data. *IEEE Trans. on Geoscience and Remote Sensing*, 29(4):518–528, 1991.

[127] R. Kohavi. A Study on Cross-Validation and Bootstrap for Accuracy Estimation and Model Selection. In *Proc. of the 15th Intl. Joint Conf. on Artificial Intelligence*, pages 1137–1145, Montreal, Canada, August 1995.

[128] S. R. Kulkarni, G. Lugosi, and S. S. Venkatesh. Learning Pattern Classification—A Survey. *IEEE Tran. Inf. Theory*, 44(6):2178–2206, 1998.

[129] V. Kumar, M. V. Joshi, E.-H. Han, P. N. Tan, and M. Steinbach. High Performance Data Mining. In *High Performance Computing for Computational Science (VECPAR 2002)*, pages 111–125. Springer, 2002.

[130] G. Landeweerd, T. Timmers, E. Gersema, M. Bins, and M. Halic. Binary tree versus single level tree classification of white blood cells. *Pattern Recognition*, 16:571–577, 1983.

[131] M. Mehta, R. Agrawal, and J. Rissanen. SLIQ: A Fast Scalable Classifier for Data Mining. In *Proc. of the 5th Intl. Conf. on Extending Database Technology*, pages 18–32, Avignon, France, March 1996.

[132] R. S. Michalski. A theory and methodology of inductive learning. *Artificial Intelligence*, 20:111–116, 1983.

[133] D. Michie, D. J. Spiegelhalter, and C. C. Taylor. *Machine Learning, Neural and Statistical Classification*. Ellis Horwood, Upper Saddle River, NJ, 1994.

[134] J. Mingers. Expert Systems—Rule Induction with Statistical Data. *J Operational Research Society*, 38:39–47, 1987.

[135] J. Mingers. An empirical comparison of pruning methods for decision tree induction. *Machine Learning*, 4:227–243, 1989.

[136] T. Mitchell. *Machine Learning*. McGraw-Hill, Boston, MA, 1997.

[137] B. M. E. Moret. Decision Trees and Diagrams. *Computing Surveys*, 14(4):593–623, 1982.

[138] S. K. Murthy. Automatic Construction of Decision Trees from Data: A Multi-Disciplinary Survey. *Data Mining and Knowledge Discovery*, 2(4):345–389, 1998.

[139] S. K. Murthy, S. Kasif, and S. Salzberg. A system for induction of oblique decision trees. *J of Artificial Intelligence Research*, 2:1–33, 1994.

[140] T. Niblett. Constructing decision trees in noisy domains. In *Proc. of the 2nd European Working Session on Learning*, pages 67–78, Bled, Yugoslavia, May 1987.

[141] T. Niblett and I. Bratko. Learning Decision Rules in Noisy Domains. In *Research and Development in Expert Systems III*, Cambridge, 1986. Cambridge University Press.

[142] K. R. Pattipati and M. G. Alexandridis. Application of heuristic search and information theory to sequential fault diagnosis. *IEEE Trans. on Systems, Man, and Cybernetics*, 20(4):872–887, 1990.

[143] J. R. Quinlan. Discovering rules by induction from large collection of examples. In D. Michie, editor, *Expert Systems in the Micro Electronic Age*. Edinburgh University Press, Edinburgh, UK, 1979.

[144] J. R. Quinlan. Simplifying Decision Trees. *Intl. J. Man-Machine Studies*, 27:221–234, 1987.

[145] J. R. Quinlan. *C4.5: Programs for Machine Learning*. Morgan-Kaufmann Publishers, San Mateo, CA, 1993.

[146] J. R. Quinlan and R. L. Rivest. Inferring Decision Trees Using the Minimum Description Length Principle. *Information and Computation*, 80(3):227–248, 1989.

[147] S. R. Safavian and D. Landgrebe. A Survey of Decision Tree Classifier Methodology. *IEEE Trans. Systems, Man and Cybernetics*, 22:660–674, May/June 1998.

[148] C. Schaffer. Overfitting avoidance as bias. *Machine Learning*, 10:153–178, 1993.

[149] R. E. Schapire. The Boosting Approach to Machine Learning: An Overview. In *MSRI Workshop on Nonlinear Estimation and Classification*, 2002.

[150] J. Schuermann and W. Doster. A decision-theoretic approach in hierarchical classifier design. *Pattern Recognition*, 17:359–369, 1984.

[151] J. C. Shafer, R. Agrawal, and M. Mehta. SPRINT: A Scalable Parallel Classifier for Data Mining. In *Proc. of the 22nd VLDB Conf.*, pages 544–555, Bombay, India, September 1996.

[152] P. E. Utgoff and C. E. Brodley. An incremental method for finding multivariate splits for decision trees. In *Proc. of the 7th Intl. Conf. on Machine Learning*, pages 58–65, Austin, TX, June 1990.

[153] H. Wang and C. Zaniolo. CMP: A Fast Decision Tree Classifier Using Multivariate Predictions. In *Proc. of the 16th Intl. Conf. on Data Engineering*, pages 449–460, San Diego, CA, March 2000.

[154] Q. R. Wang and C. Y. Suen. Large tree classifier with heuristic search and global training. *IEEE Trans. on Pattern Analysis and Machine Intelligence*, 9(1):91–102, 1987.

4.8 Exercises

1. Draw the full decision tree for the parity function of four Boolean attributes, A, B, C, and D. Is it possible to simplify the tree?

2. Consider the training examples shown in Table 4.7 for a binary classification problem.

   (a) Compute the Gini index for the overall collection of training examples.

   (b) Compute the Gini index for the **Customer ID** attribute.

   (c) Compute the Gini index for the **Gender** attribute.

   (d) Compute the Gini index for the **Car Type** attribute using multiway split.

   (e) Compute the Gini index for the **Shirt Size** attribute using multiway split.

   (f) Which attribute is better, **Gender**, **Car Type**, or **Shirt Size**?

   (g) Explain why **Customer ID** should not be used as the attribute test condition even though it has the lowest Gini.

3. Consider the training examples shown in Table 4.8 for a binary classification problem.

   (a) What is the entropy of this collection of training examples with respect to the positive class?

Table 4.7. Data set for Exercise 2.

Customer ID	Gender	Car Type	Shirt Size	Class
1	M	Family	Small	C0
2	M	Sports	Medium	C0
3	M	Sports	Medium	C0
4	M	Sports	Large	C0
5	M	Sports	Extra Large	C0
6	M	Sports	Extra Large	C0
7	F	Sports	Small	C0
8	F	Sports	Small	C0
9	F	Sports	Medium	C0
10	F	Luxury	Large	C0
11	M	Family	Large	C1
12	M	Family	Extra Large	C1
13	M	Family	Medium	C1
14	M	Luxury	Extra Large	C1
15	F	Luxury	Small	C1
16	F	Luxury	Small	C1
17	F	Luxury	Medium	C1
18	F	Luxury	Medium	C1
19	F	Luxury	Medium	C1
20	F	Luxury	Large	C1

Table 4.8. Data set for Exercise 3.

Instance	a_1	a_2	a_3	Target Class
1	T	T	1.0	+
2	T	T	6.0	+
3	T	F	5.0	−
4	F	F	4.0	+
5	F	T	7.0	−
6	F	T	3.0	−
7	F	F	8.0	−
8	T	F	7.0	+
9	F	T	5.0	−

(b) What are the information gains of a_1 and a_2 relative to these training examples?

(c) For a_3, which is a continuous attribute, compute the information gain for every possible split.

199

(d) What is the best split (among a_1, a_2, and a_3) according to the information gain?

(e) What is the best split (between a_1 and a_2) according to the classification error rate?

(f) What is the best split (between a_1 and a_2) according to the Gini index?

4. Show that the entropy of a node never increases after splitting it into smaller successor nodes.

5. Consider the following data set for a binary class problem.

A	B	Class Label
T	F	+
T	T	+
T	T	+
T	F	−
T	T	+
F	F	−
F	F	−
F	F	−
T	T	−
T	F	−

(a) Calculate the information gain when splitting on A and B. Which attribute would the decision tree induction algorithm choose?

(b) Calculate the gain in the Gini index when splitting on A and B. Which attribute would the decision tree induction algorithm choose?

(c) Figure 4.13 shows that entropy and the Gini index are both monotonously increasing on the range [0, 0.5] and they are both monotonously decreasing on the range [0.5, 1]. Is it possible that information gain and the gain in the Gini index favor different attributes? Explain.

6. Consider the following set of training examples.

X	Y	Z	No. of Class C1 Examples	No. of Class C2 Examples
0	0	0	5	40
0	0	1	0	15
0	1	0	10	5
0	1	1	45	0
1	0	0	10	5
1	0	1	25	0
1	1	0	5	20
1	1	1	0	15

(a) Compute a two-level decision tree using the greedy approach described in this chapter. Use the classification error rate as the criterion for splitting. What is the overall error rate of the induced tree?

(b) Repeat part (a) using X as the first splitting attribute and then choose the best remaining attribute for splitting at each of the two successor nodes. What is the error rate of the induced tree?

(c) Compare the results of parts (a) and (b). Comment on the suitability of the greedy heuristic used for splitting attribute selection.

7. The following table summarizes a data set with three attributes A, B, C and two class labels $+$, $-$. Build a two-level decision tree.

A	B	C	Number of Instances	
			+	−
T	T	T	5	0
F	T	T	0	20
T	F	T	20	0
F	F	T	0	5
T	T	F	0	0
F	T	F	25	0
T	F	F	0	0
F	F	F	0	25

(a) According to the classification error rate, which attribute would be chosen as the first splitting attribute? For each attribute, show the contingency table and the gains in classification error rate.

(b) Repeat for the two children of the root node.

(c) How many instances are misclassified by the resulting decision tree?

(d) Repeat parts (a), (b), and (c) using C as the splitting attribute.

(e) Use the results in parts (c) and (d) to conclude about the greedy nature of the decision tree induction algorithm.

8. Consider the decision tree shown in Figure 4.30.

(a) Compute the generalization error rate of the tree using the optimistic approach.

(b) Compute the generalization error rate of the tree using the pessimistic approach. (For simplicity, use the strategy of adding a factor of 0.5 to each leaf node.)

(c) Compute the generalization error rate of the tree using the validation set shown above. This approach is known as **reduced error pruning**.

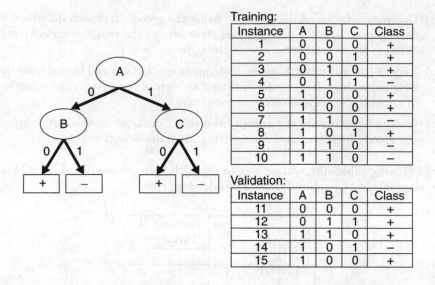

Figure 4.30. Decision tree and data sets for Exercise 8.

9. Consider the decision trees shown in Figure 4.31. Assume they are generated from a data set that contains 16 binary attributes and 3 classes, C_1, C_2, and C_3.

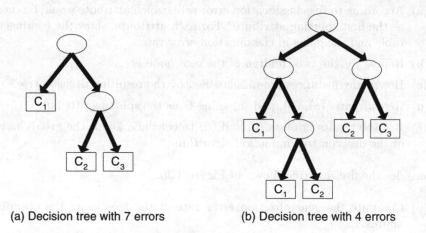

(a) Decision tree with 7 errors   (b) Decision tree with 4 errors

Figure 4.31. Decision trees for Exercise 9.

Compute the total description length of each decision tree according to the minimum description length principle.

- The total description length of a tree is given by:

$$Cost(tree, data) = Cost(tree) + Cost(data|tree).$$

- Each internal node of the tree is encoded by the ID of the splitting attribute. If there are m attributes, the cost of encoding each attribute is $\log_2 m$ bits.

- Each leaf is encoded using the ID of the class it is associated with. If there are k classes, the cost of encoding a class is $\log_2 k$ bits.

- $Cost(tree)$ is the cost of encoding all the nodes in the tree. To simplify the computation, you can assume that the total cost of the tree is obtained by adding up the costs of encoding each internal node and each leaf node.

- $Cost(data|tree)$ is encoded using the classification errors the tree commits on the training set. Each error is encoded by $\log_2 n$ bits, where n is the total number of training instances.

Which decision tree is better, according to the MDL principle?

10. While the .632 bootstrap approach is useful for obtaining a reliable estimate of model accuracy, it has a known limitation [127]. Consider a two-class problem, where there are equal number of positive and negative examples in the data. Suppose the class labels for the examples are generated randomly. The classifier used is an unpruned decision tree (i.e., a perfect memorizer). Determine the accuracy of the classifier using each of the following methods.

(a) The holdout method, where two-thirds of the data are used for training and the remaining one-third are used for testing.

(b) Ten-fold cross-validation.

(c) The .632 bootstrap method.

(d) From the results in parts (a), (b), and (c), which method provides a more reliable evaluation of the classifier's accuracy?

11. Consider the following approach for testing whether a classifier A beats another classifier B. Let N be the size of a given data set, p_A be the accuracy of classifier A, p_B be the accuracy of classifier B, and $p = (p_A + p_B)/2$ be the average accuracy for both classifiers. To test whether classifier A is significantly better than B, the following Z-statistic is used:

$$Z = \frac{p_A - p_B}{\sqrt{\frac{2p(1-p)}{N}}}.$$

Classifier A is assumed to be better than classifier B if Z > 1.96.

Table 4.9 compares the accuracies of three different classifiers, decision tree classifiers, naïve Bayes classifiers, and support vector machines, on various data sets. (The latter two classifiers are described in Chapter 5.)

Table 4.9. Comparing the accuracy of various classification methods.

Data Set	Size (N)	Decision Tree (%)	naïve Bayes (%)	Support vector machine (%)
Anneal	898	92.09	79.62	87.19
Australia	690	85.51	76.81	84.78
Auto	205	81.95	58.05	70.73
Breast	699	95.14	95.99	96.42
Cleve	303	76.24	83.50	84.49
Credit	690	85.80	77.54	85.07
Diabetes	768	72.40	75.91	76.82
German	1000	70.90	74.70	74.40
Glass	214	67.29	48.59	59.81
Heart	270	80.00	84.07	83.70
Hepatitis	155	81.94	83.23	87.10
Horse	368	85.33	78.80	82.61
Ionosphere	351	89.17	82.34	88.89
Iris	150	94.67	95.33	96.00
Labor	57	78.95	94.74	92.98
Led7	3200	73.34	73.16	73.56
Lymphography	148	77.03	83.11	86.49
Pima	768	74.35	76.04	76.95
Sonar	208	78.85	69.71	76.92
Tic-tac-toe	958	83.72	70.04	98.33
Vehicle	846	71.04	45.04	74.94
Wine	178	94.38	96.63	98.88
Zoo	101	93.07	93.07	96.04

Summarize the performance of the classifiers given in Table 4.9 using the following 3 × 3 table:

win-loss-draw	Decision tree	Naïve Bayes	Support vector machine
Decision tree	0 - 0 - 23		
Naïve Bayes		0 - 0 - 23	
Support vector machine			0 - 0 - 23

Each cell in the table contains the number of wins, losses, and draws when comparing the classifier in a given row to the classifier in a given column.

12. Let X be a binomial random variable with mean Np and variance $Np(1 - p)$. Show that the ratio X/N also has a binomial distribution with mean p and variance $p(1 - p)/N$.

5

Classification: Alternative Techniques

The previous chapter described a simple, yet quite effective, classification technique known as decision tree induction. Issues such as model overfitting and classifier evaluation were also discussed in great detail. This chapter presents alternative techniques for building classification models—from simple techniques such as rule-based and nearest-neighbor classifiers to more advanced techniques such as support vector machines and ensemble methods. Other key issues such as the class imbalance and multiclass problems are also discussed at the end of the chapter.

5.1   Rule-Based Classifier

A rule-based classifier is a technique for classifying records using a collection of "if ...then..." rules. Table 5.1 shows an example of a model generated by a rule-based classifier for the vertebrate classification problem. The rules for the model are represented in a disjunctive normal form, $R = (r_1 \vee r_2 \vee \ldots r_k)$, where R is known as the **rule set** and r_i's are the classification rules or disjuncts.

Table 5.1. Example of a rule set for the vertebrate classification problem.

r_1:	(Gives Birth = no) $\wedge$ (Aerial Creature = yes) $\longrightarrow$ Birds
r_2:	(Gives Birth = no) $\wedge$ (Aquatic Creature = yes) $\longrightarrow$ Fishes
r_3:	(Gives Birth = yes) $\wedge$ (Body Temperature = warm-blooded) $\longrightarrow$ Mammals
r_4:	(Gives Birth = no) $\wedge$ (Aerial Creature = no) $\longrightarrow$ Reptiles
r_5:	(Aquatic Creature = semi) $\longrightarrow$ Amphibians

From Chapter 5 of *Introduction to Data Mining*, First Edition. Pang-Ning Tan, Michael Steinbach, Vipin Kumar. Copyright © 2006 by Pearson Education, Inc. All rights reserved.

Each classification rule can be expressed in the following way:

$$r_i : \quad (Condition_i) \longrightarrow y_i. \tag{5.1}$$

The left-hand side of the rule is called the **rule antecedent** or **precondition**. It contains a conjunction of attribute tests:

$$Condition_i = (A_1 \ op \ v_1) \wedge (A_2 \ op \ v_2) \wedge \ldots (A_k \ op \ v_k), \tag{5.2}$$

where (A_j, v_j) is an attribute-value pair and op is a logical operator chosen from the set $\{=, \neq, <, >, \leq, \geq\}$. Each attribute test $(A_j \ op \ v_j)$ is known as a conjunct. The right-hand side of the rule is called the **rule consequent**, which contains the predicted class y_i.

A rule r covers a record x if the precondition of r matches the attributes of x. r is also said to be fired or triggered whenever it covers a given record. For an illustration, consider the rule r_1 given in Table 5.1 and the following attributes for two vertebrates: hawk and grizzly bear.

Name	Body Temperature	Skin Cover	Gives Birth	Aquatic Creature	Aerial Creature	Has Legs	Hiber- nates
hawk	warm-blooded	feather	no	no	yes	yes	no
grizzly bear	warm-blooded	fur	yes	no	no	yes	yes

r_1 covers the first vertebrate because its precondition is satisfied by the hawk's attributes. The rule does not cover the second vertebrate because grizzly bears give birth to their young and cannot fly, thus violating the precondition of r_1.

The quality of a classification rule can be evaluated using measures such as coverage and accuracy. Given a data set D and a classification rule $r : A \longrightarrow y$, the coverage of the rule is defined as the fraction of records in D that trigger the rule r. On the other hand, its accuracy or confidence factor is defined as the fraction of records triggered by r whose class labels are equal to y. The formal definitions of these measures are

$$\text{Coverage}(r) = \frac{|A|}{|D|}$$
$$\text{Accuracy}(r) = \frac{|A \cap y|}{|A|}, \tag{5.3}$$

where $|A|$ is the number of records that satisfy the rule antecedent, $|A \cap y|$ is the number of records that satisfy both the antecedent and consequent, and $|D|$ is the total number of records.

Table 5.2. The vertebrate data set.

Name	Body Temperature	Skin Cover	Gives Birth	Aquatic Creature	Aerial Creature	Has Legs	Hiber-nates	Class Label
human	warm-blooded	hair	yes	no	no	yes	no	Mammals
python	cold-blooded	scales	no	no	no	no	yes	Reptiles
salmon	cold-blooded	scales	no	yes	no	no	no	Fishes
whale	warm-blooded	hair	yes	yes	no	no	no	Mammals
frog	cold-blooded	none	no	semi	no	yes	yes	Amphibians
komodo dragon	cold-blooded	scales	no	no	no	yes	no	Reptiles
bat	warm-blooded	hair	yes	no	yes	yes	yes	Mammals
pigeon	warm-blooded	feathers	no	no	yes	yes	no	Birds
cat	warm-blooded	fur	yes	no	no	yes	no	Mammals
guppy	cold-blooded	scales	yes	yes	no	no	no	Fishes
alligator	cold-blooded	scales	no	semi	no	yes	no	Reptiles
penguin	warm-blooded	feathers	no	semi	no	yes	no	Birds
porcupine	warm-blooded	quills	yes	no	no	yes	yes	Mammals
eel	cold-blooded	scales	no	yes	no	no	no	Fishes
salamander	cold-blooded	none	no	semi	no	yes	yes	Amphibians

Example 5.1. Consider the data set shown in Table 5.2. The rule

$$(\texttt{Gives Birth} = \texttt{yes}) \wedge (\texttt{Body Temperature} = \texttt{warm-blooded}) \longrightarrow \texttt{Mammals}$$

has a coverage of 33% since five of the fifteen records support the rule antecedent. The rule accuracy is 100% because all five vertebrates covered by the rule are mammals. ∎

5.1.1 How a Rule-Based Classifier Works

A rule-based classifier classifies a test record based on the rule triggered by the record. To illustrate how a rule-based classifier works, consider the rule set shown in Table 5.1 and the following vertebrates:

Name	Body Temperature	Skin Cover	Gives Birth	Aquatic Creature	Aerial Creature	Has Legs	Hiber-nates
lemur	warm-blooded	fur	yes	no	no	yes	yes
turtle	cold-blooded	scales	no	semi	no	yes	no
dogfish shark	cold-blooded	scales	yes	yes	no	no	no

- The first vertebrate, which is a lemur, is warm-blooded and gives birth to its young. It triggers the rule r_3, and thus, is classified as a mammal.

- The second vertebrate, which is a turtle, triggers the rules r_4 and r_5. Since the classes predicted by the rules are contradictory (reptiles versus amphibians), their conflicting classes must be resolved.

- None of the rules are applicable to a dogfish shark. In this case, we need to ensure that the classifier can still make a reliable prediction even though a test record is not covered by any rule.

The previous example illustrates two important properties of the rule set generated by a rule-based classifier.

Mutually Exclusive Rules   The rules in a rule set R are mutually exclusive if no two rules in R are triggered by the same record. This property ensures that every record is covered by at most one rule in R. An example of a mutually exclusive rule set is shown in Table 5.3.

Exhaustive Rules   A rule set R has exhaustive coverage if there is a rule for each combination of attribute values. This property ensures that every record is covered by at least one rule in R. Assuming that Body Temperature and Gives Birth are binary variables, the rule set shown in Table 5.3 has exhaustive coverage.

Table 5.3. Example of a mutually exclusive and exhaustive rule set.

r_1: (Body Temperature = cold-blooded) $\longrightarrow$ Non-mammals
r_2: (Body Temperature = warm-blooded) $\wedge$ (Gives Birth = yes) $\longrightarrow$ Mammals
r_3: (Body Temperature = warm-blooded) $\wedge$ (Gives Birth = no) $\longrightarrow$ Non-mammals

Together, these properties ensure that every record is covered by exactly one rule. Unfortunately, many rule-based classifiers, including the one shown in Table 5.1, do not have such properties. If the rule set is not exhaustive, then a default rule, $r_d : () \longrightarrow y_d$, must be added to cover the remaining cases. A default rule has an empty antecedent and is triggered when all other rules have failed. y_d is known as the default class and is typically assigned to the majority class of training records not covered by the existing rules.

If the rule set is not mutually exclusive, then a record can be covered by several rules, some of which may predict conflicting classes. There are two ways to overcome this problem.

Ordered Rules In this approach, the rules in a rule set are ordered in decreasing order of their priority, which can be defined in many ways (e.g., based on accuracy, coverage, total description length, or the order in which the rules are generated). An ordered rule set is also known as a **decision list**. When a test record is presented, it is classified by the highest-ranked rule that covers the record. This avoids the problem of having conflicting classes predicted by multiple classification rules.

Unordered Rules This approach allows a test record to trigger multiple classification rules and considers the consequent of each rule as a vote for a particular class. The votes are then tallied to determine the class label of the test record. The record is usually assigned to the class that receives the highest number of votes. In some cases, the vote may be weighted by the rule's accuracy. Using unordered rules to build a rule-based classifier has both advantages and disadvantages. Unordered rules are less susceptible to errors caused by the wrong rule being selected to classify a test record (unlike classifiers based on ordered rules, which are sensitive to the choice of rule-ordering criteria). Model building is also less expensive because the rules do not have to be kept in sorted order. Nevertheless, classifying a test record can be quite an expensive task because the attributes of the test record must be compared against the precondition of every rule in the rule set.

In the remainder of this section, we will focus on rule-based classifiers that use ordered rules.

5.1.2 Rule-Ordering Schemes

Rule ordering can be implemented on a rule-by-rule basis or on a class-by-class basis. The difference between these schemes is illustrated in Figure 5.1.

Rule-Based Ordering Scheme This approach orders the individual rules by some rule quality measure. This ordering scheme ensures that every test record is classified by the "best" rule covering it. A potential drawback of this scheme is that lower-ranked rules are much harder to interpret because they assume the negation of the rules preceding them. For example, the fourth rule shown in Figure 5.1 for rule-based ordering,

$$\text{Aquatic Creature} = \text{semi} \longrightarrow \text{Amphibians},$$

has the following interpretation: If the vertebrate does not have any feathers or cannot fly, and is cold-blooded and semi-aquatic, then it is an amphibian.

```
┌─────────────────────────────────────┬─────────────────────────────────────┐
│          Rule-Based Ordering         │          Class-Based Ordering        │
│                                      │                                      │
│  (Skin Cover=feathers, Aerial        │  (Skin Cover=feathers, Aerial        │
│      Creature=yes)                   │      Creature=yes)                   │
│      ==> Birds                       │      ==> Birds                       │
│                                      │                                      │
│  (Body temperature=warm-blooded,     │  (Body temperature=warm-blooded,     │
│  Gives Birth=yes) ==> Mammals        │  Gives Birth=no) ==> Birds           │
│                                      │                                      │
│  (Body temperature=warm-blooded,     │  (Body temperature=warm-blooded,     │
│  Gives Birth=no) ==> Birds           │  Gives Birth=yes) ==> Mammals        │
│                                      │                                      │
│  (Aquatic Creature=semi)) ==> Amphibians │  (Aquatic Creature=semi)) ==> Amphibians │
│                                      │                                      │
│  (Skin Cover=scales, Aquatic Creature=no) │  (Skin Cover=none) ==> Amphibians    │
│      ==> Reptiles                    │                                      │
│                                      │  (Skin Cover=scales, Aquatic Creature=no) │
│  (Skin Cover=scales, Aquatic Creature=yes) │      ==> Reptiles               │
│      ==> Fishes                      │                                      │
│                                      │  (Skin Cover=scales, Aquatic Creature=yes) │
│  (Skin Cover=none) ==> Amphibians    │      ==> Fishes                      │
└─────────────────────────────────────┴─────────────────────────────────────┘
```

Figure 5.1. Comparison between rule-based and class-based ordering schemes.

The additional conditions (that the vertebrate does not have any feathers or cannot fly, and is cold-blooded) are due to the fact that the vertebrate does not satisfy the first three rules. If the number of rules is large, interpreting the meaning of the rules residing near the bottom of the list can be a cumbersome task.

Class-Based Ordering Scheme   In this approach, rules that belong to the same class appear together in the rule set R. The rules are then collectively sorted on the basis of their class information. The relative ordering among the rules from the same class is not important; as long as one of the rules fires, the class will be assigned to the test record. This makes rule interpretation slightly easier. However, it is possible for a high-quality rule to be overlooked in favor of an inferior rule that happens to predict the higher-ranked class.

Since most of the well-known rule-based classifiers (such as C4.5rules and RIPPER) employ the class-based ordering scheme, the discussion in the remainder of this section focuses mainly on this type of ordering scheme.

5.1.3   How to Build a Rule-Based Classifier

To build a rule-based classifier, we need to extract a set of rules that identifies key relationships between the attributes of a data set and the class label.

There are two broad classes of methods for extracting classification rules: (1) direct methods, which extract classification rules directly from data, and (2) indirect methods, which extract classification rules from other classification models, such as decision trees and neural networks.

Direct methods partition the attribute space into smaller subspaces so that all the records that belong to a subspace can be classified using a single classification rule. Indirect methods use the classification rules to provide a succinct description of more complex classification models. Detailed discussions of these methods are presented in Sections 5.1.4 and 5.1.5, respectively.

5.1.4 Direct Methods for Rule Extraction

The **sequential covering** algorithm is often used to extract rules directly from data. Rules are grown in a greedy fashion based on a certain evaluation measure. The algorithm extracts the rules one class at a time for data sets that contain more than two classes. For the vertebrate classification problem, the sequential covering algorithm may generate rules for classifying birds first, followed by rules for classifying mammals, amphibians, reptiles, and finally, fishes (see Figure 5.1). The criterion for deciding which class should be generated first depends on a number of factors, such as the class prevalence (i.e., fraction of training records that belong to a particular class) or the cost of misclassifying records from a given class.

A summary of the sequential covering algorithm is given in Algorithm 5.1. The algorithm starts with an empty decision list, R. The Learn-One-Rule function is then used to extract the best rule for class y that covers the current set of training records. During rule extraction, all training records for class y are considered to be positive examples, while those that belong to

---

Algorithm 5.1 Sequential covering algorithm.

1: Let E be the training records and A be the set of attribute-value pairs, $\{(A_j, v_j)\}$.
2: Let Y_o be an ordered set of classes $\{y_1, y_2, \ldots, y_k\}$.
3: Let $R = \{\ \}$ be the initial rule list.
4: **for** each class $y \in Y_o - \{y_k\}$ **do**
5:     **while** stopping condition is not met **do**
6:         $r \leftarrow$ Learn-One-Rule (E, A, y).
7:         Remove training records from E that are covered by r.
8:         Add r to the bottom of the rule list: $R \longrightarrow R \vee r$.
9:     **end while**
10: **end for**
11: Insert the default rule, $\{\} \longrightarrow y_k$, to the bottom of the rule list R.

---

other classes are considered to be negative examples. A rule is desirable if it covers most of the positive examples and none (or very few) of the negative examples. Once such a rule is found, the training records covered by the rule are eliminated. The new rule is added to the bottom of the decision list R. This procedure is repeated until the stopping criterion is met. The algorithm then proceeds to generate rules for the next class.

Figure 5.2 demonstrates how the sequential covering algorithm works for a data set that contains a collection of positive and negative examples. The rule $R1$, whose coverage is shown in Figure 5.2(b), is extracted first because it covers the largest fraction of positive examples. All the training records covered by $R1$ are subsequently removed and the algorithm proceeds to look for the next best rule, which is $R2$.

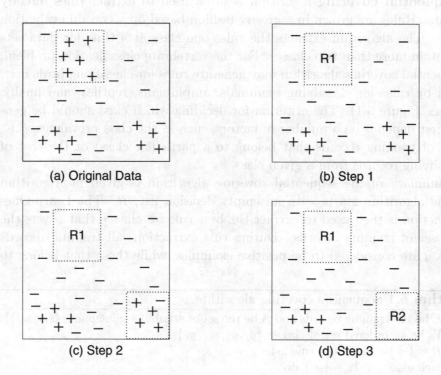

Figure 5.2. An example of the sequential covering algorithm.

Learn-One-Rule Function

The objective of the Learn-One-Rule function is to extract a classification rule that covers many of the positive examples and none (or very few) of the negative examples in the training set. However, finding an optimal rule is computationally expensive given the exponential size of the search space. The Learn-One-Rule function addresses the exponential search problem by growing the rules in a greedy fashion. It generates an initial rule r and keeps refining the rule until a certain stopping criterion is met. The rule is then pruned to improve its generalization error.

Rule-Growing Strategy   There are two common strategies for growing a classification rule: general-to-specific or specific-to-general. Under the general-to-specific strategy, an initial rule $r : \{\} \longrightarrow y$ is created, where the left-hand side is an empty set and the right-hand side contains the target class. The rule has poor quality because it covers all the examples in the training set. New

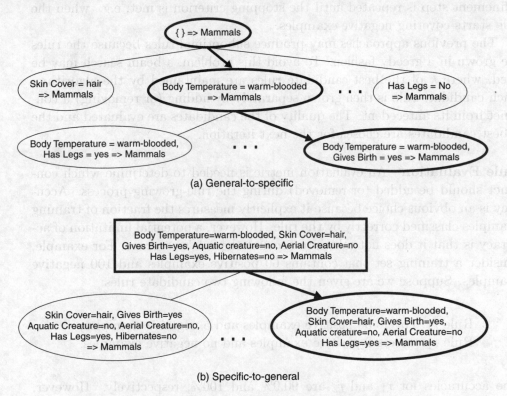

(a) General-to-specific

(b) Specific-to-general

Figure 5.3. General-to-specific and specific-to-general rule-growing strategies.

conjuncts are subsequently added to improve the rule's quality. Figure 5.3(a) shows the general-to-specific rule-growing strategy for the vertebrate classification problem. The conjunct `Body Temperature=warm-blooded` is initially chosen to form the rule antecedent. The algorithm then explores all the possible candidates and greedily chooses the next conjunct, `Gives Birth=yes`, to be added into the rule antecedent. This process continues until the stopping criterion is met (e.g., when the added conjunct does not improve the quality of the rule).

For the specific-to-general strategy, one of the positive examples is randomly chosen as the initial seed for the rule-growing process. During the refinement step, the rule is generalized by removing one of its conjuncts so that it can cover more positive examples. Figure 5.3(b) shows the specific-to-general approach for the vertebrate classification problem. Suppose a positive example for mammals is chosen as the initial seed. The initial rule contains the same conjuncts as the attribute values of the seed. To improve its coverage, the rule is generalized by removing the conjunct `Hibernate=no`. The refinement step is repeated until the stopping criterion is met, e.g., when the rule starts covering negative examples.

The previous approaches may produce suboptimal rules because the rules are grown in a greedy fashion. To avoid this problem, a beam search may be used, where k of the best candidate rules are maintained by the algorithm. Each candidate rule is then grown separately by adding (or removing) a conjunct from its antecedent. The quality of the candidates are evaluated and the k best candidates are chosen for the next iteration.

Rule Evaluation   An evaluation metric is needed to determine which conjunct should be added (or removed) during the rule-growing process. Accuracy is an obvious choice because it explicitly measures the fraction of training examples classified correctly by the rule. However, a potential limitation of accuracy is that it does not take into account the rule's coverage. For example, consider a training set that contains 60 positive examples and 100 negative examples. Suppose we are given the following two candidate rules:

> Rule r_1: covers 50 positive examples and 5 negative examples,
> Rule r_2: covers 2 positive examples and no negative examples.

The accuracies for r_1 and r_2 are 90.9% and 100%, respectively. However, r_1 is the better rule despite its lower accuracy. The high accuracy for r_2 is potentially spurious because the coverage of the rule is too low.

5.1 Rule-Based Classifier

The following approaches can be used to handle this problem.

1. A statistical test can be used to prune rules that have poor coverage. For example, we may compute the following likelihood ratio statistic:

$$R = 2 \sum_{i=1}^{k} f_i \log(f_i/e_i),$$

where k is the number of classes, f_i is the observed frequency of class i examples that are covered by the rule, and e_i is the expected frequency of a rule that makes random predictions. Note that R has a chi-square distribution with $k - 1$ degrees of freedom. A large R value suggests that the number of correct predictions made by the rule is significantly larger than that expected by random guessing. For example, since r_1 covers 55 examples, the expected frequency for the positive class is $e_+ = 55 \times 60/160 = 20.625$, while the expected frequency for the negative class is $e_- = 55 \times 100/160 = 34.375$. Thus, the likelihood ratio for r_1 is

$$R(r_1) = 2 \times [50 \times \log_2(50/20.625) + 5 \times \log_2(5/34.375)] = 99.9.$$

Similarly, the expected frequencies for r_2 are $e_+ = 2 \times 60/160 = 0.75$ and $e_- = 2 \times 100/160 = 1.25$. The likelihood ratio statistic for r_2 is

$$R(r_2) = 2 \times [2 \times \log_2(2/0.75) + 0 \times \log_2(0/1.25)] = 5.66.$$

This statistic therefore suggests that r_1 is a better rule than r_2.

2. An evaluation metric that takes into account the rule coverage can be used. Consider the following evaluation metrics:

$$\text{Laplace} = \frac{f_+ + 1}{n + k}, \tag{5.4}$$

$$\text{m-estimate} = \frac{f_+ + kp_+}{n + k}, \tag{5.5}$$

where n is the number of examples covered by the rule, f_+ is the number of positive examples covered by the rule, k is the total number of classes, and p_+ is the prior probability for the positive class. Note that the m-estimate is equivalent to the Laplace measure by choosing $p_+ = 1/k$. Depending on the rule coverage, these measures capture the trade-off between rule accuracy and the prior probability of the positive class. If the rule does not cover any training example, then the Laplace measure reduces to $1/k$, which is the prior probability of the positive class assuming a uniform class distribution. The m-estimate also reduces to the prior probability (p_+) when $n = 0$. However, if the rule coverage is large, then both measures asymptotically approach the rule accuracy, f_+/n. Going back to the previous example, the Laplace measure for r_1 is $51/57 = 89.47\%$, which is quite close to its accuracy. Conversely, the Laplace measure for r_2 (75%) is significantly lower than its accuracy because r_2 has a much lower coverage.

3. An evaluation metric that takes into account the support count of the rule can be used. One such metric is the **FOIL's information gain**. The support count of a rule corresponds to the number of positive examples covered by the rule. Suppose the rule $r : A \longrightarrow +$ covers p_0 positive examples and n_0 negative examples. After adding a new conjunct B, the extended rule $r' : A \wedge B \longrightarrow +$ covers p_1 positive examples and n_1 negative examples. Given this information, the FOIL's information gain of the extended rule is defined as follows:

$$\text{FOIL's information gain} = p_1 \times \left(\log_2 \frac{p_1}{p_1 + n_1} - \log_2 \frac{p_0}{p_0 + n_0} \right). \quad (5.6)$$

Since the measure is proportional to p_1 and $p_1/(p_1 + n_1)$, it prefers rules that have high support count and accuracy. The FOIL's information gains for rules r_1 and r_2 given in the preceding example are 43.12 and 2, respectively. Therefore, r_1 is a better rule than r_2.

Rule Pruning   The rules generated by the Learn-One-Rule function can be pruned to improve their generalization errors. To determine whether pruning is necessary, we may apply the methods described in Section 4.4 on page 172 to estimate the generalization error of a rule. For example, if the error on validation set decreases after pruning, we should keep the simplified rule. Another approach is to compare the pessimistic error of the rule before and after pruning (see Section 4.4.4 on page 179). The simplified rule is retained in place of the original rule if the pessimistic error improves after pruning.

Rationale for Sequential Covering

After a rule is extracted, the sequential covering algorithm must eliminate all the positive and negative examples covered by the rule. The rationale for doing this is given in the next example.

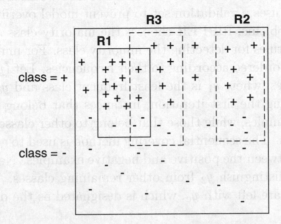

Figure 5.4. Elimination of training records by the sequential covering algorithm. $R1$, $R2$, and $R3$ represent regions covered by three different rules.

Figure 5.4 shows three possible rules, $R1$, $R2$, and $R3$, extracted from a data set that contains 29 positive examples and 21 negative examples. The accuracies of $R1$, $R2$, and $R3$ are 12/15 (80%), 7/10 (70%), and 8/12 (66.7%), respectively. $R1$ is generated first because it has the highest accuracy. After generating $R1$, it is clear that the positive examples covered by the rule must be removed so that the next rule generated by the algorithm is different than $R1$. Next, suppose the algorithm is given the choice of generating either $R2$ or $R3$. Even though $R2$ has higher accuracy than $R3$, $R1$ and $R3$ together cover 18 positive examples and 5 negative examples (resulting in an overall accuracy of 78.3%), whereas $R1$ and $R2$ together cover 19 positive examples and 6 negative examples (resulting in an overall accuracy of 76%). The incremental impact of $R2$ or $R3$ on accuracy is more evident when the positive and negative examples covered by $R1$ are removed before computing their accuracies. In particular, if positive examples covered by $R1$ are not removed, then we may overestimate the effective accuracy of $R3$, and if negative examples are not removed, then we may underestimate the accuracy of $R3$. In the latter case, we might end up preferring $R2$ over $R3$ even though half of the false positive errors committed by $R3$ have already been accounted for by the preceding rule, $R1$.

RIPPER Algorithm

To illustrate the direct method, we consider a widely used rule induction algorithm called RIPPER. This algorithm scales almost linearly with the number of training examples and is particularly suited for building models from data sets with imbalanced class distributions. RIPPER also works well with noisy data sets because it uses a validation set to prevent model overfitting.

For two-class problems, RIPPER chooses the majority class as its default class and learns the rules for detecting the minority class. For multiclass problems, the classes are ordered according to their frequencies. Let $(y_1, y_2, \ldots, y_c)$ be the ordered classes, where y_1 is the least frequent class and y_c is the most frequent class. During the first iteration, instances that belong to y_1 are labeled as positive examples, while those that belong to other classes are labeled as negative examples. The sequential covering method is used to generate rules that discriminate between the positive and negative examples. Next, RIPPER extracts rules that distinguish y_2 from other remaining classes. This process is repeated until we are left with y_c, which is designated as the default class.

Rule Growing   RIPPER employs a general-to-specific strategy to grow a rule and the FOIL's information gain measure to choose the best conjunct to be added into the rule antecedent. It stops adding conjuncts when the rule starts covering negative examples. The new rule is then pruned based on its performance on the validation set. The following metric is computed to determine whether pruning is needed: $(p-n)/(p+n)$, where p (n) is the number of positive (negative) examples in the validation set covered by the rule. This metric is monotonically related to the rule's accuracy on the validation set. If the metric improves after pruning, then the conjunct is removed. Pruning is done starting from the last conjunct added to the rule. For example, given a rule $ABCD \longrightarrow y$, RIPPER checks whether D should be pruned first, followed by CD, BCD, etc. While the original rule covers only positive examples, the pruned rule may cover some of the negative examples in the training set.

Building the Rule Set   After generating a rule, all the positive and negative examples covered by the rule are eliminated. The rule is then added into the rule set as long as it does not violate the stopping condition, which is based on the minimum description length principle. If the new rule increases the total description length of the rule set by at least d bits, then RIPPER stops adding rules into its rule set (by default, d is chosen to be 64 bits). Another stopping condition used by RIPPER is that the error rate of the rule on the validation set must not exceed 50%.

RIPPER also performs additional optimization steps to determine whether some of the existing rules in the rule set can be replaced by better alternative rules. Readers who are interested in the details of the optimization method may refer to the reference cited at the end of this chapter.

5.1.5   Indirect Methods for Rule Extraction

This section presents a method for generating a rule set from a decision tree. In principle, every path from the root node to the leaf node of a decision tree can be expressed as a classification rule. The test conditions encountered along the path form the conjuncts of the rule antecedent, while the class label at the leaf node is assigned to the rule consequent. Figure 5.5 shows an example of a rule set generated from a decision tree. Notice that the rule set is exhaustive and contains mutually exclusive rules. However, some of the rules can be simplified as shown in the next example.

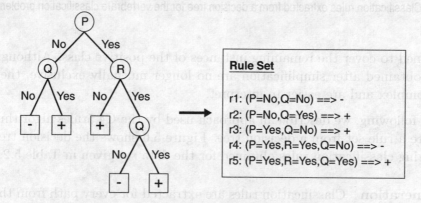

Figure 5.5. Converting a decision tree into classification rules.

Example 5.2. Consider the following three rules from Figure 5.5:

$$r2 : (P = No) \wedge (Q = Yes) \longrightarrow +$$
$$r3 : (P = Yes) \wedge (R = No) \longrightarrow +$$
$$r5 : (P = Yes) \wedge (R = Yes) \wedge (Q = Yes) \longrightarrow +$$

Observe that the rule set always predicts a positive class when the value of Q is Yes. Therefore, we may simplify the rules as follows:

$$r2' : (Q = Yes) \longrightarrow +$$
$$r3 : (P = Yes) \wedge (R = No) \longrightarrow +$$

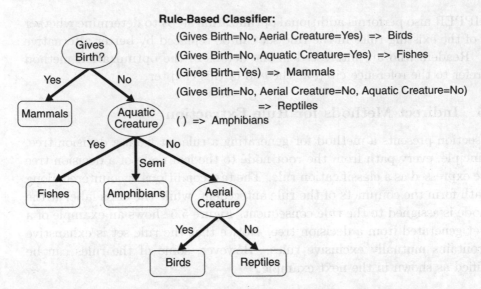

Figure 5.6. Classification rules extracted from a decision tree for the vertebrate classification problem.

r_3 is retained to cover the remaining instances of the positive class. Although the rules obtained after simplification are no longer mutually exclusive, they are less complex and are easier to interpret.   ∎

In the following, we describe an approach used by the C4.5rules algorithm to generate a rule set from a decision tree. Figure 5.6 shows the decision tree and resulting classification rules obtained for the data set given in Table 5.2.

Rule Generation   Classification rules are extracted for every path from the root to one of the leaf nodes in the decision tree. Given a classification rule $r : A \longrightarrow y$, we consider a simplified rule, $r' : A' \longrightarrow y$, where A' is obtained by removing one of the conjuncts in A. The simplified rule with the lowest pessimistic error rate is retained provided its error rate is less than that of the original rule. The rule-pruning step is repeated until the pessimistic error of the rule cannot be improved further. Because some of the rules may become identical after pruning, the duplicate rules must be discarded.

Rule Ordering   After generating the rule set, C4.5rules uses the class-based ordering scheme to order the extracted rules. Rules that predict the same class are grouped together into the same subset. The total description length for each subset is computed, and the classes are arranged in increasing order of their total description length. The class that has the smallest description length is given the highest priority because it is expected to contain the best set of rules. The total description length for a class is given by $L_{\text{exception}} + g \times L_{\text{model}}$, where $L_{\text{exception}}$ is the number of bits needed to encode the misclassified examples, L_{model} is the number of bits needed to encode the model, and g is a tuning parameter whose default value is 0.5. The tuning parameter depends on the number of redundant attributes present in the model. The value of the tuning parameter is small if the model contains many redundant attributes.

5.1.6 Characteristics of Rule-Based Classifiers

A rule-based classifier has the following characteristics:

- The expressiveness of a rule set is almost equivalent to that of a decision tree because a decision tree can be represented by a set of mutually exclusive and exhaustive rules. Both rule-based and decision tree classifiers create rectilinear partitions of the attribute space and assign a class to each partition. Nevertheless, if the rule-based classifier allows multiple rules to be triggered for a given record, then a more complex decision boundary can be constructed.

- Rule-based classifiers are generally used to produce descriptive models that are easier to interpret, but gives comparable performance to the decision tree classifier.

- The class-based ordering approach adopted by many rule-based classifiers (such as RIPPER) is well suited for handling data sets with imbalanced class distributions.

5.2 Nearest-Neighbor classifiers

The classification framework shown in Figure 4.3 involves a two-step process: (1) an inductive step for constructing a classification model from data, and (2) a deductive step for applying the model to test examples. Decision tree and rule-based classifiers are examples of **eager learners** because they are designed to learn a model that maps the input attributes to the class label as soon as the training data becomes available. An opposite strategy would be to delay the process of modeling the training data until it is needed to classify the test examples. Techniques that employ this strategy are known as **lazy learners**. An example of a lazy learner is the **Rote classifier**, which memorizes the entire training data and performs classification only if the attributes of a test instance match one of the training examples exactly. An obvious drawback of

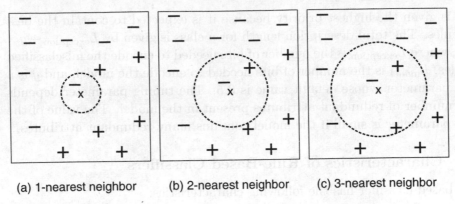

(a) 1-nearest neighbor   (b) 2-nearest neighbor   (c) 3-nearest neighbor

Figure 5.7. The 1-, 2-, and 3-nearest neighbors of an instance.

this approach is that some test records may not be classified because they do not match any training example.

One way to make this approach more flexible is to find all the training examples that are relatively similar to the attributes of the test example. These examples, which are known as **nearest neighbors**, can be used to determine the class label of the test example. The justification for using nearest neighbors is best exemplified by the following saying: *"If it walks like a duck, quacks like a duck, and looks like a duck, then it's probably a duck."* A nearest-neighbor classifier represents each example as a data point in a d-dimensional space, where d is the number of attributes. Given a test example, we compute its proximity to the rest of the data points in the training set, using one of the proximity measures described in Section 2.4 on page 65. The k-nearest neighbors of a given example z refer to the k points that are closest to z.

Figure 5.7 illustrates the 1-, 2-, and 3-nearest neighbors of a data point located at the center of each circle. The data point is classified based on the class labels of its neighbors. In the case where the neighbors have more than one label, the data point is assigned to the majority class of its nearest neighbors. In Figure 5.7(a), the 1-nearest neighbor of the data point is a negative example. Therefore the data point is assigned to the negative class. If the number of nearest neighbors is three, as shown in Figure 5.7(c), then the neighborhood contains two positive examples and one negative example. Using the majority voting scheme, the data point is assigned to the positive class. In the case where there is a tie between the classes (see Figure 5.7(b)), we may randomly choose one of them to classify the data point.

The preceding discussion underscores the importance of choosing the right value for k. If k is too small, then the nearest-neighbor classifier may be

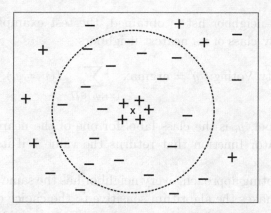

Figure 5.8. k-nearest neighbor classification with large k.

susceptible to overfitting because of noise in the training data. On the other hand, if k is too large, the nearest-neighbor classifier may misclassify the test instance because its list of nearest neighbors may include data points that are located far away from its neighborhood (see Figure 5.8).

5.2.1 Algorithm

A high-level summary of the nearest-neighbor classification method is given in Algorithm 5.2. The algorithm computes the distance (or similarity) between each test example $z = (\mathbf{x}', y')$ and all the training examples $(\mathbf{x}, y) \in D$ to determine its nearest-neighbor list, D_z. Such computation can be costly if the number of training examples is large. However, efficient indexing techniques are available to reduce the amount of computations needed to find the nearest neighbors of a test example.

Algorithm 5.2 The k-nearest neighbor classification algorithm.

1: Let k be the number of nearest neighbors and D be the set of training examples.
2: **for** each test example $z = (\mathbf{x}', y')$ **do**
3:     Compute $d(\mathbf{x}', \mathbf{x})$, the distance between z and every example, $(\mathbf{x}, y) \in D$.
4:     Select $D_z \subseteq D$, the set of k closest training examples to z.
5:     $y' = \underset{v}{\operatorname{argmax}} \sum_{(\mathbf{x}_i, y_i) \in D_z} I(v = y_i)$
6: **end for**

Once the nearest-neighbor list is obtained, the test example is classified based on the majority class of its nearest neighbors:

$$\text{Majority Voting: } y' = \underset{v}{\text{argmax}} \sum_{(\mathbf{x}_i, y_i) \in D_z} I(v = y_i), \qquad (5.7)$$

where v is a class label, y_i is the class label for one of the nearest neighbors, and $I(\cdot)$ is an indicator function that returns the value 1 if its argument is true and 0 otherwise.

In the majority voting approach, every neighbor has the same impact on the classification. This makes the algorithm sensitive to the choice of k, as shown in Figure 5.7. One way to reduce the impact of k is to weight the influence of each nearest neighbor $\mathbf{x}_i$ according to its distance: $w_i = 1/d(\mathbf{x}', \mathbf{x}_i)^2$. As a result, training examples that are located far away from z have a weaker impact on the classification compared to those that are located close to z. Using the distance-weighted voting scheme, the class label can be determined as follows:

$$\text{Distance-Weighted Voting: } y' = \underset{v}{\text{argmax}} \sum_{(\mathbf{x}_i, y_i) \in D_z} w_i \times I(v = y_i). \qquad (5.8)$$

5.2.2 Characteristics of Nearest-Neighbor Classifiers

The characteristics of the nearest-neighbor classifier are summarized below:

- Nearest-neighbor classification is part of a more general technique known as instance-based learning, which uses specific training instances to make predictions without having to maintain an abstraction (or model) derived from data. Instance-based learning algorithms require a proximity measure to determine the similarity or distance between instances and a classification function that returns the predicted class of a test instance based on its proximity to other instances.

- Lazy learners such as nearest-neighbor classifiers do not require model building. However, classifying a test example can be quite expensive because we need to compute the proximity values individually between the test and training examples. In contrast, eager learners often spend the bulk of their computing resources for model building. Once a model has been built, classifying a test example is extremely fast.

- Nearest-neighbor classifiers make their predictions based on local information, whereas decision tree and rule-based classifiers attempt to find a global model that fits the entire input space. Because the classification decisions are made locally, nearest-neighbor classifiers (with small values of k) are quite susceptible to noise.

- Nearest-neighbor classifiers can produce arbitrarily shaped decision boundaries. Such boundaries provide a more flexible model representation compared to decision tree and rule-based classifiers that are often constrained to rectilinear decision boundaries. The decision boundaries of nearest-neighbor classifiers also have high variability because they depend on the composition of training examples. Increasing the number of nearest neighbors may reduce such variability.

- Nearest-neighbor classifiers can produce wrong predictions unless the appropriate proximity measure and data preprocessing steps are taken. For example, suppose we want to classify a group of people based on attributes such as height (measured in meters) and weight (measured in pounds). The height attribute has a low variability, ranging from 1.5 m to 1.85 m, whereas the weight attribute may vary from 90 lb. to 250 lb. If the scale of the attributes are not taken into consideration, the proximity measure may be dominated by differences in the weights of a person.

5.3   Bayesian Classifiers

In many applications the relationship between the attribute set and the class variable is non-deterministic. In other words, the class label of a test record cannot be predicted with certainty even though its attribute set is identical to some of the training examples. This situation may arise because of noisy data or the presence of certain confounding factors that affect classification but are not included in the analysis. For example, consider the task of predicting whether a person is at risk for heart disease based on the person's diet and workout frequency. Although most people who eat healthily and exercise regularly have less chance of developing heart disease, they may still do so because of other factors such as heredity, excessive smoking, and alcohol abuse. Determining whether a person's diet is healthy or the workout frequency is sufficient is also subject to interpretation, which in turn may introduce uncertainties into the learning problem.

This section presents an approach for modeling probabilistic relationships between the attribute set and the class variable. The section begins with an introduction to the **Bayes theorem**, a statistical principle for combining prior knowledge of the classes with new evidence gathered from data. The use of the Bayes theorem for solving classification problems will be explained, followed by a description of two implementations of Bayesian classifiers: naïve Bayes and the Bayesian belief network.

5.3.1   Bayes Theorem

Consider a football game between two rival teams: Team 0 and Team 1. Suppose Team 0 wins 65% of the time and Team 1 wins the remaining matches. Among the games won by Team 0, only 30% of them come from playing on Team 1's football field. On the other hand, 75% of the victories for Team 1 are obtained while playing at home. If Team 1 is to host the next match between the two teams, which team will most likely emerge as the winner?

This question can be answered by using the well-known Bayes theorem. For completeness, we begin with some basic definitions from probability theory. Readers who are unfamiliar with concepts in probability may refer to Appendix C for a brief review of this topic.

Let X and Y be a pair of random variables. Their joint probability, $P(X = x, Y = y)$, refers to the probability that variable X will take on the value x and variable Y will take on the value y. A conditional probability is the probability that a random variable will take on a particular value given that the outcome for another random variable is known. For example, the conditional probability $P(Y = y | X = x)$ refers to the probability that the variable Y will take on the value y, given that the variable X is observed to have the value x. The joint and conditional probabilities for X and Y are related in the following way:

$$P(X, Y) = P(Y|X) \times P(X) = P(X|Y) \times P(Y). \qquad (5.9)$$

Rearranging the last two expressions in Equation 5.9 leads to the following formula, known as the Bayes theorem:

$$P(Y|X) = \frac{P(X|Y)P(Y)}{P(X)}. \qquad (5.10)$$

The Bayes theorem can be used to solve the prediction problem stated at the beginning of this section. For notational convenience, let X be the random variable that represents the team hosting the match and Y be the random variable that represents the winner of the match. Both X and Y can take on values from the set $\{0, 1\}$. We can summarize the information given in the problem as follows:

Probability Team 0 wins is $P(Y = 0) = 0.65$.
Probability Team 1 wins is $P(Y = 1) = 1 - P(Y = 0) = 0.35$.
Probability Team 1 hosted the match it won is $P(X = 1|Y = 1) = 0.75$.
Probability Team 1 hosted the match won by Team 0 is $P(X = 1|Y = 0) = 0.3$.

Our objective is to compute $P(Y = 1|X = 1)$, which is the conditional probability that Team 1 wins the next match it will be hosting, and compares it against $P(Y = 0|X = 1)$. Using the Bayes theorem, we obtain

$$
\begin{aligned}
P(Y = 1|X = 1) &= \frac{P(X = 1|Y = 1) \times P(Y = 1)}{P(X = 1)} \\
&= \frac{P(X = 1|Y = 1) \times P(Y = 1)}{P(X = 1, Y = 1) + P(X = 1, Y = 0)} \\
&= \frac{P(X = 1|Y = 1) \times P(Y = 1)}{P(X = 1|Y = 1)P(Y = 1) + P(X = 1|Y = 0)P(Y = 0)} \\
&= \frac{0.75 \times 0.35}{0.75 \times 0.35 + 0.3 \times 0.65} \\
&= 0.5738,
\end{aligned}
$$

where the law of total probability (see Equation C.5 on page 722) was applied in the second line. Furthermore, $P(Y = 0|X = 1) = 1 - P(Y = 1|X = 1) = 0.4262$. Since $P(Y = 1|X = 1) > P(Y = 0|X = 1)$, Team 1 has a better chance than Team 0 of winning the next match.

5.3.2   Using the Bayes Theorem for Classification

Before describing how the Bayes theorem can be used for classification, let us formalize the classification problem from a statistical perspective. Let $\mathbf{X}$ denote the attribute set and Y denote the class variable. If the class variable has a non-deterministic relationship with the attributes, then we can treat $\mathbf{X}$ and Y as random variables and capture their relationship probabilistically using $P(Y|\mathbf{X})$. This conditional probability is also known as the **posterior probability** for Y, as opposed to its **prior probability**, $P(Y)$.

During the training phase, we need to learn the posterior probabilities $P(Y|\mathbf{X})$ for every combination of $\mathbf{X}$ and Y based on information gathered from the training data. By knowing these probabilities, a test record $\mathbf{X}'$ can be classified by finding the class Y' that maximizes the posterior probability,

$P(Y'|\mathbf{X}')$. To illustrate this approach, consider the task of predicting whether a loan borrower will default on their payments. Figure 5.9 shows a training set with the following attributes: Home Owner, Marital Status, and Annual Income. Loan borrowers who defaulted on their payments are classified as Yes, while those who repaid their loans are classified as No.

Tid	Home Owner	Marital Status	Annual Income	Defaulted Borrower
1	Yes	Single	125K	No
2	No	Married	100K	No
3	No	Single	70K	No
4	Yes	Married	120K	No
5	No	Divorced	95K	Yes
6	No	Married	60K	No
7	Yes	Divorced	220K	No
8	No	Single	85K	Yes
9	No	Married	75K	No
10	No	Single	90K	Yes

Figure 5.9. Training set for predicting the loan default problem.

Suppose we are given a test record with the following attribute set: $\mathbf{X} =$ (Home Owner = No, Marital Status = Married, Annual Income = \$120K). To classify the record, we need to compute the posterior probabilities $P(\text{Yes}|\mathbf{X})$ and $P(\text{No}|\mathbf{X})$ based on information available in the training data. If $P(\text{Yes}|\mathbf{X}) > P(\text{No}|\mathbf{X})$, then the record is classified as Yes; otherwise, it is classified as No.

Estimating the posterior probabilities accurately for every possible combination of class label and attribute value is a difficult problem because it requires a very large training set, even for a moderate number of attributes. The Bayes theorem is useful because it allows us to express the posterior probability in terms of the prior probability $P(Y)$, the **class-conditional** probability $P(\mathbf{X}|Y)$, and the evidence, $P(\mathbf{X})$:

$$P(Y|\mathbf{X}) = \frac{P(\mathbf{X}|Y) \times P(Y)}{P(\mathbf{X})}. \tag{5.11}$$

When comparing the posterior probabilities for different values of Y, the denominator term, $P(\mathbf{X})$, is always constant, and thus, can be ignored. The prior probability $P(Y)$ can be easily estimated from the training set by computing the fraction of training records that belong to each class. To estimate the class-conditional probabilities $P(\mathbf{X}|Y)$, we present two implementations of Bayesian classification methods: the naïve Bayes classifier and the Bayesian belief network. These implementations are described in Sections 5.3.3 and 5.3.5, respectively.

5.3.3   Naïve Bayes Classifier

A naïve Bayes classifier estimates the class-conditional probability by assuming that the attributes are conditionally independent, given the class label y. The conditional independence assumption can be formally stated as follows:

$$P(\mathbf{X}|Y = y) = \prod_{i=1}^{d} P(X_i|Y = y), \qquad (5.12)$$

where each attribute set $\mathbf{X} = \{X_1, X_2, \ldots, X_d\}$ consists of d attributes.

Conditional Independence

Before delving into the details of how a naïve Bayes classifier works, let us examine the notion of conditional independence. Let $\mathbf{X}$, $\mathbf{Y}$, and $\mathbf{Z}$ denote three sets of random variables. The variables in $\mathbf{X}$ are said to be conditionally independent of $\mathbf{Y}$, given $\mathbf{Z}$, if the following condition holds:

$$P(\mathbf{X}|\mathbf{Y}, \mathbf{Z}) = P(\mathbf{X}|\mathbf{Z}). \qquad (5.13)$$

An example of conditional independence is the relationship between a person's arm length and his or her reading skills. One might observe that people with longer arms tend to have higher levels of reading skills. This relationship can be explained by the presence of a confounding factor, which is age. A young child tends to have short arms and lacks the reading skills of an adult. If the age of a person is fixed, then the observed relationship between arm length and reading skills disappears. Thus, we can conclude that arm length and reading skills are conditionally independent when the age variable is fixed.

The conditional independence between $\mathbf{X}$ and $\mathbf{Y}$ can also be written into a form that looks similar to Equation 5.12:

$$P(\mathbf{X}, \mathbf{Y}|\mathbf{Z}) = \frac{P(\mathbf{X}, \mathbf{Y}, \mathbf{Z})}{P(\mathbf{Z})}$$

$$= \frac{P(\mathbf{X}, \mathbf{Y}, \mathbf{Z})}{P(\mathbf{Y}, \mathbf{Z})} \times \frac{P(\mathbf{Y}, \mathbf{Z})}{P(\mathbf{Z})}$$

$$= P(\mathbf{X}|\mathbf{Y}, \mathbf{Z}) \times P(\mathbf{Y}|\mathbf{Z})$$

$$= P(\mathbf{X}|\mathbf{Z}) \times P(\mathbf{Y}|\mathbf{Z}), \qquad (5.14)$$

where Equation 5.13 was used to obtain the last line of Equation 5.14.

How a Naïve Bayes Classifier Works

With the conditional independence assumption, instead of computing the class-conditional probability for every combination of $\mathbf{X}$, we only have to estimate the conditional probability of each X_i, given Y. The latter approach is more practical because it does not require a very large training set to obtain a good estimate of the probability.

To classify a test record, the naïve Bayes classifier computes the posterior probability for each class Y:

$$P(Y|\mathbf{X}) = \frac{P(Y) \prod_{i=1}^{d} P(X_i|Y)}{P(\mathbf{X})}. \qquad (5.15)$$

Since $P(\mathbf{X})$ is fixed for every Y, it is sufficient to choose the class that maximizes the numerator term, $P(Y) \prod_{i=1}^{d} P(X_i|Y)$. In the next two subsections, we describe several approaches for estimating the conditional probabilities $P(X_i|Y)$ for categorical and continuous attributes.

Estimating Conditional Probabilities for Categorical Attributes

For a categorical attribute X_i, the conditional probability $P(X_i = x_i|Y = y)$ is estimated according to the fraction of training instances in class y that take on a particular attribute value x_i. For example, in the training set given in Figure 5.9, three out of the seven people who repaid their loans also own a home. As a result, the conditional probability for $P(\texttt{Home Owner=Yes|No})$ is equal to 3/7. Similarly, the conditional probability for defaulted borrowers who are single is given by $P(\texttt{Marital Status = Single|Yes}) = 2/3$.

Estimating Conditional Probabilities for Continuous Attributes

There are two ways to estimate the class-conditional probabilities for continuous attributes in naïve Bayes classifiers:

1. We can discretize each continuous attribute and then replace the continuous attribute value with its corresponding discrete interval. This approach transforms the continuous attributes into ordinal attributes. The conditional probability $P(X_i|Y = y)$ is estimated by computing the fraction of training records belonging to class y that falls within the corresponding interval for X_i. The estimation error depends on the discretization strategy (as described in Section 2.3.6 on page 57), as well as the number of discrete intervals. If the number of intervals is too large, there are too few training records in each interval to provide a reliable estimate for $P(X_i|Y)$. On the other hand, if the number of intervals is too small, then some intervals may aggregate records from different classes and we may miss the correct decision boundary.

2. We can assume a certain form of probability distribution for the continuous variable and estimate the parameters of the distribution using the training data. A Gaussian distribution is usually chosen to represent the class-conditional probability for continuous attributes. The distribution is characterized by two parameters, its mean, μ, and variance, σ^2. For each class y_j, the class-conditional probability for attribute X_i is

$$P(X_i = x_i|Y = y_j) = \frac{1}{\sqrt{2\pi}\sigma_{ij}} \exp^{-\frac{(x_i-\mu_{ij})^2}{2\sigma_{ij}^2}}. \qquad (5.16)$$

The parameter μ_{ij} can be estimated based on the sample mean of X_i ($\overline{x}$) for all training records that belong to the class y_j. Similarly, σ_{ij}^2 can be estimated from the sample variance (s^2) of such training records. For example, consider the annual income attribute shown in Figure 5.9. The sample mean and variance for this attribute with respect to the class No are

$$\overline{x} = \frac{125 + 100 + 70 + \ldots + 75}{7} = 110$$

$$s^2 = \frac{(125 - 110)^2 + (100 - 110)^2 + \ldots + (75 - 110)^2}{7(6)} = 2975$$

$$s = \sqrt{2975} = 54.54.$$

Given a test record with taxable income equal to \$120K, we can compute its class-conditional probability as follows:

$$P(\texttt{Income=120|No}) = \frac{1}{\sqrt{2\pi}(54.54)} \exp^{-\frac{(120-110)^2}{2\times 2975}} = 0.0072.$$

Note that the preceding interpretation of class-conditional probability is somewhat misleading. The right-hand side of Equation 5.16 corresponds to a **probability density function**, $f(X_i; \mu_{ij}, \sigma_{ij})$. Since the function is continuous, the probability that the random variable X_i takes a particular value is zero. Instead, we should compute the conditional probability that X_i lies within some interval, x_i and $x_i + \epsilon$, where ϵ is a small constant:

$$
\begin{aligned}
P(x_i \leq X_i \leq x_i + \epsilon | Y = y_j) &= \int_{x_i}^{x_i+\epsilon} f(X_i; \mu_{ij}, \sigma_{ij}) dX_i \\
&\approx f(x_i; \mu_{ij}, \sigma_{ij}) \times \epsilon. \quad (5.17)
\end{aligned}
$$

Since ϵ appears as a constant multiplicative factor for each class, it cancels out when we normalize the posterior probability for $P(Y|\mathbf{X})$. Therefore, we can still apply Equation 5.16 to approximate the class-conditional probability $P(X_i|Y)$.

Example of the Naïve Bayes Classifier

Consider the data set shown in Figure 5.10(a). We can compute the class-conditional probability for each categorical attribute, along with the sample mean and variance for the continuous attribute using the methodology described in the previous subsections. These probabilities are summarized in Figure 5.10(b).

To predict the class label of a test record $\mathbf{X} = (\texttt{Home Owner=No}, \texttt{Marital Status = Married}, \texttt{Income = \$120K})$, we need to compute the posterior probabilities $P(\texttt{No}|\mathbf{X})$ and $P(\texttt{Yes}|\mathbf{X})$. Recall from our earlier discussion that these posterior probabilities can be estimated by computing the product between the prior probability $P(Y)$ and the class-conditional probabilities $\prod_i P(X_i|Y)$, which corresponds to the numerator of the right-hand side term in Equation 5.15.

The prior probabilities of each class can be estimated by calculating the fraction of training records that belong to each class. Since there are three records that belong to the class **Yes** and seven records that belong to the class

Tid	Home Owner	Marital Status	Annual Income	Defaulted Borrower
1	Yes	Single	125K	No
2	No	Married	100K	No
3	No	Single	70K	No
4	Yes	Married	120K	No
5	No	Divorced	95K	Yes
6	No	Married	60K	No
7	Yes	Divorced	220K	No
8	No	Single	85K	Yes
9	No	Married	75K	No
10	No	Single	90K	Yes

(a)

P(Home Owner=Yes|No) = 3/7
P(Home Owner=No|No) = 4/7
P(Home Owner=Yes|Yes) = 0
P(Home Owner=No|Yes) = 1
P(Marital Status=Single|No) = 2/7
P(Marital Status=Divorced|No) = 1/7
P(Marital Status=Married|No) = 4/7
P(Marital Status=Single|Yes) = 2/3
P(Marital Status=Divorced|Yes) = 1/3
P(Marital Status=Married|Yes) = 0

For Annual Income:
If class=No: sample mean=110
              sample variance=2975
If class=Yes: sample mean=90
              sample variance=25

(b)

Figure 5.10. The naïve Bayes classifier for the loan classification problem.

No, $P(\text{Yes}) = 0.3$ and $P(\text{No}) = 0.7$. Using the information provided in Figure 5.10(b), the class-conditional probabilities can be computed as follows:

$$
\begin{aligned}
P(\mathbf{X}|\text{No}) &= P(\text{Home Owner} = \text{No}|\text{No}) \times P(\text{Status} = \text{Married}|\text{No}) \\
&\quad \times P(\text{Annual Income} = \$120K|\text{No}) \\
&= 4/7 \times 4/7 \times 0.0072 = 0.0024.
\end{aligned}
$$

$$
\begin{aligned}
P(\mathbf{X}|\text{Yes}) &= P(\text{Home Owner} = \text{No}|\text{Yes}) \times P(\text{Status} = \text{Married}|\text{Yes}) \\
&\quad \times P(\text{Annual Income} = \$120K|\text{Yes}) \\
&= 1 \times 0 \times 1.2 \times 10^{-9} = 0.
\end{aligned}
$$

Putting them together, the posterior probability for class No is $P(\text{No}|\mathbf{X}) = \alpha \times 7/10 \times 0.0024 = 0.0016\alpha$, where $\alpha = 1/P(\mathbf{X})$ is a constant term. Using a similar approach, we can show that the posterior probability for class Yes is zero because its class-conditional probability is zero. Since $P(\text{No}|\mathbf{X}) > P(\text{Yes}|\mathbf{X})$, the record is classified as No.

M-estimate of Conditional Probability

The preceding example illustrates a potential problem with estimating posterior probabilities from training data. If the class-conditional probability for one of the attributes is zero, then the overall posterior probability for the class vanishes. This approach of estimating class-conditional probabilities using simple fractions may seem too brittle, especially when there are few training examples available and the number of attributes is large.

In a more extreme case, if the training examples do not cover many of the attribute values, we may not be able to classify some of the test records. For example, if $P(\text{Marital Status} = \text{Divorced}|\text{No})$ is zero instead of 1/7, then a record with attribute set $\mathbf{X} = (\text{Home Owner} = \text{Yes}, \text{Marital Status} = \text{Divorced}, \text{Income} = \$120\text{K})$ has the following class-conditional probabilities:

$$P(\mathbf{X}|\text{No}) = 3/7 \times 0 \times 0.0072 = 0.$$
$$P(\mathbf{X}|\text{Yes}) = 0 \times 1/3 \times 1.2 \times 10^{-9} = 0.$$

The naïve Bayes classifier will not be able to classify the record. This problem can be addressed by using the m-estimate approach for estimating the conditional probabilities:

$$P(x_i|y_j) = \frac{n_c + mp}{n + m}, \tag{5.18}$$

where n is the total number of instances from class y_j, n_c is the number of training examples from class y_j that take on the value x_i, m is a parameter known as the equivalent sample size, and p is a user-specified parameter. If there is no training set available (i.e., $n = 0$), then $P(x_i|y_j) = p$. Therefore p can be regarded as the prior probability of observing the attribute value x_i among records with class y_j. The equivalent sample size determines the tradeoff between the prior probability p and the observed probability n_c/n.

In the example given in the previous section, the conditional probability $P(\text{Status} = \text{Married}|\text{Yes}) = 0$ because none of the training records for the class has the particular attribute value. Using the m-estimate approach with $m = 3$ and $p = 1/3$, the conditional probability is no longer zero:

$$P(\text{Marital Status} = \text{Married}|\text{Yes}) = (0 + 3 \times 1/3)/(3 + 3) = 1/6.$$

If we assume $p = 1/3$ for all attributes of class Yes and $p = 2/3$ for all attributes of class No, then

$$
\begin{aligned}
P(\mathbf{X}|\text{No}) &= P(\text{Home Owner} = \text{No}|\text{No}) \times P(\text{Status} = \text{Married}|\text{No}) \\
&\quad \times P(\text{Annual Income} = \$120\text{K}|\text{No}) \\
&= 6/10 \times 6/10 \times 0.0072 = 0.0026.
\end{aligned}
$$

$$
\begin{aligned}
P(\mathbf{X}|\text{Yes}) &= P(\text{Home Owner} = \text{No}|\text{Yes}) \times P(\text{Status} = \text{Married}|\text{Yes}) \\
&\quad \times P(\text{Annual Income} = \$120\text{K}|\text{Yes}) \\
&= 4/6 \times 1/6 \times 1.2 \times 10^{-9} = 1.3 \times 10^{-10}.
\end{aligned}
$$

The posterior probability for class No is $P(\text{No}|\mathbf{X}) = \alpha \times 7/10 \times 0.0026 = 0.0018\alpha$, while the posterior probability for class Yes is $P(\text{Yes}|\mathbf{X}) = \alpha \times 3/10 \times 1.3 \times 10^{-10} = 4.0 \times 10^{-11}\alpha$. Although the classification decision has not changed, the m-estimate approach generally provides a more robust way for estimating probabilities when the number of training examples is small.

Characteristics of Naïve Bayes Classifiers

Naïve Bayes classifiers generally have the following characteristics:

- They are robust to isolated noise points because such points are averaged out when estimating conditional probabilities from data. Naïve Bayes classifiers can also handle missing values by ignoring the example during model building and classification.

- They are robust to irrelevant attributes. If X_i is an irrelevant attribute, then $P(X_i|Y)$ becomes almost uniformly distributed. The class-conditional probability for X_i has no impact on the overall computation of the posterior probability.

- Correlated attributes can degrade the performance of naïve Bayes classifiers because the conditional independence assumption no longer holds for such attributes. For example, consider the following probabilities:

$$
P(A = 0|Y = 0) = 0.4, \quad P(A = 1|Y = 0) = 0.6,
$$
$$
P(A = 0|Y = 1) = 0.6, \quad P(A = 1|Y = 1) = 0.4,
$$

where A is a binary attribute and Y is a binary class variable. Suppose there is another binary attribute B that is perfectly correlated with A

when $Y = 0$, but is independent of A when $Y = 1$. For simplicity, assume that the class-conditional probabilities for B are the same as for A. Given a record with attributes $A = 0, B = 0$, we can compute its posterior probabilities as follows:

$$P(Y = 0|A = 0, B = 0) = \frac{P(A = 0|Y = 0)P(B = 0|Y = 0)P(Y = 0)}{P(A = 0, B = 0)}$$

$$= \frac{0.16 \times P(Y = 0)}{P(A = 0, B = 0)}.$$

$$P(Y = 1|A = 0, B = 0) = \frac{P(A = 0|Y = 1)P(B = 0|Y = 1)P(Y = 1)}{P(A = 0, B = 0)}$$

$$= \frac{0.36 \times P(Y = 1)}{P(A = 0, B = 0)}.$$

If $P(Y = 0) = P(Y = 1)$, then the naïve Bayes classifier would assign the record to class 1. However, the truth is,

$$P(A = 0, B = 0|Y = 0) = P(A = 0|Y = 0) = 0.4,$$

because A and B are perfectly correlated when $Y = 0$. As a result, the posterior probability for $Y = 0$ is

$$P(Y = 0|A = 0, B = 0) = \frac{P(A = 0, B = 0|Y = 0)P(Y = 0)}{P(A = 0, B = 0)}$$

$$= \frac{0.4 \times P(Y = 0)}{P(A = 0, B = 0)},$$

which is larger than that for $Y = 1$. The record should have been classified as class 0.

5.3.4 Bayes Error Rate

Suppose we know the true probability distribution that governs $P(\mathbf{X}|Y)$. The Bayesian classification method allows us to determine the ideal decision boundary for the classification task, as illustrated in the following example.

Example 5.3. Consider the task of identifying alligators and crocodiles based on their respective lengths. The average length of an adult crocodile is about 15 feet, while the average length of an adult alligator is about 12 feet. Assuming

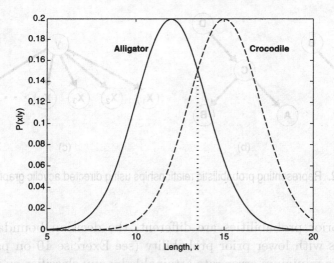

Figure 5.11. Comparing the likelihood functions of a crocodile and an alligator.

that their length x follows a Gaussian distribution with a standard deviation equal to 2 feet, we can express their class-conditional probabilities as follows:

$$P(X|\text{Crocodile}) = \frac{1}{\sqrt{2\pi} \cdot 2} \exp\left[-\frac{1}{2}\left(\frac{X-15}{2}\right)^2\right] \quad (5.19)$$

$$P(X|\text{Alligator}) = \frac{1}{\sqrt{2\pi} \cdot 2} \exp\left[-\frac{1}{2}\left(\frac{X-12}{2}\right)^2\right] \quad (5.20)$$

Figure 5.11 shows a comparison between the class-conditional probabilities for a crocodile and an alligator. Assuming that their prior probabilities are the same, the ideal decision boundary is located at some length $\hat{x}$ such that

$$P(X = \hat{x}|\text{Crocodile}) = P(X = \hat{x}|\text{Alligator}).$$

Using Equations 5.19 and 5.20, we obtain

$$\left(\frac{\hat{x}-15}{2}\right)^2 = \left(\frac{\hat{x}-12}{2}\right)^2,$$

which can be solved to yield $\hat{x} = 13.5$. The decision boundary for this example is located halfway between the two means. ∎

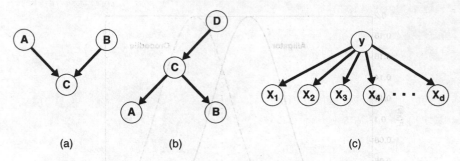

(a)   (b)   (c)

Figure 5.12. Representing probabilistic relationships using directed acyclic graphs.

When the prior probabilities are different, the decision boundary shifts toward the class with lower prior probability (see Exercise 10 on page 319). Furthermore, the minimum error rate attainable by any classifier on the given data can also be computed. The ideal decision boundary in the preceding example classifies all creatures whose lengths are less than $\hat{x}$ as alligators and those whose lengths are greater than $\hat{x}$ as crocodiles. The error rate of the classifier is given by the sum of the area under the posterior probability curve for crocodiles (from length 0 to $\hat{x}$) and the area under the posterior probability curve for alligators (from $\hat{x}$ to ∞):

$$\text{Error} = \int_0^{\hat{x}} P(\texttt{Crocodile}|X)dX + \int_{\hat{x}}^{\infty} P(\texttt{Alligator}|X)dX.$$

The total error rate is known as the **Bayes error rate**.

5.3.5   Bayesian Belief Networks

The conditional independence assumption made by naïve Bayes classifiers may seem too rigid, especially for classification problems in which the attributes are somewhat correlated. This section presents a more flexible approach for modeling the class-conditional probabilities $P(\mathbf{X}|Y)$. Instead of requiring all the attributes to be conditionally independent given the class, this approach allows us to specify which pair of attributes are conditionally independent. We begin with a discussion on how to represent and build such a probabilistic model, followed by an example of how to make inferences from the model.

Model Representation

A Bayesian belief network (BBN), or simply, Bayesian network, provides a graphical representation of the probabilistic relationships among a set of random variables. There are two key elements of a Bayesian network:

1. A directed acyclic graph (dag) encoding the dependence relationships among a set of variables.

2. A probability table associating each node to its immediate parent nodes.

Consider three random variables, A, B, and C, in which A and B are independent variables and each has a direct influence on a third variable, C. The relationships among the variables can be summarized into the directed acyclic graph shown in Figure 5.12(a). Each node in the graph represents a variable, and each arc asserts the dependence relationship between the pair of variables. If there is a directed arc from X to Y, then X is the **parent** of Y and Y is the **child** of X. Furthermore, if there is a directed path in the network from X to Z, then X is an **ancestor** of Z, while Z is a **descendant** of X. For example, in the diagram shown in Figure 5.12(b), A is a descendant of D and D is an ancestor of B. Both B and D are also non-descendants of A. An important property of the Bayesian network can be stated as follows:

Property 1 (Conditional Independence). *A node in a Bayesian network is conditionally independent of its non-descendants, if its parents are known.*

In the diagram shown in Figure 5.12(b), A is conditionally independent of both B and D given C because the nodes for B and D are non-descendants of node A. The conditional independence assumption made by a naïve Bayes classifier can also be represented using a Bayesian network, as shown in Figure 5.12(c), where y is the target class and $\{X_1, X_2, \ldots, X_d\}$ is the attribute set.

Besides the conditional independence conditions imposed by the network topology, each node is also associated with a probability table.

1. If a node X does not have any parents, then the table contains only the prior probability $P(X)$.

2. If a node X has only one parent, Y, then the table contains the conditional probability $P(X|Y)$.

3. If a node X has multiple parents, $\{Y_1, Y_2, \ldots, Y_k\}$, then the table contains the conditional probability $P(X|Y_1, Y_2, \ldots, Y_k)$.

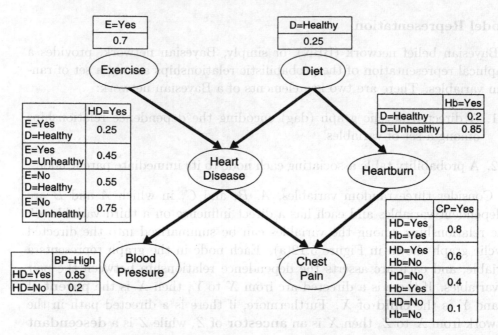

Figure 5.13. A Bayesian belief network for detecting heart disease and heartburn in patients.

Figure 5.13 shows an example of a Bayesian network for modeling patients with heart disease or heartburn problems. Each variable in the diagram is assumed to be binary-valued. The parent nodes for heart disease (HD) correspond to risk factors that may affect the disease, such as exercise (E) and diet (D). The child nodes for heart disease correspond to symptoms of the disease, such as chest pain (CP) and high blood pressure (BP). For example, the diagram shows that heartburn (Hb) may result from an unhealthy diet and may lead to chest pain.

The nodes associated with the risk factors contain only the prior probabilities, whereas the nodes for heart disease, heartburn, and their corresponding symptoms contain the conditional probabilities. To save space, some of the probabilities have been omitted from the diagram. The omitted probabilities can be recovered by noting that $P(X = \bar{x}) = 1 - P(X = x)$ and $P(X = \bar{x}|Y) = 1 - P(X = x|Y)$, where $\bar{x}$ denotes the opposite outcome of x. For example, the conditional probability

$$P(\text{Heart Disease} = \text{No}|\text{Exercise} = \text{No}, \text{Diet} = \text{Healthy})$$
$$= 1 - P(\text{Heart Disease} = \text{Yes}|\text{Exercise} = \text{No}, \text{Diet} = \text{Healthy})$$
$$= 1 - 0.55 = 0.45.$$

Model Building

Model building in Bayesian networks involves two steps: (1) creating the structure of the network, and (2) estimating the probability values in the tables associated with each node. The network topology can be obtained by encoding the subjective knowledge of domain experts. Algorithm 5.3 presents a systematic procedure for inducing the topology of a Bayesian network.

Algorithm 5.3 Algorithm for generating the topology of a Bayesian network.

1: Let $T = (X_1, X_2, \ldots, X_d)$ denote a total order of the variables.
2: **for** $j = 1$ to d **do**
3:     Let $X_{T(j)}$ denote the jth highest order variable in T.
4:     Let $\pi(X_{T(j)}) = \{X_{T(1)}, X_{T(2)}, \ldots, X_{T(j-1)}\}$ denote the set of variables preceding $X_{T(j)}$.
5:     Remove the variables from $\pi(X_{T(j)})$ that do not affect X_j (using prior knowledge).
6:     Create an arc between $X_{T(j)}$ and the remaining variables in $\pi(X_{T(j)})$.
7: **end for**

Example 5.4. Consider the variables shown in Figure 5.13. After performing Step 1, let us assume that the variables are ordered in the following way: (E, D, HD, Hb, CP, BP). From Steps 2 to 7, starting with variable D, we obtain the following conditional probabilities:

- $P(D|E)$ is simplified to $P(D)$.

- $P(HD|E, D)$ cannot be simplified.

- $P(Hb|HD, E, D)$ is simplified to $P(Hb|D)$.

- $P(CP|Hb, HD, E, D)$ is simplified to $P(CP|Hb, HD)$.

- $P(BP|CP, Hb, HD, E, D)$ is simplified to $P(BP|HD)$.

Based on these conditional probabilities, we can create arcs between the nodes (E, HD), (D, HD), (D, Hb), (HD, CP), (Hb, CP), and (HD, BP). These arcs result in the network structure shown in Figure 5.13. ∎

Algorithm 5.3 guarantees a topology that does not contain any cycles. The proof for this is quite straightforward. If a cycle exists, then there must be at least one arc connecting the lower-ordered nodes to the higher-ordered nodes, and at least another arc connecting the higher-ordered nodes to the lower-ordered nodes. Since Algorithm 5.3 prevents any arc from connecting the lower-ordered nodes to the higher-ordered nodes, there cannot be any cycles in the topology.

Nevertheless, the network topology may change if we apply a different ordering scheme to the variables. Some topology may be inferior because it produces many arcs connecting between different pairs of nodes. In principle, we may have to examine all $d!$ possible orderings to determine the most appropriate topology, a task that can be computationally expensive. An alternative approach is to divide the variables into causal and effect variables, and then draw the arcs from each causal variable to its corresponding effect variables. This approach eases the task of building the Bayesian network structure.

Once the right topology has been found, the probability table associated with each node is determined. Estimating such probabilities is fairly straightforward and is similar to the approach used by naïve Bayes classifiers.

Example of Inferencing Using BBN

Suppose we are interested in using the BBN shown in Figure 5.13 to diagnose whether a person has heart disease. The following cases illustrate how the diagnosis can be made under different scenarios.

Case 1: No Prior Information

Without any prior information, we can determine whether the person is likely to have heart disease by computing the prior probabilities $P(\text{HD} = \text{Yes})$ and $P(\text{HD} = \text{No})$. To simplify the notation, let $\alpha \in \{\text{Yes}, \text{No}\}$ denote the binary values of Exercise and $\beta \in \{\text{Healthy}, \text{Unhealthy}\}$ denote the binary values of Diet.

$$
\begin{aligned}
P(\text{HD} = \text{Yes}) &= \sum_{\alpha} \sum_{\beta} P(\text{HD} = \text{Yes}|E = \alpha, D = \beta) P(E = \alpha, D = \beta) \\
&= \sum_{\alpha} \sum_{\beta} P(\text{HD} = \text{Yes}|E = \alpha, D = \beta) P(E = \alpha) P(D = \beta) \\
&= 0.25 \times 0.7 \times 0.25 + 0.45 \times 0.7 \times 0.75 + 0.55 \times 0.3 \times 0.25 \\
&\quad + 0.75 \times 0.3 \times 0.75 \\
&= 0.49.
\end{aligned}
$$

Since $P(\text{HD} = \text{no}) = 1 - P(\text{HD} = \text{yes}) = 0.51$, the person has a slightly higher chance of not getting the disease.

Case 2: High Blood Pressure

If the person has high blood pressure, we can make a diagnosis about heart disease by comparing the posterior probabilities, $P(\text{HD} = \text{Yes}|\text{BP} = \text{High})$ against $P(\text{HD} = \text{No}|\text{BP} = \text{High})$. To do this, we must compute $P(\text{BP} = \text{High})$:

$$P(\text{BP} = \text{High}) = \sum_{\gamma} P(\text{BP} = \text{High}|\text{HD} = \gamma)P(\text{HD} = \gamma)$$

$$= 0.85 \times 0.49 + 0.2 \times 0.51 = 0.5185.$$

where $\gamma \in \{\text{Yes}, \text{No}\}$. Therefore, the posterior probability the person has heart disease is

$$P(\text{HD} = \text{Yes}|\text{BP} = \text{High}) = \frac{P(\text{BP} = \text{High}|\text{HD} = \text{Yes})P(\text{HD} = \text{Yes})}{P(\text{BP} = \text{High})}$$

$$= \frac{0.85 \times 0.49}{0.5185} = 0.8033.$$

Similarly, $P(\text{HD} = \text{No}|\text{BP} = \text{High}) = 1 - 0.8033 = 0.1967$. Therefore, when a person has high blood pressure, it increases the risk of heart disease.

Case 3: High Blood Pressure, Healthy Diet, and Regular Exercise

Suppose we are told that the person exercises regularly and eats a healthy diet. How does the new information affect our diagnosis? With the new information, the posterior probability that the person has heart disease is

$$P(\text{HD} = \text{Yes}|\text{BP} = \text{High}, D = \text{Healthy}, E = \text{Yes})$$

$$= \left[\frac{P(\text{BP} = \text{High}|\text{HD} = \text{Yes}, D = \text{Healthy}, E = \text{Yes})}{P(\text{BP} = \text{High}|D = \text{Healthy}, E = \text{Yes})}\right]$$

$$\times P(\text{HD} = \text{Yes}|D = \text{Healthy}, E = \text{Yes})$$

$$= \frac{P(\text{BP} = \text{High}|\text{HD} = \text{Yes})P(\text{HD} = \text{Yes}|D = \text{Healthy}, E = \text{Yes})}{\sum_{\gamma} P(\text{BP} = \text{High}|\text{HD} = \gamma)P(\text{HD} = \gamma|D = \text{Healthy}, E = \text{Yes})}$$

$$= \frac{0.85 \times 0.25}{0.85 \times 0.25 + 0.2 \times 0.75}$$

$$= 0.5862,$$

while the probability that the person does not have heart disease is

$$P(\text{HD} = \text{No}|\text{BP} = \text{High}, D = \text{Healthy}, E = \text{Yes}) = 1 - 0.5862 = 0.4138.$$

The model therefore suggests that eating healthily and exercising regularly may reduce a person's risk of getting heart disease.

Characteristics of BBN

Following are some of the general characteristics of the BBN method:

1. BBN provides an approach for capturing the prior knowledge of a particular domain using a graphical model. The network can also be used to encode causal dependencies among variables.

2. Constructing the network can be time consuming and requires a large amount of effort. However, once the structure of the network has been determined, adding a new variable is quite straightforward.

3. Bayesian networks are well suited to dealing with incomplete data. Instances with missing attributes can be handled by summing or integrating the probabilities over all possible values of the attribute.

4. Because the data is combined probabilistically with prior knowledge, the method is quite robust to model overfitting.

5.4   Artificial Neural Network (ANN)

The study of artificial neural networks (ANN) was inspired by attempts to simulate biological neural systems. The human brain consists primarily of nerve cells called **neurons**, linked together with other neurons via strands of fiber called **axons**. Axons are used to transmit nerve impulses from one neuron to another whenever the neurons are stimulated. A neuron is connected to the axons of other neurons via **dendrites**, which are extensions from the cell body of the neuron. The contact point between a dendrite and an axon is called a **synapse**. Neurologists have discovered that the human brain learns by changing the strength of the synaptic connection between neurons upon repeated stimulation by the same impulse.

Analogous to human brain structure, an ANN is composed of an interconnected assembly of nodes and directed links. In this section, we will examine a family of ANN models, starting with the simplest model called **perceptron**, and show how the models can be trained to solve classification problems.

5.4.1 Perceptron

Consider the diagram shown in Figure 5.14. The table on the left shows a data set containing three boolean variables (x_1, x_2, x_3) and an output variable, y, that takes on the value -1 if at least two of the three inputs are zero, and $+1$ if at least two of the inputs are greater than zero.

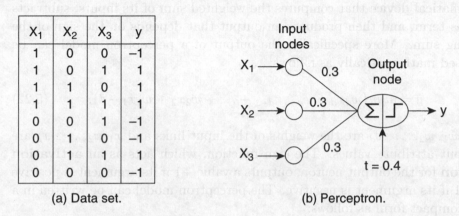

X_1	X_2	X_3	y
1	0	0	-1
1	0	1	1
1	1	0	1
1	1	1	1
0	0	1	-1
0	1	0	-1
0	1	1	1
0	0	0	-1

(a) Data set.

(b) Perceptron.

Figure 5.14. Modeling a boolean function using a perceptron.

Figure 5.14(b) illustrates a simple neural network architecture known as a perceptron. The perceptron consists of two types of nodes: input nodes, which are used to represent the input attributes, and an output node, which is used to represent the model output. The nodes in a neural network architecture are commonly known as neurons or units. In a perceptron, each input node is connected via a weighted link to the output node. The weighted link is used to emulate the strength of synaptic connection between neurons. As in biological neural systems, training a perceptron model amounts to adapting the weights of the links until they fit the input-output relationships of the underlying data.

A perceptron computes its output value, $\hat{y}$, by performing a weighted sum on its inputs, subtracting a bias factor t from the sum, and then examining the sign of the result. The model shown in Figure 5.14(b) has three input nodes, each of which has an identical weight of 0.3 to the output node and a bias factor of $t = 0.4$. The output computed by the model is

$$\hat{y} = \begin{cases} 1, & \text{if } 0.3x_1 + 0.3x_2 + 0.3x_3 - 0.4 > 0; \\ -1, & \text{if } 0.3x_1 + 0.3x_2 + 0.3x_3 - 0.4 < 0. \end{cases} \quad (5.21)$$

For example, if $x_1 = 1, x_2 = 1, x_3 = 0$, then $\hat{y} = +1$ because $0.3x_1 + 0.3x_2 + 0.3x_3 - 0.4$ is positive. On the other hand, if $x_1 = 0, x_2 = 1, x_3 = 0$, then $\hat{y} = -1$ because the weighted sum subtracted by the bias factor is negative.

Note the difference between the input and output nodes of a perceptron. An input node simply transmits the value it receives to the outgoing link without performing any transformation. The output node, on the other hand, is a mathematical device that computes the weighted sum of its inputs, subtracts the bias term, and then produces an output that depends on the sign of the resulting sum. More specifically, the output of a perceptron model can be expressed mathematically as follows:

$$\hat{y} = sign(w_d x_d + w_{d-1} x_{d-1} + \ldots + w_2 x_2 + w_1 x_1 - t), \qquad (5.22)$$

where $w_1, w_2, \ldots, w_d$ are the weights of the input links and $x_1, x_2, \ldots, x_d$ are the input attribute values. The sign function, which acts as an **activation function** for the output neuron, outputs a value $+1$ if its argument is positive and -1 if its argument is negative. The perceptron model can be written in a more compact form as follows:

$$\hat{y} = sign[w_d x_d + w_{d-1} x_{d-1} + \ldots + w_1 x_1 + w_0 x_0] = sign(\mathbf{w} \cdot \mathbf{x}), \qquad (5.23)$$

where $w_0 = -t$, $x_0 = 1$, and $\mathbf{w} \cdot \mathbf{x}$ is the dot product between the weight vector $\mathbf{w}$ and the input attribute vector $\mathbf{x}$.

Learning Perceptron Model

During the training phase of a perceptron model, the weight parameters $\mathbf{w}$ are adjusted until the outputs of the perceptron become consistent with the true outputs of training examples. A summary of the perceptron learning algorithm is given in Algorithm 5.4.

The key computation for this algorithm is the weight update formula given in Step 7 of the algorithm:

$$w_j^{(k+1)} = w_j^{(k)} + \lambda \left(y_i - \hat{y}_i^{(k)} \right) x_{ij}, \qquad (5.24)$$

where $w^{(k)}$ is the weight parameter associated with the ith input link after the kth iteration, λ is a parameter known as the **learning rate**, and x_{ij} is the value of the jth attribute of the training example $\mathbf{x}_i$. The justification for the weight update formula is rather intuitive. Equation 5.24 shows that the new weight $w^{(k+1)}$ is a combination of the old weight $w^{(k)}$ and a term proportional

---

Algorithm 5.4 Perceptron learning algorithm.

1: Let $D = \{(\mathbf{x}_i, y_i) \mid i = 1, 2, \ldots, N\}$ be the set of training examples.
2: Initialize the weight vector with random values, $\mathbf{w}^{(0)}$
3: **repeat**
4:    **for** each training example $(\mathbf{x}_i, y_i) \in D$ **do**
5:      Compute the predicted output $\hat{y}_i^{(k)}$
6:      **for** each weight w_j **do**
7:         Update the weight, $w_j^{(k+1)} = w_j^{(k)} + \lambda\big(y_i - \hat{y}_i^{(k)}\big)x_{ij}$.
8:      **end for**
9:    **end for**
10: **until** stopping condition is met

---

to the prediction error, $(y - \hat{y})$. If the prediction is correct, then the weight remains unchanged. Otherwise, it is modified in the following ways:

- If $y = +1$ and $\hat{y} = -1$, then the prediction error is $(y - \hat{y}) = 2$. To compensate for the error, we need to increase the value of the predicted output by increasing the weights of all links with positive inputs and decreasing the weights of all links with negative inputs.

- If $y_i = -1$ and $\hat{y} = +1$, then $(y - \hat{y}) = -2$. To compensate for the error, we need to decrease the value of the predicted output by decreasing the weights of all links with positive inputs and increasing the weights of all links with negative inputs.

In the weight update formula, links that contribute the most to the error term are the ones that require the largest adjustment. However, the weights should not be changed too drastically because the error term is computed only for the current training example. Otherwise, the adjustments made in earlier iterations will be undone. The learning rate λ, a parameter whose value is between 0 and 1, can be used to control the amount of adjustments made in each iteration. If λ is close to 0, then the new weight is mostly influenced by the value of the old weight. On the other hand, if λ is close to 1, then the new weight is sensitive to the amount of adjustment performed in the current iteration. In some cases, an adaptive λ value can be used; initially, λ is moderately large during the first few iterations and then gradually decreases in subsequent iterations.

The perceptron model shown in Equation 5.23 is linear in its parameters $\mathbf{w}$ and attributes $\mathbf{x}$. Because of this, the decision boundary of a perceptron, which is obtained by setting $\hat{y} = 0$, is a linear hyperplane that separates the data into two classes, -1 and $+1$. Figure 5.15 shows the decision boundary

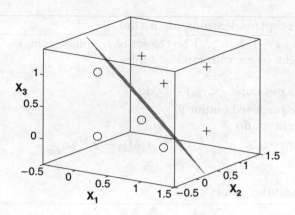

Figure 5.15. Perceptron decision boundary for the data given in Figure 5.14.

obtained by applying the perceptron learning algorithm to the data set given in Figure 5.14. The perceptron learning algorithm is guaranteed to converge to an optimal solution (as long as the learning rate is sufficiently small) for linearly separable classification problems. If the problem is not linearly separable, the algorithm fails to converge. Figure 5.16 shows an example of nonlinearly separable data given by the XOR function. Perceptron cannot find the right solution for this data because there is no linear hyperplane that can perfectly separate the training instances.

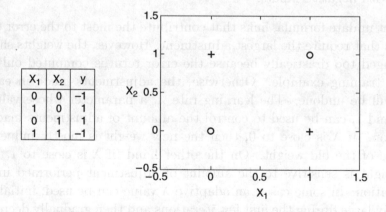

X_1	X_2	y
0	0	−1
1	0	1
0	1	1
1	1	−1

Figure 5.16. XOR classification problem. No linear hyperplane can separate the two classes.

5.4.2 Multilayer Artificial Neural Network

An artificial neural network has a more complex structure than that of a perceptron model. The additional complexities may arise in a number of ways:

1. The network may contain several intermediary layers between its input and output layers. Such intermediary layers are called **hidden layers** and the nodes embedded in these layers are called **hidden nodes**. The resulting structure is known as a multilayer neural network (see Figure 5.17). In a **feed-forward** neural network, the nodes in one layer

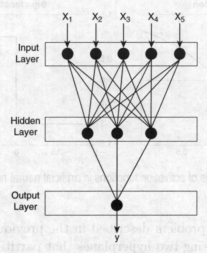

Figure 5.17. Example of a multilayer feed-forward artificial neural network (ANN).

are connected only to the nodes in the next layer. The perceptron is a single-layer, feed-forward neural network because it has only one layer of nodes—the output layer—that performs complex mathematical operations. In a **recurrent** neural network, the links may connect nodes within the same layer or nodes from one layer to the previous layers.

2. The network may use types of activation functions other than the sign function. Examples of other activation functions include linear, sigmoid (logistic), and hyperbolic tangent functions, as shown in Figure 5.18. These activation functions allow the hidden and output nodes to produce output values that are nonlinear in their input parameters.

These additional complexities allow multilayer neural networks to model more complex relationships between the input and output variables. For ex-

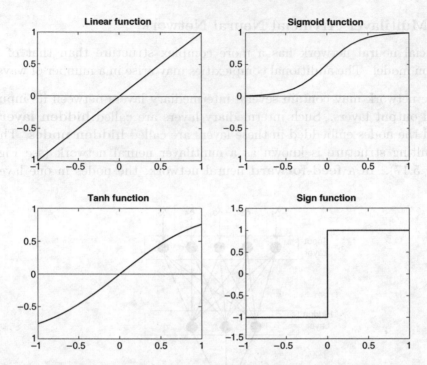

Figure 5.18. Types of activation functions in artificial neural networks.

ample, consider the XOR problem described in the previous section. The instances can be classified using two hyperplanes that partition the input space into their respective classes, as shown in Figure 5.19(a). Because a perceptron can create only one hyperplane, it cannot find the optimal solution. This problem can be addressed using a two-layer, feed-forward neural network, as shown in Figure 5.19(b). Intuitively, we can think of each hidden node as a perceptron that tries to construct one of the two hyperplanes, while the output node simply combines the results of the perceptrons to yield the decision boundary shown in Figure 5.19(a).

To learn the weights of an ANN model, we need an efficient algorithm that converges to the right solution when a sufficient amount of training data is provided. One approach is to treat each hidden node or output node in the network as an independent perceptron unit and to apply the same weight update formula as Equation 5.24. Obviously, this approach will not work because we lack *a priori* knowledge about the true outputs of the hidden nodes. This makes it difficult to determine the error term, $(y - \hat{y})$, associated

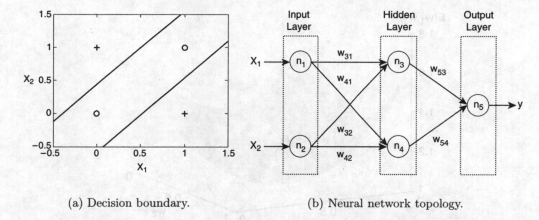

(a) Decision boundary.   (b) Neural network topology.

Figure 5.19. A two-layer, feed-forward neural network for the XOR problem.

with each hidden node. A methodology for learning the weights of a neural network based on the gradient descent approach is presented next.

Learning the ANN Model

The goal of the ANN learning algorithm is to determine a set of weights $\mathbf{w}$ that minimize the total sum of squared errors:

$$E(\mathbf{w}) = \frac{1}{2} \sum_{i=1}^{N} (y_i - \hat{y}_i)^2. \tag{5.25}$$

Note that the sum of squared errors depends on $\mathbf{w}$ because the predicted class $\hat{y}$ is a function of the weights assigned to the hidden and output nodes. Figure 5.20 shows an example of the error surface as a function of its two parameters, w_1 and w_2. This type of error surface is typically encountered when $\hat{y}_i$ is a linear function of its parameters, $\mathbf{w}$. If we replace $\hat{y} = \mathbf{w} \cdot \mathbf{x}$ into Equation 5.25, then the error function becomes quadratic in its parameters and a global minimum solution can be easily found.

In most cases, the output of an ANN is a nonlinear function of its parameters because of the choice of its activation functions (e.g., sigmoid or tanh function). As a result, it is no longer straightforward to derive a solution for $\mathbf{w}$ that is guaranteed to be globally optimal. Greedy algorithms such as those based on the gradient descent method have been developed to efficiently solve the optimization problem. The weight update formula used by the gradient

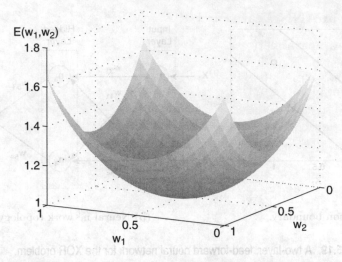

Figure 5.20. Error surface $E(w_1, w_2)$ for a two-parameter model.

descent method can be written as follows:

$$w_j \longleftarrow w_j - \lambda \frac{\partial E(\mathbf{w})}{\partial w_j}, \qquad (5.26)$$

where λ is the learning rate. The second term states that the weight should be increased in a direction that reduces the overall error term. However, because the error function is nonlinear, it is possible that the gradient descent method may get trapped in a local minimum.

The gradient descent method can be used to learn the weights of the output and hidden nodes of a neural network. For hidden nodes, the computation is not trivial because it is difficult to assess their error term, $\partial E / \partial w_j$, without knowing what their output values should be. A technique known as **back-propagation** has been developed to address this problem. There are two phases in each iteration of the algorithm: the forward phase and the backward phase. During the forward phase, the weights obtained from the previous iteration are used to compute the output value of each neuron in the network. The computation progresses in the forward direction; i.e., outputs of the neurons at level k are computed prior to computing the outputs at level $k + 1$. During the backward phase, the weight update formula is applied in the reverse direction. In other words, the weights at level $k + 1$ are updated before the weights at level k are updated. This back-propagation approach allows us to use the errors for neurons at layer $k + 1$ to estimate the errors for neurons at layer k.

Design Issues in ANN Learning

Before we train a neural network to learn a classification task, the following design issues must be considered.

1. The number of nodes in the input layer should be determined. Assign an input node to each numerical or binary input variable. If the input variable is categorical, we could either create one node for each categorical value or encode the k-ary variable using $\lceil \log_2 k \rceil$ input nodes.

2. The number of nodes in the output layer should be established. For a two-class problem, it is sufficient to use a single output node. For a k-class problem, there are k output nodes.

3. The network topology (e.g., the number of hidden layers and hidden nodes, and feed-forward or recurrent network architecture) must be selected. Note that the target function representation depends on the weights of the links, the number of hidden nodes and hidden layers, biases in the nodes, and type of activation function. Finding the right topology is not an easy task. One way to do this is to start from a fully connected network with a sufficiently large number of nodes and hidden layers, and then repeat the model-building procedure with a smaller number of nodes. This approach can be very time consuming. Alternatively, instead of repeating the model-building procedure, we could remove some of the nodes and repeat the model evaluation procedure to select the right model complexity.

4. The weights and biases need to be initialized. Random assignments are usually acceptable.

5. Training examples with missing values should be removed or replaced with most likely values.

5.4.3   Characteristics of ANN

Following is a summary of the general characteristics of an artificial neural network:

1. Multilayer neural networks with at least one hidden layer are **universal approximators**; i.e., they can be used to approximate any target functions. Since an ANN has a very expressive hypothesis space, it is important to choose the appropriate network topology for a given problem to avoid model overfitting.

2. ANN can handle redundant features because the weights are automatically learned during the training step. The weights for redundant features tend to be very small.

3. Neural networks are quite sensitive to the presence of noise in the training data. One approach to handling noise is to use a validation set to determine the generalization error of the model. Another approach is to decrease the weight by some factor at each iteration.

4. The gradient descent method used for learning the weights of an ANN often converges to some local minimum. One way to escape from the local minimum is to add a momentum term to the weight update formula.

5. Training an ANN is a time consuming process, especially when the number of hidden nodes is large. Nevertheless, test examples can be classified rapidly.

5.5   Support Vector Machine (SVM)

A classification technique that has received considerable attention is support vector machine (SVM). This technique has its roots in statistical learning theory and has shown promising empirical results in many practical applications, from handwritten digit recognition to text categorization. SVM also works very well with high-dimensional data and avoids the curse of dimensionality problem. Another unique aspect of this approach is that it represents the decision boundary using a subset of the training examples, known as the **support vectors**.

To illustrate the basic idea behind SVM, we first introduce the concept of a **maximal margin hyperplane** and explain the rationale of choosing such a hyperplane. We then describe how a linear SVM can be trained to explicitly look for this type of hyperplane in linearly separable data. We conclude by showing how the SVM methodology can be extended to non-linearly separable data.

5.5.1   Maximum Margin Hyperplanes

Figure 5.21 shows a plot of a data set containing examples that belong to two different classes, represented as squares and circles. The data set is also linearly separable; i.e., we can find a hyperplane such that all the squares reside on one side of the hyperplane and all the circles reside on the other

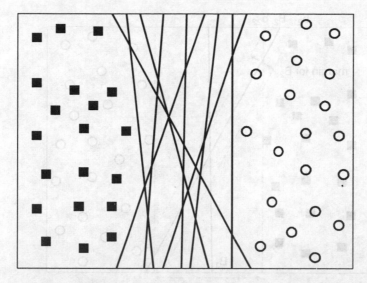

Figure 5.21. Possible decision boundaries for a linearly separable data set.

side. However, as shown in Figure 5.21, there are infinitely many such hyper-planes possible. Although their training errors are zero, there is no guarantee that the hyperplanes will perform equally well on previously unseen examples. The classifier must choose one of these hyperplanes to represent its decision boundary, based on how well they are expected to perform on test examples.

To get a clearer picture of how the different choices of hyperplanes affect the generalization errors, consider the two decision boundaries, B_1 and B_2, shown in Figure 5.22. Both decision boundaries can separate the training examples into their respective classes without committing any misclassification errors. Each decision boundary B_i is associated with a pair of hyperplanes, denoted as b_{i1} and b_{i2}, respectively. b_{i1} is obtained by moving a parallel hyperplane away from the decision boundary until it touches the closest square(s), whereas b_{i2} is obtained by moving the hyperplane until it touches the closest circle(s). The distance between these two hyperplanes is known as the margin of the classifier. From the diagram shown in Figure 5.22, notice that the margin for B_1 is considerably larger than that for B_2. In this example, B_1 turns out to be the maximum margin hyperplane of the training instances.

Rationale for Maximum Margin

Decision boundaries with large margins tend to have better generalization errors than those with small margins. Intuitively, if the margin is small, then

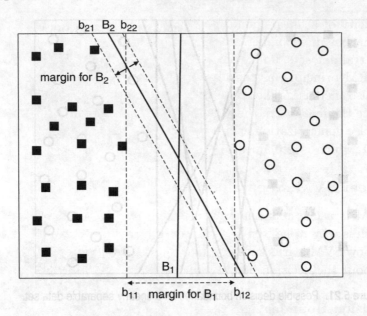

Figure 5.22. Margin of a decision boundary.

any slight perturbations to the decision boundary can have quite a significant impact on its classification. Classifiers that produce decision boundaries with small margins are therefore more susceptible to model overfitting and tend to generalize poorly on previously unseen examples.

A more formal explanation relating the margin of a linear classifier to its generalization error is given by a statistical learning principle known as **structural risk minimization** (SRM). This principle provides an upper bound to the generalization error of a classifier (R) in terms of its training error (R_e), the number of training examples (N), and the model complexity, otherwise known as its **capacity** (h). More specifically, with a probability of $1 - \eta$, the generalization error of the classifier can be at worst

$$R \le R_e + \varphi\left(\frac{h}{N}, \frac{\log(\eta)}{N}\right), \tag{5.27}$$

where φ is a monotone increasing function of the capacity h. The preceding inequality may seem quite familiar to the readers because it resembles the equation given in Section 4.4.4 (on page 179) for the minimum description length (MDL) principle. In this regard, SRM is another way to express generalization error as a tradeoff between training error and model complexity.

The capacity of a linear model is inversely related to its margin. Models with small margins have higher capacities because they are more flexible and can fit many training sets, unlike models with large margins. However, according to the SRM principle, as the capacity increases, the generalization error bound will also increase. Therefore, it is desirable to design linear classifiers that maximize the margins of their decision boundaries in order to ensure that their worst-case generalization errors are minimized. One such classifier is the **linear SVM**, which is explained in the next section.

5.5.2   Linear SVM: Separable Case

A linear SVM is a classifier that searches for a hyperplane with the largest margin, which is why it is often known as a **maximal margin classifier**. To understand how SVM learns such a boundary, we begin with some preliminary discussion about the decision boundary and margin of a linear classifier.

Linear Decision Boundary

Consider a binary classification problem consisting of N training examples. Each example is denoted by a tuple $(\mathbf{x_i}, y_i)$ $(i = 1, 2, \ldots, N)$, where $\mathbf{x}_i = (x_{i1}, x_{i2}, \ldots, x_{id})^T$ corresponds to the attribute set for the ith example. By convention, let $y_i \in \{-1, 1\}$ denote its class label. The decision boundary of a linear classifier can be written in the following form:

$$\mathbf{w} \cdot \mathbf{x} + b = 0, \tag{5.28}$$

where $\mathbf{w}$ and b are parameters of the model.

Figure 5.23 shows a two-dimensional training set consisting of squares and circles. A decision boundary that bisects the training examples into their respective classes is illustrated with a solid line. Any example located along the decision boundary must satisfy Equation 5.28. For example, if $\mathbf{x}_a$ and $\mathbf{x}_b$ are two points located on the decision boundary, then

$$\mathbf{w} \cdot \mathbf{x}_a + b = 0,$$
$$\mathbf{w} \cdot \mathbf{x}_b + b = 0.$$

Subtracting the two equations will yield the following:

$$\mathbf{w} \cdot (\mathbf{x}_b - \mathbf{x}_a) = 0,$$

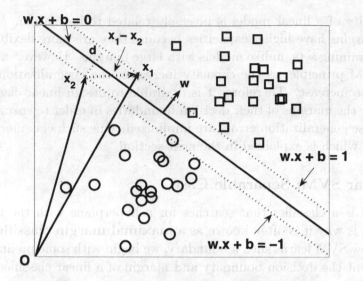

Figure 5.23. Decision boundary and margin of SVM.

where $\mathbf{x}_b - \mathbf{x}_a$ is a vector parallel to the decision boundary and is directed from $\mathbf{x}_a$ to $\mathbf{x}_b$. Since the dot product is zero, the direction for $\mathbf{w}$ must be perpendicular to the decision boundary, as shown in Figure 5.23.

For any square $\mathbf{x}_s$ located above the decision boundary, we can show that

$$\mathbf{w} \cdot \mathbf{x}_s + b = k, \qquad (5.29)$$

where $k > 0$. Similarly, for any circle $\mathbf{x}_c$ located below the decision boundary, we can show that

$$\mathbf{w} \cdot \mathbf{x}_c + b = k', \qquad (5.30)$$

where $k' < 0$. If we label all the squares as class $+1$ and all the circles as class -1, then we can predict the class label y for any test example $\mathbf{z}$ in the following way:

$$y = \begin{cases} 1, & \text{if } \mathbf{w} \cdot \mathbf{z} + b > 0; \\ -1, & \text{if } \mathbf{w} \cdot \mathbf{z} + b < 0. \end{cases} \qquad (5.31)$$

Margin of a Linear Classifier

Consider the square and the circle that are closest to the decision boundary. Since the square is located above the decision boundary, it must satisfy Equation 5.29 for some positive value k, whereas the circle must satisfy Equation

5.30 for some negative value k'. We can rescale the parameters $\mathbf{w}$ and b of the decision boundary so that the two parallel hyperplanes b_{i1} and b_{i2} can be expressed as follows:

$$b_{i1}:\ \mathbf{w}\cdot\mathbf{x}+b=1, \tag{5.32}$$

$$b_{i2}:\ \mathbf{w}\cdot\mathbf{x}+b=-1. \tag{5.33}$$

The margin of the decision boundary is given by the distance between these two hyperplanes. To compute the margin, let $\mathbf{x}_1$ be a data point located on b_{i1} and $\mathbf{x}_2$ be a data point on b_{i2}, as shown in Figure 5.23. Upon substituting these points into Equations 5.32 and 5.33, the margin d can be computed by subtracting the second equation from the first equation:

$$\mathbf{w}\cdot(\mathbf{x}_1-\mathbf{x}_2)=2$$
$$\|\mathbf{w}\|\times d=2$$
$$\therefore d=\frac{2}{\|\mathbf{w}\|}. \tag{5.34}$$

Learning a Linear SVM Model

The training phase of SVM involves estimating the parameters $\mathbf{w}$ and b of the decision boundary from the training data. The parameters must be chosen in such a way that the following two conditions are met:

$$\mathbf{w}\cdot\mathbf{x_i}+b\geq\ 1\ \text{if}\ y_i=1,$$
$$\mathbf{w}\cdot\mathbf{x_i}+b\leq-1\ \text{if}\ y_i=-1. \tag{5.35}$$

These conditions impose the requirements that all training instances from class $y=1$ (i.e., the squares) must be located on or above the hyperplane $\mathbf{w}\cdot\mathbf{x}+b=1$, while those instances from class $y=-1$ (i.e., the circles) must be located on or below the hyperplane $\mathbf{w}\cdot\mathbf{x}+b=-1$. Both inequalities can be summarized in a more compact form as follows:

$$y_i(\mathbf{w}\cdot\mathbf{x_i}+b)\geq1,\quad i=1,2,\ldots,N. \tag{5.36}$$

Although the preceding conditions are also applicable to any linear classifiers (including perceptrons), SVM imposes an additional requirement that the margin of its decision boundary must be maximal. Maximizing the margin, however, is equivalent to minimizing the following objective function:

$$f(\mathbf{w})=\frac{\|\mathbf{w}\|^2}{2}. \tag{5.37}$$

Definition 5.1 (Linear SVM: Separable Case). The learning task in SVM can be formalized as the following constrained optimization problem:

$$\min_{\mathbf{w}} \frac{\|\mathbf{w}\|^2}{2}$$

$$\text{subject to} \quad y_i(\mathbf{w} \cdot \mathbf{x_i} + b) \geq 1, \quad i = 1, 2, \ldots, N.$$

Since the objective function is quadratic and the constraints are linear in the parameters $\mathbf{w}$ and b, this is known as a **convex** optimization problem, which can be solved using the standard **Lagrange multiplier** method. Following is a brief sketch of the main ideas for solving the optimization problem. A more detailed discussion is given in Appendix E.

First, we must rewrite the objective function in a form that takes into account the constraints imposed on its solutions. The new objective function is known as the Lagrangian for the optimization problem:

$$L_P = \frac{1}{2}\|\mathbf{w}\|^2 - \sum_{i=1}^{N} \lambda_i \left(y_i(\mathbf{w} \cdot \mathbf{x_i} + b) - 1 \right), \quad (5.38)$$

where the parameters λ_i are called the Lagrange multipliers. The first term in the Lagrangian is the same as the original objective function, while the second term captures the inequality constraints. To understand why the objective function must be modified, consider the original objective function given in Equation 5.37. It is easy to show that the function is minimized when $\mathbf{w} = \mathbf{0}$, a null vector whose components are all zeros. Such a solution, however, violates the constraints given in Definition 5.1 because there is no feasible solution for b. The solutions for $\mathbf{w}$ and b are infeasible if they violate the inequality constraints; i.e., if $y_i(\mathbf{w} \cdot \mathbf{x_i} + b) - 1 < 0$. The Lagrangian given in Equation 5.38 incorporates this constraint by subtracting the term from its original objective function. Assuming that $\lambda_i \geq 0$, it is clear that any infeasible solution may only increase the value of the Lagrangian.

To minimize the Lagrangian, we must take the derivative of L_P with respect to $\mathbf{w}$ and b and set them to zero:

$$\frac{\partial L_p}{\partial \mathbf{w}} = 0 \implies \mathbf{w} = \sum_{i=1}^{N} \lambda_i y_i \mathbf{x}_i, \quad (5.39)$$

$$\frac{\partial L_p}{\partial b} = 0 \implies \sum_{i=1}^{N} \lambda_i y_i = 0. \quad (5.40)$$

Because the Lagrange multipliers are unknown, we still cannot solve for $\mathbf{w}$ and b. If Definition 5.1 contains only equality instead of inequality constraints, then we can use the N equations from equality constraints along with Equations 5.39 and 5.40 to find the feasible solutions for $\mathbf{w}$, b, and λ_i. Note that the Lagrange multipliers for equality constraints are free parameters that can take any values.

One way to handle the inequality constraints is to transform them into a set of equality constraints. This is possible as long as the Lagrange multipliers are restricted to be non-negative. Such transformation leads to the following constraints on the Lagrange multipliers, which are known as the Karush-Kuhn-Tucker (KKT) conditions:

$$\lambda_i \geq 0, \tag{5.41}$$

$$\lambda_i \big[y_i(\mathbf{w} \cdot \mathbf{x}_i + b) - 1 \big] = 0. \tag{5.42}$$

At first glance, it may seem that there are as many Lagrange multipliers as there are training instances. It turns out that many of the Lagrange multipliers become zero after applying the constraint given in Equation 5.42. The constraint states that the Lagrange multiplier λ_i must be zero unless the training instance $\mathbf{x}_i$ satisfies the equation $y_i(\mathbf{w} \cdot \mathbf{x}_i + b) = 1$. Such training instance, with $\lambda_i > 0$, lies along the hyperplanes b_{i1} or b_{i2} and is known as a support vector. Training instances that do not reside along these hyperplanes have $\lambda_i = 0$. Equations 5.39 and 5.42 also suggest that the parameters $\mathbf{w}$ and b, which define the decision boundary, depend only on the support vectors.

Solving the preceding optimization problem is still quite a daunting task because it involves a large number of parameters: $\mathbf{w}$, b, and λ_i. The problem can be simplified by transforming the Lagrangian into a function of the Lagrange multipliers only (this is known as the dual problem). To do this, we first substitute Equations 5.39 and 5.40 into Equation 5.38. This will lead to the following dual formulation of the optimization problem:

$$L_D = \sum_{i=1}^{N} \lambda_i - \frac{1}{2} \sum_{i,j} \lambda_i \lambda_j y_i y_j \mathbf{x_i} \cdot \mathbf{x_j}. \tag{5.43}$$

The key differences between the dual and primary Lagrangians are as follows:

1. The dual Lagrangian involves only the Lagrange multipliers and the training data, while the primary Lagrangian involves the Lagrange multipliers as well as parameters of the decision boundary. Nevertheless, the solutions for both optimization problems are equivalent.

2. The quadratic term in Equation 5.43 has a negative sign, which means that the original minimization problem involving the primary Lagrangian, L_P, has turned into a maximization problem involving the dual Lagrangian, L_D.

For large data sets, the dual optimization problem can be solved using numerical techniques such as quadratic programming, a topic that is beyond the scope of this book. Once the λ_i's are found, we can use Equations 5.39 and 5.42 to obtain the feasible solutions for $\mathbf{w}$ and b. The decision boundary can be expressed as follows:

$$\left(\sum_{i=1}^{N} \lambda_i y_i \mathbf{x_i} \cdot \mathbf{x} \right) + b = 0. \tag{5.44}$$

b is obtained by solving Equation 5.42 for the support vectors. Because the λ_i's are calculated numerically and can have numerical errors, the value computed for b may not be unique. Instead it depends on the support vector used in Equation 5.42. In practice, the average value for b is chosen to be the parameter of the decision boundary.

Example 5.5. Consider the two-dimensional data set shown in Figure 5.24, which contains eight training instances. Using quadratic programming, we can solve the optimization problem stated in Equation 5.43 to obtain the Lagrange multiplier λ_i for each training instance. The Lagrange multipliers are depicted in the last column of the table. Notice that only the first two instances have non-zero Lagrange multipliers. These instances correspond to the support vectors for this data set.

Let $\mathbf{w} = (w_1, w_2)$ and b denote the parameters of the decision boundary. Using Equation 5.39, we can solve for w_1 and w_2 in the following way:

$$w_1 = \sum_i \lambda_i y_i x_{i1} = 65.5621 \times 1 \times 0.3858 + 65.5621 \times -1 \times 0.4871 = -6.64.$$

$$w_2 = \sum_i \lambda_i y_i x_{i2} = 65.5621 \times 1 \times 0.4687 + 65.5621 \times -1 \times 0.611 = -9.32.$$

The bias term b can be computed using Equation 5.42 for each support vector:

$$b^{(1)} = 1 - \mathbf{w} \cdot \mathbf{x_1} = 1 - (-6.64)(0.3858) - (-9.32)(0.4687) = 7.9300.$$
$$b^{(2)} = -1 - \mathbf{w} \cdot \mathbf{x_2} = -1 - (-6.64)(0.4871) - (-9.32)(0.611) = 7.9289.$$

Averaging these values, we obtain $b = 7.93$. The decision boundary corresponding to these parameters is shown in Figure 5.24. ∎

x_1	x_2	y	Lagrange Multiplier
0.3858	0.4687	1	65.5261
0.4871	0.611	−1	65.5261
0.9218	0.4103	−1	0
0.7382	0.8936	−1	0
0.1763	0.0579	1	0
0.4057	0.3529	1	0
0.9355	0.8132	−1	0
0.2146	0.0099	1	0

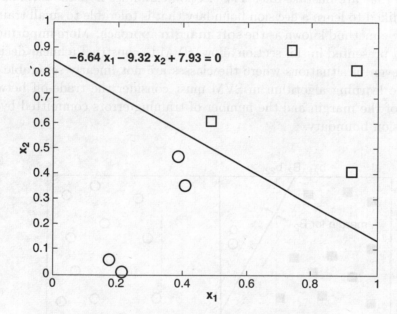

Figure 5.24. Example of a linearly separable data set.

Once the parameters of the decision boundary are found, a test instance $\mathbf{z}$ is classified as follows:

$$f(\mathbf{z}) = sign(\mathbf{w} \cdot \mathbf{z} + b) = sign\left(\sum_{i=1}^{N} \lambda_i y_i \mathbf{x_i} \cdot \mathbf{z} + b\right).$$

If $f(\mathbf{z}) = 1$, then the test instance is classified as a positive class; otherwise, it is classified as a negative class.

5.5.3   Linear SVM: Nonseparable Case

Figure 5.25 shows a data set that is similar to Figure 5.22, except it has two new examples, P and Q. Although the decision boundary B_1 misclassifies the new examples, while B_2 classifies them correctly, this does not mean that B_2 is a better decision boundary than B_1 because the new examples may correspond to noise in the training data. B_1 should still be preferred over B_2 because it has a wider margin, and thus, is less susceptible to overfitting. However, the SVM formulation presented in the previous section constructs only decision boundaries that are mistake-free. This section examines how the formulation can be modified to learn a decision boundary that is tolerable to small training errors using a method known as the **soft margin** approach. More importantly, the method presented in this section allows SVM to construct a linear decision boundary even in situations where the classes are not linearly separable. To do this, the learning algorithm in SVM must consider the trade-off between the width of the margin and the number of training errors committed by the linear decision boundary.

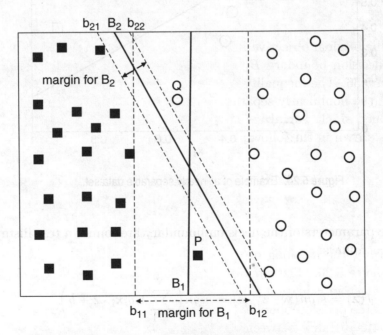

Figure 5.25. Decision boundary of SVM for the nonseparable case.

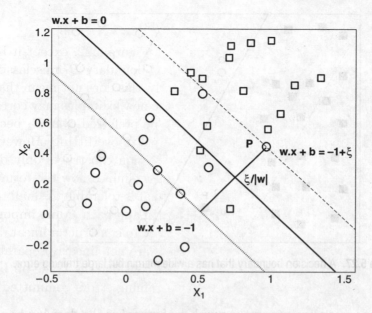

Figure 5.26. Slack variables for nonseparable data.

While the original objective function given in Equation 5.37 is still applicable, the decision boundary B_1 no longer satisfies all the constraints given in Equation 5.36. The inequality constraints must therefore be relaxed to accommodate the nonlinearly separable data. This can be done by introducing positive-valued **slack variables** (ξ) into the constraints of the optimization problem, as shown in the following equations:

$$\mathbf{w} \cdot \mathbf{x_i} + b \geq 1 - \xi_i \text{ if } y_i = 1,$$
$$\mathbf{w} \cdot \mathbf{x_i} + b \leq -1 + \xi_i \text{ if } y_i = -1, \tag{5.45}$$

where $\forall i : \xi_i > 0$.

To interpret the meaning of the slack variables ξ_i, consider the diagram shown in Figure 5.26. The circle **P** is one of the instances that violates the constraints given in Equation 5.35. Let $\mathbf{w} \cdot \mathbf{x} + b = -1 + \xi$ denote a line that is parallel to the decision boundary and passes through the point **P**. It can be shown that the distance between this line and the hyperplane $\mathbf{w} \cdot \mathbf{x} + b = -1$ is $\xi/\|\mathbf{w}\|$. Thus, ξ provides an estimate of the error of the decision boundary on the training example **P**.

In principle, we can apply the same objective function as before and impose the conditions given in Equation 5.45 to find the decision boundary. However,

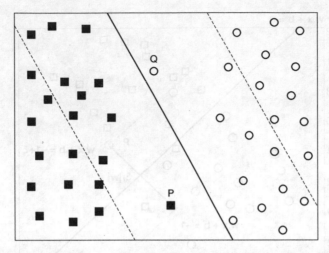

Figure 5.27. A decision boundary that has a wide margin but large training error.

since there are no constraints on the number of mistakes the decision boundary can make, the learning algorithm may find a decision boundary with a very wide margin but misclassifies many of the training examples, as shown in Figure 5.27. To avoid this problem, the objective function must be modified to penalize a decision boundary with large values of slack variables. The modified objective function is given by the following equation:

$$f(\mathbf{w}) = \frac{\|\mathbf{w}\|^2}{2} + C\left(\sum_{i=1}^{N} \xi_i\right)^k,$$

where C and k are user-specified parameters representing the penalty of misclassifying the training instances. For the remainder of this section, we assume $k = 1$ to simplify the problem. The parameter C can be chosen based on the model's performance on the validation set.

It follows that the Lagrangian for this constrained optimization problem can be written as follows:

$$L_P = \frac{1}{2}\|\mathbf{w}\|^2 + C\sum_{i=1}^{N} \xi_i - \sum_{i=1}^{N} \lambda_i\{y_i(\mathbf{w} \cdot \mathbf{x_i} + b) - 1 + \xi_i\} - \sum_{i=1}^{N} \mu_i\xi_i, \quad (5.46)$$

where the first two terms are the objective function to be minimized, the third term represents the inequality constraints associated with the slack variables, and the last term is the result of the non-negativity requirements on the values of ξ_i's. Furthermore, the inequality constraints can be transformed into equality constraints using the following KKT conditions:

$$\xi_i \geq 0, \quad \lambda_i \geq 0, \quad \mu_i \geq 0, \tag{5.47}$$

$$\lambda_i\{y_i(\mathbf{w} \cdot \mathbf{x}_i + b) - 1 + \xi_i\} = 0, \tag{5.48}$$

$$\mu_i \xi_i = 0. \tag{5.49}$$

Note that the Lagrange multiplier λ_i given in Equation 5.48 is non-vanishing only if the training instance resides along the lines $\mathbf{w} \cdot \mathbf{x}_i + b = \pm 1$ or has $\xi_i > 0$. On the other hand, the Lagrange multipliers μ_i given in Equation 5.49 are zero for any training instances that are misclassified (i.e., having $\xi_i > 0$).

Setting the first-order derivative of L with respect to $\mathbf{w}$, b, and ξ_i to zero would result in the following equations:

$$\frac{\partial L}{\partial w_j} = w_j - \sum_{i=1}^{N} \lambda_i y_i x_{ij} = 0 \implies w_j = \sum_{i=1}^{N} \lambda_i y_i x_{ij}. \tag{5.50}$$

$$\frac{\partial L}{\partial b} = -\sum_{i=1}^{N} \lambda_i y_i = 0 \implies \sum_{i=1}^{N} \lambda_i y_i = 0. \tag{5.51}$$

$$\frac{\partial L}{\partial \xi_i} = C - \lambda_i - \mu_i = 0 \implies \lambda_i + \mu_i = C. \tag{5.52}$$

Substituting Equations 5.50, 5.51, and 5.52 into the Lagrangian will produce the following dual Lagrangian:

$$\begin{aligned}
L_D &= \frac{1}{2} \sum_{i,j} \lambda_i \lambda_j y_i y_j \mathbf{x}_i \cdot \mathbf{x}_j + C \sum_i \xi_i \\
&\quad - \sum_i \lambda_i \{y_i(\sum_j \lambda_j y_j \mathbf{x}_i \cdot \mathbf{x}_j + b) - 1 + \xi_i\} \\
&\quad - \sum_i (C - \lambda_i)\xi_i \\
&= \sum_{i=1}^{N} \lambda_i - \frac{1}{2} \sum_{i,j} \lambda_i \lambda_j y_i y_j \mathbf{x_i} \cdot \mathbf{x_j},
\end{aligned} \tag{5.53}$$

which turns out to be identical to the dual Lagrangian for linearly separable data (see Equation 5.40 on page 262). Nevertheless, the constraints imposed on the Lagrange multipliers λ_i's are slightly different those in the linearly separable case. In the linearly separable case, the Lagrange multipliers must be non-negative, i.e., $\lambda_i \geq 0$. On the other hand, Equation 5.52 suggests that λ_i should not exceed C (since both μ_i and λ_i are non-negative). Therefore, the Lagrange multipliers for nonlinearly separable data are restricted to $0 \leq \lambda_i \leq C$.

The dual problem can then be solved numerically using quadratic programming techniques to obtain the Lagrange multipliers λ_i. These multipliers can be replaced into Equation 5.50 and the KKT conditions to obtain the parameters of the decision boundary.

5.5.4 Nonlinear SVM

The SVM formulations described in the previous sections construct a linear decision boundary to separate the training examples into their respective classes. This section presents a methodology for applying SVM to data sets that have nonlinear decision boundaries. The trick here is to transform the data from its original coordinate space in $\mathbf{x}$ into a new space $\Phi(\mathbf{x})$ so that a linear decision boundary can be used to separate the instances in the transformed space. After doing the transformation, we can apply the methodology presented in the previous sections to find a linear decision boundary in the transformed space.

Attribute Transformation

To illustrate how attribute transformation can lead to a linear decision boundary, Figure 5.28(a) shows an example of a two-dimensional data set consisting of squares (classified as $y = 1$) and circles (classified as $y = -1$). The data set is generated in such a way that all the circles are clustered near the center of the diagram and all the squares are distributed farther away from the center. Instances of the data set can be classified using the following equation:

$$y(x_1, x_2) = \begin{cases} 1 & \text{if } \sqrt{(x_1 - 0.5)^2 + (x_2 - 0.5)^2} > 0.2, \\ -1 & \text{otherwise.} \end{cases} \quad (5.54)$$

The decision boundary for the data can therefore be written as follows:

$$\sqrt{(x_1 - 0.5)^2 + (x_2 - 0.5)^2} = 0.2,$$

which can be further simplified into the following quadratic equation:

$$x_1^2 - x_1 + x_2^2 - x_2 = -0.46.$$

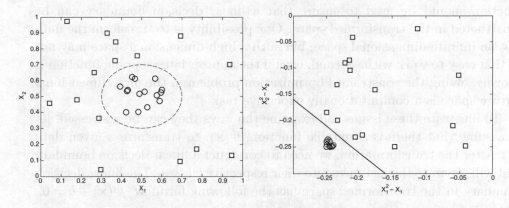

(a) Decision boundary in the original two-dimensional space.

(b) Decision boundary in the transformed space.

Figure 5.28. Classifying data with a nonlinear decision boundary.

A nonlinear transformation Φ is needed to map the data from its original feature space into a new space where the decision boundary becomes linear. Suppose we choose the following transformation:

$$\Phi : (x_1, x_2) \longrightarrow (x_1^2, x_2^2, \sqrt{2}x_1, \sqrt{2}x_2, 1). \tag{5.55}$$

In the transformed space, we can find the parameters $\mathbf{w} = (w_0, w_1, ..., w_4)$ such that:

$$w_4 x_1^2 + w_3 x_2^2 + w_2 \sqrt{2}x_1 + w_1 \sqrt{2}x_2 + w_0 = 0.$$

For illustration purposes, let us plot the graph of $x_2^2 - x_2$ versus $x_1^2 - x_1$ for the previously given instances. Figure 5.28(b) shows that in the transformed space, all the circles are located in the lower right-hand side of the diagram. A linear decision boundary can therefore be constructed to separate the instances into their respective classes.

One potential problem with this approach is that it may suffer from the curse of dimensionality problem often associated with high-dimensional data. We will show how nonlinear SVM avoids this problem (using a method known as the kernel trick) later in this section.

Learning a Nonlinear SVM Model

Although the attribute transformation approach seems promising, it raises several implementation issues. First, it is not clear what type of mapping function should be used to ensure that a linear decision boundary can be constructed in the transformed space. One possibility is to transform the data into an infinite dimensional space, but such a high-dimensional space may not be that easy to work with. Second, even if the appropriate mapping function is known, solving the constrained optimization problem in the high-dimensional feature space is a computationally expensive task.

To illustrate these issues and examine the ways they can be addressed, let us assume that there is a suitable function, $\Phi(\mathbf{x})$, to transform a given data set. After the transformation, we need to construct a linear decision boundary that will separate the instances into their respective classes. The linear decision boundary in the transformed space has the following form: $\mathbf{w} \cdot \Phi(\mathbf{x}) + b = 0$.

Definition 5.2 (Nonlinear SVM). The learning task for a nonlinear SVM can be formalized as the following optimization problem:

$$\min_{\mathbf{w}} \frac{\|\mathbf{w}\|^2}{2}$$

$$\text{subject to} \qquad y_i(\mathbf{w} \cdot \Phi(\mathbf{x}_i) + b) \geq 1, \quad i = 1, 2, \ldots, N.$$

Note the similarity between the learning task of a nonlinear SVM to that of a linear SVM (see Definition 5.1 on page 262). The main difference is that, instead of using the original attributes $\mathbf{x}$, the learning task is performed on the transformed attributes $\Phi(\mathbf{x})$. Following the approach taken in Sections 5.5.2 and 5.5.3 for linear SVM, we may derive the following dual Lagrangian for the constrained optimization problem:

$$L_D = \sum_{i=1}^{n} \lambda_i - \frac{1}{2} \sum_{i,j} \lambda_i \lambda_j y_i y_j \Phi(\mathbf{x}_i) \cdot \Phi(\mathbf{x}_j) \tag{5.56}$$

Once the λ_i's are found using quadratic programming techniques, the parameters $\mathbf{w}$ and b can be derived using the following equations:

$$\mathbf{w} = \sum_{i} \lambda_i y_i \Phi(\mathbf{x}_i) \tag{5.57}$$

$$\lambda_i \{ y_i (\sum_{j} \lambda_j y_j \Phi(\mathbf{x}_j) \cdot \Phi(\mathbf{x}_i) + b) - 1 \} = 0, \tag{5.58}$$

which are analogous to Equations 5.39 and 5.40 for linear SVM. Finally, a test instance z can be classified using the following equation:

$$f(\mathbf{z}) = sign(\mathbf{w} \cdot \Phi(\mathbf{z}) + b) = sign\left(\sum_{i=1}^{n} \lambda_i y_i \Phi(\mathbf{x}_i) \cdot \Phi(\mathbf{z}) + b \right). \tag{5.59}$$

Except for Equation 5.57, note that the rest of the computations (Equations 5.58 and 5.59) involve calculating the dot product (i.e., similarity) between pairs of vectors in the transformed space, $\Phi(\mathbf{x}_i) \cdot \Phi(\mathbf{x}_j)$. Such computation can be quite cumbersome and may suffer from the curse of dimensionality problem. A breakthrough solution to this problem comes in the form of a method known as the **kernel trick**.

Kernel Trick

The dot product is often regarded as a measure of similarity between two input vectors. For example, the cosine similarity described in Section 2.4.5 on page 73 can be defined as the dot product between two vectors that are normalized to unit length. Analogously, the dot product $\Phi(\mathbf{x}_i) \cdot \Phi(\mathbf{x}_j)$ can also be regarded as a measure of similarity between two instances, $\mathbf{x}_i$ and $\mathbf{x}_j$, in the transformed space.

The kernel trick is a method for computing similarity in the transformed space using the original attribute set. Consider the mapping function Φ given in Equation 5.55. The dot product between two input vectors $\mathbf{u}$ and $\mathbf{v}$ in the transformed space can be written as follows:

$$\begin{aligned} \Phi(\mathbf{u}) \cdot \Phi(\mathbf{v}) &= (u_1^2, u_2^2, \sqrt{2}u_1, \sqrt{2}u_2, 1) \cdot (v_1^2, v_2^2, \sqrt{2}v_1, \sqrt{2}v_2, 1) \\ &= u_1^2 v_1^2 + u_2^2 v_2^2 + 2u_1 v_1 + 2u_2 v_2 + 1 \\ &= (\mathbf{u} \cdot \mathbf{v} + 1)^2. \end{aligned} \tag{5.60}$$

This analysis shows that the dot product in the transformed space can be expressed in terms of a similarity function in the original space:

$$K(\mathbf{u}, \mathbf{v}) = \Phi(\mathbf{u}) \cdot \Phi(\mathbf{v}) = (\mathbf{u} \cdot \mathbf{v} + 1)^2. \tag{5.61}$$

The similarity function, K, which is computed in the original attribute space, is known as the **kernel function**. The kernel trick helps to address some of the concerns about how to implement nonlinear SVM. First, we do not have to know the exact form of the mapping function Φ because the kernel functions used in nonlinear SVM must satisfy a mathematical principle known as **Mercer's theorem**. This principle ensures that the kernel functions can always be expressed as the dot product between two input vectors in some high-dimensional space. The transformed space of the SVM kernels is called a **reproducing kernel Hilbert space** (RKHS). Second, computing the dot products using kernel functions is considerably cheaper than using the transformed attribute set $\Phi(\mathbf{x})$. Third, since the computations are performed in the original space, issues associated with the curse of dimensionality problem can be avoided.

Figure 5.29 shows the nonlinear decision boundary obtained by SVM using the polynomial kernel function given in Equation 5.61. A test instance $\mathbf{x}$ is classified according to the following equation:

$$
\begin{aligned}
f(\mathbf{z}) &= sign(\sum_{i=1}^{n} \lambda_i y_i \Phi(\mathbf{x}_i) \cdot \Phi(\mathbf{z}) + b) \\
&= sign(\sum_{i=1}^{n} \lambda_i y_i K(\mathbf{x}_i, \mathbf{z}) + b) \\
&= sign(\sum_{i=1}^{n} \lambda_i y_i (\mathbf{x}_i \cdot \mathbf{z} + 1)^2 + b),
\end{aligned}
\tag{5.62}
$$

where b is the parameter obtained using Equation 5.58. The decision boundary obtained by nonlinear SVM is quite close to the true decision boundary shown in Figure 5.28(a).

Mercer's Theorem

The main requirement for the kernel function used in nonlinear SVM is that there must exist a corresponding transformation such that the kernel function computed for a pair of vectors is equivalent to the dot product between the vectors in the transformed space. This requirement can be formally stated in the form of Mercer's theorem.

Theorem 5.1 (Mercer's Theorem). *A kernel function K can be expressed as*

$$
K(\boldsymbol{u}, \boldsymbol{v}) = \Phi(\boldsymbol{u}) \cdot \Phi(\boldsymbol{v})
$$

if and only if, for any function $g(x)$ such that $\int g(\boldsymbol{x})^2 d\boldsymbol{x}$ is finite, then

$$
\int K(\boldsymbol{x}, \boldsymbol{y}) \, g(\boldsymbol{x}) \, g(\boldsymbol{y}) \, d\boldsymbol{x} \, d\boldsymbol{y} \geq 0.
$$

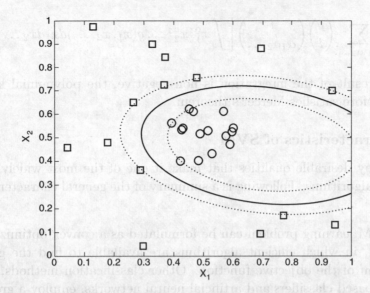

Figure 5.29. Decision boundary produced by a nonlinear SVM with polynomial kernel.

Kernel functions that satisfy Theorem 5.1 are called positive definite kernel functions. Examples of such functions are listed below:

$$K(\mathbf{x}, \mathbf{y}) = (\mathbf{x} \cdot \mathbf{y} + 1)^p \qquad (5.63)$$

$$K(\mathbf{x}, \mathbf{y}) = e^{-\|\mathbf{x}-\mathbf{y}\|^2/(2\sigma^2)} \qquad (5.64)$$

$$K(\mathbf{x}, \mathbf{y}) = \tanh(k\mathbf{x} \cdot \mathbf{y} - \delta) \qquad (5.65)$$

Example 5.6. Consider the polynomial kernel function given in Equation 5.63. Let $g(x)$ be a function that has a finite L_2 norm, i.e., $\int g(\mathbf{x})^2 d\mathbf{x} < \infty$.

$$\int (\mathbf{x} \cdot \mathbf{y} + 1)^p g(\mathbf{x}) g(\mathbf{y}) d\mathbf{x} d\mathbf{y}$$

$$= \int \sum_{i=0}^{p} \binom{p}{i} (\mathbf{x} \cdot \mathbf{y})^i g(\mathbf{x}) g(\mathbf{y}) d\mathbf{x} d\mathbf{y}$$

$$= \sum_{i=0}^{p} \binom{p}{i} \int \sum_{\alpha_1, \alpha_2, \ldots} \binom{i}{\alpha_1 \alpha_2 \ldots} \left[(x_1 y_1)^{\alpha_1} (x_2 y_2)^{\alpha_2} (x_3 y_3)^{\alpha_3} \ldots \right]$$

$$g(x_1, x_2, \ldots) \ g(y_1, y_2, \ldots) dx_1 dx_2 \ldots dy_1 dy_2 \ldots$$

$$= \sum_{i=0}^{p} \sum_{\alpha_1, \alpha_2, \ldots} \binom{p}{i} \binom{i}{\alpha_1 \alpha_2 \ldots} \left[\int x_1^{\alpha_1} x_2^{\alpha_2} \ldots g(x_1, x_2, \ldots) dx_1 dx_2 \ldots \right]^2.$$

Because the result of the integration is non-negative, the polynomial kernel function therefore satisfies Mercer's theorem. ∎

5.5.5   Characteristics of SVM

SVM has many desirable qualities that make it one of the most widely used classification algorithms. Following is a summary of the general characteristics of SVM:

1. The SVM learning problem can be formulated as a convex optimization problem, in which efficient algorithms are available to find the global minimum of the objective function. Other classification methods, such as rule-based classifiers and artificial neural networks, employ a greedy-based strategy to search the hypothesis space. Such methods tend to find only locally optimum solutions.

2. SVM performs capacity control by maximizing the margin of the decision boundary. Nevertheless, the user must still provide other parameters such as the type of kernel function to use and the cost function C for introducing each slack variable.

3. SVM can be applied to categorical data by introducing dummy variables for each categorical attribute value present in the data. For example, if `Marital Status` has three values {`Single`, `Married`, `Divorced`}, we can introduce a binary variable for each of the attribute values.

4. The SVM formulation presented in this chapter is for binary class problems. Some of the methods available to extend SVM to multiclass problems are presented in Section 5.8.

5.6   Ensemble Methods

The classification techniques we have seen so far in this chapter, with the exception of the nearest-neighbor method, predict the class labels of unknown examples using a single classifier induced from training data. This section presents techniques for improving classification accuracy by aggregating the predictions of multiple classifiers. These techniques are known as the **ensemble** or **classifier combination** methods. An ensemble method constructs a set of **base classifiers** from training data and performs classification by taking a vote on the predictions made by each base classifier. This section explains why ensemble methods tend to perform better than any single classifier and presents techniques for constructing the classifier ensemble.

5.6.1 Rationale for Ensemble Method

The following example illustrates how an ensemble method can improve a classifier's performance.

Example 5.7. Consider an ensemble of twenty-five binary classifiers, each of which has an error rate of $\epsilon = 0.35$. The ensemble classifier predicts the class label of a test example by taking a majority vote on the predictions made by the base classifiers. If the base classifiers are identical, then the ensemble will misclassify the same examples predicted incorrectly by the base classifiers. Thus, the error rate of the ensemble remains 0.35. On the other hand, if the base classifiers are independent—i.e., their errors are uncorrelated—then the ensemble makes a wrong prediction only if more than half of the base classifiers predict incorrectly. In this case, the error rate of the ensemble classifier is

$$e_{\text{ensemble}} = \sum_{i=13}^{25} \binom{25}{i} \epsilon^i (1-\epsilon)^{25-i} = 0.06, \qquad (5.66)$$

which is considerably lower than the error rate of the base classifiers. ∎

Figure 5.30 shows the error rate of an ensemble of twenty-five binary classifiers (e_{ensemble}) for different base classifier error rates (ϵ). The diagonal line represents the case in which the base classifiers are identical, while the solid line represents the case in which the base classifiers are independent. Observe that the ensemble classifier performs worse than the base classifiers when ϵ is larger than 0.5.

The preceding example illustrates two necessary conditions for an ensemble classifier to perform better than a single classifier: (1) the base classifiers should be independent of each other, and (2) the base classifiers should do better than a classifier that performs random guessing. In practice, it is difficult to ensure total independence among the base classifiers. Nevertheless, improvements in classification accuracies have been observed in ensemble methods in which the base classifiers are slightly correlated.

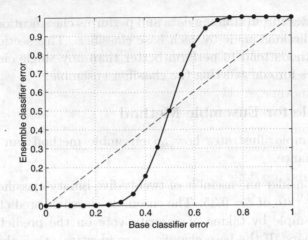

Figure 5.30. Comparison between errors of base classifiers and errors of the ensemble classifier.

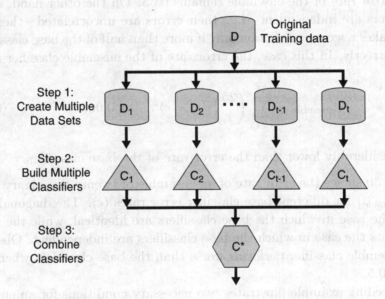

Figure 5.31. A logical view of the ensemble learning method.

5.6.2 Methods for Constructing an Ensemble Classifier

A logical view of the ensemble method is presented in Figure 5.31. The basic idea is to construct multiple classifiers from the original data and then aggregate their predictions when classifying unknown examples. The ensemble of classifiers can be constructed in many ways:

1. **By manipulating the training set.** In this approach, multiple training sets are created by resampling the original data according to some sampling distribution. The sampling distribution determines how likely it is that an example will be selected for training, and it may vary from one trial to another. A classifier is then built from each training set using a particular learning algorithm. **Bagging** and **boosting** are two examples of ensemble methods that manipulate their training sets. These methods are described in further detail in Sections 5.6.4 and 5.6.5.

2. **By manipulating the input features.** In this approach, a subset of input features is chosen to form each training set. The subset can be either chosen randomly or based on the recommendation of domain experts. Some studies have shown that this approach works very well with data sets that contain highly redundant features. **Random forest**, which is described in Section 5.6.6, is an ensemble method that manipulates its input features and uses decision trees as its base classifiers.

3. **By manipulating the class labels.** This method can be used when the number of classes is sufficiently large. The training data is transformed into a binary class problem by randomly partitioning the class labels into two disjoint subsets, A_0 and A_1. Training examples whose class label belongs to the subset A_0 are assigned to class 0, while those that belong to the subset A_1 are assigned to class 1. The relabeled examples are then used to train a base classifier. By repeating the class-relabeling and model-building steps multiple times, an ensemble of base classifiers is obtained. When a test example is presented, each base classifier C_i is used to predict its class label. If the test example is predicted as class 0, then all the classes that belong to A_0 will receive a vote. Conversely, if it is predicted to be class 1, then all the classes that belong to A_1 will receive a vote. The votes are tallied and the class that receives the highest vote is assigned to the test example. An example of this approach is the **error-correcting output coding** method described on page 307.

4. **By manipulating the learning algorithm.** Many learning algorithms can be manipulated in such a way that applying the algorithm several times on the same training data may result in different models. For example, an artificial neural network can produce different models by changing its network topology or the initial weights of the links between neurons. Similarly, an ensemble of decision trees can be constructed by injecting randomness into the tree-growing procedure. For

example, instead of choosing the best splitting attribute at each node, we can randomly choose one of the top k attributes for splitting.

The first three approaches are generic methods that are applicable to any classifiers, whereas the fourth approach depends on the type of classifier used. The base classifiers for most of these approaches can be generated sequentially (one after another) or in parallel (all at once). Algorithm 5.5 shows the steps needed to build an ensemble classifier in a sequential manner. The first step is to create a training set from the original data D. Depending on the type of ensemble method used, the training sets are either identical to or slight modifications of D. The size of the training set is often kept the same as the original data, but the distribution of examples may not be identical; i.e., some examples may appear multiple times in the training set, while others may not appear even once. A base classifier C_i is then constructed from each training set D_i. Ensemble methods work better with **unstable classifiers**, i.e., base classifiers that are sensitive to minor perturbations in the training set. Examples of unstable classifiers include decision trees, rule-based classifiers, and artificial neural networks. As will be discussed in Section 5.6.3, the variability among training examples is one of the primary sources of errors in a classifier. By aggregating the base classifiers built from different training sets, this may help to reduce such types of errors.

Finally, a test example $\mathbf{x}$ is classified by combining the predictions made by the base classifiers $C_i(\mathbf{x})$:

$$C^*(\mathbf{x}) = Vote(C_1(\mathbf{x}), C_2(\mathbf{x}), \ldots, C_k(\mathbf{x})).$$

The class can be obtained by taking a majority vote on the individual predictions or by weighting each prediction with the accuracy of the base classifier.

Algorithm 5.5 General procedure for ensemble method.

1: Let D denote the original training data, k denote the number of base classifiers, and T be the test data.
2: **for** $i = 1$ to k **do**
3:    Create training set, D_i from D.
4:    Build a base classifier C_i from D_i.
5: **end for**
6: **for** each test record $x \in T$ **do**
7:    $C^*(x) = Vote(C_1(\mathbf{x}), C_2(\mathbf{x}), \ldots, C_k(\mathbf{x}))$
8: **end for**

5.6.3 Bias-Variance Decomposition

Bias-variance decomposition is a formal method for analyzing the prediction error of a predictive model. The following example gives an intuitive explanation for this method.

Figure 5.32 shows the trajectories of a projectile launched at a particular angle. Suppose the projectile hits the floor surface at some location x, at a distance d away from the target position t. Depending on the force applied to the projectile, the observed distance may vary from one trial to another. The observed distance can be decomposed into several components. The first component, which is known as **bias**, measures the average distance between the target position and the location where the projectile hits the floor. The amount of bias depends on the angle of the projectile launcher. The second component, which is known as **variance**, measures the deviation between x and the average position $\overline{x}$ where the projectile hits the floor. The variance can be explained as a result of changes in the amount of force applied to the projectile. Finally, if the target is not stationary, then the observed distance is also affected by changes in the location of the target. This is considered the **noise** component associated with variability in the target position. Putting these components together, the average distance can be expressed as:

$$d_{f,\theta}(y,t) \;=\; \text{Bias}_\theta + \text{Variance}_f + \text{Noise}_t, \qquad (5.67)$$

where f refers to the amount of force applied and θ is the angle of the launcher.

The task of predicting the class label of a given example can be analyzed using the same approach. For a given classifier, some predictions may turn out to be correct, while others may be completely off the mark. We can decompose the expected error of a classifier as a sum of the three terms given in Equation 5.67, where expected error is the probability that the classifier misclassifies a

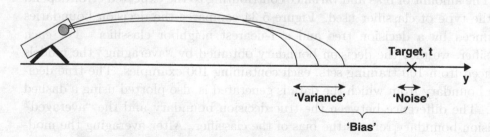

Figure 5.32. Bias-variance decomposition.

given example. The remainder of this section examines the meaning of bias, variance, and noise in the context of classification.

A classifier is usually trained to minimize its training error. However, to be useful, the classifier must be able to make an informed guess about the class labels of examples it has never seen before. This requires the classifier to generalize its decision boundary to regions where there are no training examples available—a decision that depends on the design choice of the classifier. For example, a key design issue in decision tree induction is the amount of pruning needed to obtain a tree with low expected error. Figure 5.33 shows two decision trees, T_1 and T_2, that are generated from the same training data, but have different complexities. T_2 is obtained by pruning T_1 until a tree with maximum depth of two is obtained. T_1, on the other hand, performs very little pruning on its decision tree. These design choices will introduce a bias into the classifier that is analogous to the bias of the projectile launcher described in the previous example. In general, the stronger the assumptions made by a classifier about the nature of its decision boundary, the larger the classifier's bias will be. T_2 therefore has a larger bias because it makes stronger assumptions about its decision boundary (which is reflected by the size of the tree) compared to T_1. Other design choices that may introduce a bias into a classifier include the network topology of an artificial neural network and the number of neighbors considered by a nearest-neighbor classifier.

The expected error of a classifier is also affected by variability in the training data because different compositions of the training set may lead to different decision boundaries. This is analogous to the variance in x when different amounts of force are applied to the projectile. The last component of the expected error is associated with the intrinsic noise in the target class. The target class for some domains can be non-deterministic; i.e., instances with the same attribute values can have different class labels. Such errors are unavoidable even when the true decision boundary is known.

The amount of bias and variance contributing to the expected error depend on the type of classifier used. Figure 5.34 compares the decision boundaries produced by a decision tree and a 1-nearest neighbor classifier. For each classifier, we plot the decision boundary obtained by "averaging" the models induced from 100 training sets, each containing 100 examples. The true decision boundary from which the data is generated is also plotted using a dashed line. The difference between the true decision boundary and the "averaged" decision boundary reflects the bias of the classifier. After averaging the models, observe that the difference between the true decision boundary and the decision boundary produced by the 1-nearest neighbor classifier is smaller than

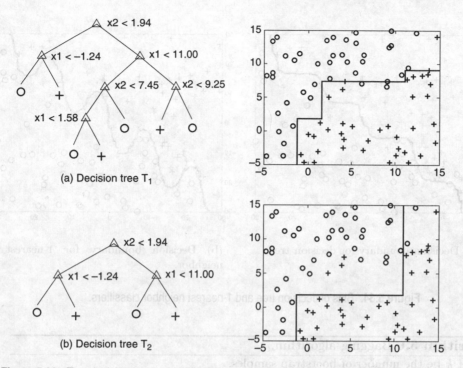

(a) Decision tree T_1

(b) Decision tree T_2

Figure 5.33. Two decision trees with different complexities induced from the same training data.

the observed difference for a decision tree classifier. This result suggests that the bias of a 1-nearest neighbor classifier is lower than the bias of a decision tree classifier.

On the other hand, the 1-nearest neighbor classifier is more sensitive to the composition of its training examples. If we examine the models induced from different training sets, there is more variability in the decision boundary of a 1-nearest neighbor classifier than a decision tree classifier. Therefore, the decision boundary of a decision tree classifier has a lower variance than the 1-nearest neighbor classifier.

5.6.4 Bagging

Bagging, which is also known as bootstrap aggregating, is a technique that repeatedly samples (with replacement) from a data set according to a uniform probability distribution. Each bootstrap sample has the same size as the original data. Because the sampling is done with replacement, some instances may appear several times in the same training set, while others may be omitted from the training set. On average, a bootstrap sample D_i contains approxi-

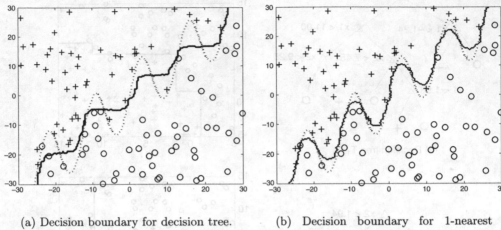

(a) Decision boundary for decision tree.   (b) Decision boundary for 1-nearest neighbor.

Figure 5.34. Bias of decision tree and 1-nearest neighbor classifiers.

Algorithm 5.6 Bagging algorithm.

1: Let k be the number of bootstrap samples.
2: **for** $i = 1$ to k **do**
3:     Create a bootstrap sample of size N, D_i.
4:     Train a base classifier C_i on the bootstrap sample D_i.
5: **end for**
6: $C^*(x) = \underset{y}{\operatorname{argmax}} \sum_i \delta\big(C_i(x) = y\big)$.

    $\{\delta(\cdot) = 1$ if its argument is true and 0 otherwise$\}$.

---

mately 63% of the original training data because each sample has a probability $1 - (1 - 1/N)^N$ of being selected in each D_i. If N is sufficiently large, this probability converges to $1 - 1/e \simeq 0.632$. The basic procedure for bagging is summarized in Algorithm 5.6. After training the k classifiers, a test instance is assigned to the class that receives the highest number of votes.

To illustrate how bagging works, consider the data set shown in Table 5.4. Let x denote a one-dimensional attribute and y denote the class label. Suppose we apply a classifier that induces only one-level binary decision trees, with a test condition $x \leq k$, where k is a split point chosen to minimize the entropy of the leaf nodes. Such a tree is also known as a **decision stump**.

Without bagging, the best decision stump we can produce splits the records at either $x \leq 0.35$ or $x \leq 0.75$. Either way, the accuracy of the tree is at

Table 5.4. Example of data set used to construct an ensemble of bagging classifiers.

x	0.1	0.2	0.3	0.4	0.5	0.6	0.7	0.8	0.9	1
y	1	1	1	−1	−1	−1	−1	1	1	1

most 70%. Suppose we apply the bagging procedure on the data set using ten bootstrap samples. The examples chosen for training in each bagging round are shown in Figure 5.35. On the right-hand side of each table, we also illustrate the decision boundary produced by the classifier.

We classify the entire data set given in Table 5.4 by taking a majority vote among the predictions made by each base classifier. The results of the predictions are shown in Figure 5.36. Since the class labels are either −1 or +1, taking the majority vote is equivalent to summing up the predicted values of y and examining the sign of the resulting sum (refer to the second to last row in Figure 5.36). Notice that the ensemble classifier perfectly classifies all ten examples in the original data.

The preceding example illustrates another advantage of using ensemble methods in terms of enhancing the representation of the target function. Even though each base classifier is a decision stump, combining the classifiers can lead to a decision tree of depth 2.

Bagging improves generalization error by reducing the variance of the base classifiers. The performance of bagging depends on the stability of the base classifier. If a base classifier is unstable, bagging helps to reduce the errors associated with random fluctuations in the training data. If a base classifier is stable, i.e., robust to minor perturbations in the training set, then the error of the ensemble is primarily caused by bias in the base classifier. In this situation, bagging may not be able to improve the performance of the base classifiers significantly. It may even degrade the classifier's performance because the effective size of each training set is about 37% smaller than the original data.

Finally, since every sample has an equal probability of being selected, bagging does not focus on any particular instance of the training data. It is therefore less susceptible to model overfitting when applied to noisy data.

5.6.5 Boosting

Boosting is an iterative procedure used to adaptively change the distribution of training examples so that the base classifiers will focus on examples that are hard to classify. Unlike bagging, boosting assigns a weight to each training

Bagging Round 1:

x	0.1	0.2	0.2	0.3	0.4	0.4	0.5	0.6	0.9	0.9
y	1	1	1	1	-1	-1	-1	-1	1	1

x <= 0.35 ==> y = 1
x > 0.35 ==> y = -1

Bagging Round 2:

x	0.1	0.2	0.3	0.4	0.5	0.8	0.9	1	1	1
y	1	1	1	-1	-1	1	1	1	1	1

x <= 0.65 ==> y = 1
x > 0.65 ==> y = 1

Bagging Round 3:

x	0.1	0.2	0.3	0.4	0.4	0.5	0.7	0.7	0.8	0.9
y	1	1	1	-1	-1	-1	-1	-1	1	1

x <= 0.35 ==> y = 1
x > 0.35 ==> y = -1

Bagging Round 4:

x	0.1	0.1	0.2	0.4	0.4	0.5	0.5	0.7	0.8	0.9
y	1	1	1	-1	-1	-1	-1	-1	1	1

x <= 0.3 ==> y = 1
x > 0.3 ==> y = -1

Bagging Round 5:

x	0.1	0.1	0.2	0.5	0.6	0.6	0.6	1	1	1
y	1	1	1	-1	-1	-1	-1	1	1	1

x <= 0.35 ==> y = 1
x > 0.35 ==> y = -1

Bagging Round 6:

x	0.2	0.4	0.5	0.6	0.7	0.7	0.7	0.8	0.9	1
y	1	-1	-1	-1	-1	-1	-1	1	1	1

x <= 0.75 ==> y = -1
x > 0.75 ==> y = 1

Bagging Round 7:

x	0.1	0.4	0.4	0.6	0.7	0.8	0.9	0.9	0.9	1
y	1	-1	-1	-1	-1	1	1	1	1	1

x <= 0.75 ==> y = -1
x > 0.75 ==> y = 1

Bagging Round 8:

x	0.1	0.2	0.5	0.5	0.5	0.7	0.7	0.8	0.9	1
y	1	1	-1	-1	-1	-1	-1	1	1	1

x <= 0.75 ==> y = -1
x > 0.75 ==> y = 1

Bagging Round 9:

x	0.1	0.3	0.4	0.4	0.6	0.7	0.7	0.8	1	1
y	1	1	-1	-1	-1	-1	-1	1	1	1

x <= 0.75 ==> y = -1
x > 0.75 ==> y = 1

Bagging Round 10:

x	0.1	0.1	0.1	0.1	0.3	0.3	0.8	0.8	0.9	0.9
y	1	1	1	1	1	1	1	1	1	1

x <= 0.05 ==> y = -1
x > 0.05 ==> y = 1

Figure 5.35. Example of bagging.

example and may adaptively change the weight at the end of each boosting round. The weights assigned to the training examples can be used in the following ways:

1. They can be used as a sampling distribution to draw a set of bootstrap samples from the original data.

2. They can be used by the base classifier to learn a model that is biased toward higher-weight examples.

Round	x=0.1	x=0.2	x=0.3	x=0.4	x=0.5	x=0.6	x=0.7	x=0.8	x=0.9	x=1.0
1	1	1	1	-1	-1	-1	-1	-1	-1	-1
2	1	1	1	1	1	1	1	1	1	1
3	1	1	1	-1	-1	-1	-1	-1	-1	-1
4	1	1	1	-1	-1	-1	-1	-1	-1	-1
5	1	1	1	-1	-1	-1	-1	-1	-1	-1
6	-1	-1	-1	-1	-1	-1	-1	1	1	1
7	-1	-1	-1	-1	-1	-1	-1	1	1	1
8	-1	-1	-1	-1	-1	-1	-1	1	1	1
9	-1	-1	-1	-1	-1	-1	-1	1	1	1
10	1	1	1	1	1	1	1	1	1	1
Sum	2	2	2	-6	-6	-6	-6	2	2	2
Sign	1	1	1	-1	-1	-1	-1	1	1	1
True Class	1	1	1	-1	-1	-1	-1	1	1	1

Figure 5.36. Example of combining classifiers constructed using the bagging approach.

This section describes an algorithm that uses weights of examples to determine the sampling distribution of its training set. Initially, the examples are assigned equal weights, $1/N$, so that they are equally likely to be chosen for training. A sample is drawn according to the sampling distribution of the training examples to obtain a new training set. Next, a classifier is induced from the training set and used to classify all the examples in the original data. The weights of the training examples are updated at the end of each boosting round. Examples that are classified incorrectly will have their weights increased, while those that are classified correctly will have their weights decreased. This forces the classifier to focus on examples that are difficult to classify in subsequent iterations.

The following table shows the examples chosen during each boosting round.

Boosting (Round 1):	7	3	2	8	7	9	4	10	6	3
Boosting (Round 2):	5	4	9	4	2	5	1	7	4	2
Boosting (Round 3):	4	4	8	10	4	5	4	6	3	4

Initially, all the examples are assigned the same weights. However, some examples may be chosen more than once, e.g., examples 3 and 7, because the sampling is done with replacement. A classifier built from the data is then used to classify all the examples. Suppose example 4 is difficult to classify. The weight for this example will be increased in future iterations as it gets misclassified repeatedly. Meanwhile, examples that were not chosen in the previous round, e.g., examples 1 and 5, also have a better chance of being selected in the next round since their predictions in the previous round were likely to be wrong. As the boosting rounds proceed, examples that are the hardest to classify tend to become even more prevalent. The final ensemble is obtained by aggregating the base classifiers obtained from each boosting round.

Over the years, several implementations of the boosting algorithm have been developed. These algorithms differ in terms of (1) how the weights of the training examples are updated at the end of each boosting round, and (2) how the predictions made by each classifier are combined. An implementation called AdaBoost is explored in the next section.

AdaBoost

Let $\{(\mathbf{x}_j, y_j) \mid j = 1, 2, \ldots, N\}$ denote a set of N training examples. In the AdaBoost algorithm, the importance of a base classifier C_i depends on its error rate, which is defined as

$$\epsilon_i = \frac{1}{N} \left[\sum_{j=1}^{N} w_j \, I\left(C_i(\mathbf{x}_j) \neq y_j \right) \right], \tag{5.68}$$

where $I(p) = 1$ if the predicate p is true, and 0 otherwise. The importance of a classifier C_i is given by the following parameter,

$$\alpha_i = \frac{1}{2} \ln\left(\frac{1 - \epsilon_i}{\epsilon_i} \right).$$

Note that α_i has a large positive value if the error rate is close to 0 and a large negative value if the error rate is close to 1, as shown in Figure 5.37.

The α_i parameter is also used to update the weight of the training examples. To illustrate, let $w_i^{(j)}$ denote the weight assigned to example $(\mathbf{x}_i, y_i)$ during the jth boosting round. The weight update mechanism for AdaBoost is given by the equation:

$$w_i^{(j+1)} = \frac{w_i^{(j)}}{Z_j} \times \begin{cases} \exp^{-\alpha_j} & \text{if } C_j(\mathbf{x_i}) = y_i \\ \exp^{\alpha_j} & \text{if } C_j(\mathbf{x_i}) \neq y_i \end{cases}, \tag{5.69}$$

where Z_j is the normalization factor used to ensure that $\sum_i w_i^{(j+1)} = 1$. The weight update formula given in Equation 5.69 increases the weights of incorrectly classified examples and decreases the weights of those classified correctly.

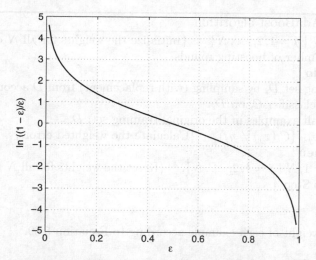

Figure 5.37. Plot of α as a function of training error ϵ.

Instead of using a majority voting scheme, the prediction made by each classifier C_j is weighted according to α_j. This approach allows AdaBoost to penalize models that have poor accuracy, e.g., those generated at the earlier boosting rounds. In addition, if any intermediate rounds produce an error rate higher than 50%, the weights are reverted back to their original uniform values, $w_i = 1/N$, and the resampling procedure is repeated. The AdaBoost algorithm is summarized in Algorithm 5.7.

Let us examine how the boosting approach works on the data set shown in Table 5.4. Initially, all the examples have identical weights. After three boosting rounds, the examples chosen for training are shown in Figure 5.38(a). The weights for each example are updated at the end of each boosting round using Equation 5.69.

Without boosting, the accuracy of the decision stump is, at best, 70%. With AdaBoost, the results of the predictions are given in Figure 5.39(b). The final prediction of the ensemble classifier is obtained by taking a weighted average of the predictions made by each base classifier, which is shown in the last row of Figure 5.39(b). Notice that AdaBoost perfectly classifies all the examples in the training data.

An important analytical result of boosting shows that the training error of the ensemble is bounded by the following expression:

$$e_{\text{ensemble}} \leq \prod_{i} \left[\sqrt{\epsilon_i (1 - \epsilon_i)} \right], \tag{5.70}$$

Algorithm 5.7 AdaBoost algorithm.

1: $\mathbf{w} = \{w_j = 1/N \mid j = 1, 2, \ldots, N\}$.   {Initialize the weights for all N examples.}
2: Let k be the number of boosting rounds.
3: **for** $i = 1$ to k **do**
4:     Create training set D_i by sampling (with replacement) from D according to $\mathbf{w}$.
5:     Train a base classifier C_i on D_i.
6:     Apply C_i to all examples in the original training set, D.
7:     $\epsilon_i = \frac{1}{N}\left[\sum_j w_j \, \delta\big(C_i(x_j) \neq y_j\big)\right]$ {Calculate the weighted error.}
8:     **if** $\epsilon_i > 0.5$ **then**
9:         $\mathbf{w} = \{w_j = 1/N \mid j = 1, 2, \ldots, N\}$.   {Reset the weights for all N examples.}
10:        Go back to Step 4.
11:    **end if**
12:    $\alpha_i = \frac{1}{2}\ln\frac{1-\epsilon_i}{\epsilon_i}$.
13:    Update the weight of each example according to Equation 5.69.
14: **end for**
15: $C^*(\mathbf{x}) = \underset{y}{\operatorname{argmax}} \sum_{j=1}^{T} \alpha_j \delta(C_j(\mathbf{x}) = y)$.

---

where ϵ_i is the error rate of each base classifier i. If the error rate of the base classifier is less than 50%, we can write $\epsilon_i = 0.5 - \gamma_i$, where γ_i measures how much better the classifier is than random guessing. The bound on the training error of the ensemble becomes

$$e_{\text{ensemble}} \leq \prod_i \sqrt{1 - 4\gamma_i^2} \leq \exp\left(-2\sum_i \gamma_i^2\right). \tag{5.71}$$

If $\gamma_i < \gamma*$ for all i's, then the training error of the ensemble decreases exponentially, which leads to the fast convergence of the algorithm. Nevertheless, because of its tendency to focus on training examples that are wrongly classified, the boosting technique can be quite susceptible to overfitting.

5.6.6   Random Forests

Random forest is a class of ensemble methods specifically designed for decision tree classifiers. It combines the predictions made by multiple decision trees, where each tree is generated based on the values of an independent set of random vectors, as shown in Figure 5.40. The random vectors are generated from a fixed probability distribution, unlike the adaptive approach used in AdaBoost, where the probability distribution is varied to focus on examples that are hard to classify. Bagging using decision trees is a special case of random forests, where randomness is injected into the model-building process

Boosting Round 1:

x	0.1	0.4	0.5	0.6	0.6	0.7	0.7	0.7	0.8	1
y	1	-1	-1	-1	-1	-1	-1	-1	1	1

Boosting Round 2:

x	0.1	0.1	0.2	0.2	0.2	0.2	0.3	0.3	0.3	0.3
y	1	1	1	1	1	1	1	1	1	1

Boosting Round 3:

x	0.2	0.2	0.4	0.4	0.4	0.4	0.5	0.6	0.6	0.7
y	1	1	-1	-1	-1	-1	-1	-1	-1	-1

(a) Training records chosen during boosting

Round	x=0.1	x=0.2	x=0.3	x=0.4	x=0.5	x=0.6	x=0.7	x=0.8	x=0.9	x=1.0
1	0.1	0.1	0.1	0.1	0.1	0.1	0.1	0.1	0.1	0.1
2	0.311	0.311	0.311	0.01	0.01	0.01	0.01	0.01	0.01	0.01
3	0.029	0.029	0.029	0.228	0.228	0.228	0.228	0.009	0.009	0.009

(b) Weights of training records

Figure 5.38. Example of boosting.

by randomly choosing N samples, with replacement, from the original training set. Bagging also uses the same uniform probability distribution to generate its bootstrapped samples throughout the entire model-building process.

It was theoretically proven that the upper bound for generalization error of random forests converges to the following expression, when the number of trees is sufficiently large.

$$\text{Generalization error} \leq \frac{\overline{\rho}(1 - s^2)}{s^2}, \qquad (5.72)$$

where $\overline{\rho}$ is the average correlation among the trees and s is a quantity that measures the "strength" of the tree classifiers. The strength of a set of classifiers refers to the average performance of the classifiers, where performance is measured probabilistically in terms of the classifier's margin:

$$\text{margin, } M(\mathbf{X}, Y) = P(\hat{Y}_\theta = Y) - \max_{Z \neq Y} P(\hat{Y}_\theta = Z), \qquad (5.73)$$

where $\hat{Y}_\theta$ is the predicted class of $\mathbf{X}$ according to a classifier built from some random vector θ. The higher the margin is, the more likely it is that the

Round	Split Point	Left Class	Right Class	α
1	0.75	-1	1	1.738
2	0.05	1	1	2.7784
3	0.3	1	-1	4.1195

(a)

Round	x=0.1	x=0.2	x=0.3	x=0.4	x=0.5	x=0.6	x=0.7	x=0.8	x=0.9	x=1.0
1	-1	-1	-1	-1	-1	-1	-1	1	1	1
2	1	1	1	1	1	1	1	1	1	1
3	1	1	1	-1	-1	-1	-1	-1	-1	-1
Sum	5.16	5.16	5.16	-3.08	-3.08	-3.08	-3.08	0.397	0.397	0.397
Sign	1	1	1	-1	-1	-1	-1	1	1	1

(b)

Figure 5.39. Example of combining classifiers constructed using the AdaBoost approach.

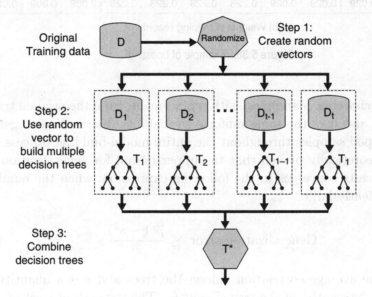

Figure 5.40. Random forests.

classifier correctly predicts a given example **X**. Equation 5.72 is quite intuitive; as the trees become more correlated or the strength of the ensemble decreases, the generalization error bound tends to increase. Randomization helps to reduce the correlation among decision trees so that the generalization error of the ensemble can be improved.

Each decision tree uses a random vector that is generated from some fixed probability distribution. A random vector can be incorporated into the tree-growing process in many ways. The first approach is to randomly select F input features to split at each node of the decision tree. As a result, instead of examining all the available features, the decision to split a node is determined from these selected F features. The tree is then grown to its entirety without any pruning. This may help reduce the bias present in the resulting tree. Once the trees have been constructed, the predictions are combined using a majority voting scheme. This approach is known as Forest-RI, where RI refers to random input selection. To increase randomness, bagging can also be used to generate bootstrap samples for Forest-RI. The strength and correlation of random forests may depend on the size of F. If F is sufficiently small, then the trees tend to become less correlated. On the other hand, the strength of the tree classifier tends to improve with a larger number of features, F. As a tradeoff, the number of features is commonly chosen to be $F = \log_2 d + 1$, where d is the number of input features. Since only a subset of the features needs to be examined at each node, this approach helps to significantly reduce the runtime of the algorithm.

If the number of original features d is too small, then it is difficult to choose an independent set of random features for building the decision trees. One way to increase the feature space is to create linear combinations of the input features. Specifically, at each node, a new feature is generated by randomly selecting L of the input features. The input features are linearly combined using coefficients generated from a uniform distribution in the range of $[-1, 1]$. At each node, F of such randomly combined new features are generated, and the best of them is subsequently selected to split the node. This approach is known as Forest-RC.

A third approach for generating the random trees is to randomly select one of the F best splits at each node of the decision tree. This approach may potentially generate trees that are more correlated than Forest-RI and Forest-RC, unless F is sufficiently large. It also does not have the runtime savings of Forest-RI and Forest-RC because the algorithm must examine all the splitting features at each node of the decision tree.

It has been shown empirically that the classification accuracies of random forests are quite comparable to the AdaBoost algorithm. It is also more robust to noise and runs much faster than the AdaBoost algorithm. The classification accuracies of various ensemble algorithms are compared in the next section.

Table 5.5. Comparing the accuracy of a decision tree classifier against three ensemble methods.

Data Set	Number of (Attributes, Classes, Records)	Decision Tree (%)	Bagging (%)	Boosting (%)	RF (%)
Anneal	(39, 6, 898)	92.09	94.43	95.43	95.43
Australia	(15, 2, 690)	85.51	87.10	85.22	85.80
Auto	(26, 7, 205)	81.95	85.37	85.37	84.39
Breast	(11, 2, 699)	95.14	96.42	97.28	96.14
Cleve	(14, 2, 303)	76.24	81.52	82.18	82.18
Credit	(16, 2, 690)	85.8	86.23	86.09	85.8
Diabetes	(9, 2, 768)	72.40	76.30	73.18	75.13
German	(21, 2, 1000)	70.90	73.40	73.00	74.5
Glass	(10, 7, 214)	67.29	76.17	77.57	78.04
Heart	(14, 2, 270)	80.00	81.48	80.74	83.33
Hepatitis	(20, 2, 155)	81.94	81.29	83.87	83.23
Horse	(23, 2, 368)	85.33	85.87	81.25	85.33
Ionosphere	(35, 2, 351)	89.17	92.02	93.73	93.45
Iris	(5, 3, 150)	94.67	94.67	94.00	93.33
Labor	(17, 2, 57)	78.95	84.21	89.47	84.21
Led7	(8, 10, 3200)	73.34	73.66	73.34	73.06
Lymphography	(19, 4, 148)	77.03	79.05	85.14	82.43
Pima	(9, 2, 768)	74.35	76.69	73.44	77.60
Sonar	(61, 2, 208)	78.85	78.85	84.62	85.58
Tic-tac-toe	(10, 2, 958)	83.72	93.84	98.54	95.82
Vehicle	(19, 4, 846)	71.04	74.11	78.25	74.94
Waveform	(22, 3, 5000)	76.44	83.30	83.90	84.04
Wine	(14, 3, 178)	94.38	96.07	97.75	97.75
Zoo	(17, 7, 101)	93.07	93.07	95.05	97.03

5.6.7   Empirical Comparison among Ensemble Methods

Table 5.5 shows the empirical results obtained when comparing the performance of a decision tree classifier against bagging, boosting, and random forest. The base classifiers used in each ensemble method consist of fifty decision trees. The classification accuracies reported in this table are obtained from ten-fold cross-validation. Notice that the ensemble classifiers generally outperform a single decision tree classifier on many of the data sets.

5.7   Class Imbalance Problem

Data sets with imbalanced class distributions are quite common in many real applications. For example, an automated inspection system that monitors products that come off a manufacturing assembly line may find that the number of defective products is significantly fewer than that of non-defective products. Similarly, in credit card fraud detection, fraudulent transactions are outnumbered by legitimate transactions. In both of these examples, there is a disproportionate number of instances that belong to different classes. The degree of imbalance varies from one application to another—a manufacturing plant operating under the six sigma principle may discover four defects in a million products shipped to their customers, while the amount of credit card fraud may be of the order of 1 in 100. Despite their infrequent occurrences, a correct classification of the rare class in these applications often has greater value than a correct classification of the majority class. However, because the class distribution is imbalanced, this presents a number of problems to existing classification algorithms.

The accuracy measure, which is used extensively to compare the performance of classifiers, may not be well suited for evaluating models derived from imbalanced data sets. For example, if 1% of the credit card transactions are fraudulent, then a model that predicts every transaction as legitimate has an accuracy of 99% even though it fails to detect any of the fraudulent activities. Additionally, measures that are used to guide the learning algorithm (e.g., information gain for decision tree induction) may need to be modified to focus on the rare class.

Detecting instances of the rare class is akin to finding a needle in a haystack. Because their instances occur infrequently, models that describe the rare class tend to be highly specialized. For example, in a rule-based classifier, the rules extracted for the rare class typically involve a large number of attributes and cannot be easily simplified into more general rules with broader coverage (unlike the rules for the majority class). Such models are also susceptible to the presence of noise in training data. As a result, many of the existing classification algorithms may not effectively detect instances of the rare class.

This section presents some of the methods developed for handling the class imbalance problem. First, alternative metrics besides accuracy are introduced, along with a graphical method called ROC analysis. We then describe how cost-sensitive learning and sampling-based methods may be used to improve the detection of rare classes.

5.7.1   Alternative Metrics

Since the accuracy measure treats every class as equally important, it may not be suitable for analyzing imbalanced data sets, where the rare class is considered more interesting than the majority class. For binary classification, the rare class is often denoted as the positive class, while the majority class is

Table 5.6. A confusion matrix for a binary classification problem in which the classes are not equally important.

		Predicted Class	
		+	−
Actual	+	f_{++} (TP)	f_{+-} (FN)
Class	−	f_{-+} (FP)	f_{--} (TN)

denoted as the negative class. A confusion matrix that summarizes the number of instances predicted correctly or incorrectly by a classification model is shown in Table 5.6.

The following terminology is often used when referring to the counts tabulated in a confusion matrix:

- True positive (TP) or f_{++}, which corresponds to the number of positive examples correctly predicted by the classification model.

- False negative (FN) or f_{+-}, which corresponds to the number of positive examples wrongly predicted as negative by the classification model.

- False positive (FP) or f_{-+}, which corresponds to the number of negative examples wrongly predicted as positive by the classification model.

- True negative (TN) or f_{--}, which corresponds to the number of negative examples correctly predicted by the classification model.

The counts in a confusion matrix can also be expressed in terms of percentages. The **true positive rate** (TPR) or **sensitivity** is defined as the fraction of positive examples predicted correctly by the model, i.e.,

$$TPR = TP/(TP + FN).$$

Similarly, the **true negative rate** (TNR) or **specificity** is defined as the fraction of negative examples predicted correctly by the model, i.e.,

$$TNR = TN/(TN + FP).$$

Finally, the **false positive rate** (FPR) is the fraction of negative examples predicted as a positive class, i.e.,

$$FPR = FP/(TN + FP),$$

while the **false negative rate** (FNR) is the fraction of positive examples predicted as a negative class, i.e.,

$$FNR = FN/(TP + FN).$$

Recall and **precision** are two widely used metrics employed in applications where successful detection of one of the classes is considered more significant than detection of the other classes. A formal definition of these metrics is given below.

$$\text{Precision, } p = \frac{TP}{TP + FP} \tag{5.74}$$

$$\text{Recall, } r = \frac{TP}{TP + FN} \tag{5.75}$$

Precision determines the fraction of records that actually turns out to be positive in the group the classifier has declared as a positive class. The higher the precision is, the lower the number of false positive errors committed by the classifier. Recall measures the fraction of positive examples correctly predicted by the classifier. Classifiers with large recall have very few positive examples misclassified as the negative class. In fact, the value of recall is equivalent to the true positive rate.

It is often possible to construct baseline models that maximize one metric but not the other. For example, a model that declares every record to be the positive class will have a perfect recall, but very poor precision. Conversely, a model that assigns a positive class to every test record that matches one of the positive records in the training set has very high precision, but low recall. Building a model that maximizes both precision and recall is the key challenge of classification algorithms.

Precision and recall can be summarized into another metric known as the F_1 measure.

$$F_1 = \frac{2rp}{r + p} = \frac{2 \times TP}{2 \times TP + FP + FN} \tag{5.76}$$

In principle, F_1 represents a harmonic mean between recall and precision, i.e.,

$$F_1 = \frac{2}{\frac{1}{r} + \frac{1}{p}}.$$

The harmonic mean of two numbers x and y tends to be closer to the smaller of the two numbers. Hence, a high value of F_1-measure ensures that both precision and recall are reasonably high. A comparison among harmonic, geometric, and arithmetic means is given in the next example.

Example 5.8. Consider two positive numbers $a = 1$ and $b = 5$. Their arithmetic mean is $\mu_a = (a+b)/2 = 3$ and their geometric mean is $\mu_g = \sqrt{ab} = 2.236$. Their harmonic mean is $\mu_h = (2 \times 1 \times 5)/6 = 1.667$, which is closer to the smaller value between a and b than the arithmetic and geometric means. ∎

More generally, the F_β measure can be used to examine the tradeoff between recall and precision:

$$F_\beta = \frac{(\beta^2 + 1)rp}{r + \beta^2 p} = \frac{(\beta^2 + 1) \times TP}{(\beta^2 + 1)TP + \beta^2 FP + FN}. \tag{5.77}$$

Both precision and recall are special cases of F_β by setting $\beta = 0$ and $\beta = \infty$, respectively. Low values of β make F_β closer to precision, and high values make it closer to recall.

A more general metric that captures F_β as well as accuracy is the weighted accuracy measure, which is defined by the following equation:

$$\text{Weighted accuracy} = \frac{w_1 TP + w_4 TN}{w_1 TP + w_2 FP + w_3 FN + w_4 TN}. \tag{5.78}$$

The relationship between weighted accuracy and other performance metrics is summarized in the following table:

Measure	w_1	w_2	w_3	w_4
Recall	1	1	0	0
Precision	1	0	1	0
F_β	$\beta^2 + 1$	β^2	1	0
Accuracy	1	1	1	1

5.7.2   The Receiver Operating Characteristic Curve

A receiver operating characteristic (ROC) curve is a graphical approach for displaying the tradeoff between true positive rate and false positive rate of a classifier. In an ROC curve, the true positive rate (TPR) is plotted along the y axis and the false positive rate (FPR) is shown on the x axis. Each point along the curve corresponds to one of the models induced by the classifier. Figure 5.41 shows the ROC curves for a pair of classifiers, M_1 and M_2.

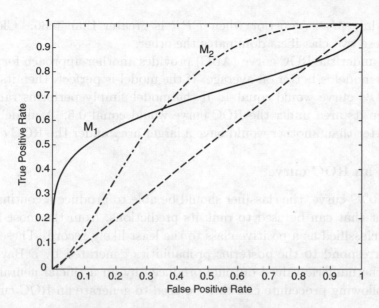

Figure 5.41. ROC curves for two different classifiers.

There are several critical points along an ROC curve that have well-known interpretations:

(TPR=0, FPR=0): Model predicts every instance to be a negative class.
(TPR=1, FPR=1): Model predicts every instance to be a positive class.
(TPR=1, FPR=0): The ideal model.

A good classification model should be located as close as possible to the upper left corner of the diagram, while a model that makes random guesses should reside along the main diagonal, connecting the points $(TPR = 0, FPR = 0)$ and $(TPR = 1, FPR = 1)$. Random guessing means that a record is classified as a positive class with a fixed probability p, irrespective of its attribute set. For example, consider a data set that contains n_+ positive instances and n_- negative instances. The random classifier is expected to correctly classify pn_+ of the positive instances and to misclassify pn_- of the negative instances. Therefore, the TPR of the classifier is $(pn_+)/n_+ = p$, while its FPR is $(pn_-)/p = p$. Since the TPR and FPR are identical, the ROC curve for a random classifier always reside along the main diagonal.

An ROC curve is useful for comparing the relative performance among different classifiers. In Figure 5.41, M_1 is better than M_2 when FPR is less than 0.36, while M_2 is superior when FPR is greater than 0.36. Clearly, neither of these two classifiers dominates the other.

The area under the ROC curve (AUC) provides another approach for evaluating which model is better on average. If the model is perfect, then its area under the ROC curve would equal 1. If the model simply performs random guessing, then its area under the ROC curve would equal 0.5. A model that is strictly better than another would have a larger area under the ROC curve.

Generating an ROC curve

To draw an ROC curve, the classifier should be able to produce a continuous-valued output that can be used to rank its predictions, from the most likely record to be classified as a positive class to the least likely record. These outputs may correspond to the posterior probabilities generated by a Bayesian classifier or the numeric-valued outputs produced by an artificial neural network. The following procedure can then be used to generate an ROC curve:

1. Assuming that the continuous-valued outputs are defined for the positive class, sort the test records in increasing order of their output values.

2. Select the lowest ranked test record (i.e., the record with lowest output value). Assign the selected record and those ranked above it to the positive class. This approach is equivalent to classifying all the test records as positive class. Because all the positive examples are classified correctly and the negative examples are misclassified, $TPR = FPR = 1$.

3. Select the next test record from the sorted list. Classify the selected record and those ranked above it as positive, while those ranked below it as negative. Update the counts of TP and FP by examining the actual class label of the previously selected record. If the previously selected record is a positive class, the TP count is decremented and the FP count remains the same as before. If the previously selected record is a negative class, the FP count is decremented and TP count remains the same as before.

4. Repeat Step 3 and update the TP and FP counts accordingly until the highest ranked test record is selected.

5. Plot the TPR against FPR of the classifier.

Figure 5.42 shows an example of how to compute the ROC curve. There are five positive examples and five negative examples in the test set. The class

Class	+	−	+	−	−	−	+	−	+	+	
	0.25	0.43	0.53	0.76	0.85	0.85	0.85	0.87	0.93	0.95	1.00
TP	5	4	4	3	3	3	3	2	2	1	0
FP	5	5	4	4	3	2	1	1	0	0	0
TN	0	0	1	1	2	3	4	4	5	5	5
FN	0	1	1	2	2	2	2	3	3	4	5
TPR	1	0.8	0.8	0.6	0.6	0.6	0.6	0.4	0.4	0.2	0
FPR	1	1	0.8	0.8	0.6	0.4	0.2	0.2	0	0	0

Figure 5.42. Constructing an ROC curve.

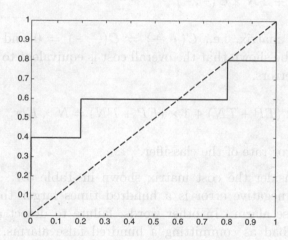

Figure 5.43. ROC curve for the data shown in Figure 5.42.

labels of the test records are shown in the first row of the table. The second row corresponds to the sorted output values for each record. For example, they may correspond to the posterior probabilities $P(+|\mathbf{x})$ generated by a naïve Bayes classifier. The next six rows contain the counts of TP, FP, TN, and FN, along with their corresponding TPR and FPR. The table is then filled from left to right. Initially, all the records are predicted to be positive. Thus, $TP = FP = 5$ and $TPR = FPR = 1$. Next, we assign the test record with the lowest output value as the negative class. Because the selected record is actually a positive example, the TP count reduces from 5 to 4 and the FP count is the same as before. The FPR and TPR are updated accordingly. This process is repeated until we reach the end of the list, where $TPR = 0$ and $FPR = 0$. The ROC curve for this example is shown in Figure 5.43.

5.7.3   Cost-Sensitive Learning

A cost matrix encodes the penalty of classifying records from one class as another. Let $C(i, j)$ denote the cost of predicting a record from class i as class j. With this notation, $C(+, -)$ is the cost of committing a false negative error, while $C(-, +)$ is the cost of generating a false alarm. A negative entry in the cost matrix represents the reward for making correct classification. Given a collection of N test records, the overall cost of a model M is

$$
\begin{aligned}
C_t(M) = \quad & TP \times C(+, +) + FP \times C(-, +) + FN \times C(+, -) \\
& + TN \times C(-, -).
\end{aligned}
\tag{5.79}
$$

Under the 0/1 cost matrix, i.e., $C(+, +) = C(-, -) = 0$ and $C(+, -) = C(-, +) = 1$, it can be shown that the overall cost is equivalent to the number of misclassification errors.

$$
C_t(M) = 0 \times (TP + TN) + 1 \times (FP + FN) = N \times Err,
\tag{5.80}
$$

where Err is the error rate of the classifier.

Example 5.9. Consider the cost matrix shown in Table 5.7: The cost of committing a false negative error is a hundred times larger than the cost of committing a false alarm. In other words, failure to detect any positive example is just as bad as committing a hundred false alarms. Given the classification models with the confusion matrices shown in Table 5.8, the total cost for each model is

$$
\begin{aligned}
C_t(M_1) &= 150 \times (-1) + 60 \times 1 + 40 \times 100 = 3910, \\
C_t(M_2) &= 250 \times (-1) + 5 \times 1 + 45 \times 100 = 4255.
\end{aligned}
$$

Table 5.7. Cost matrix for Example 5.9.

		Predicted Class	
		Class = +	Class = −
Actual	Class = +	−1	100
Class	Class = −	1	0

Table 5.8. Confusion matrix for two classification models.

Model M_1		Predicted Class		Model M_2		Predicted Class	
		Class +	Class –			Class +	Class –
Actual	Class +	150	40	Actual	Class +	250	45
Class	Class –	60	250	Class	Class –	5	200

Notice that despite improving both of its true positive and false positive counts, model M_2 is still inferior since the improvement comes at the expense of increasing the more costly false negative errors. A standard accuracy measure would have preferred model M_2 over M_1.   ∎

A cost-sensitive classification technique takes the cost matrix into consideration during model building and generates a model that has the lowest cost. For example, if false negative errors are the most costly, the learning algorithm will try to reduce these errors by extending its decision boundary toward the negative class, as shown in Figure 5.44. In this way, the generated model can cover more positive examples, although at the expense of generating additional false alarms.

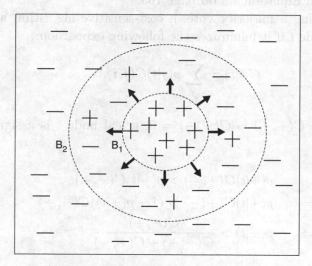

Figure 5.44. Modifying the decision boundary (from B_1 to B_2) to reduce the false negative errors of a classifier.

There are various ways to incorporate cost information into classification algorithms. For example, in the context of decision tree induction, the cost information can be used to: (1) choose the best attribute to use for splitting the data, (2) determine whether a subtree should be pruned, (3) manipulate the weights of the training records so that the learning algorithm converges to a decision tree that has the lowest cost, and (4) modify the decision rule at each leaf node. To illustrate the last approach, let $p(i|t)$ denote the fraction of training records from class i that belong to the leaf node t. A typical decision rule for a binary classification problem assigns the positive class to node t if the following condition holds.

$$
\begin{aligned}
& p(+|t) > p(-|t) \\
\Longrightarrow \quad & p(+|t) > (1 - p(+|t)) \\
\Longrightarrow \quad & 2p(+|t) > 1 \\
\Longrightarrow \quad & p(+|t) > 0.5.
\end{aligned}
\tag{5.81}
$$

The preceding decision rule suggests that the class label of a leaf node depends on the majority class of the training records that reach the particular node. Note that this rule assumes that the misclassification costs are identical for both positive and negative examples. This decision rule is equivalent to the expression given in Equation 4.8 on page 165.

Instead of taking a majority vote, a cost-sensitive algorithm assigns the class label i to node t if it minimizes the following expression:

$$
C(i|t) = \sum_j p(j|t)C(j, i).
\tag{5.82}
$$

In the case where $C(+, +) = C(-, -) = 0$, a leaf node t is assigned to the positive class if:

$$
\begin{aligned}
& p(+|t)C(+, -) > p(-|t)C(-, +) \\
\Longrightarrow \quad & p(+|t)C(+, -) > (1 - p(+|t))C(-, +) \\
\Longrightarrow \quad & p(+|t) > \frac{C(-, +)}{C(-, +) + C(+, -)}.
\end{aligned}
\tag{5.83}
$$

This expression suggests that we can modify the threshold of the decision rule from 0.5 to $C(-, +)/(C(-, +) + C(+, -))$ to obtain a cost-sensitive classifier. If $C(-, +) < C(+, -)$, then the threshold will be less than 0.5. This result makes sense because the cost of making a false negative error is more expensive than that for generating a false alarm. Lowering the threshold will expand the decision boundary toward the negative class, as shown in Figure 5.44.

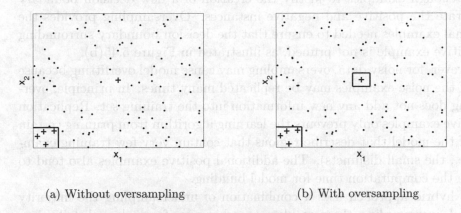

(a) Without oversampling   (b) With oversampling

Figure 5.45. Illustrating the effect of oversampling of the rare class.

5.7.4 Sampling-Based Approaches

Sampling is another widely used approach for handling the class imbalance problem. The idea of sampling is to modify the distribution of instances so that the rare class is well represented in the training set. Some of the available techniques for sampling include undersampling, oversampling, and a hybrid of both approaches. To illustrate these techniques, consider a data set that contains 100 positive examples and 1000 negative examples.

In the case of undersampling, a random sample of 100 negative examples is chosen to form the training set along with all the positive examples. One potential problem with this approach is that some of the useful negative examples may not be chosen for training, therefore, resulting in a less than optimal model. A potential method to overcome this problem is to perform undersampling multiple times and to induce multiple classifiers similar to the ensemble learning approach. Focused undersampling methods may also be used, where the sampling procedure makes an informed choice with regard to the negative examples that should be eliminated, e.g., those located far away from the decision boundary.

Oversampling replicates the positive examples until the training set has an equal number of positive and negative examples. Figure 5.45 illustrates the effect of oversampling on the construction of a decision boundary using a classifier such as a decision tree. Without oversampling, only the positive examples at the bottom right-hand side of Figure 5.45(a) are classified correctly. The positive example in the middle of the diagram is misclassified because there are not enough examples to justify the creation of a new decision boundary to separate the positive and negative instances. Oversampling provides the additional examples needed to ensure that the decision boundary surrounding the positive example is not pruned, as illustrated in Figure 5.45(b).

However, for noisy data, oversampling may cause model overfitting because some of the noise examples may be replicated many times. In principle, oversampling does not add any new information into the training set. Replication of positive examples only prevents the learning algorithm from pruning certain parts of the model that describe regions that contain very few training examples (i.e., the small disjuncts). The additional positive examples also tend to increase the computation time for model building.

The hybrid approach uses a combination of undersampling the majority class and oversampling the rare class to achieve uniform class distribution. Undersampling can be performed using random or focused subsampling. Oversampling, on the other hand, can be done by replicating the existing positive examples or generating new positive examples in the neighborhood of the existing positive examples. In the latter approach, we must first determine the k-nearest neighbors for each existing positive example. A new positive example is then generated at some random point along the line segment that joins the positive example to one of its k-nearest neighbors. This process is repeated until the desired number of positive examples is reached. Unlike the data replication approach, the new examples allow us to extend the decision boundary for the positive class outward, similar to the approach shown in Figure 5.44. Nevertheless, this approach may still be quite susceptible to model overfitting.

5.8   Multiclass Problem

Some of the classification techniques described in this chapter, such as support vector machines and AdaBoost, are originally designed for binary classification problems. Yet there are many real-world problems, such as character recognition, face identification, and text classification, where the input data is divided into more than two categories. This section presents several approaches for extending the binary classifiers to handle multiclass problems. To illustrate these approaches, let $Y = \{y_1, y_2, \ldots, y_K\}$ be the set of classes of the input data.

The first approach decomposes the multiclass problem into K binary problems. For each class $y_i \in Y$, a binary problem is created where all instances that belong to y_i are considered positive examples, while the remaining instances are considered negative examples. A binary classifier is then constructed to separate instances of class y_i from the rest of the classes. This is known as the one-against-rest (1-r) approach.

The second approach, which is known as the one-against-one (1-1) approach, constructs $K(K-1)/2$ binary classifiers, where each classifier is used to distinguish between a pair of classes, (y_i, y_j). Instances that do not belong to either y_i or y_j are ignored when constructing the binary classifier for (y_i, y_j). In both 1-r and 1-1 approaches, a test instance is classified by combining the predictions made by the binary classifiers. A voting scheme is typically employed to combine the predictions, where the class that receives the highest number of votes is assigned to the test instance. In the 1-r approach, if an instance is classified as negative, then all classes except for the positive class receive a vote. This approach, however, may lead to ties among the different classes. Another possibility is to transform the outputs of the binary classifiers into probability estimates and then assign the test instance to the class that has the highest probability.

Example 5.10. Consider a multiclass problem where $Y = \{y_1, y_2, y_3, y_4\}$. Suppose a test instance is classified as $(+, -, -, -)$ according to the 1-r approach. In other words, it is classified as positive when y_1 is used as the positive class and negative when y_2, y_3, and y_4 are used as the positive class. Using a simple majority vote, notice that y_1 receives the highest number of votes, which is four, while the remaining classes receive only three votes. The test instance is therefore classified as y_1.

Suppose the test instance is classified as follows using the 1-1 approach:

Binary pair of classes	+: y_1 −: y_2	+: y_1 −: y_3	+: y_1 −: y_4	+: y_2 −: y_3	+: y_2 −: y_4	+: y_3 −: y_4
Classification	+	+	−	+	−	+

The first two rows in this table correspond to the pair of classes (y_i, y_j) chosen to build the classifier and the last row represents the predicted class for the test instance. After combining the predictions, y_1 and y_4 each receive two votes, while y_2 and y_3 each receives only one vote. The test instance is therefore classified as either y_1 or y_4, depending on the tie-breaking procedure. ∎

Error-Correcting Output Coding

A potential problem with the previous two approaches is that they are sensitive to the binary classification errors. For the 1-r approach given in Example 5.10, if at least of one of the binary classifiers makes a mistake in its prediction, then the ensemble may end up declaring a tie between classes or making a wrong prediction. For example, suppose the test instance is classified as $(+, -, +, -)$ due to misclassification by the third classifier. In this case, it will be difficult to tell whether the instance should be classified as y_1 or y_3, unless the probability associated with each class prediction is taken into account.

The error-correcting output coding (ECOC) method provides a more robust way for handling multiclass problems. The method is inspired by an information-theoretic approach for sending messages across noisy channels. The idea behind this approach is to add redundancy into the transmitted message by means of a codeword, so that the receiver may detect errors in the received message and perhaps recover the original message if the number of errors is small.

For multiclass learning, each class y_i is represented by a unique bit string of length n known as its codeword. We then train n binary classifiers to predict each bit of the codeword string. The predicted class of a test instance is given by the codeword whose Hamming distance is closest to the codeword produced by the binary classifiers. Recall that the Hamming distance between a pair of bit strings is given by the number of bits that differ.

Example 5.11. Consider a multiclass problem where $Y = \{y_1, y_2, y_3, y_4\}$. Suppose we encode the classes using the following 7-bit codewords:

Class	Codeword						
y_1	1	1	1	1	1	1	1
y_2	0	0	0	0	1	1	1
y_3	0	0	1	1	0	0	1
y_4	0	1	0	1	0	1	0

Each bit of the codeword is used to train a binary classifier. If a test instance is classified as (0,1,1,1,1,1,1) by the binary classifiers, then the Hamming distance between the codeword and y_1 is 1, while the Hamming distance to the remaining classes is 3. The test instance is therefore classified as y_1. ∎

An interesting property of an error-correcting code is that if the minimum Hamming distance between any pair of codewords is d, then any $\lfloor (d-1)/2 \rfloor$ errors in the output code can be corrected using its nearest codeword. In Example 5.11, because the minimum Hamming distance between any pair of codewords is 4, the ensemble may tolerate errors made by one of the seven binary classifiers. If there is more than one classifier that makes a mistake, then the ensemble may not be able to compensate for the error.

An important issue is how to design the appropriate set of codewords for different classes. From coding theory, a vast number of algorithms have been developed for generating n-bit codewords with bounded Hamming distance. However, the discussion of these algorithms is beyond the scope of this book. It is worthwhile mentioning that there is a significant difference between the design of error-correcting codes for communication tasks compared to those used for multiclass learning. For communication, the codewords should maximize the Hamming distance between the rows so that error correction can be performed. Multiclass learning, however, requires that the row-wise and column-wise distances of the codewords must be well separated. A larger column-wise distance ensures that the binary classifiers are mutually independent, which is an important requirement for ensemble learning methods.

5.9 Bibliographic Notes

Mitchell [208] provides an excellent coverage on many classification techniques from a machine learning perspective. Extensive coverage on classification can also be found in Duda et al. [180], Webb [219], Fukunaga [187], Bishop [159], Hastie et al. [192], Cherkassky and Mulier [167], Witten and Frank [221], Hand et al. [190], Han and Kamber [189], and Dunham [181].

Direct methods for rule-based classifiers typically employ the sequential covering scheme for inducing classification rules. Holte's 1R [195] is the simplest form of a rule-based classifier because its rule set contains only a single rule. Despite its simplicity, Holte found that for some data sets that exhibit a strong one-to-one relationship between the attributes and the class label, 1R performs just as well as other classifiers. Other examples of rule-based classifiers include IREP [184], RIPPER [170], CN2 [168, 169], AQ [207], RISE [176], and ITRULE [214]. Table 5.9 shows a comparison of the characteristics of four of these classifiers.

For rule-based classifiers, the rule antecedent can be generalized to include any propositional or first-order logical expression (e.g., Horn clauses). Readers who are interested in first-order logic rule-based classifiers may refer to references such as [208] or the vast literature on inductive logic programming [209]. Quinlan [211] proposed the C4.5rules algorithm for extracting classification rules from decision trees. An indirect method for extracting rules from artificial neural networks was given by Andrews et al. in [157].

Table 5.9. Comparison of various rule-based classifiers.

	RIPPER	CN2 (unordered)	CN2 (ordered)	AQR
Rule-growing strategy	General-to-specific	General-to-specific	General-to-specific	General-to-specific (seeded by a positive example)
Evaluation Metric	FOIL's Info gain	Laplace	Entropy and likelihood ratio	Number of true positives
Stopping condition for rule-growing	All examples belong to the same class	No performance gain	No performance gain	Rules cover only positive class
Rule Pruning	Reduced error pruning	None	None	None
Instance Elimination	Positive and negative	Positive only	Positive only	Positive and negative
Stopping condition for adding rules	Error > 50% or based on MDL	No performance gain	No performance gain	All positive examples are covered
Rule Set Pruning	Replace or modify rules	Statistical tests	None	None
Search strategy	Greedy	Beam search	Beam search	Beam search

Cover and Hart [172] presented an overview of the nearest-neighbor classification method from a Bayesian perspective. Aha provided both theoretical and empirical evaluations for instance-based methods in [155]. PEBLS, which was developed by Cost and Salzberg [171], is a nearest-neighbor classification algorithm that can handle data sets containing nominal attributes. Each training example in PEBLS is also assigned a weight factor that depends on the number of times the example helps make a correct prediction. Han et al. [188] developed a weight-adjusted nearest-neighbor algorithm, in which the feature weights are learned using a greedy, hill-climbing optimization algorithm.

Naïve Bayes classifiers have been investigated by many authors, including Langley et al. [203], Ramoni and Sebastiani [212], Lewis [204], and Domingos and Pazzani [178]. Although the independence assumption used in naïve Bayes classifiers may seem rather unrealistic, the method has worked surprisingly well for applications such as text classification. Bayesian belief networks provide a more flexible approach by allowing some of the attributes to be interdependent. An excellent tutorial on Bayesian belief networks is given by Heckerman in [194].

Vapnik [217, 218] had written two authoritative books on Support Vector Machines (SVM). Other useful resources on SVM and kernel methods include the books by Cristianini and Shawe-Taylor [173] and Schölkopf and Smola

[213]. There are several survey articles on SVM, including those written by Burges [164], Bennet et al. [158], Hearst [193], and Mangasarian [205].

A survey of ensemble methods in machine learning was given by Dietterich [174]. The bagging method was proposed by Breiman [161]. Freund and Schapire [186] developed the AdaBoost algorithm. Arcing, which stands for adaptive resampling and combining, is a variant of the boosting algorithm proposed by Breiman [162]. It uses the non-uniform weights assigned to training examples to resample the data for building an ensemble of training sets. Unlike AdaBoost, the votes of the base classifiers are not weighted when determining the class label of test examples. The random forest method was introduced by Breiman in [163].

Related work on mining rare and imbalanced data sets can be found in the survey papers written by Chawla et al. [166] and Weiss [220]. Sampling-based methods for mining imbalanced data sets have been investigated by many authors, such as Kubat and Matwin [202], Japkowitz [196], and Drummond and Holte [179]. Joshi et al. [199] discussed the limitations of boosting algorithms for rare class modeling. Other algorithms developed for mining rare classes include SMOTE [165], PNrule [198], and CREDOS [200].

Various alternative metrics that are well-suited for class imbalanced problems are available. The precision, recall, and F_1-measure are widely used metrics in information retrieval [216]. ROC analysis was originally used in signal detection theory. Bradley [160] investigated the use of area under the ROC curve as a performance metric for machine learning algorithms. A method for comparing classifier performance using the convex hull of ROC curves was suggested by Provost and Fawcett in [210]. Ferri et al. [185] developed a methodology for performing ROC analysis on decision tree classifiers. They had also proposed a methodology for incorporating area under the ROC curve (AUC) as the splitting criterion during the tree-growing process. Joshi [197] examined the performance of these measures from the perspective of analyzing rare classes.

A vast amount of literature on cost-sensitive learning can be found in the online proceedings of the ICML'2000 Workshop on cost-sensitive learning. The properties of a cost matrix had been studied by Elkan in [182]. Margineantu and Dietterich [206] examined various methods for incorporating cost information into the C4.5 learning algorithm, including wrapper methods, class distribution-based methods, and loss-based methods. Other cost-sensitive learning methods that are algorithm-independent include AdaCost [183], MetaCost [177], and costing [222].

Extensive literature is also available on the subject of multiclass learning. This includes the works of Hastie and Tibshirani [191], Allwein et al. [156], Kong and Dietterich [201], and Tax and Duin [215]. The error-correcting output coding (ECOC) method was proposed by Dietterich and Bakiri [175]. They had also investigated techniques for designing codes that are suitable for solving multiclass problems.

Bibliography

[155] D. W. Aha. *A study of instance-based algorithms for supervised learning tasks: mathematical, empirical, and psychological evaluations.* PhD thesis, University of California, Irvine, 1990.

[156] E. L. Allwein, R. E. Schapire, and Y. Singer. Reducing Multiclass to Binary: A Unifying Approach to Margin Classifiers. *Journal of Machine Learning Research*, 1: 113–141, 2000.

[157] R. Andrews, J. Diederich, and A. Tickle. A Survey and Critique of Techniques For Extracting Rules From Trained Artificial Neural Networks. *Knowledge Based Systems*, 8(6):373–389, 1995.

[158] K. Bennett and C. Campbell. Support Vector Machines: Hype or Hallelujah. *SIGKDD Explorations*, 2(2):1–13, 2000.

[159] C. M. Bishop. *Neural Networks for Pattern Recognition.* Oxford University Press, Oxford, U.K., 1995.

[160] A. P. Bradley. The use of the area under the ROC curve in the Evaluation of Machine Learning Algorithms. *Pattern Recognition*, 30(7):1145–1149, 1997.

[161] L. Breiman. Bagging Predictors. *Machine Learning*, 24(2):123–140, 1996.

[162] L. Breiman. Bias, Variance, and Arcing Classifiers. Technical Report 486, University of California, Berkeley, CA, 1996.

[163] L. Breiman. Random Forests. *Machine Learning*, 45(1):5–32, 2001.

[164] C. J. C. Burges. A Tutorial on Support Vector Machines for Pattern Recognition. *Data Mining and Knowledge Discovery*, 2(2):121–167, 1998.

[165] N. V. Chawla, K. W. Bowyer, L. O. Hall, and W. P. Kegelmeyer. SMOTE: Synthetic Minority Over-sampling Technique. *Journal of Artificial Intelligence Research*, 16:321–357, 2002.

[166] N. V. Chawla, N. Japkowicz, and A. Kolcz. Editorial: Special Issue on Learning from Imbalanced Data Sets. *SIGKDD Explorations*, 6(1):1–6, 2004.

[167] V. Cherkassky and F. Mulier. *Learning from Data: Concepts, Theory, and Methods.* Wiley Interscience, 1998.

[168] P. Clark and R. Boswell. Rule Induction with CN2: Some Recent Improvements. In *Machine Learning: Proc. of the 5th European Conf. (EWSL-91)*, pages 151–163, 1991.

[169] P. Clark and T. Niblett. The CN2 Induction Algorithm. *Machine Learning*, 3(4): 261–283, 1989.

[170] W. W. Cohen. Fast Effective Rule Induction. In *Proc. of the 12th Intl. Conf. on Machine Learning*, pages 115–123, Tahoe City, CA, July 1995.

[171] S. Cost and S. Salzberg. A Weighted Nearest Neighbor Algorithm for Learning with Symbolic Features. *Machine Learning*, 10:57–78, 1993.

[172] T. M. Cover and P. E. Hart. Nearest Neighbor Pattern Classification. *Knowledge Based Systems*, 8(6):373–389, 1995.

[173] N. Cristianini and J. Shawe-Taylor. *An Introduction to Support Vector Machines and Other Kernel-based Learning Methods*. Cambridge University Press, 2000.

[174] T. G. Dietterich. Ensemble Methods in Machine Learning. In *First Intl. Workshop on Multiple Classifier Systems*, Cagliari, Italy, 2000.

[175] T. G. Dietterich and G. Bakiri. Solving Multiclass Learning Problems via Error-Correcting Output Codes. *Journal of Artificial Intelligence Research*, 2:263–286, 1995.

[176] P. Domingos. The RISE system: Conquering without separating. In *Proc. of the 6th IEEE Intl. Conf. on Tools with Artificial Intelligence*, pages 704–707, New Orleans, LA, 1994.

[177] P. Domingos. MetaCost: A General Method for Making Classifiers Cost-Sensitive. In *Proc. of the 5th Intl. Conf. on Knowledge Discovery and Data Mining*, pages 155–164, San Diego, CA, August 1999.

[178] P. Domingos and M. Pazzani. On the Optimality of the Simple Bayesian Classifier under Zero-One Loss. *Machine Learning*, 29(2-3):103–130, 1997.

[179] C. Drummond and R. C. Holte. C4.5, Class imbalance, and Cost sensitivity: Why under-sampling beats over-sampling. In *ICML'2004 Workshop on Learning from Imbalanced Data Sets II*, Washington, DC, August 2003.

[180] R. O. Duda, P. E. Hart, and D. G. Stork. *Pattern Classification*. John Wiley & Sons, Inc., New York, 2nd edition, 2001.

[181] M. H. Dunham. *Data Mining: Introductory and Advanced Topics*. Prentice Hall, 2002.

[182] C. Elkan. The Foundations of Cost-Sensitive Learning. In *Proc. of the 17th Intl. Joint Conf. on Artificial Intelligence*, pages 973–978, Seattle, WA, August 2001.

[183] W. Fan, S. J. Stolfo, J. Zhang, and P. K. Chan. AdaCost: misclassification cost-sensitive boosting. In *Proc. of the 16th Intl. Conf. on Machine Learning*, pages 97–105, Bled, Slovenia, June 1999.

[184] J. Fürnkranz and G. Widmer. Incremental reduced error pruning. In *Proc. of the 11th Intl. Conf. on Machine Learning*, pages 70–77, New Brunswick, NJ, July 1994.

[185] C. Ferri, P. Flach, and J. Hernandez-Orallo. Learning Decision Trees Using the Area Under the ROC Curve. In *Proc. of the 19th Intl. Conf. on Machine Learning*, pages 139–146, Sydney, Australia, July 2002.

[186] Y. Freund and R. E. Schapire. A decision-theoretic generalization of on-line learning and an application to boosting. *Journal of Computer and System Sciences*, 55(1):119–139, 1997.

[187] K. Fukunaga. *Introduction to Statistical Pattern Recognition*. Academic Press, New York, 1990.

[188] E.-H. Han, G. Karypis, and V. Kumar. Text Categorization Using Weight Adjusted k-Nearest Neighbor Classification. In *Proc. of the 5th Pacific-Asia Conf. on Knowledge Discovery and Data Mining*, Lyon, France, 2001.

[189] J. Han and M. Kamber. *Data Mining: Concepts and Techniques*. Morgan Kaufmann Publishers, San Francisco, 2001.

[190] D. J. Hand, H. Mannila, and P. Smyth. *Principles of Data Mining*. MIT Press, 2001.

[191] T. Hastie and R. Tibshirani. Classification by pairwise coupling. *Annals of Statistics*, 26(2):451–471, 1998.

[192] T. Hastie, R. Tibshirani, and J. H. Friedman. *The Elements of Statistical Learning: Data Mining, Inference, Prediction*. Springer, New York, 2001.

[193] M. Hearst. Trends & Controversies: Support Vector Machines. *IEEE Intelligent Systems*, 13(4):18–28, 1998.

[194] D. Heckerman. Bayesian Networks for Data Mining. *Data Mining and Knowledge Discovery*, 1(1):79–119, 1997.

[195] R. C. Holte. Very Simple Classification Rules Perform Well on Most Commonly Used Data sets. *Machine Learning*, 11:63–91, 1993.

[196] N. Japkowicz. The Class Imbalance Problem: Significance and Strategies. In *Proc. of the 2000 Intl. Conf. on Artificial Intelligence: Special Track on Inductive Learning*, volume 1, pages 111–117, Las Vegas, NV, June 2000.

[197] M. V. Joshi. On Evaluating Performance of Classifiers for Rare Classes. In *Proc. of the 2002 IEEE Intl. Conf. on Data Mining*, Maebashi City, Japan, December 2002.

[198] M. V. Joshi, R. C. Agarwal, and V. Kumar. Mining Needles in a Haystack: Classifying Rare Classes via Two-Phase Rule Induction. In *Proc. of 2001 ACM-SIGMOD Intl. Conf. on Management of Data*, pages 91–102, Santa Barbara, CA, June 2001.

[199] M. V. Joshi, R. C. Agarwal, and V. Kumar. Predicting rare classes: can boosting make any weak learner strong? In *Proc. of the 8th Intl. Conf. on Knowledge Discovery and Data Mining*, pages 297–306, Edmonton, Canada, July 2002.

[200] M. V. Joshi and V. Kumar. CREDOS: Classification Using Ripple Down Structure (A Case for Rare Classes). In *Proc. of the SIAM Intl. Conf. on Data Mining*, pages 321–332, Orlando, FL, April 2004.

[201] E. B. Kong and T. G. Dietterich. Error-Correcting Output Coding Corrects Bias and Variance. In *Proc. of the 12th Intl. Conf. on Machine Learning*, pages 313–321, Tahoe City, CA, July 1995.

[202] M. Kubat and S. Matwin. Addressing the Curse of Imbalanced Training Sets: One Sided Selection. In *Proc. of the 14th Intl. Conf. on Machine Learning*, pages 179–186, Nashville, TN, July 1997.

[203] P. Langley, W. Iba, and K. Thompson. An analysis of Bayesian classifiers. In *Proc. of the 10th National Conf. on Artificial Intelligence*, pages 223–228, 1992.

[204] D. D. Lewis. Naive Bayes at Forty: The Independence Assumption in Information Retrieval. In *Proc. of the 10th European Conf. on Machine Learning (ECML 1998)*, pages 4–15, 1998.

[205] O. Mangasarian. Data Mining via Support Vector Machines. Technical Report Technical Report 01-05, Data Mining Institute, May 2001.

[206] D. D. Margineantu and T. G. Dietterich. Learning Decision Trees for Loss Minimization in Multi-Class Problems. Technical Report 99-30-03, Oregon State University, 1999.

[207] R. S. Michalski, I. Mozetic, J. Hong, and N. Lavrac. The Multi-Purpose Incremental Learning System AQ15 and Its Testing Application to Three Medical Domains. In *Proc. of 5th National Conf. on Artificial Intelligence*, Orlando, August 1986.

[208] T. Mitchell. *Machine Learning*. McGraw-Hill, Boston, MA, 1997.

[209] S. Muggleton. *Foundations of Inductive Logic Programming*. Prentice Hall, Englewood Cliffs, NJ, 1995.

[210] F. J. Provost and T. Fawcett. Analysis and Visualization of Classifier Performance: Comparison under Imprecise Class and Cost Distributions. In *Proc. of the 3rd Intl. Conf. on Knowledge Discovery and Data Mining*, pages 43–48, Newport Beach, CA, August 1997.

[211] J. R. Quinlan. *C4.5: Programs for Machine Learning*. Morgan-Kaufmann Publishers, San Mateo, CA, 1993.

[212] M. Ramoni and P. Sebastiani. Robust Bayes classifiers. *Artificial Intelligence*, 125: 209–226, 2001.

[213] B. Schölkopf and A. J. Smola. *Learning with Kernels: Support Vector Machines, Regularization, Optimization, and Beyond.* MIT Press, 2001.

[214] P. Smyth and R. M. Goodman. An Information Theoretic Approach to Rule Induction from Databases. *IEEE Trans. on Knowledge and Data Engineering,* 4(4):301–316, 1992.

[215] D. M. J. Tax and R. P. W. Duin. Using Two-Class Classifiers for Multiclass Classification. In *Proc. of the 16th Intl. Conf. on Pattern Recognition (ICPR 2002),* pages 124–127, Quebec, Canada, August 2002.

[216] C. J. van Rijsbergen. *Information Retrieval.* Butterworth-Heinemann, Newton, MA, 1978.

[217] V. Vapnik. *The Nature of Statistical Learning Theory.* Springer Verlag, New York, 1995.

[218] V. Vapnik. *Statistical Learning Theory.* John Wiley & Sons, New York, 1998.

[219] A. R. Webb. *Statistical Pattern Recognition.* John Wiley & Sons, 2nd edition, 2002.

[220] G. M. Weiss. Mining with Rarity: A Unifying Framework. *SIGKDD Explorations,* 6 (1):7–19, 2004.

[221] I. H. Witten and E. Frank. *Data Mining: Practical Machine Learning Tools and Techniques with Java Implementations.* Morgan Kaufmann, 1999.

[222] B. Zadrozny, J. C. Langford, and N. Abe. Cost-Sensitive Learning by Cost-Proportionate Example Weighting. In *Proc. of the 2003 IEEE Intl. Conf. on Data Mining,* pages 435–442, Melbourne, FL, August 2003.

5.10   Exercises

1. Consider a binary classification problem with the following set of attributes and attribute values:

   - Air Conditioner = {Working, Broken}
   - Engine = {Good, Bad}
   - Mileage = {High, Medium, Low}
   - Rust = {Yes, No}

   Suppose a rule-based classifier produces the following rule set:

Mileage = High $\longrightarrow$ Value = Low
Mileage = Low $\longrightarrow$ Value = High
Air Conditioner = Working, Engine = Good $\longrightarrow$ Value = High
Air Conditioner = Working, Engine = Bad $\longrightarrow$ Value = Low
Air Conditioner = Broken $\longrightarrow$ Value = Low

   (a) Are the rules mutually exclustive?

   (b) Is the rule set exhaustive?

   (c) Is ordering needed for this set of rules?

   (d) Do you need a default class for the rule set?

2. The RIPPER algorithm (by Cohen [170]) is an extension of an earlier algorithm called IREP (by Fürnkranz and Widmer [184]). Both algorithms apply the **reduced-error pruning** method to determine whether a rule needs to be pruned. The reduced error pruning method uses a validation set to estimate the generalization error of a classifier. Consider the following pair of rules:

$$R_1: \quad A \longrightarrow C$$
$$R_2: \quad A \wedge B \longrightarrow C$$

R_2 is obtained by adding a new conjunct, B, to the left-hand side of R_1. For this question, you will be asked to determine whether R_2 is preferred over R_1 from the perspectives of rule-growing and rule-pruning. To determine whether a rule should be pruned, IREP computes the following measure:

$$v_{IREP} = \frac{p + (N - n)}{P + N},$$

where P is the total number of positive examples in the validation set, N is the total number of negative examples in the validation set, p is the number of positive examples in the validation set covered by the rule, and n is the number of negative examples in the validation set covered by the rule. v_{IREP} is actually similar to classification accuracy for the validation set. IREP favors rules that have higher values of v_{IREP}. On the other hand, RIPPER applies the following measure to determine whether a rule should be pruned:

$$v_{RIPPER} = \frac{p - n}{p + n}.$$

   (a) Suppose R_1 is covered by 350 positive examples and 150 negative examples, while R_2 is covered by 300 positive examples and 50 negative examples. Compute the FOIL's information gain for the rule R_2 with respect to R_1.

   (b) Consider a validation set that contains 500 positive examples and 500 negative examples. For R_1, suppose the number of positive examples covered by the rule is 200, and the number of negative examples covered by the rule is 50. For R_2, suppose the number of positive examples covered by the rule is 100 and the number of negative examples is 5. Compute v_{IREP} for both rules. Which rule does IREP prefer?

   (c) Compute v_{RIPPER} for the previous problem. Which rule does RIPPER prefer?

3. C4.5rules is an implementation of an indirect method for generating rules from a decision tree. RIPPER is an implementation of a direct method for generating rules directly from data.

   (a) Discuss the strengths and weaknesses of both methods.

   (b) Consider a data set that has a large difference in the class size (i.e., some classes are much bigger than others). Which method (between C4.5rules and RIPPER) is better in terms of finding high accuracy rules for the small classes?

4. Consider a training set that contains 100 positive examples and 400 negative examples. For each of the following candidate rules,

   R_1: $A \longrightarrow +$ (covers 4 positive and 1 negative examples),
   R_2: $B \longrightarrow +$ (covers 30 positive and 10 negative examples),
   R_3: $C \longrightarrow +$ (covers 100 positive and 90 negative examples),

   determine which is the best and worst candidate rule according to:

   (a) Rule accuracy.

   (b) FOIL's information gain.

   (c) The likelihood ratio statistic.

   (d) The Laplace measure.

   (e) The m-estimate measure (with $k = 2$ and $p_+ = 0.2$).

5. Figure 5.4 illustrates the coverage of the classification rules $R1$, $R2$, and $R3$. Determine which is the best and worst rule according to:

   (a) The likelihood ratio statistic.

   (b) The Laplace measure.

   (c) The m-estimate measure (with $k = 2$ and $p_+ = 0.58$).

   (d) The rule accuracy after $R1$ has been discovered, where none of the examples covered by $R1$ are discarded).

   (e) The rule accuracy after $R1$ has been discovered, where only the positive examples covered by $R1$ are discarded).

   (f) The rule accuracy after $R1$ has been discovered, where both positive and negative examples covered by $R1$ are discarded.

6. (a) Suppose the fraction of undergraduate students who smoke is 15% and the fraction of graduate students who smoke is 23%. If one-fifth of the college students are graduate students and the rest are undergraduates, what is the probability that a student who smokes is a graduate student?

(b) Given the information in part (a), is a randomly chosen college student more likely to be a graduate or undergraduate student?

(c) Repeat part (b) assuming that the student is a smoker.

(d) Suppose 30% of the graduate students live in a dorm but only 10% of the undergraduate students live in a dorm. If a student smokes and lives in the dorm, is he or she more likely to be a graduate or undergraduate student? You can assume independence between students who live in a dorm and those who smoke.

7. Consider the data set shown in Table 5.10

Table 5.10. Data set for Exercise 7.

Record	A	B	C	Class
1	0	0	0	+
2	0	0	1	−
3	0	1	1	−
4	0	1	1	−
5	0	0	1	+
6	1	0	1	+
7	1	0	1	−
8	1	0	1	−
9	1	1	1	+
10	1	0	1	+

(a) Estimate the conditional probabilities for $P(A|+)$, $P(B|+)$, $P(C|+)$, $P(A|-)$, $P(B|-)$, and $P(C|-)$.

(b) Use the estimate of conditional probabilities given in the previous question to predict the class label for a test sample $(A = 0, B = 1, C = 0)$ using the naïve Bayes approach.

(c) Estimate the conditional probabilities using the m-estimate approach, with $p = 1/2$ and $m = 4$.

(d) Repeat part (b) using the conditional probabilities given in part (c).

(e) Compare the two methods for estimating probabilities. Which method is better and why?

8. Consider the data set shown in Table 5.11.

(a) Estimate the conditional probabilities for $P(A = 1|+)$, $P(B = 1|+)$, $P(C = 1|+)$, $P(A = 1|-)$, $P(B = 1|-)$, and $P(C = 1|-)$ using the same approach as in the previous problem.

Table 5.11. Data set for Exercise 8.

Instance	A	B	C	Class
1	0	0	1	−
2	1	0	1	+
3	0	1	0	−
4	1	0	0	−
5	1	0	1	+
6	0	0	1	+
7	1	1	0	−
8	0	0	0	−
9	0	1	0	+
10	1	1	1	+

(b) Use the conditional probabilities in part (a) to predict the class label for a test sample $(A = 1, B = 1, C = 1)$ using the naïve Bayes approach.

(c) Compare $P(A = 1)$, $P(B = 1)$, and $P(A = 1, B = 1)$. State the relationships between A and B.

(d) Repeat the analysis in part (c) using $P(A = 1)$, $P(B = 0)$, and $P(A = 1, B = 0)$.

(e) Compare $P(A = 1, B = 1|Class = +)$ against $P(A = 1|Class = +)$ and $P(B = 1|Class = +)$. Are the variables conditionally independent given the class?

9. (a) Explain how naïve Bayes performs on the data set shown in Figure 5.46.

(b) If each class is further divided such that there are four classes ($A1$, $A2$, $B1$, and $B2$), will naïve Bayes perform better?

(c) How will a decision tree perform on this data set (for the two-class problem)? What if there are four classes?

10. Repeat the analysis shown in Example 5.3 for finding the location of a decision boundary using the following information:

(a) The prior probabilities are $P(\texttt{Crocodile}) = 2 \times P(\texttt{Alligator})$.

(b) The prior probabilities are $P(\texttt{Alligator}) = 2 \times P(\texttt{Crocodile})$.

(c) The prior probabilities are the same, but their standard deviations are different; i.e., $\sigma(\texttt{Crocodile}) = 4$ and $\sigma(\texttt{Alligator}) = 2$.

11. Figure 5.47 illustrates the Bayesian belief network for the data set shown in Table 5.12. (Assume that all the attributes are binary).

(a) Draw the probability table for each node in the network.

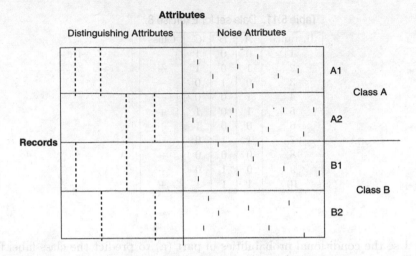

Figure 5.46. Data set for Exercise 9.

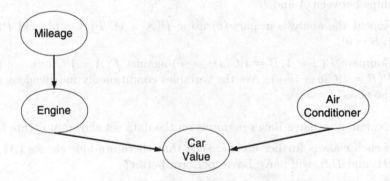

Figure 5.47. Bayesian belief network.

(b) Use the Bayesian network to compute P(Engine = Bad, Air Conditioner = Broken).

12. Given the Bayesian network shown in Figure 5.48, compute the following probabilities:

    (a) $P(B = good, F = empty, G = empty, S = yes)$.

    (b) $P(B = bad, F = empty, G = not empty, S = no)$.

    (c) Given that the battery is bad, compute the probability that the car will start.

13. Consider the one-dimensional data set shown in Table 5.13.

Table 5.12. Data set for Exercise 11.

Mileage	Engine	Air Conditioner	Number of Records with Car Value=Hi	Number of Records with Car Value=Lo
Hi	Good	Working	3	4
Hi	Good	Broken	1	2
Hi	Bad	Working	1	5
Hi	Bad	Broken	0	4
Lo	Good	Working	9	0
Lo	Good	Broken	5	1
Lo	Bad	Working	1	2
Lo	Bad	Broken	0	2

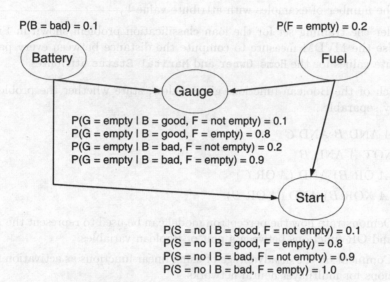

$P(B = bad) = 0.1$ $P(F = empty) = 0.2$

$P(G = empty \mid B = good, F = not\ empty) = 0.1$
$P(G = empty \mid B = good, F = empty) = 0.8$
$P(G = empty \mid B = bad, F = not\ empty) = 0.2$
$P(G = empty \mid B = bad, F = empty) = 0.9$

$P(S = no \mid B = good, F = not\ empty) = 0.1$
$P(S = no \mid B = good, F = empty) = 0.8$
$P(S = no \mid B = bad, F = not\ empty) = 0.9$
$P(S = no \mid B = bad, F = empty) = 1.0$

Figure 5.48. Bayesian belief network for Exercise 12.

(a) Classify the data point $x = 5.0$ according to its 1-, 3-, 5-, and 9-nearest neighbors (using majority vote).

(b) Repeat the previous analysis using the distance-weighted voting approach described in Section 5.2.1.

14. The nearest-neighbor algorithm described in Section 5.2 can be extended to handle nominal attributes. A variant of the algorithm called PEBLS (Parallel Examplar-Based Learning System) by Cost and Salzberg [171] measures the distance between two values of a nominal attribute using the modified value difference metric (MVDM). Given a pair of nominal attribute values, V_1 and

Table 5.13. Data set for Exercise 13.

x	0.5	3.0	4.5	4.6	4.9	5.2	5.3	5.5	7.0	9.5
y	−	−	+	+	+	−	−	+	−	−

V_2, the distance between them is defined as follows:

$$d(V_1, V_2) = \sum_{i=1}^{k} \left| \frac{n_{i1}}{n_1} - \frac{n_{i2}}{n_2} \right|, \qquad (5.84)$$

where n_{ij} is the number of examples from class i with attribute value V_j and n_j is the number of examples with attribute value V_j.

Consider the training set for the loan classification problem shown in Figure 5.9. Use the MVDM measure to compute the distance between every pair of attribute values for the **Home Owner** and **Marital Status** attributes.

15. For each of the Boolean functions given below, state whether the problem is linearly separable.

    (a) A AND B AND C

    (b) NOT A AND B

    (c) $(A$ OR $B)$ AND $(A$ OR $C)$

    (d) $(A$ XOR $B)$ AND $(A$ OR $B)$

16. (a) Demonstrate how the perceptron model can be used to represent the AND and OR functions between a pair of Boolean variables.

    (b) Comment on the disadvantage of using linear functions as activation functions for multilayer neural networks.

17. You are asked to evaluate the performance of two classification models, M_1 and M_2. The test set you have chosen contains 26 binary attributes, labeled as A through Z.

    Table 5.14 shows the posterior probabilities obtained by applying the models to the test set. (Only the posterior probabilities for the positive class are shown). As this is a two-class problem, $P(-) = 1 - P(+)$ and $P(-|A,...,Z) = 1 - P(+|A,...,Z)$. Assume that we are mostly interested in detecting instances from the positive class.

    (a) Plot the ROC curve for both M_1 and M_2. (You should plot them on the same graph.) Which model do you think is better? Explain your reasons.

    (b) For model M_1, suppose you choose the cutoff threshold to be $t = 0.5$. In other words, any test instances whose posterior probability is greater than t will be classified as a positive example. Compute the precision, recall, and F-measure for the model at this threshold value.

Table 5.14. Posterior probabilities for Exercise 17.

Instance	True Class	$P(+|A,\ldots,Z,M_1)$	$P(+|A,\ldots,Z,M_2)$
1	+	0.73	0.61
2	+	0.69	0.03
3	−	0.44	0.68
4	−	0.55	0.31
5	+	0.67	0.45
6	+	0.47	0.09
7	−	0.08	0.38
8	−	0.15	0.05
9	+	0.45	0.01
10	−	0.35	0.04

(c) Repeat the analysis for part (c) using the same cutoff threshold on model M_2. Compare the F-measure results for both models. Which model is better? Are the results consistent with what you expect from the ROC curve?

(d) Repeat part (c) for model M_1 using the threshold $t = 0.1$. Which threshold do you prefer, $t = 0.5$ or $t = 0.1$? Are the results consistent with what you expect from the ROC curve?

18. Following is a data set that contains two attributes, X and Y, and two class labels, "+" and "−". Each attribute can take three different values: $0, 1$, or 2.

X	Y	Number of Instances	
		+	−
0	0	0	100
1	0	0	0
2	0	0	100
0	1	10	100
1	1	10	0
2	1	10	100
0	2	0	100
1	2	0	0
2	2	0	100

The concept for the "+" class is $Y = 1$ and the concept for the "−" class is $X = 0 \vee X = 2$.

(a) Build a decision tree on the data set. Does the tree capture the "+" and "−" concepts?

(b) What are the accuracy, precision, recall, and F_1-measure of the decision tree? (Note that precision, recall, and F_1-measure are defined with respect to the "+" class.)

(c) Build a new decision tree with the following cost function:

$$
C(i,j) = \begin{cases}
0, & \text{if } i = j; \\
1, & \text{if } i = +, j = -; \\
\dfrac{\text{Number of } - \text{ instances}}{\text{Number of } + \text{ instances}}, & \text{if } i = -, j = +.
\end{cases}
$$

(Hint: only the leaves of the old decision tree need to be changed.) Does the decision tree capture the "+" concept?

(d) What are the accuracy, precision, recall, and F_1-measure of the new decision tree?

19. (a) Consider the cost matrix for a two-class problem. Let $C(+,+) = C(-,-) = p$, $C(+,-) = C(-,+) = q$, and $q > p$. Show that minimizing the cost function is equivalent to maximizing the classifier's accuracy.

    (b) Show that a cost matrix is scale-invariant. For example, if the cost matrix is rescaled from $C(i,j) \longrightarrow \beta C(i,j)$, where β is the scaling factor, the decision threshold (Equation 5.82) will remain unchanged.

    (c) Show that a cost matrix is translation-invariant. In other words, adding a constant factor to all entries in the cost matrix will not affect the decision threshold (Equation 5.82).

20. Consider the task of building a classifier from random data, where the attribute values are generated randomly irrespective of the class labels. Assume the data set contains records from two classes, "+" and "−." Half of the data set is used for training while the remaining half is used for testing.

    (a) Suppose there are an equal number of positive and negative records in the data and the decision tree classifier predicts every test record to be positive. What is the expected error rate of the classifier on the test data?

    (b) Repeat the previous analysis assuming that the classifier predicts each test record to be positive class with probability 0.8 and negative class with probability 0.2.

    (c) Suppose two-thirds of the data belong to the positive class and the remaining one-third belong to the negative class. What is the expected error of a classifier that predicts every test record to be positive?

    (d) Repeat the previous analysis assuming that the classifier predicts each test record to be positive class with probability 2/3 and negative class with probability 1/3.

21. Derive the dual Lagrangian for the linear SVM with nonseparable data where the objective function is

$$f(\mathbf{w}) = \frac{\|\mathbf{w}\|^2}{2} + C\left(\sum_{i=1}^{N} \xi_i\right)^2.$$

22. Consider the XOR problem where there are four training points:

$$(1,1,-),(1,0,+),(0,1,+),(0,0,-).$$

Transform the data into the following feature space:

$$\Phi = (1, \sqrt{2}x_1, \sqrt{2}x_2, \sqrt{2}x_1x_2, x_1^2, x_2^2).$$

Find the maximum margin linear decision boundary in the transformed space.

23. Given the data sets shown in Figures 5.49, explain how the decision tree, naïve Bayes, and k-nearest neighbor classifiers would perform on these data sets.

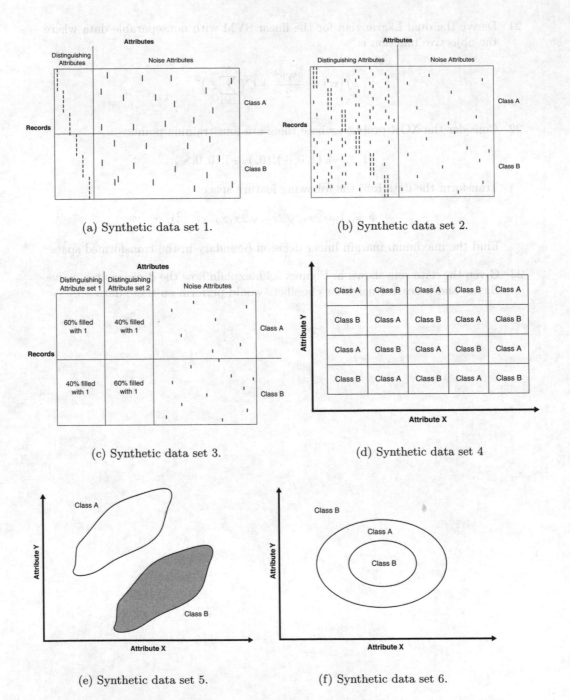

(a) Synthetic data set 1.

(b) Synthetic data set 2.

(c) Synthetic data set 3.

(d) Synthetic data set 4

(e) Synthetic data set 5.

(f) Synthetic data set 6.

Figure 5.49. Data set for Exercise 23.

6

Association Analysis: Basic Concepts and Algorithms

Many business enterprises accumulate large quantities of data from their day-to-day operations. For example, huge amounts of customer purchase data are collected daily at the checkout counters of grocery stores. Table 6.1 illustrates an example of such data, commonly known as **market basket transactions**. Each row in this table corresponds to a transaction, which contains a unique identifier labeled TID and a set of items bought by a given customer. Retailers are interested in analyzing the data to learn about the purchasing behavior of their customers. Such valuable information can be used to support a variety of business-related applications such as marketing promotions, inventory management, and customer relationship management.

This chapter presents a methodology known as **association analysis**, which is useful for discovering interesting relationships hidden in large data sets. The uncovered relationships can be represented in the form of associa-

Table 6.1. An example of market basket transactions.

TID	Items
1	{Bread, Milk}
2	{Bread, Diapers, Beer, Eggs}
3	{Milk, Diapers, Beer, Cola}
4	{Bread, Milk, Diapers, Beer}
5	{Bread, Milk, Diapers, Cola}

From Chapter 6 of *Introduction to Data Mining*, First Edition. Pang-Ning Tan, Michael Steinbach, Vipin Kumar.

tion rules or sets of frequent items. For example, the following rule can be extracted from the data set shown in Table 6.1:

$$\{\texttt{Diapers}\} \longrightarrow \{\texttt{Beer}\}.$$

The rule suggests that a strong relationship exists between the sale of diapers and beer because many customers who buy diapers also buy beer. Retailers can use this type of rules to help them identify new opportunities for cross-selling their products to the customers.

Besides market basket data, association analysis is also applicable to other application domains such as bioinformatics, medical diagnosis, Web mining, and scientific data analysis. In the analysis of Earth science data, for example, the association patterns may reveal interesting connections among the ocean, land, and atmospheric processes. Such information may help Earth scientists develop a better understanding of how the different elements of the Earth system interact with each other. Even though the techniques presented here are generally applicable to a wider variety of data sets, for illustrative purposes, our discussion will focus mainly on market basket data.

There are two key issues that need to be addressed when applying association analysis to market basket data. First, discovering patterns from a large transaction data set can be computationally expensive. Second, some of the discovered patterns are potentially spurious because they may happen simply by chance. The remainder of this chapter is organized around these two issues. The first part of the chapter is devoted to explaining the basic concepts of association analysis and the algorithms used to efficiently mine such patterns. The second part of the chapter deals with the issue of evaluating the discovered patterns in order to prevent the generation of spurious results.

6.1   Problem Definition

This section reviews the basic terminology used in association analysis and presents a formal description of the task.

Binary Representation   Market basket data can be represented in a binary format as shown in Table 6.2, where each row corresponds to a transaction and each column corresponds to an item. An item can be treated as a binary variable whose value is one if the item is present in a transaction and zero otherwise. Because the presence of an item in a transaction is often considered more important than its absence, an item is an **asymmetric** binary variable.

Table 6.2. A binary 0/1 representation of market basket data.

TID	Bread	Milk	Diapers	Beer	Eggs	Cola
1	1	1	0	0	0	0
2	1	0	1	1	1	0
3	0	1	1	1	0	1
4	1	1	1	1	0	0
5	1	1	1	0	0	1

This representation is perhaps a very simplistic view of real market basket data because it ignores certain important aspects of the data such as the quantity of items sold or the price paid to purchase them. Methods for handling such non-binary data will be explained in Chapter 7.

Itemset and Support Count   Let $I = \{i_1, i_2, \ldots, i_d\}$ be the set of all items in a market basket data and $T = \{t_1, t_2, \ldots, t_N\}$ be the set of all transactions. Each transaction t_i contains a subset of items chosen from I. In association analysis, a collection of zero or more items is termed an itemset. If an itemset contains k items, it is called a k-itemset. For instance, {Beer, Diapers, Milk} is an example of a 3-itemset. The null (or empty) set is an itemset that does not contain any items.

The transaction width is defined as the number of items present in a transaction. A transaction t_j is said to contain an itemset X if X is a subset of t_j. For example, the second transaction shown in Table 6.2 contains the itemset {Bread, Diapers} but not {Bread, Milk}. An important property of an itemset is its support count, which refers to the number of transactions that contain a particular itemset. Mathematically, the support count, $\sigma(X)$, for an itemset X can be stated as follows:

$$\sigma(X) = \left| \{t_i | X \subseteq t_i, \ t_i \in T\} \right|,$$

where the symbol $|\cdot|$ denote the number of elements in a set. In the data set shown in Table 6.2, the support count for {Beer, Diapers, Milk} is equal to two because there are only two transactions that contain all three items.

Association Rule   An association rule is an implication expression of the form $X \longrightarrow Y$, where X and Y are disjoint itemsets, i.e., $X \cap Y = \emptyset$. The strength of an association rule can be measured in terms of its **support** and **confidence**. Support determines how often a rule is applicable to a given data set, while confidence determines how frequently items in Y appear in transactions that contain X. The formal definitions of these metrics are

$$\text{Support, } s(X \longrightarrow Y) = \frac{\sigma(X \cup Y)}{N}; \tag{6.1}$$

$$\text{Confidence, } c(X \longrightarrow Y) = \frac{\sigma(X \cup Y)}{\sigma(X)}. \tag{6.2}$$

Example 6.1. Consider the rule {Milk, Diapers} $\longrightarrow$ {Beer}. Since the support count for {Milk, Diapers, Beer} is 2 and the total number of transactions is 5, the rule's support is $2/5 = 0.4$. The rule's confidence is obtained by dividing the support count for {Milk, Diapers, Beer} by the support count for {Milk, Diapers}. Since there are 3 transactions that contain milk and diapers, the confidence for this rule is $2/3 = 0.67$. ∎

Why Use Support and Confidence? Support is an important measure because a rule that has very low support may occur simply by chance. A low support rule is also likely to be uninteresting from a business perspective because it may not be profitable to promote items that customers seldom buy together (with the exception of the situation described in Section 6.8). For these reasons, support is often used to eliminate uninteresting rules. As will be shown in Section 6.2.1, support also has a desirable property that can be exploited for the efficient discovery of association rules.

Confidence, on the other hand, measures the reliability of the inference made by a rule. For a given rule $X \longrightarrow Y$, the higher the confidence, the more likely it is for Y to be present in transactions that contain X. Confidence also provides an estimate of the conditional probability of Y given X.

Association analysis results should be interpreted with caution. The inference made by an association rule does not necessarily imply causality. Instead, it suggests a strong co-occurrence relationship between items in the antecedent and consequent of the rule. Causality, on the other hand, requires knowledge about the causal and effect attributes in the data and typically involves relationships occurring over time (e.g., ozone depletion leads to global warming).

Formulation of Association Rule Mining Problem The association rule mining problem can be formally stated as follows:

Definition 6.1 (Association Rule Discovery). Given a set of transactions T, find all the rules having support $\geq$ *minsup* and confidence $\geq$ *minconf*, where *minsup* and *minconf* are the corresponding support and confidence thresholds.

A brute-force approach for mining association rules is to compute the support and confidence for every possible rule. This approach is prohibitively expensive because there are exponentially many rules that can be extracted from a data set. More specifically, the total number of possible rules extracted from a data set that contains d items is

$$R = 3^d - 2^{d+1} + 1. \qquad (6.3)$$

The proof for this equation is left as an exercise to the readers (see Exercise 5 on page 405). Even for the small data set shown in Table 6.1, this approach requires us to compute the support and confidence for $3^6 - 2^7 + 1 = 602$ rules. More than 80% of the rules are discarded after applying $minsup = 20\%$ and $minconf = 50\%$, thus making most of the computations become wasted. To avoid performing needless computations, it would be useful to prune the rules early without having to compute their support and confidence values.

An initial step toward improving the performance of association rule mining algorithms is to decouple the support and confidence requirements. From Equation 6.2, notice that the support of a rule $X \longrightarrow Y$ depends only on the support of its corresponding itemset, $X \cup Y$. For example, the following rules have identical support because they involve items from the same itemset, {Beer, Diapers, Milk}:

{Beer, Diapers} $\longrightarrow$ {Milk}, {Beer, Milk} $\longrightarrow$ {Diapers},
{Diapers, Milk} $\longrightarrow$ {Beer}, {Beer} $\longrightarrow$ {Diapers, Milk},
{Milk} $\longrightarrow$ {Beer,Diapers}, {Diapers} $\longrightarrow$ {Beer,Milk}.

If the itemset is infrequent, then all six candidate rules can be pruned immediately without our having to compute their confidence values.

Therefore, a common strategy adopted by many association rule mining algorithms is to decompose the problem into two major subtasks:

1. **Frequent Itemset Generation**, whose objective is to find all the itemsets that satisfy the *minsup* threshold. These itemsets are called frequent itemsets.

2. **Rule Generation**, whose objective is to extract all the high-confidence rules from the frequent itemsets found in the previous step. These rules are called strong rules.

The computational requirements for frequent itemset generation are generally more expensive than those of rule generation. Efficient techniques for generating frequent itemsets and association rules are discussed in Sections 6.2 and 6.3, respectively.

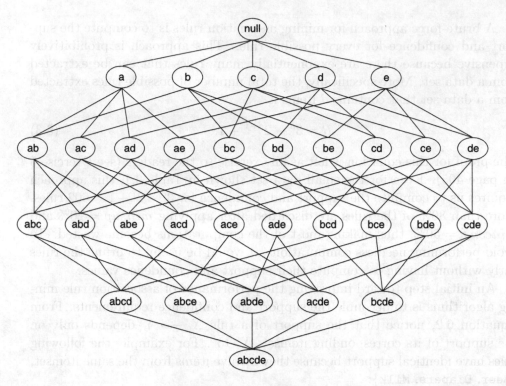

Figure 6.1. An itemset lattice.

6.2   Frequent Itemset Generation

A lattice structure can be used to enumerate the list of all possible itemsets. Figure 6.1 shows an itemset lattice for $I = \{a, b, c, d, e\}$. In general, a data set that contains k items can potentially generate up to $2^k - 1$ frequent itemsets, excluding the null set. Because k can be very large in many practical applications, the search space of itemsets that need to be explored is exponentially large.

A brute-force approach for finding frequent itemsets is to determine the support count for every **candidate itemset** in the lattice structure. To do this, we need to compare each candidate against every transaction, an operation that is shown in Figure 6.2. If the candidate is contained in a transaction, its support count will be incremented. For example, the support for {Bread, Milk} is incremented three times because the itemset is contained in transactions 1, 4, and 5. Such an approach can be very expensive because it requires $O(NMw)$ comparisons, where N is the number of transactions, $M = 2^k - 1$ is the number of candidate itemsets, and w is the maximum transaction width.

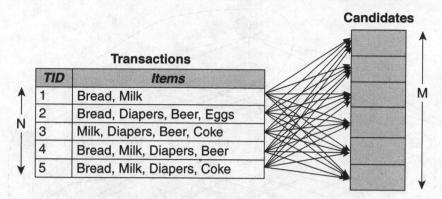

Figure 6.2. Counting the support of candidate itemsets.

There are several ways to reduce the computational complexity of frequent itemset generation.

1. **Reduce the number of candidate itemsets (M).** The *Apriori* principle, described in the next section, is an effective way to eliminate some of the candidate itemsets without counting their support values.

2. **Reduce the number of comparisons.** Instead of matching each candidate itemset against every transaction, we can reduce the number of comparisons by using more advanced data structures, either to store the candidate itemsets or to compress the data set. We will discuss these strategies in Sections 6.2.4 and 6.6.

6.2.1   The *Apriori* Principle

This section describes how the support measure helps to reduce the number of candidate itemsets explored during frequent itemset generation. The use of support for pruning candidate itemsets is guided by the following principle.

Theorem 6.1 (*Apriori* Principle). *If an itemset is frequent, then all of its subsets must also be frequent.*

To illustrate the idea behind the *Apriori* principle, consider the itemset lattice shown in Figure 6.3. Suppose $\{c, d, e\}$ is a frequent itemset. Clearly, any transaction that contains $\{c, d, e\}$ must also contain its subsets, $\{c, d\}$, $\{c, e\}$, $\{d, e\}$, $\{c\}$, $\{d\}$, and $\{e\}$. As a result, if $\{c, d, e\}$ is frequent, then all subsets of $\{c, d, e\}$ (i.e., the shaded itemsets in this figure) must also be frequent.

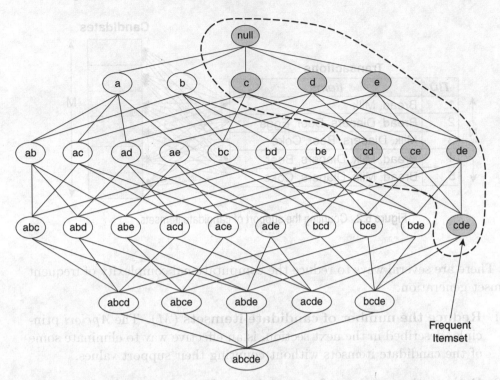

Figure 6.3. An illustration of the *Apriori* principle. If $\{c, d, e\}$ is frequent, then all subsets of this itemset are frequent.

Conversely, if an itemset such as $\{a, b\}$ is infrequent, then all of its supersets must be infrequent too. As illustrated in Figure 6.4, the entire subgraph containing the supersets of $\{a, b\}$ can be pruned immediately once $\{a, b\}$ is found to be infrequent. This strategy of trimming the exponential search space based on the support measure is known as **support-based pruning**. Such a pruning strategy is made possible by a key property of the support measure, namely, that the support for an itemset never exceeds the support for its subsets. This property is also known as the **anti-monotone** property of the support measure.

Definition 6.2 (Monotonicity Property). Let I be a set of items, and $J = 2^I$ be the power set of I. A measure f is monotone (or upward closed) if

$$\forall X, Y \in J: \ (X \subseteq Y) \longrightarrow f(X) \leq f(Y),$$

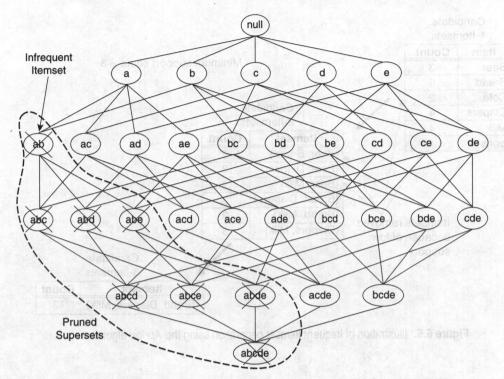

Figure 6.4. An illustration of support-based pruning. If $\{a, b\}$ is infrequent, then all supersets of $\{a, b\}$ are infrequent.

which means that if X is a subset of Y, then $f(X)$ must not exceed $f(Y)$. On the other hand, f is anti-monotone (or downward closed) if

$$\forall X, Y \in J : (X \subseteq Y) \longrightarrow f(Y) \leq f(X),$$

which means that if X is a subset of Y, then $f(Y)$ must not exceed $f(X)$.

Any measure that possesses an anti-monotone property can be incorporated directly into the mining algorithm to effectively prune the exponential search space of candidate itemsets, as will be shown in the next section.

6.2.2 Frequent Itemset Generation in the *Apriori* Algorithm

Apriori is the first association rule mining algorithm that pioneered the use of support-based pruning to systematically control the exponential growth of candidate itemsets. Figure 6.5 provides a high-level illustration of the frequent itemset generation part of the *Apriori* algorithm for the transactions shown in

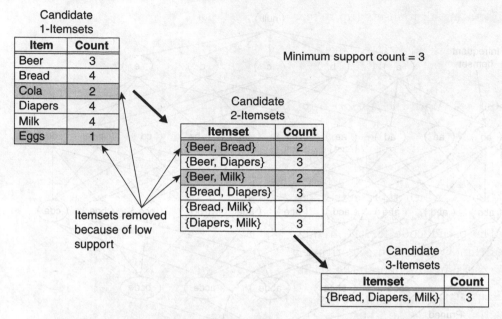

Figure 6.5. Illustration of frequent itemset generation using the *Apriori* algorithm.

Table 6.1. We assume that the support threshold is 60%, which is equivalent to a minimum support count equal to 3.

Initially, every item is considered as a candidate 1-itemset. After counting their supports, the candidate itemsets {Cola} and {Eggs} are discarded because they appear in fewer than three transactions. In the next iteration, candidate 2-itemsets are generated using only the frequent 1-itemsets because the *Apriori* principle ensures that all supersets of the infrequent 1-itemsets must be infrequent. Because there are only four frequent 1-itemsets, the number of candidate 2-itemsets generated by the algorithm is $\binom{4}{2} = 6$. Two of these six candidates, {Beer, Bread} and {Beer, Milk}, are subsequently found to be infrequent after computing their support values. The remaining four candidates are frequent, and thus will be used to generate candidate 3-itemsets. Without support-based pruning, there are $\binom{6}{3} = 20$ candidate 3-itemsets that can be formed using the six items given in this example. With the *Apriori* principle, we only need to keep candidate 3-itemsets whose subsets are frequent. The only candidate that has this property is {Bread, Diapers, Milk}.

The effectiveness of the *Apriori* pruning strategy can be shown by counting the number of candidate itemsets generated. A brute-force strategy of enumerating all itemsets (up to size 3) as candidates will produce

$$\binom{6}{1} + \binom{6}{2} + \binom{6}{3} = 6 + 15 + 20 = 41$$

candidates. With the *Apriori* principle, this number decreases to

$$\binom{6}{1} + \binom{4}{2} + 1 = 6 + 6 + 1 = 13$$

candidates, which represents a 68% reduction in the number of candidate itemsets even in this simple example.

The pseudocode for the frequent itemset generation part of the *Apriori* algorithm is shown in Algorithm 6.1. Let C_k denote the set of candidate k-itemsets and F_k denote the set of frequent k-itemsets:

- The algorithm initially makes a single pass over the data set to determine the support of each item. Upon completion of this step, the set of all frequent 1-itemsets, F_1, will be known (steps 1 and 2).

- Next, the algorithm will iteratively generate new candidate k-itemsets using the frequent $(k-1)$-itemsets found in the previous iteration (step 5). Candidate generation is implemented using a function called apriori-gen, which is described in Section 6.2.3.

Algorithm 6.1 Frequent itemset generation of the *Apriori* algorithm.

1: $k = 1$.
2: $F_k = \{\, i \mid i \in I \wedge \sigma(\{i\}) \geq N \times minsup \,\}$.   {Find all frequent 1-itemsets}
3: **repeat**
4:     $k = k + 1$.
5:     $C_k = $ apriori-gen(F_{k-1}).   {Generate candidate itemsets}
6:     **for** each transaction $t \in T$ **do**
7:         $C_t = $ subset(C_k, t).   {Identify all candidates that belong to t}
8:         **for** each candidate itemset $c \in C_t$ **do**
9:             $\sigma(c) = \sigma(c) + 1$.   {Increment support count}
10:        **end for**
11:    **end for**
12:    $F_k = \{\, c \mid c \in C_k \wedge \sigma(c) \geq N \times minsup \,\}$.   {Extract the frequent k-itemsets}
13: **until** $F_k = \emptyset$
14: Result $= \bigcup F_k$.

- To count the support of the candidates, the algorithm needs to make an additional pass over the data set (steps 6–10). The subset function is used to determine all the candidate itemsets in C_k that are contained in each transaction t. The implementation of this function is described in Section 6.2.4.

- After counting their supports, the algorithm eliminates all candidate itemsets whose support counts are less than *minsup* (step 12).

- The algorithm terminates when there are no new frequent itemsets generated, i.e., $F_k = \emptyset$ (step 13).

The frequent itemset generation part of the *Apriori* algorithm has two important characteristics. First, it is a **level-wise** algorithm; i.e., it traverses the itemset lattice one level at a time, from frequent 1-itemsets to the maximum size of frequent itemsets. Second, it employs a **generate-and-test** strategy for finding frequent itemsets. At each iteration, new candidate itemsets are generated from the frequent itemsets found in the previous iteration. The support for each candidate is then counted and tested against the *minsup* threshold. The total number of iterations needed by the algorithm is $k_{\max} + 1$, where $k_{\max}$ is the maximum size of the frequent itemsets.

6.2.3 Candidate Generation and Pruning

The apriori-gen function shown in Step 5 of Algorithm 6.1 generates candidate itemsets by performing the following two operations:

1. **Candidate Generation.** This operation generates new candidate k-itemsets based on the frequent $(k-1)$-itemsets found in the previous iteration.

2. **Candidate Pruning.** This operation eliminates some of the candidate k-itemsets using the support-based pruning strategy.

To illustrate the candidate pruning operation, consider a candidate k-itemset, $X = \{i_1, i_2, \ldots, i_k\}$. The algorithm must determine whether all of its proper subsets, $X - \{i_j\}$ ($\forall j = 1, 2, \ldots, k$), are frequent. If one of them is infrequent, then X is immediately pruned. This approach can effectively reduce the number of candidate itemsets considered during support counting. The complexity of this operation is $O(k)$ for each candidate k-itemset. However, as will be shown later, we do not have to examine all k subsets of a given candidate itemset. If m of the k subsets were used to generate a candidate, we only need to check the remaining $k - m$ subsets during candidate pruning.

In principle, there are many ways to generate candidate itemsets. The following is a list of requirements for an effective candidate generation procedure:

1. It should avoid generating too many unnecessary candidates. A candidate itemset is unnecessary if at least one of its subsets is infrequent. Such a candidate is guaranteed to be infrequent according to the anti-monotone property of support.

2. It must ensure that the candidate set is complete, i.e., no frequent itemsets are left out by the candidate generation procedure. To ensure completeness, the set of candidate itemsets must subsume the set of all frequent itemsets, i.e., $\forall k : F_k \subseteq C_k$.

3. It should not generate the same candidate itemset more than once. For example, the candidate itemset $\{a, b, c, d\}$ can be generated in many ways—by merging $\{a, b, c\}$ with $\{d\}$, $\{b, d\}$ with $\{a, c\}$, $\{c\}$ with $\{a, b, d\}$, etc. Generation of duplicate candidates leads to wasted computations and thus should be avoided for efficiency reasons.

Next, we will briefly describe several candidate generation procedures, including the one used by the apriori-gen function.

Brute-Force Method   The brute-force method considers every k-itemset as a potential candidate and then applies the candidate pruning step to remove any unnecessary candidates (see Figure 6.6). The number of candidate itemsets generated at level k is equal to $\binom{d}{k}$, where d is the total number of items. Although candidate generation is rather trivial, candidate pruning becomes extremely expensive because a large number of itemsets must be examined. Given that the amount of computations needed for each candidate is $O(k)$, the overall complexity of this method is $O\left(\sum_{k=1}^{d} k \times \binom{d}{k}\right) = O(d \cdot 2^{d-1})$.

$\mathbf{F}_{k-1} \times \mathbf{F}_1$ Method   An alternative method for candidate generation is to extend each frequent $(k - 1)$-itemset with other frequent items. Figure 6.7 illustrates how a frequent 2-itemset such as {Beer, Diapers} can be augmented with a frequent item such as Bread to produce a candidate 3-itemset {Beer, Diapers, Bread}. This method will produce $O(|F_{k-1}| \times |F_1|)$ candidate k-itemsets, where $|F_j|$ is the number of frequent j-itemsets. The overall complexity of this step is $O(\sum_k k |F_{k-1}||F_1|)$.

The procedure is complete because every frequent k-itemset is composed of a frequent $(k - 1)$-itemset and a frequent 1-itemset. Therefore, all frequent k-itemsets are part of the candidate k-itemsets generated by this procedure.

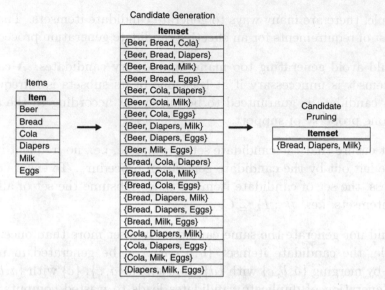

Figure 6.6. A brute-force method for generating candidate 3-itemsets.

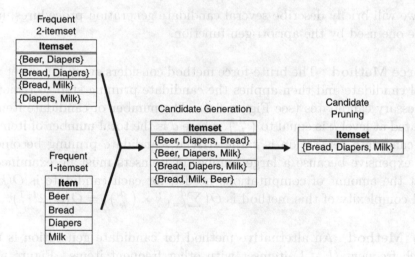

Figure 6.7. Generating and pruning candidate k-itemsets by merging a frequent $(k-1)$-itemset with a frequent item. Note that some of the candidates are unnecessary because their subsets are infrequent.

This approach, however, does not prevent the same candidate itemset from being generated more than once. For instance, {Bread, Diapers, Milk} can be generated by merging {Bread, Diapers} with {Milk}, {Bread, Milk} with {Diapers}, or {Diapers, Milk} with {Bread}. One way to avoid generating duplicate candidates is by ensuring that the items in each frequent itemset are kept sorted in their lexicographic order. Each frequent $(k-1)$-itemset X is then extended with frequent items that are lexicographically larger than the items in X. For example, the itemset {Bread, Diapers} can be augmented with {Milk} since Milk is lexicographically larger than Bread and Diapers. However, we should not augment {Diapers, Milk} with {Bread} nor {Bread, Milk} with {Diapers} because they violate the lexicographic ordering condition.

While this procedure is a substantial improvement over the brute-force method, it can still produce a large number of unnecessary candidates. For example, the candidate itemset obtained by merging {Beer, Diapers} with {Milk} is unnecessary because one of its subsets, {Beer, Milk}, is infrequent. There are several heuristics available to reduce the number of unnecessary candidates. For example, note that, for every candidate k-itemset that survives the pruning step, every item in the candidate must be contained in at least $k-1$ of the frequent $(k-1)$-itemsets. Otherwise, the candidate is guaranteed to be infrequent. For example, {Beer, Diapers, Milk} is a viable candidate 3-itemset only if every item in the candidate, including Beer, is contained in at least two frequent 2-itemsets. Since there is only one frequent 2-itemset containing Beer, all candidate itemsets involving Beer must be infrequent.

$\mathbf{F}_{k-1} \times \mathbf{F}_{k-1}$ **Method** The candidate generation procedure in the apriori-gen function merges a pair of frequent $(k-1)$-itemsets only if their first $k-2$ items are identical. Let $A = \{a_1, a_2, \ldots, a_{k-1}\}$ and $B = \{b_1, b_2, \ldots, b_{k-1}\}$ be a pair of frequent $(k-1)$-itemsets. A and B are merged if they satisfy the following conditions:

$$a_i = b_i \text{ (for } i = 1, 2, \ldots, k-2) \text{ and } a_{k-1} \neq b_{k-1}.$$

In Figure 6.8, the frequent itemsets {Bread, Diapers} and {Bread, Milk} are merged to form a candidate 3-itemset {Bread, Diapers, Milk}. The algorithm does not have to merge {Beer, Diapers} with {Diapers, Milk} because the first item in both itemsets is different. Indeed, if {Beer, Diapers, Milk} is a viable candidate, it would have been obtained by merging {Beer, Diapers} with {Beer, Milk} instead. This example illustrates both the completeness of the candidate generation procedure and the advantages of using lexicographic ordering to prevent duplicate candidates. However, because each candidate is obtained by merging a pair of frequent $(k-1)$-itemsets, an additional candidate pruning step is needed to ensure that the remaining $k-2$ subsets of the candidate are frequent.

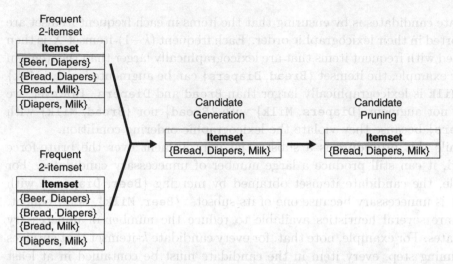

Figure 6.8. Generating and pruning candidate k-itemsets by merging pairs of frequent $(k-1)$-itemsets.

6.2.4   Support Counting

Support counting is the process of determining the frequency of occurrence for every candidate itemset that survives the candidate pruning step of the apriori-gen function. Support counting is implemented in steps 6 through 11 of Algorithm 6.1. One approach for doing this is to compare each transaction against every candidate itemset (see Figure 6.2) and to update the support counts of candidates contained in the transaction. This approach is computationally expensive, especially when the numbers of transactions and candidate itemsets are large.

An alternative approach is to enumerate the itemsets contained in each transaction and use them to update the support counts of their respective candidate itemsets. To illustrate, consider a transaction t that contains five items, $\{1, 2, 3, 5, 6\}$. There are $\binom{5}{3} = 10$ itemsets of size 3 contained in this transaction. Some of the itemsets may correspond to the candidate 3-itemsets under investigation, in which case, their support counts are incremented. Other subsets of t that do not correspond to any candidates can be ignored.

Figure 6.9 shows a systematic way for enumerating the 3-itemsets contained in t. Assuming that each itemset keeps its items in increasing lexicographic order, an itemset can be enumerated by specifying the smallest item first, followed by the larger items. For instance, given $t = \{1, 2, 3, 5, 6\}$, all the 3-itemsets contained in t must begin with item 1, 2, or 3. It is not possible to construct a 3-itemset that begins with items 5 or 6 because there are only two

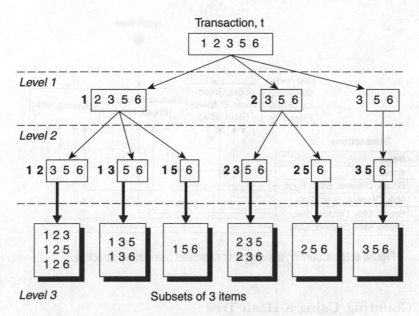

Figure 6.9. Enumerating subsets of three items from a transaction t.

items in t whose labels are greater than or equal to 5. The number of ways to specify the first item of a 3-itemset contained in t is illustrated by the Level 1 prefix structures depicted in Figure 6.9. For instance, 1 $\boxed{2\ 3\ 5\ 6}$ represents a 3-itemset that begins with item 1, followed by two more items chosen from the set $\{2, 3, 5, 6\}$.

After fixing the first item, the prefix structures at Level 2 represent the number of ways to select the second item. For example, 1 2 $\boxed{3\ 5\ 6}$ corresponds to itemsets that begin with prefix (1 2) and are followed by items 3, 5, or 6. Finally, the prefix structures at Level 3 represent the complete set of 3-itemsets contained in t. For example, the 3-itemsets that begin with prefix $\{1\ 2\}$ are $\{1, 2, 3\}$, $\{1, 2, 5\}$, and $\{1, 2, 6\}$, while those that begin with prefix $\{2\ 3\}$ are $\{2, 3, 5\}$ and $\{2, 3, 6\}$.

The prefix structures shown in Figure 6.9 demonstrate how itemsets contained in a transaction can be systematically enumerated, i.e., by specifying their items one by one, from the leftmost item to the rightmost item. We still have to determine whether each enumerated 3-itemset corresponds to an existing candidate itemset. If it matches one of the candidates, then the support count of the corresponding candidate is incremented. In the next section, we illustrate how this matching operation can be performed efficiently using a hash tree structure.

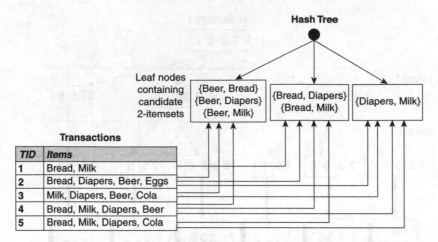

Figure 6.10. Counting the support of itemsets using hash structure.

Support Counting Using a Hash Tree

In the *Apriori* algorithm, candidate itemsets are partitioned into different buckets and stored in a hash tree. During support counting, itemsets contained in each transaction are also hashed into their appropriate buckets. That way, instead of comparing each itemset in the transaction with every candidate itemset, it is matched only against candidate itemsets that belong to the same bucket, as shown in Figure 6.10.

Figure 6.11 shows an example of a hash tree structure. Each internal node of the tree uses the following hash function, $h(p) = p \bmod 3$, to determine which branch of the current node should be followed next. For example, items 1, 4, and 7 are hashed to the same branch (i.e., the leftmost branch) because they have the same remainder after dividing the number by 3. All candidate itemsets are stored at the leaf nodes of the hash tree. The hash tree shown in Figure 6.11 contains 15 candidate 3-itemsets, distributed across 9 leaf nodes.

Consider a transaction, $t = \{1, 2, 3, 5, 6\}$. To update the support counts of the candidate itemsets, the hash tree must be traversed in such a way that all the leaf nodes containing candidate 3-itemsets belonging to t must be visited at least once. Recall that the 3-itemsets contained in t must begin with items 1, 2, or 3, as indicated by the Level 1 prefix structures shown in Figure 6.9. Therefore, at the root node of the hash tree, the items 1, 2, and 3 of the transaction are hashed separately. Item 1 is hashed to the left child of the root node, item 2 is hashed to the middle child, and item 3 is hashed to the right child. At the next level of the tree, the transaction is hashed on the second

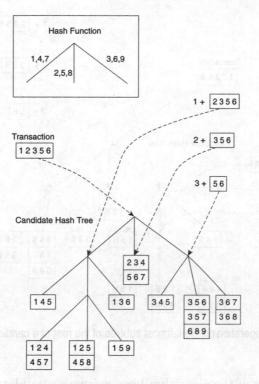

Figure 6.11. Hashing a transaction at the root node of a hash tree.

item listed in the Level 2 structures shown in Figure 6.9. For example, after hashing on item 1 at the root node, items 2, 3, and 5 of the transaction are hashed. Items 2 and 5 are hashed to the middle child, while item 3 is hashed to the right child, as shown in Figure 6.12. This process continues until the leaf nodes of the hash tree are reached. The candidate itemsets stored at the visited leaf nodes are compared against the transaction. If a candidate is a subset of the transaction, its support count is incremented. In this example, 5 out of the 9 leaf nodes are visited and 9 out of the 15 itemsets are compared against the transaction.

6.2.5 Computational Complexity

The computational complexity of the *Apriori* algorithm can be affected by the following factors.

Support Threshold Lowering the support threshold often results in more itemsets being declared as frequent. This has an adverse effect on the com-

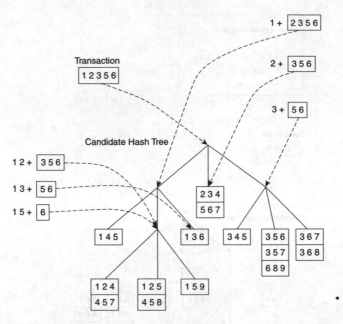

Figure 6.12. Subset operation on the leftmost subtree of the root of a candidate hash tree.

putational complexity of the algorithm because more candidate itemsets must be generated and counted, as shown in Figure 6.13. The maximum size of frequent itemsets also tends to increase with lower support thresholds. As the maximum size of the frequent itemsets increases, the algorithm will need to make more passes over the data set.

Number of Items (Dimensionality) As the number of items increases, more space will be needed to store the support counts of items. If the number of frequent items also grows with the dimensionality of the data, the computation and I/O costs will increase because of the larger number of candidate itemsets generated by the algorithm.

Number of Transactions Since the *Apriori* algorithm makes repeated passes over the data set, its run time increases with a larger number of transactions.

Average Transaction Width For dense data sets, the average transaction width can be very large. This affects the complexity of the *Apriori* algorithm in two ways. First, the maximum size of frequent itemsets tends to increase as the

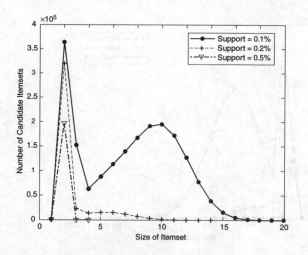

(a) Number of candidate itemsets.

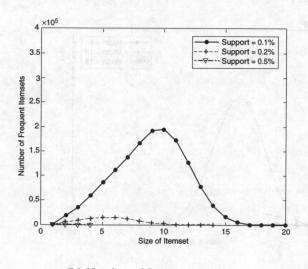

(b) Number of frequent itemsets.

Figure 6.13. Effect of support threshold on the number of candidate and frequent itemsets.

average transaction width increases. As a result, more candidate itemsets must be examined during candidate generation and support counting, as illustrated in Figure 6.14. Second, as the transaction width increases, more itemsets

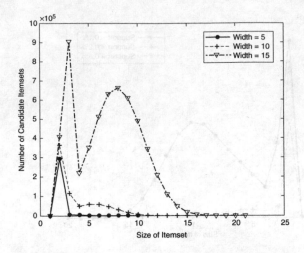

(a) Number of candidate itemsets.

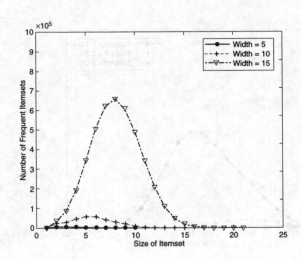

(b) Number of Frequent Itemsets.

Figure 6.14. Effect of average transaction width on the number of candidate and frequent itemsets.

are contained in the transaction. This will increase the number of hash tree traversals performed during support counting.

A detailed analysis of the time complexity for the *Apriori* algorithm is presented next.

Generation of frequent 1-itemsets For each transaction, we need to update the support count for every item present in the transaction. Assuming that w is the average transaction width, this operation requires $O(Nw)$ time, where N is the total number of transactions.

Candidate generation To generate candidate k-itemsets, pairs of frequent $(k-1)$-itemsets are merged to determine whether they have at least $k-2$ items in common. Each merging operation requires at most $k-2$ equality comparisons. In the best-case scenario, every merging step produces a viable candidate k-itemset. In the worst-case scenario, the algorithm must merge every pair of frequent $(k-1)$-itemsets found in the previous iteration. Therefore, the overall cost of merging frequent itemsets is

$$\sum_{k=2}^{w}(k-2)|C_k| < \text{ Cost of merging } < \sum_{k=2}^{w}(k-2)|F_{k-1}|^2.$$

A hash tree is also constructed during candidate generation to store the candidate itemsets. Because the maximum depth of the tree is k, the cost for populating the hash tree with candidate itemsets is $O\left(\sum_{k=2}^{w}k|C_k|\right)$. During candidate pruning, we need to verify that the $k-2$ subsets of every candidate k-itemset are frequent. Since the cost for looking up a candidate in a hash tree is $O(k)$, the candidate pruning step requires $O\left(\sum_{k=2}^{w}k(k-2)|C_k|\right)$ time.

Support counting Each transaction of length $|t|$ produces $\binom{|t|}{k}$ itemsets of size k. This is also the effective number of hash tree traversals performed for each transaction. The cost for support counting is $O\left(N\sum_{k}\binom{w}{k}\alpha_k\right)$, where w is the maximum transaction width and α_k is the cost for updating the support count of a candidate k-itemset in the hash tree.

6.3 Rule Generation

This section describes how to extract association rules efficiently from a given frequent itemset. Each frequent k-itemset, Y, can produce up to $2^k - 2$ association rules, ignoring rules that have empty antecedents or consequents ($\emptyset \longrightarrow Y$ or $Y \longrightarrow \emptyset$). An association rule can be extracted by partitioning the itemset Y into two non-empty subsets, X and $Y - X$, such that $X \longrightarrow Y - X$ satisfies the confidence threshold. Note that all such rules must have already met the support threshold because they are generated from a frequent itemset.

Example 6.2. Let $X = \{1, 2, 3\}$ be a frequent itemset. There are six candidate association rules that can be generated from X: $\{1, 2\} \longrightarrow \{3\}$, $\{1, 3\} \longrightarrow \{2\}$, $\{2, 3\} \longrightarrow \{1\}$, $\{1\} \longrightarrow \{2, 3\}$, $\{2\} \longrightarrow \{1, 3\}$, and $\{3\} \longrightarrow \{1, 2\}$. As each of their support is identical to the support for X, the rules must satisfy the support threshold. ∎

Computing the confidence of an association rule does not require additional scans of the transaction data set. Consider the rule $\{1, 2\} \longrightarrow \{3\}$, which is generated from the frequent itemset $X = \{1, 2, 3\}$. The confidence for this rule is $\sigma(\{1, 2, 3\})/\sigma(\{1, 2\})$. Because $\{1, 2, 3\}$ is frequent, the anti-monotone property of support ensures that $\{1, 2\}$ must be frequent, too. Since the support counts for both itemsets were already found during frequent itemset generation, there is no need to read the entire data set again.

6.3.1   Confidence-Based Pruning

Unlike the support measure, confidence does not have any monotone property. For example, the confidence for $X \longrightarrow Y$ can be larger, smaller, or equal to the confidence for another rule $\tilde{X} \longrightarrow \tilde{Y}$, where $\tilde{X} \subseteq X$ and $\tilde{Y} \subseteq Y$ (see Exercise 3 on page 405). Nevertheless, if we compare rules generated from the same frequent itemset Y, the following theorem holds for the confidence measure.

Theorem 6.2. *If a rule $X \longrightarrow Y - X$ does not satisfy the confidence threshold, then any rule $X' \longrightarrow Y - X'$, where X' is a subset of X, must not satisfy the confidence threshold as well.*

To prove this theorem, consider the following two rules: $X' \longrightarrow Y - X'$ and $X \longrightarrow Y - X$, where $X' \subset X$. The confidence of the rules are $\sigma(Y)/\sigma(X')$ and $\sigma(Y)/\sigma(X)$, respectively. Since X' is a subset of X, $\sigma(X') \geq \sigma(X)$. Therefore, the former rule cannot have a higher confidence than the latter rule.

6.3.2   Rule Generation in *Apriori* Algorithm

The *Apriori* algorithm uses a level-wise approach for generating association rules, where each level corresponds to the number of items that belong to the rule consequent. Initially, all the high-confidence rules that have only one item in the rule consequent are extracted. These rules are then used to generate new candidate rules. For example, if $\{acd\} \longrightarrow \{b\}$ and $\{abd\} \longrightarrow \{c\}$ are high-confidence rules, then the candidate rule $\{ad\} \longrightarrow \{bc\}$ is generated by merging the consequents of both rules. Figure 6.15 shows a lattice structure for the association rules generated from the frequent itemset $\{a, b, c, d\}$. If any node in the lattice has low confidence, then according to Theorem 6.2, the

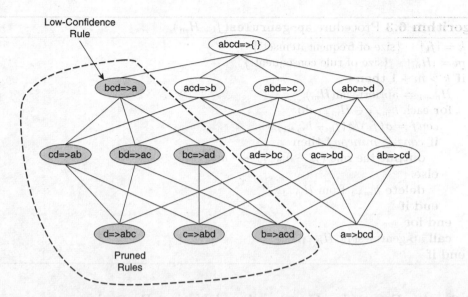

Figure 6.15. Pruning of association rules using the confidence measure.

entire subgraph spanned by the node can be pruned immediately. Suppose the confidence for $\{bcd\} \longrightarrow \{a\}$ is low. All the rules containing item a in its consequent, including $\{cd\} \longrightarrow \{ab\}$, $\{bd\} \longrightarrow \{ac\}$, $\{bc\} \longrightarrow \{ad\}$, and $\{d\} \longrightarrow \{abc\}$ can be discarded.

A pseudocode for the rule generation step is shown in Algorithms 6.2 and 6.3. Note the similarity between the ap-genrules procedure given in Algorithm 6.3 and the frequent itemset generation procedure given in Algorithm 6.1. The only difference is that, in rule generation, we do not have to make additional passes over the data set to compute the confidence of the candidate rules. Instead, we determine the confidence of each rule by using the support counts computed during frequent itemset generation.

Algorithm 6.2 Rule generation of the *Apriori* algorithm.

1: **for** each frequent k-itemset f_k, $k \geq 2$ **do**
2: $\quad H_1 = \{i \mid i \in f_k\}$ {1-item consequents of the rule.}
3: $\quad$ call ap-genrules(f_k, H_1.)
4: **end for**

Algorithm 6.3 Procedure ap-genrules(f_k, H_m).

1: $k = |f_k|$ {size of frequent itemset.}
2: $m = |H_m|$ {size of rule consequent.}
3: **if** $k > m + 1$ **then**
4:    H_{m+1} = apriori-gen(H_m).
5:    **for** each $h_{m+1} \in H_{m+1}$ **do**
6:       $conf = \sigma(f_k)/\sigma(f_k - h_{m+1})$.
7:       **if** $conf \geq minconf$ **then**
8:          **output** the rule $(f_k - h_{m+1}) \longrightarrow h_{m+1}$.
9:       **else**
10:          **delete** h_{m+1} from H_{m+1}.
11:       **end if**
12:    **end for**
13:    **call** ap-genrules(f_k, H_{m+1}.)
14: **end if**

6.3.3   An Example: Congressional Voting Records

This section demonstrates the results of applying association analysis to the voting records of members of the United States House of Representatives. The data is obtained from the 1984 Congressional Voting Records Database, which is available at the UCI machine learning data repository. Each transaction contains information about the party affiliation for a representative along with his or her voting record on 16 key issues. There are 435 transactions and 34 items in the data set. The set of items are listed in Table 6.3.

The *Apriori* algorithm is then applied to the data set with $minsup = 30\%$ and $minconf = 90\%$. Some of the high-confidence rules extracted by the algorithm are shown in Table 6.4. The first two rules suggest that most of the members who voted yes for aid to El Salvador and no for budget resolution and MX missile are Republicans; while those who voted no for aid to El Salvador and yes for budget resolution and MX missile are Democrats. These high-confidence rules show the key issues that divide members from both political parties. If $minconf$ is reduced, we may find rules that contain issues that cut across the party lines. For example, with $minconf = 40\%$, the rules suggest that corporation cutbacks is an issue that receives almost equal number of votes from both parties—52.3% of the members who voted no are Republicans, while the remaining 47.7% of them who voted no are Democrats.

Table 6.3. List of binary attributes from the 1984 United States Congressional Voting Records. Source: The UCI machine learning repository.

1. Republican
2. Democrat
3. handicapped-infants = yes
4. handicapped-infants = no
5. water project cost sharing = yes
6. water project cost sharing = no
7. budget-resolution = yes
8. budget-resolution = no
9. physician fee freeze = yes
10. physician fee freeze = no
11. aid to El Salvador = yes
12. aid to El Salvador = no
13. religious groups in schools = yes
14. religious groups in schools = no
15. anti-satellite test ban = yes
16. anti-satellite test ban = no
17. aid to Nicaragua = yes
18. aid to Nicaragua = no
19. MX-missile = yes
20. MX-missile = no
21. immigration = yes
22. immigration = no
23. synfuel corporation cutback = yes
24. synfuel corporation cutback = no
25. education spending = yes
26. education spending = no
27. right-to-sue = yes
28. right-to-sue = no
29. crime = yes
30. crime = no
31. duty-free-exports = yes
32. duty-free-exports = no
33. export administration act = yes
34. export administration act = no

Table 6.4. Association rules extracted from the 1984 United States Congressional Voting Records.

Association Rule	Confidence
{budget resolution = no, MX-missile=no, aid to El Salvador = yes } $\longrightarrow$ {Republican}	91.0%
{budget resolution = yes, MX-missile=yes, aid to El Salvador = no } $\longrightarrow$ {Democrat}	97.5%
{crime = yes, right-to-sue = yes, physician fee freeze = yes} $\longrightarrow$ {Republican}	93.5%
{crime = no, right-to-sue = no, physician fee freeze = no} $\longrightarrow$ {Democrat}	100%

6.4   Compact Representation of Frequent Itemsets

In practice, the number of frequent itemsets produced from a transaction data set can be very large. It is useful to identify a small representative set of itemsets from which all other frequent itemsets can be derived. Two such representations are presented in this section in the form of maximal and closed frequent itemsets.

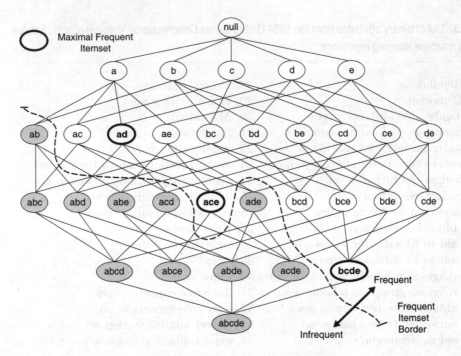

Figure 6.16. Maximal frequent itemset.

6.4.1 Maximal Frequent Itemsets

Definition 6.3 (Maximal Frequent Itemset). A maximal frequent itemset is defined as a frequent itemset for which none of its immediate supersets are frequent.

To illustrate this concept, consider the itemset lattice shown in Figure 6.16. The itemsets in the lattice are divided into two groups: those that are frequent and those that are infrequent. A frequent itemset border, which is represented by a dashed line, is also illustrated in the diagram. Every itemset located above the border is frequent, while those located below the border (the shaded nodes) are infrequent. Among the itemsets residing near the border, $\{a, d\}$, $\{a, c, e\}$, and $\{b, c, d, e\}$ are considered to be maximal frequent itemsets because their immediate supersets are infrequent. An itemset such as $\{a, d\}$ is maximal frequent because all of its immediate supersets, $\{a, b, d\}$, $\{a, c, d\}$, and $\{a, d, e\}$, are infrequent. In contrast, $\{a, c\}$ is non-maximal because one of its immediate supersets, $\{a, c, e\}$, is frequent.

Maximal frequent itemsets effectively provide a compact representation of frequent itemsets. In other words, they form the smallest set of itemsets from which all frequent itemsets can be derived. For example, the frequent itemsets shown in Figure 6.16 can be divided into two groups:

- Frequent itemsets that begin with item a and that may contain items c, d, or e. This group includes itemsets such as $\{a\}$, $\{a, c\}$, $\{a, d\}$, $\{a, e\}$, and $\{a, c, e\}$.

- Frequent itemsets that begin with items b, c, d, or e. This group includes itemsets such as $\{b\}$, $\{b, c\}$, $\{c, d\}$,$\{b, c, d, e\}$, etc.

Frequent itemsets that belong in the first group are subsets of either $\{a, c, e\}$ or $\{a, d\}$, while those that belong in the second group are subsets of $\{b, c, d, e\}$. Hence, the maximal frequent itemsets $\{a, c, e\}$, $\{a, d\}$, and $\{b, c, d, e\}$ provide a compact representation of the frequent itemsets shown in Figure 6.16.

Maximal frequent itemsets provide a valuable representation for data sets that can produce very long, frequent itemsets, as there are exponentially many frequent itemsets in such data. Nevertheless, this approach is practical only if an efficient algorithm exists to explicitly find the maximal frequent itemsets without having to enumerate all their subsets. We briefly describe one such approach in Section 6.5.

Despite providing a compact representation, maximal frequent itemsets do not contain the support information of their subsets. For example, the support of the maximal frequent itemsets $\{a, c, e\}$, $\{a, d\}$, and $\{b,c,d,e\}$ do not provide any hint about the support of their subsets. An additional pass over the data set is therefore needed to determine the support counts of the non-maximal frequent itemsets. In some cases, it might be desirable to have a minimal representation of frequent itemsets that preserves the support information. We illustrate such a representation in the next section.

6.4.2   Closed Frequent Itemsets

Closed itemsets provide a minimal representation of itemsets without losing their support information. A formal definition of a closed itemset is presented below.

Definition 6.4 (Closed Itemset).   An itemset X is closed if none of its immediate supersets has exactly the same support count as X.

Put another way, X is not closed if at least one of its immediate supersets has the same support count as X. Examples of closed itemsets are shown in Figure 6.17. To better illustrate the support count of each itemset, we have associated each node (itemset) in the lattice with a list of its corresponding

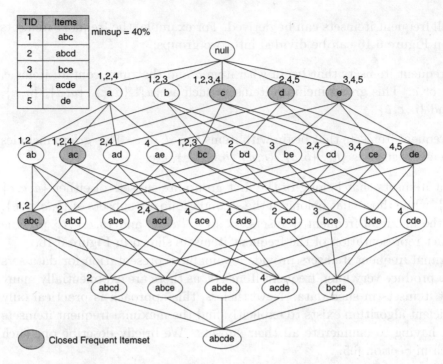

TID	Items
1	abc
2	abcd
3	bce
4	acde
5	de

minsup = 40%

Figure 6.17. An example of the closed frequent itemsets (with minimum support count equal to 40%).

transaction IDs. For example, since the node $\{b, c\}$ is associated with transaction IDs 1, 2, and 3, its support count is equal to three. From the transactions given in this diagram, notice that every transaction that contains b also contains c. Consequently, the support for $\{b\}$ is identical to $\{b, c\}$ and $\{b\}$ should not be considered a closed itemset. Similarly, since c occurs in every transaction that contains both a and d, the itemset $\{a, d\}$ is not closed. On the other hand, $\{b, c\}$ is a closed itemset because it does not have the same support count as any of its supersets.

Definition 6.5 (Closed Frequent Itemset). An itemset is a closed frequent itemset if it is closed and its support is greater than or equal to *minsup*.

In the previous example, assuming that the support threshold is 40%, {b,c} is a closed frequent itemset because its support is 60%. The rest of the closed frequent itemsets are indicated by the shaded nodes.

Algorithms are available to explicitly extract closed frequent itemsets from a given data set. Interested readers may refer to the bibliographic notes at the end of this chapter for further discussions of these algorithms. We can use the closed frequent itemsets to determine the support counts for the non-closed

---

Algorithm 6.4 Support counting using closed frequent itemsets.

1: Let C denote the set of closed frequent itemsets
2: Let $k_{\max}$ denote the maximum size of closed frequent itemsets
3: $F_{k_{\max}} = \{f | f \in C, \ |f| = k_{\max}\}$ {Find all frequent itemsets of size $k_{\max}$.}
4: **for** $k = k_{\max} - 1$ downto 1 **do**
5:    $F_k = \{f | f \subset F_{k+1}, \ |f| = k\}$ {Find all frequent itemsets of size k.}
6:    **for** each $f \in F_k$ **do**
7:       **if** $f \notin C$ **then**
8:          $f.support = \max\{f'.support | f' \in F_{k+1}, \ f \subset f'\}$
9:       **end if**
10:   **end for**
11: **end for**

---

frequent itemsets. For example, consider the frequent itemset $\{a, d\}$ shown in Figure 6.17. Because the itemset is not closed, its support count must be identical to one of its immediate supersets. The key is to determine which superset (among $\{a, b, d\}$, $\{a, c, d\}$, or $\{a, d, e\}$) has exactly the same support count as $\{a, d\}$. The *Apriori* principle states that any transaction that contains the superset of $\{a, d\}$ must also contain $\{a, d\}$. However, any transaction that contains $\{a, d\}$ does not have to contain the supersets of $\{a, d\}$. For this reason, the support for $\{a, d\}$ must be equal to the largest support among its supersets. Since $\{a, c, d\}$ has a larger support than both $\{a, b, d\}$ and $\{a, d, e\}$, the support for $\{a, d\}$ must be identical to the support for $\{a, c, d\}$. Using this methodology, an algorithm can be developed to compute the support for the non-closed frequent itemsets. The pseudocode for this algorithm is shown in Algorithm 6.4. The algorithm proceeds in a specific-to-general fashion, i.e., from the largest to the smallest frequent itemsets. This is because, in order to find the support for a non-closed frequent itemset, the support for all of its supersets must be known.

To illustrate the advantage of using closed frequent itemsets, consider the data set shown in Table 6.5, which contains ten transactions and fifteen items. The items can be divided into three groups: (1) Group A, which contains items a_1 through a_5; (2) Group B, which contains items b_1 through b_5; and (3) Group C, which contains items c_1 through c_5. Note that items within each group are perfectly associated with each other and they do not appear with items from another group. Assuming the support threshold is 20%, the total number of frequent itemsets is $3 \times (2^5 - 1) = 93$. However, there are only three closed frequent itemsets in the data: ($\{a_1, a_2, a_3, a_4, a_5\}$, $\{b_1, b_2, b_3, b_4, b_5\}$, and $\{c_1, c_2, c_3, c_4, c_5\}$). It is often sufficient to present only the closed frequent itemsets to the analysts instead of the entire set of frequent itemsets.

Table 6.5. A transaction data set for mining closed itemsets.

TID	a_1	a_2	a_3	a_4	a_5	b_1	b_2	b_3	b_4	b_5	c_1	c_2	c_3	c_4	c_5
1	1	1	1	1	1	0	0	0	0	0	0	0	0	0	0
2	1	1	1	1	1	0	0	0	0	0	0	0	0	0	0
3	1	1	1	1	1	0	0	0	0	0	0	0	0	0	0
4	0	0	0	0	0	1	1	1	1	1	0	0	0	0	0
5	0	0	0	0	0	1	1	1	1	1	0	0	0	0	0
6	0	0	0	0	0	1	1	1	1	1	0	0	0	0	0
7	0	0	0	0	0	0	0	0	0	0	1	1	1	1	1
8	0	0	0	0	0	0	0	0	0	0	1	1	1	1	1
9	0	0	0	0	0	0	0	0	0	0	1	1	1	1	1
10	0	0	0	0	0	0	0	0	0	0	1	1	1	1	1

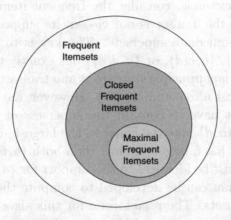

Figure 6.18. Relationships among frequent, maximal frequent, and closed frequent itemsets.

Closed frequent itemsets are useful for removing some of the redundant association rules. An association rule $X \longrightarrow Y$ is redundant if there exists another rule $X' \longrightarrow Y'$, where X is a subset of X' and Y is a subset of Y', such that the support and confidence for both rules are identical. In the example shown in Figure 6.17, $\{b\}$ is not a closed frequent itemset while $\{b, c\}$ is closed. The association rule $\{b\} \longrightarrow \{d, e\}$ is therefore redundant because it has the same support and confidence as $\{b, c\} \longrightarrow \{d, e\}$. Such redundant rules are not generated if closed frequent itemsets are used for rule generation.

Finally, note that all maximal frequent itemsets are closed because none of the maximal frequent itemsets can have the same support count as their immediate supersets. The relationships among frequent, maximal frequent, and closed frequent itemsets are shown in Figure 6.18.

6.5 Alternative Methods for Generating Frequent Itemsets

Apriori is one of the earliest algorithms to have successfully addressed the combinatorial explosion of frequent itemset generation. It achieves this by applying the *Apriori* principle to prune the exponential search space. Despite its significant performance improvement, the algorithm still incurs considerable I/O overhead since it requires making several passes over the transaction data set. In addition, as noted in Section 6.2.5, the performance of the *Apriori* algorithm may degrade significantly for dense data sets because of the increasing width of transactions. Several alternative methods have been developed to overcome these limitations and improve upon the efficiency of the *Apriori* algorithm. The following is a high-level description of these methods.

Traversal of Itemset Lattice A search for frequent itemsets can be conceptually viewed as a traversal on the itemset lattice shown in Figure 6.1. The search strategy employed by an algorithm dictates how the lattice structure is traversed during the frequent itemset generation process. Some search strategies are better than others, depending on the configuration of frequent itemsets in the lattice. An overview of these strategies is presented next.

- **General-to-Specific versus Specific-to-General:** The *Apriori* algorithm uses a general-to-specific search strategy, where pairs of frequent $(k-1)$-itemsets are merged to obtain candidate k-itemsets. This general-to-specific search strategy is effective, provided the maximum length of a frequent itemset is not too long. The configuration of frequent itemsets that works best with this strategy is shown in Figure 6.19(a), where the darker nodes represent infrequent itemsets. Alternatively, a specific-to-general search strategy looks for more specific frequent itemsets first, before finding the more general frequent itemsets. This strategy is useful to discover maximal frequent itemsets in dense transactions, where the frequent itemset border is located near the bottom of the lattice, as shown in Figure 6.19(b). The *Apriori* principle can be applied to prune all subsets of maximal frequent itemsets. Specifically, if a candidate k-itemset is maximal frequent, we do not have to examine any of its subsets of size $k - 1$. However, if the candidate k-itemset is infrequent, we need to check all of its $k - 1$ subsets in the next iteration. Another approach is to combine both general-to-specific and specific-to-general search strategies. This bidirectional approach requires more space to

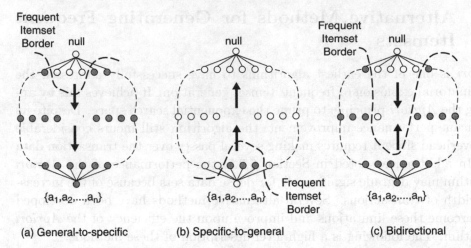

Figure 6.19. General-to-specific, specific-to-general, and bidirectional search.

store the candidate itemsets, but it can help to rapidly identify the frequent itemset border, given the configuration shown in Figure 6.19(c).

- **Equivalence Classes:** Another way to envision the traversal is to first partition the lattice into disjoint groups of nodes (or equivalence classes). A frequent itemset generation algorithm searches for frequent itemsets within a particular equivalence class first before moving to another equivalence class. As an example, the level-wise strategy used in the *Apriori* algorithm can be considered to be partitioning the lattice on the basis of itemset sizes; i.e., the algorithm discovers all frequent 1-itemsets first before proceeding to larger-sized itemsets. Equivalence classes can also be defined according to the prefix or suffix labels of an itemset. In this case, two itemsets belong to the same equivalence class if they share a common prefix or suffix of length k. In the prefix-based approach, the algorithm can search for frequent itemsets starting with the prefix a before looking for those starting with prefixes b, c, and so on. Both prefix-based and suffix-based equivalence classes can be demonstrated using the tree-like structure shown in Figure 6.20.

- **Breadth-First versus Depth-First:** The *Apriori* algorithm traverses the lattice in a breadth-first manner, as shown in Figure 6.21(a). It first discovers all the frequent 1-itemsets, followed by the frequent 2-itemsets, and so on, until no new frequent itemsets are generated. The itemset

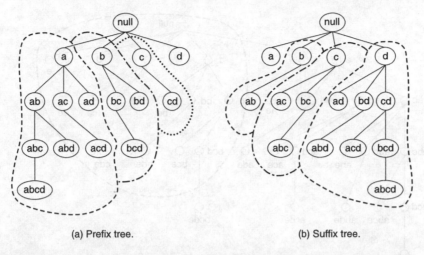

(a) Prefix tree.   (b) Suffix tree.

Figure 6.20. Equivalence classes based on the prefix and suffix labels of itemsets.

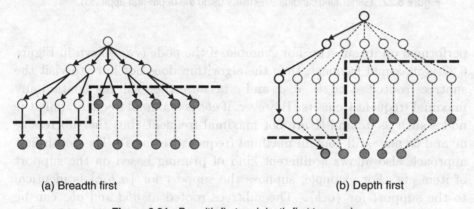

(a) Breadth first   (b) Depth first

Figure 6.21. Breadth-first and depth-first traversals.

lattice can also be traversed in a depth-first manner, as shown in Figures 6.21(b) and 6.22. The algorithm can start from, say, node *a* in Figure 6.22, and count its support to determine whether it is frequent. If so, the algorithm progressively expands the next level of nodes, i.e., *ab*, *abc*, and so on, until an infrequent node is reached, say, *abcd*. It then backtracks to another branch, say, *abce*, and continues the search from there.

The depth-first approach is often used by algorithms designed to find maximal frequent itemsets. This approach allows the frequent itemset border to be detected more quickly than using a breadth-first approach. Once a maximal frequent itemset is found, substantial pruning can be

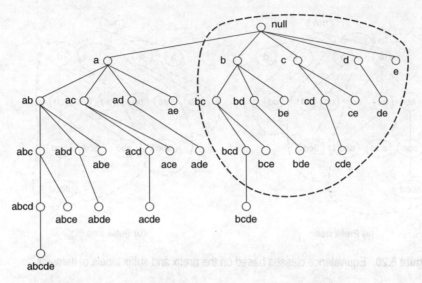

Figure 6.22. Generating candidate itemsets using the depth-first approach.

performed on its subsets. For example, if the node *bcde* shown in Figure 6.22 is maximal frequent, then the algorithm does not have to visit the subtrees rooted at *bd*, *be*, *c*, *d*, and *e* because they will not contain any maximal frequent itemsets. However, if *abc* is maximal frequent, only the nodes such as *ac* and *bc* are not maximal frequent (but the subtrees of *ac* and *bc* may still contain maximal frequent itemsets). The depth-first approach also allows a different kind of pruning based on the support of itemsets. For example, suppose the support for $\{a, b, c\}$ is identical to the support for $\{a, b\}$. The subtrees rooted at *abd* and *abe* can be skipped because they are guaranteed not to have any maximal frequent itemsets. The proof of this is left as an exercise to the readers.

Representation of Transaction Data Set   There are many ways to represent a transaction data set. The choice of representation can affect the I/O costs incurred when computing the support of candidate itemsets. Figure 6.23 shows two different ways of representing market basket transactions. The representation on the left is called a **horizontal** data layout, which is adopted by many association rule mining algorithms, including *Apriori*. Another possibility is to store the list of transaction identifiers (TID-list) associated with each item. Such a representation is known as the **vertical** data layout. The support for each candidate itemset is obtained by intersecting the TID-lists of its subset items. The length of the TID-lists shrinks as we progress to larger

Horizontal
Data Layout

TID	Items
1	a,b,e
2	b,c,d
3	c,e
4	a,c,d
5	a,b,c,d
6	a,e
7	a,b
8	a,b,c
9	a,c,d
10	b

Vertical Data Layout

a	b	c	d	e
1	1	2	2	1
4	2	3	4	3
5	5	4	5	6
6	7	8	9	
7	8	9		
8	10			
9				

Figure 6.23. Horizontal and vertical data format.

sized itemsets. However, one problem with this approach is that the initial set of TID-lists may be too large to fit into main memory, thus requiring more sophisticated techniques to compress the TID-lists. We describe another effective approach to represent the data in the next section.

6.6   FP-Growth Algorithm

This section presents an alternative algorithm called **FP-growth** that takes a radically different approach to discovering frequent itemsets. The algorithm does not subscribe to the generate-and-test paradigm of *Apriori*. Instead, it encodes the data set using a compact data structure called an **FP-tree** and extracts frequent itemsets directly from this structure. The details of this approach are presented next.

6.6.1   FP-Tree Representation

An FP-tree is a compressed representation of the input data. It is constructed by reading the data set one transaction at a time and mapping each transaction onto a path in the FP-tree. As different transactions can have several items in common, their paths may overlap. The more the paths overlap with one another, the more compression we can achieve using the FP-tree structure. If the size of the FP-tree is small enough to fit into main memory, this will allow us to extract frequent itemsets directly from the structure in memory instead of making repeated passes over the data stored on disk.

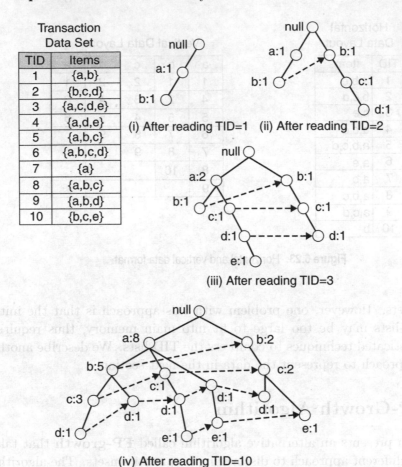

Figure 6.24. Construction of an FP-tree.

Figure 6.24 shows a data set that contains ten transactions and five items. The structures of the FP-tree after reading the first three transactions are also depicted in the diagram. Each node in the tree contains the label of an item along with a counter that shows the number of transactions mapped onto the given path. Initially, the FP-tree contains only the root node represented by the **null** symbol. The FP-tree is subsequently extended in the following way:

1. The data set is scanned once to determine the support count of each item. Infrequent items are discarded, while the frequent items are sorted in decreasing support counts. For the data set shown in Figure 6.24, *a* is the most frequent item, followed by *b*, *c*, *d*, and *e*.

2. The algorithm makes a second pass over the data to construct the FP-tree. After reading the first transaction, $\{a, b\}$, the nodes labeled as a and b are created. A path is then formed from $\texttt{null} \rightarrow a \rightarrow b$ to encode the transaction. Every node along the path has a frequency count of 1.

3. After reading the second transaction, $\{b,c,d\}$, a new set of nodes is created for items b, c, and d. A path is then formed to represent the transaction by connecting the nodes $\texttt{null} \rightarrow b \rightarrow c \rightarrow d$. Every node along this path also has a frequency count equal to one. Although the first two transactions have an item in common, which is b, their paths are disjoint because the transactions do not share a common prefix.

4. The third transaction, $\{a,c,d,e\}$, shares a common prefix item (which is a) with the first transaction. As a result, the path for the third transaction, $\texttt{null} \rightarrow a \rightarrow c \rightarrow d \rightarrow e$, overlaps with the path for the first transaction, $\texttt{null} \rightarrow a \rightarrow b$. Because of their overlapping path, the frequency count for node a is incremented to two, while the frequency counts for the newly created nodes, c, d, and e, are equal to one.

5. This process continues until every transaction has been mapped onto one of the paths given in the FP-tree. The resulting FP-tree after reading all the transactions is shown at the bottom of Figure 6.24.

The size of an FP-tree is typically smaller than the size of the uncompressed data because many transactions in market basket data often share a few items in common. In the best-case scenario, where all the transactions have the same set of items, the FP-tree contains only a single branch of nodes. The worst-case scenario happens when every transaction has a unique set of items. As none of the transactions have any items in common, the size of the FP-tree is effectively the same as the size of the original data. However, the physical storage requirement for the FP-tree is higher because it requires additional space to store pointers between nodes and counters for each item.

The size of an FP-tree also depends on how the items are ordered. If the ordering scheme in the preceding example is reversed, i.e., from lowest to highest support item, the resulting FP-tree is shown in Figure 6.25. The tree appears to be denser because the branching factor at the root node has increased from 2 to 5 and the number of nodes containing the high support items such as a and b has increased from 3 to 12. Nevertheless, ordering by decreasing support counts does not always lead to the smallest tree. For example, suppose we augment the data set given in Figure 6.24 with 100 transactions that contain $\{e\}$, 80 transactions that contain $\{d\}$, 60 transactions

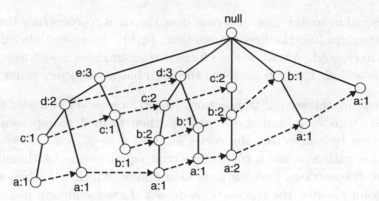

Figure 6.25. An FP-tree representation for the data set shown in Figure 6.24 with a different item ordering scheme.

that contain $\{c\}$, and 40 transactions that contain $\{b\}$. Item e is now most frequent, followed by d, c, b, and a. With the augmented transactions, ordering by decreasing support counts will result in an FP-tree similar to Figure 6.25, while a scheme based on increasing support counts produces a smaller FP-tree similar to Figure 6.24(iv).

An FP-tree also contains a list of pointers connecting between nodes that have the same items. These pointers, represented as dashed lines in Figures 6.24 and 6.25, help to facilitate the rapid access of individual items in the tree. We explain how to use the FP-tree and its corresponding pointers for frequent itemset generation in the next section.

6.6.2   Frequent Itemset Generation in FP-Growth Algorithm

FP-growth is an algorithm that generates frequent itemsets from an FP-tree by exploring the tree in a bottom-up fashion. Given the example tree shown in Figure 6.24, the algorithm looks for frequent itemsets ending in e first, followed by d, c, b, and finally, a. This bottom-up strategy for finding frequent itemsets ending with a particular item is equivalent to the suffix-based approach described in Section 6.5. Since every transaction is mapped onto a path in the FP-tree, we can derive the frequent itemsets ending with a particular item, say, e, by examining only the paths containing node e. These paths can be accessed rapidly using the pointers associated with node e. The extracted paths are shown in Figure 6.26(a). The details on how to process the paths to obtain frequent itemsets will be explained later.

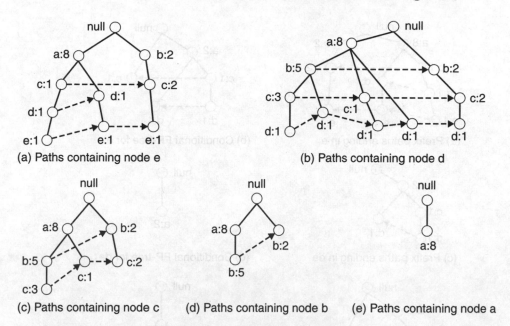

Figure 6.26. Decomposing the frequent itemset generation problem into multiple subproblems, where each subproblem involves finding frequent itemsets ending in e, d, c, b, and a.

Table 6.6. The list of frequent itemsets ordered by their corresponding suffixes.

Suffix	Frequent Itemsets
e	{e}, {d,e}, {a,d,e}, {c,e},{a,e}
d	{d}, {c,d}, {b,c,d}, {a,c,d}, {b,d}, {a,b,d}, {a,d}
c	{c}, {b,c}, {a,b,c}, {a,c}
b	{b}, {a,b}
a	{a}

After finding the frequent itemsets ending in e, the algorithm proceeds to look for frequent itemsets ending in d by processing the paths associated with node d. The corresponding paths are shown in Figure 6.26(b). This process continues until all the paths associated with nodes c, b, and finally a, are processed. The paths for these items are shown in Figures 6.26(c), (d), and (e), while their corresponding frequent itemsets are summarized in Table 6.6.

FP-growth finds all the frequent itemsets ending with a particular suffix by employing a divide-and-conquer strategy to split the problem into smaller subproblems. For example, suppose we are interested in finding all frequent

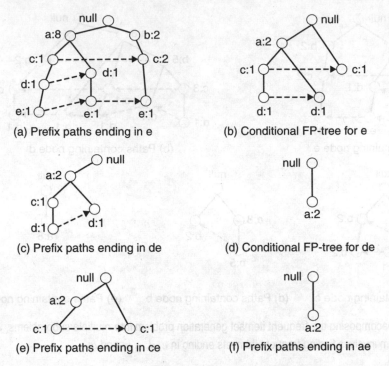

(a) Prefix paths ending in e

(b) Conditional FP-tree for e

(c) Prefix paths ending in de

(d) Conditional FP-tree for de

(e) Prefix paths ending in ce

(f) Prefix paths ending in ae

Figure 6.27. Example of applying the FP-growth algorithm to find frequent itemsets ending in e.

itemsets ending in e. To do this, we must first check whether the itemset $\{e\}$ itself is frequent. If it is frequent, we consider the subproblem of finding frequent itemsets ending in de, followed by ce, be, and ae. In turn, each of these subproblems are further decomposed into smaller subproblems. By merging the solutions obtained from the subproblems, all the frequent itemsets ending in e can be found. This divide-and-conquer approach is the key strategy employed by the FP-growth algorithm.

For a more concrete example on how to solve the subproblems, consider the task of finding frequent itemsets ending with e.

1. The first step is to gather all the paths containing node e. These initial paths are called **prefix paths** and are shown in Figure 6.27(a).

2. From the prefix paths shown in Figure 6.27(a), the support count for e is obtained by adding the support counts associated with node e. Assuming that the minimum support count is 2, $\{e\}$ is declared a frequent itemset because its support count is 3.

3. Because $\{e\}$ is frequent, the algorithm has to solve the subproblems of finding frequent itemsets ending in de, ce, be, and ae. Before solving these subproblems, it must first convert the prefix paths into a **conditional FP-tree**, which is structurally similar to an FP-tree, except it is used to find frequent itemsets ending with a particular suffix. A conditional FP-tree is obtained in the following way:

   (a) First, the support counts along the prefix paths must be updated because some of the counts include transactions that do not contain item e. For example, the rightmost path shown in Figure 6.27(a), $\text{null} \longrightarrow b:2 \longrightarrow c:2 \longrightarrow e:1$, includes a transaction $\{b, c\}$ that does not contain item e. The counts along the prefix path must therefore be adjusted to 1 to reflect the actual number of transactions containing $\{b, c, e\}$.

   (b) The prefix paths are truncated by removing the nodes for e. These nodes can be removed because the support counts along the prefix paths have been updated to reflect only transactions that contain e and the subproblems of finding frequent itemsets ending in de, ce, be, and ae no longer need information about node e.

   (c) After updating the support counts along the prefix paths, some of the items may no longer be frequent. For example, the node b appears only once and has a support count equal to 1, which means that there is only one transaction that contains both b and e. Item b can be safely ignored from subsequent analysis because all itemsets ending in be must be infrequent.

   The conditional FP-tree for e is shown in Figure 6.27(b). The tree looks different than the original prefix paths because the frequency counts have been updated and the nodes b and e have been eliminated.

4. FP-growth uses the conditional FP-tree for e to solve the subproblems of finding frequent itemsets ending in de, ce, and ae. To find the frequent itemsets ending in de, the prefix paths for d are gathered from the conditional FP-tree for e (Figure 6.27(c)). By adding the frequency counts associated with node d, we obtain the support count for $\{d, e\}$. Since the support count is equal to 2, $\{d, e\}$ is declared a frequent itemset. Next, the algorithm constructs the conditional FP-tree for de using the approach described in step 3. After updating the support counts and removing the infrequent item c, the conditional FP-tree for de is shown in Figure 6.27(d). Since the conditional FP-tree contains only one item,

a, whose support is equal to *minsup*, the algorithm extracts the frequent itemset $\{a, d, e\}$ and moves on to the next subproblem, which is to generate frequent itemsets ending in *ce*. After processing the prefix paths for c, only $\{c, e\}$ is found to be frequent. The algorithm proceeds to solve the next subprogram and found $\{a, e\}$ to be the only frequent itemset remaining.

This example illustrates the divide-and-conquer approach used in the FP-growth algorithm. At each recursive step, a conditional FP-tree is constructed by updating the frequency counts along the prefix paths and removing all infrequent items. Because the subproblems are disjoint, FP-growth will not generate any duplicate itemsets. In addition, the counts associated with the nodes allow the algorithm to perform support counting while generating the common suffix itemsets.

FP-growth is an interesting algorithm because it illustrates how a compact representation of the transaction data set helps to efficiently generate frequent itemsets. In addition, for certain transaction data sets, FP-growth outperforms the standard *Apriori* algorithm by several orders of magnitude. The run-time performance of FP-growth depends on the **compaction factor** of the data set. If the resulting conditional FP-trees are very bushy (in the worst case, a full prefix tree), then the performance of the algorithm degrades significantly because it has to generate a large number of subproblems and merge the results returned by each subproblem.

6.7 Evaluation of Association Patterns

Association analysis algorithms have the potential to generate a large number of patterns. For example, although the data set shown in Table 6.1 contains only six items, it can produce up to hundreds of association rules at certain support and confidence thresholds. As the size and dimensionality of real commercial databases can be very large, we could easily end up with thousands or even millions of patterns, many of which might not be interesting. Sifting through the patterns to identify the most interesting ones is not a trivial task because "one person's trash might be another person's treasure." It is therefore important to establish a set of well-accepted criteria for evaluating the quality of association patterns.

The first set of criteria can be established through statistical arguments. Patterns that involve a set of mutually independent items or cover very few transactions are considered uninteresting because they may capture spurious relationships in the data. Such patterns can be eliminated by applying an

objective interestingness measure that uses statistics derived from data to determine whether a pattern is interesting. Examples of objective interestingness measures include support, confidence, and correlation.

The second set of criteria can be established through subjective arguments. A pattern is considered subjectively uninteresting unless it reveals unexpected information about the data or provides useful knowledge that can lead to profitable actions. For example, the rule $\{Butter\} \longrightarrow \{Bread\}$ may not be interesting, despite having high support and confidence values, because the relationship represented by the rule may seem rather obvious. On the other hand, the rule $\{Diapers\} \longrightarrow \{Beer\}$ is interesting because the relationship is quite unexpected and may suggest a new cross-selling opportunity for retailers. Incorporating subjective knowledge into pattern evaluation is a difficult task because it requires a considerable amount of prior information from the domain experts.

The following are some of the approaches for incorporating subjective knowledge into the pattern discovery task.

Visualization   This approach requires a user-friendly environment to keep the human user in the loop. It also allows the domain experts to interact with the data mining system by interpreting and verifying the discovered patterns.

Template-based approach   This approach allows the users to constrain the type of patterns extracted by the mining algorithm. Instead of reporting all the extracted rules, only rules that satisfy a user-specified template are returned to the users.

Subjective interestingness measure   A subjective measure can be defined based on domain information such as concept hierarchy (to be discussed in Section 7.3) or profit margin of items. The measure can then be used to filter patterns that are obvious and non-actionable.

Readers interested in subjective interestingness measures may refer to resources listed in the bibliography at the end of this chapter.

6.7.1   Objective Measures of Interestingness

An objective measure is a data-driven approach for evaluating the quality of association patterns. It is domain-independent and requires minimal input from the users, other than to specify a threshold for filtering low-quality patterns. An objective measure is usually computed based on the frequency

Table 6.7. A 2-way contingency table for variables A and B.

	B	$\overline{B}$	
A	f_{11}	f_{10}	f_{1+}
$\overline{A}$	f_{01}	f_{00}	f_{0+}
	f_{+1}	f_{+0}	N

counts tabulated in a **contingency table**. Table 6.7 shows an example of a contingency table for a pair of binary variables, A and B. We use the notation $\overline{A}$ ($\overline{B}$) to indicate that A (B) is absent from a transaction. Each entry f_{ij} in this 2×2 table denotes a frequency count. For example, f_{11} is the number of times A and B appear together in the same transaction, while f_{01} is the number of transactions that contain B but not A. The row sum f_{1+} represents the support count for A, while the column sum f_{+1} represents the support count for B. Finally, even though our discussion focuses mainly on asymmetric binary variables, note that contingency tables are also applicable to other attribute types such as symmetric binary, nominal, and ordinal variables.

Limitations of the Support-Confidence Framework Existing association rule mining formulation relies on the support and confidence measures to eliminate uninteresting patterns. The drawback of support was previously described in Section 6.8, in which many potentially interesting patterns involving low support items might be eliminated by the support threshold. The drawback of confidence is more subtle and is best demonstrated with the following example.

Example 6.3. Suppose we are interested in analyzing the relationship between people who drink tea and coffee. We may gather information about the beverage preferences among a group of people and summarize their responses into a table such as the one shown in Table 6.8.

Table 6.8. Beverage preferences among a group of 1000 people.

	$Coffee$	$\overline{Coffee}$	
Tea	150	50	200
$\overline{Tea}$	650	150	800
	800	200	1000

The information given in this table can be used to evaluate the association rule $\{Tea\} \longrightarrow \{Coffee\}$. At first glance, it may appear that people who drink tea also tend to drink coffee because the rule's support (15%) and confidence (75%) values are reasonably high. This argument would have been acceptable except that the fraction of people who drink coffee, regardless of whether they drink tea, is 80%, while the fraction of tea drinkers who drink coffee is only 75%. Thus knowing that a person is a tea drinker actually decreases her probability of being a coffee drinker from 80% to 75%! The rule $\{Tea\} \longrightarrow \{Coffee\}$ is therefore misleading despite its high confidence value. ■

The pitfall of confidence can be traced to the fact that the measure ignores the support of the itemset in the rule consequent. Indeed, if the support of coffee drinkers is taken into account, we would not be surprised to find that many of the people who drink tea also drink coffee. What is more surprising is that the fraction of tea drinkers who drink coffee is actually less than the overall fraction of people who drink coffee, which points to an inverse relationship between tea drinkers and coffee drinkers.

Because of the limitations in the support-confidence framework, various objective measures have been used to evaluate the quality of association patterns. Below, we provide a brief description of these measures and explain some of their strengths and limitations.

Interest Factor   The tea-coffee example shows that high-confidence rules can sometimes be misleading because the confidence measure ignores the support of the itemset appearing in the rule consequent. One way to address this problem is by applying a metric known as **lift**:

$$Lift = \frac{c(A \longrightarrow B)}{s(B)}, \qquad (6.4)$$

which computes the ratio between the rule's confidence and the support of the itemset in the rule consequent. For binary variables, lift is equivalent to another objective measure called **interest factor**, which is defined as follows:

$$I(A, B) = \frac{s(A, B)}{s(A) \times s(B)} = \frac{N f_{11}}{f_{1+} f_{+1}}. \qquad (6.5)$$

Interest factor compares the frequency of a pattern against a baseline frequency computed under the statistical independence assumption. The baseline frequency for a pair of mutually independent variables is

$$\frac{f_{11}}{N} = \frac{f_{1+}}{N} \times \frac{f_{+1}}{N}, \quad \text{or equivalently,} \quad f_{11} = \frac{f_{1+} f_{+1}}{N}. \qquad (6.6)$$

Table 6.9. Contingency tables for the word pairs ({p,q} and {r,s}.

	p	$\bar{p}$	
q	880	50	930
$\bar{q}$	50	20	70
	930	70	1000

	r	$\bar{r}$	
s	20	50	70
$\bar{s}$	50	880	930
	70	930	1000

This equation follows from the standard approach of using simple fractions as estimates for probabilities. The fraction f_{11}/N is an estimate for the joint probability $P(A, B)$, while f_{1+}/N and f_{+1}/N are the estimates for $P(A)$ and $P(B)$, respectively. If A and B are statistically independent, then $P(A, B) = P(A) \times P(B)$, thus leading to the formula shown in Equation 6.6. Using Equations 6.5 and 6.6, we can interpret the measure as follows:

$$I(A, B) \begin{cases} = 1, & \text{if } A \text{ and } B \text{ are independent;} \\ > 1, & \text{if } A \text{ and } B \text{ are positively correlated;} \\ < 1, & \text{if } A \text{ and } B \text{ are negatively correlated.} \end{cases} \quad (6.7)$$

For the tea-coffee example shown in Table 6.8, $I = \frac{0.15}{0.2 \times 0.8} = 0.9375$, thus suggesting a slight negative correlation between tea drinkers and coffee drinkers.

Limitations of Interest Factor We illustrate the limitation of interest factor with an example from the text mining domain. In the text domain, it is reasonable to assume that the association between a pair of words depends on the number of documents that contain both words. For example, because of their stronger association, we expect the words data and mining to appear together more frequently than the words compiler and mining in a collection of computer science articles.

Table 6.9 shows the frequency of occurrences between two pairs of words, {p, q} and {r, s}. Using the formula given in Equation 6.5, the interest factor for {p, q} is 1.02 and for {r, s} is 4.08. These results are somewhat troubling for the following reasons. Although p and q appear together in 88% of the documents, their interest factor is close to 1, which is the value when p and q are statistically independent. On the other hand, the interest factor for {r, s} is higher than {p, q} even though r and s seldom appear together in the same document. Confidence is perhaps the better choice in this situation because it considers the association between p and q (94.6%) to be much stronger than that between r and s (28.6%).

Correlation Analysis   Correlation analysis is a statistical-based technique for analyzing relationships between a pair of variables. For continuous variables, correlation is defined using Pearson's correlation coefficient (see Equation 2.10 on page 77). For binary variables, correlation can be measured using the ϕ-coefficient, which is defined as

$$\phi = \frac{f_{11}f_{00} - f_{01}f_{10}}{\sqrt{f_{1+}f_{+1}f_{0+}f_{+0}}}. \tag{6.8}$$

The value of correlation ranges from -1 (perfect negative correlation) to $+1$ (perfect positive correlation). If the variables are statistically independent, then $\phi = 0$. For example, the correlation between the tea and coffee drinkers given in Table 6.8 is -0.0625.

Limitations of Correlation Analysis   The drawback of using correlation can be seen from the word association example given in Table 6.9. Although the words p and q appear together more often than r and s, their ϕ-coefficients are identical, i.e., $\phi(p, q) = \phi(r, s) = 0.232$. This is because the ϕ-coefficient gives equal importance to both co-presence and co-absence of items in a transaction. It is therefore more suitable for analyzing symmetric binary variables. Another limitation of this measure is that it does not remain invariant when there are proportional changes to the sample size. This issue will be discussed in greater detail when we describe the properties of objective measures on page 377.

IS Measure IS is an alternative measure that has been proposed for handling asymmetric binary variables. The measure is defined as follows:

$$IS(A, B) = \sqrt{I(A, B) \times s(A, B)} = \frac{s(A, B)}{\sqrt{s(A)s(B)}}. \tag{6.9}$$

Note that IS is large when the interest factor and support of the pattern are large. For example, the value of IS for the word pairs $\{p, q\}$ and $\{r, s\}$ shown in Table 6.9 are 0.946 and 0.286, respectively. Contrary to the results given by interest factor and the ϕ-coefficient, the IS measure suggests that the association between $\{p, q\}$ is stronger than $\{r, s\}$, which agrees with what we expect from word associations in documents.

It is possible to show that IS is mathematically equivalent to the cosine measure for binary variables (see Equation 2.7 on page 75). In this regard, we

Table 6.10. Example of a contingency table for items p and q.

	q	$\bar{q}$	
p	800	100	900
$\bar{p}$	100	0	100
	900	100	1000

consider **A** and **B** as a pair of bit vectors, $\mathbf{A} \bullet \mathbf{B} = s(A, B)$ the dot product between the vectors, and $|\mathbf{A}| = \sqrt{s(A)}$ the magnitude of vector **A**. Therefore:

$$IS(A, B) = \frac{s(A, B)}{\sqrt{s(A) \times s(B)}} = \frac{\mathbf{A} \bullet \mathbf{B}}{|\mathbf{A}| \times |\mathbf{B}|} = cosine(\mathbf{A}, \mathbf{B}). \qquad (6.10)$$

The IS measure can also be expressed as the geometric mean between the confidence of association rules extracted from a pair of binary variables:

$$IS(A, B) = \sqrt{\frac{s(A, B)}{s(A)} \times \frac{s(A, B)}{s(B)}} = \sqrt{c(A \rightarrow B) \times c(B \rightarrow A)}. \qquad (6.11)$$

Because the geometric mean between any two numbers is always closer to the smaller number, the IS value of an itemset $\{p, q\}$ is low whenever one of its rules, $p \longrightarrow q$ or $q \longrightarrow p$, has low confidence.

Limitations of IS Measure   The IS value for a pair of independent itemsets, A and B, is

$$IS_{\text{indep}}(A, B) = \frac{s(A, B)}{\sqrt{s(A) \times s(B)}} = \frac{s(A) \times s(B)}{\sqrt{s(A) \times s(B)}} = \sqrt{s(A) \times s(B)}.$$

Since the value depends on $s(A)$ and $s(B)$, IS shares a similar problem as the confidence measure—that the value of the measure can be quite large, even for uncorrelated and negatively correlated patterns. For example, despite the large IS value between items p and q given in Table 6.10 (0.889), it is still less than the expected value when the items are statistically independent ($IS_{\text{indep}} = 0.9$).

Alternative Objective Interestingness Measures

Besides the measures we have described so far, there are other alternative measures proposed for analyzing relationships between pairs of binary variables. These measures can be divided into two categories, **symmetric** and **asymmetric** measures. A measure M is symmetric if $M(A \longrightarrow B) = M(B \longrightarrow A)$. For example, interest factor is a symmetric measure because its value is identical for the rules $A \longrightarrow B$ and $B \longrightarrow A$. In contrast, confidence is an asymmetric measure since the confidence for $A \longrightarrow B$ and $B \longrightarrow A$ may not be the same. Symmetric measures are generally used for evaluating itemsets, while asymmetric measures are more suitable for analyzing association rules. Tables 6.11 and 6.12 provide the definitions for some of these measures in terms of the frequency counts of a 2×2 contingency table.

Consistency among Objective Measures

Given the wide variety of measures available, it is reasonable to question whether the measures can produce similar ordering results when applied to a set of association patterns. If the measures are consistent, then we can choose any one of them as our evaluation metric. Otherwise, it is important to understand what their differences are in order to determine which measure is more suitable for analyzing certain types of patterns.

Table 6.11. Examples of symmetric objective measures for the itemset $\{A, B\}$.

Measure (Symbol)	Definition
Correlation (ϕ)	$\dfrac{N f_{11} - f_{1+} f_{+1}}{\sqrt{f_{1+} f_{+1} f_{0+} f_{+0}}}$
Odds ratio (α)	$(f_{11} f_{00})/(f_{10} f_{01})$
Kappa (κ)	$\dfrac{N f_{11} + N f_{00} - f_{1+} f_{+1} - f_{0+} f_{+0}}{N^2 - f_{1+} f_{+1} - f_{0+} f_{+0}}$
Interest (I)	$(N f_{11})/(f_{1+} f_{+1})$
Cosine (IS)	$(f_{11})/(\sqrt{f_{1+} f_{+1}})$
Piatetsky-Shapiro (PS)	$\dfrac{f_{11}}{N} - \dfrac{f_{1+} f_{+1}}{N^2}$
Collective strength (S)	$\dfrac{f_{11} + f_{00}}{f_{1+} f_{+1} + f_{0+} f_{+0}} \times \dfrac{N - f_{1+} f_{+1} - f_{0+} f_{+0}}{N - f_{11} - f_{00}}$
Jaccard (ζ)	$f_{11}/(f_{1+} + f_{+1} - f_{11})$
All-confidence (h)	$\min \left[\dfrac{f_{11}}{f_{1+}}, \dfrac{f_{11}}{f_{+1}} \right]$

Table 6.12. Examples of asymmetric objective measures for the rule $A \longrightarrow B$.

Measure (Symbol)	Definition
Goodman-Kruskal (λ)	$\left(\sum_j \max_k f_{jk} - max_k f_{+k}\right) / \left(N - \max_k f_{+k}\right)$
Mutual Information (M)	$\left(\sum_i \sum_j \frac{f_{ij}}{N} \log \frac{N f_{ij}}{f_{i+}f_{+j}}\right) / \left(-\sum_i \frac{f_{i+}}{N} \log \frac{f_{i+}}{N}\right)$
J-Measure (J)	$\frac{f_{11}}{N} \log \frac{N f_{11}}{f_{1+}f_{+1}} + \frac{f_{10}}{N} \log \frac{N f_{10}}{f_{1+}f_{+0}}$
Gini index (G)	$\frac{f_{1+}}{N} \times \left(\frac{f_{11}}{f_{1+}}\right)^2 + \left(\frac{f_{10}}{f_{1+}}\right)^2] - \left(\frac{f_{+1}}{N}\right)^2$
	$+ \frac{f_{0+}}{N} \times [\left(\frac{f_{01}}{f_{0+}}\right)^2 + \left(\frac{f_{00}}{f_{0+}}\right)^2] - \left(\frac{f_{+0}}{N}\right)^2$
Laplace (L)	$(f_{11} + 1)/(f_{1+} + 2)$
Conviction (V)	$(f_{1+}f_{+0})/(N f_{10})$
Certainty factor (F)	$\left(\frac{f_{11}}{f_{1+}} - \frac{f_{+1}}{N}\right) / \left(1 - \frac{f_{+1}}{N}\right)$
Added Value (AV)	$\frac{f_{11}}{f_{1+}} - \frac{f_{+1}}{N}$

Table 6.13. Example of contingency tables.

Example	f_{11}	f_{10}	f_{01}	f_{00}
E_1	8123	83	424	1370
E_2	8330	2	622	1046
E_3	3954	3080	5	2961
E_4	2886	1363	1320	4431
E_5	1500	2000	500	6000
E_6	4000	2000	1000	3000
E_7	9481	298	127	94
E_8	4000	2000	2000	2000
E_9	7450	2483	4	63
E_{10}	61	2483	4	7452

Suppose the symmetric and asymmetric measures are applied to rank the ten contingency tables shown in Table 6.13. These contingency tables are chosen to illustrate the differences among the existing measures. The ordering produced by these measures are shown in Tables 6.14 and 6.15, respectively (with 1 as the most interesting and 10 as the least interesting table). Although some of the measures appear to be consistent with each other, there are certain measures that produce quite different ordering results. For example, the rankings given by the ϕ-coefficient agree with those provided by κ and collective strength, but are somewhat different than the rankings produced by interest

Table 6.14. Rankings of contingency tables using the symmetric measures given in Table 6.11.

	ϕ	α	κ	I	IS	PS	S	ζ	h
E_1	1	3	1	6	2	2	1	2	2
E_2	2	1	2	7	3	5	2	3	3
E_3	3	2	4	4	5	1	3	6	8
E_4	4	8	3	3	7	3	4	7	5
E_5	5	7	6	2	9	6	6	9	9
E_6	6	9	5	5	6	4	5	5	7
E_7	7	6	7	9	1	8	7	1	1
E_8	8	10	8	8	8	7	8	8	7
E_9	9	4	9	10	4	9	9	4	4
E_{10}	10	5	10	1	10	10	10	10	10

Table 6.15. Rankings of contingency tables using the asymmetric measures given in Table 6.12.

	λ	M	J	G	L	V	F	AV
E_1	1	1	1	1	4	2	2	5
E_2	2	2	2	3	5	1	1	6
E_3	5	3	5	2	2	6	6	4
E_4	4	6	3	4	9	3	3	1
E_5	9	7	4	6	8	5	5	2
E_6	3	8	6	5	7	4	4	3
E_7	7	5	9	8	3	7	7	9
E_8	8	9	7	7	10	8	8	7
E_9	6	4	10	9	1	9	9	10
E_{10}	10	10	8	10	6	10	10	8

factor and odds ratio. Furthermore, a contingency table such as E_{10} is ranked lowest according to the ϕ-coefficient, but highest according to interest factor.

Properties of Objective Measures

The results shown in Table 6.14 suggest that a significant number of the measures provide conflicting information about the quality of a pattern. To understand their differences, we need to examine the properties of these measures.

Inversion Property Consider the bit vectors shown in Figure 6.28. The 0/1 bit in each column vector indicates whether a transaction (row) contains a particular item (column). For example, the vector **A** indicates that item a

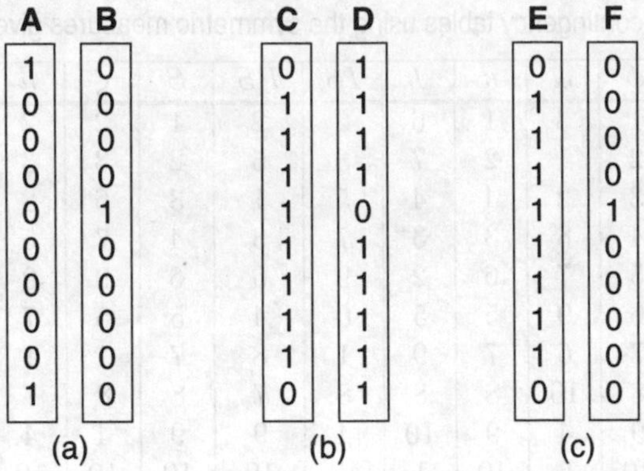

Figure 6.28. Effect of the inversion operation. The vectors C and E are inversions of vector A, while the vector D is an inversion of vectors B and F.

belongs to the first and last transactions, whereas the vector **B** indicates that item b is contained only in the fifth transaction. The vectors **C** and **E** are in fact related to the vector **A**—their bits have been inverted from 0's (absence) to 1's (presence), and vice versa. Similarly, **D** is related to vectors **B** and **F** by inverting their bits. The process of flipping a bit vector is called **inversion**. If a measure is invariant under the inversion operation, then its value for the vector pair $(\mathbf{C}, \mathbf{D})$ should be identical to its value for $(\mathbf{A}, \mathbf{B})$. The inversion property of a measure can be tested as follows.

Definition 6.6 (Inversion Property). An objective measure M is invariant under the inversion operation if its value remains the same when exchanging the frequency counts f_{11} with f_{00} and f_{10} with f_{01}.

Among the measures that remain invariant under this operation include the ϕ-coefficient, odds ratio, κ, and collective strength. These measures may not be suitable for analyzing asymmetric binary data. For example, the ϕ-coefficient between **C** and **D** is identical to the ϕ-coefficient between **A** and **B**, even though items c and d appear together more frequently than a and b. Furthermore, the ϕ-coefficient between **C** and **D** is less than that between **E** and **F** even though items e and f appear together only once! We had previously raised this issue when discussing the limitations of the ϕ-coefficient on page 375. For asymmetric binary data, measures that do not remain invariant under the inversion operation are preferred. Some of the non-invariant measures include interest factor, IS, PS, and the Jaccard coefficient.

Null Addition Property Suppose we are interested in analyzing the relationship between a pair of words, such as `data` and `mining`, in a set of documents. If a collection of articles about ice fishing is added to the data set, should the association between `data` and `mining` be affected? This process of adding unrelated data (in this case, documents) to a given data set is known as the **null addition** operation.

Definition 6.7 (Null Addition Property). An objective measure M is invariant under the null addition operation if it is not affected by increasing f_{00}, while all other frequencies in the contingency table stay the same.

For applications such as document analysis or market basket analysis, the measure is expected to remain invariant under the null addition operation. Otherwise, the relationship between words may disappear simply by adding enough documents that do not contain both words! Examples of measures that satisfy this property include cosine (IS) and Jaccard (ξ) measures, while those that violate this property include interest factor, PS, odds ratio, and the ϕ-coefficient.

Scaling Property Table 6.16 shows the contingency tables for gender and the grades achieved by students enrolled in a particular course in 1993 and 2004. The data in these tables showed that the number of male students has doubled since 1993, while the number of female students has increased by a factor of 3. However, the male students in 2004 are not performing any better than those in 1993 because the ratio of male students who achieve a high grade to those who achieve a low grade is still the same, i.e., 3:4. Similarly, the female students in 2004 are performing no better than those in 1993. The association between grade and gender is expected to remain unchanged despite changes in the sampling distribution.

Table 6.16. The grade-gender example.

	Male	Female	
High	30	20	50
Low	40	10	50
	70	30	100

(a) Sample data from 1993.

	Male	Female	
High	60	60	120
Low	80	30	110
	140	90	230

(b) Sample data from 2004.

Table 6.17. Properties of symmetric measures.

Symbol	Measure	Inversion	Null Addition	Scaling
ϕ	ϕ-coefficient	Yes	No	No
α	odds ratio	Yes	No	Yes
κ	Cohen's	Yes	No	No
I	Interest	No	No	No
IS	Cosine	No	Yes	No
PS	Piatetsky-Shapiro's	Yes	No	No
S	Collective strength	Yes	No	No
ζ	Jaccard	No	Yes	No
h	All-confidence	No	No	No
s	Support	No	No	No

Definition 6.8 (Scaling Invariance Property). An objective measure M is invariant under the row/column scaling operation if $M(T) = M(T')$, where T is a contingency table with frequency counts $[f_{11}; f_{10}; f_{01}; f_{00}]$, T' is a contingency table with scaled frequency counts $[k_1 k_3 f_{11}; k_2 k_3 f_{10}; k_1 k_4 f_{01}; k_2 k_4 f_{00}]$, and k_1, k_2, k_3, k_4 are positive constants.

From Table 6.17, notice that only the odds ratio (α) is invariant under the row and column scaling operations. All other measures such as the ϕ-coefficient, κ, IS, interest factor, and collective strength (S) change their values when the rows and columns of the contingency table are rescaled. Although we do not discuss the properties of asymmetric measures (such as confidence, J-measure, Gini index, and conviction), it is clear that such measures do not preserve their values under inversion and row/column scaling operations, but are invariant under the null addition operation.

6.7.2   Measures beyond Pairs of Binary Variables

The measures shown in Tables 6.11 and 6.12 are defined for pairs of binary variables (e.g., 2-itemsets or association rules). However, many of them, such as support and all-confidence, are also applicable to larger-sized itemsets. Other measures, such as interest factor, IS, PS, and Jaccard coefficient, can be extended to more than two variables using the frequency tables tabulated in a multidimensional contingency table. An example of a three-dimensional contingency table for a, b, and c is shown in Table 6.18. Each entry f_{ijk} in this table represents the number of transactions that contain a particular combination of items a, b, and c. For example, f_{101} is the number of transactions that contain a and c, but not b. On the other hand, a marginal frequency

Table 6.18. Example of a three-dimensional contingency table.

c	b	$\bar{b}$		$\bar{c}$	b	$\bar{b}$	
a	f_{111}	f_{101}	f_{1+1}	a	f_{110}	f_{100}	f_{1+0}
$\bar{a}$	f_{011}	f_{001}	f_{0+1}	$\bar{a}$	f_{010}	f_{000}	f_{0+0}
	f_{+11}	f_{+01}	f_{++1}		f_{+10}	f_{+00}	f_{++0}

such as f_{1+1} is the number of transactions that contain a and c, irrespective of whether b is present in the transaction.

Given a k-itemset $\{i_1, i_2, \ldots, i_k\}$, the condition for statistical independence can be stated as follows:

$$f_{i_1 i_2 \ldots i_k} = \frac{f_{i_1 + \ldots +} \times f_{+ i_2 \ldots +} \times \ldots \times f_{++ \ldots i_k}}{N^{k-1}}. \tag{6.12}$$

With this definition, we can extend objective measures such as interest factor and PS, which are based on deviations from statistical independence, to more than two variables:

$$I = \frac{N^{k-1} \times f_{i_1 i_2 \ldots i_k}}{f_{i_1 + \ldots +} \times f_{+ i_2 \ldots +} \times \ldots \times f_{++ \ldots i_k}}$$

$$PS = \frac{f_{i_1 i_2 \ldots i_k}}{N} - \frac{f_{i_1 + \ldots +} \times f_{+ i_2 \ldots +} \times \ldots \times f_{++ \ldots i_k}}{N^k}$$

Another approach is to define the objective measure as the maximum, minimum, or average value for the associations between pairs of items in a pattern. For example, given a k-itemset $X = \{i_1, i_2, \ldots, i_k\}$, we may define the ϕ-coefficient for X as the average ϕ-coefficient between every pair of items (i_p, i_q) in X. However, because the measure considers only pairwise associations, it may not capture all the underlying relationships within a pattern.

Analysis of multidimensional contingency tables is more complicated because of the presence of partial associations in the data. For example, some associations may appear or disappear when conditioned upon the value of certain variables. This problem is known as **Simpson's paradox** and is described in the next section. More sophisticated statistical techniques are available to analyze such relationships, e.g., loglinear models, but these techniques are beyond the scope of this book.

Table 6.19. A two-way contingency table between the sale of high-definition television and exercise machine.

Buy HDTV	Buy Exercise Machine		
	Yes	No	
Yes	99	81	180
No	54	66	120
	153	147	300

Table 6.20. Example of a three-way contingency table.

Customer Group	Buy HDTV	Buy Exercise Machine		Total
		Yes	No	
College Students	Yes	1	9	10
	No	4	30	34
Working Adult	Yes	98	72	170
	No	50	36	86

6.7.3 Simpson's Paradox

It is important to exercise caution when interpreting the association between variables because the observed relationship may be influenced by the presence of other confounding factors, i.e., hidden variables that are not included in the analysis. In some cases, the hidden variables may cause the observed relationship between a pair of variables to disappear or reverse its direction, a phenomenon that is known as Simpson's paradox. We illustrate the nature of this paradox with the following example.

Consider the relationship between the sale of high-definition television (HDTV) and exercise machine, as shown in Table 6.19. The rule {HDTV=Yes} $\longrightarrow$ {Exercise machine=Yes} has a confidence of 99/180 = 55% and the rule {HDTV=No} $\longrightarrow$ {Exercise machine=Yes} has a confidence of 54/120 = 45%. Together, these rules suggest that customers who buy high-definition televisions are more likely to buy exercise machines than those who do not buy high-definition televisions.

However, a deeper analysis reveals that the sales of these items depend on whether the customer is a college student or a working adult. Table 6.20 summarizes the relationship between the sale of HDTVs and exercise machines among college students and working adults. Notice that the support counts given in the table for college students and working adults sum up to the frequencies shown in Table 6.19. Furthermore, there are more working adults than college students who buy these items. For college students:

$$c(\{\text{HDTV=Yes}\} \longrightarrow \{\text{Exercise machine=Yes}\}) = 1/10 = 10\%,$$
$$c(\{\text{HDTV=No}\} \longrightarrow \{\text{Exercise machine=Yes}\}) = 4/34 = 11.8\%,$$

while for working adults:

$$c(\{\text{HDTV=Yes}\} \longrightarrow \{\text{Exercise machine=Yes}\}) = 98/170 = 57.7\%,$$
$$c(\{\text{HDTV=No}\} \longrightarrow \{\text{Exercise machine=Yes}\}) = 50/86 = 58.1\%.$$

The rules suggest that, for each group, customers who do not buy high-definition televisions are more likely to buy exercise machines, which contradict the previous conclusion when data from the two customer groups are pooled together. Even if alternative measures such as correlation, odds ratio, or interest are applied, we still find that the sale of HDTV and exercise machine is positively correlated in the combined data but is negatively correlated in the stratified data (see Exercise 20 on page 414). The reversal in the direction of association is known as Simpson's paradox.

The paradox can be explained in the following way. Notice that most customers who buy HDTVs are working adults. Working adults are also the largest group of customers who buy exercise machines. Because nearly 85% of the customers are working adults, the observed relationship between HDTV and exercise machine turns out to be stronger in the combined data than what it would have been if the data is stratified. This can also be illustrated mathematically as follows. Suppose

$$a/b < c/d \text{ and } p/q < r/s,$$

where a/b and p/q may represent the confidence of the rule $A \longrightarrow B$ in two different strata, while c/d and r/s may represent the confidence of the rule $\overline{A} \longrightarrow B$ in the two strata. When the data is pooled together, the confidence values of the rules in the combined data are $(a+p)/(b+q)$ and $(c+r)/(d+s)$, respectively. Simpson's paradox occurs when

$$\frac{a+p}{b+q} > \frac{c+r}{d+s},$$

thus leading to the wrong conclusion about the relationship between the variables. The lesson here is that proper stratification is needed to avoid generating spurious patterns resulting from Simpson's paradox. For example, market

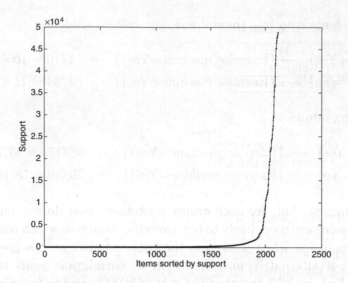

Figure 6.29. Support distribution of items in the census data set.

basket data from a major supermarket chain should be stratified according to store locations, while medical records from various patients should be stratified according to confounding factors such as age and gender.

6.8   Effect of Skewed Support Distribution

The performances of many association analysis algorithms are influenced by properties of their input data. For example, the computational complexity of the *Apriori* algorithm depends on properties such as the number of items in the data and average transaction width. This section examines another important property that has significant influence on the performance of association analysis algorithms as well as the quality of extracted patterns. More specifically, we focus on data sets with skewed support distributions, where most of the items have relatively low to moderate frequencies, but a small number of them have very high frequencies.

An example of a real data set that exhibits such a distribution is shown in Figure 6.29. The data, taken from the PUMS (Public Use Microdata Sample) census data, contains 49,046 records and 2113 asymmetric binary variables. We shall treat the asymmetric binary variables as items and records as transactions in the remainder of this section. While more than 80% of the items have support less than 1%, a handful of them have support greater than 90%.

Table 6.21. Grouping the items in the census data set based on their support values.

Group	G_1	G_2	G_3
Support	$< 1\%$	$1\% - 90\%$	$> 90\%$
Number of Items	1735	358	20

To illustrate the effect of skewed support distribution on frequent itemset mining, we divide the items into three groups, G_1, G_2, and G_3, according to their support levels. The number of items that belong to each group is shown in Table 6.21.

Choosing the right support threshold for mining this data set can be quite tricky. If we set the threshold too high (e.g., 20%), then we may miss many interesting patterns involving the low support items from G_1. In market basket analysis, such low support items may correspond to expensive products (such as jewelry) that are seldom bought by customers, but whose patterns are still interesting to retailers. Conversely, when the threshold is set too low, it becomes difficult to find the association patterns due to the following reasons. First, the computational and memory requirements of existing association analysis algorithms increase considerably with low support thresholds. Second, the number of extracted patterns also increases substantially with low support thresholds. Third, we may extract many spurious patterns that relate a high-frequency item such as milk to a low-frequency item such as caviar. Such patterns, which are called **cross-support** patterns, are likely to be spurious because their correlations tend to be weak. For example, at a support threshold equal to 0.05%, there are 18,847 frequent pairs involving items from G_1 and G_3. Out of these, 93% of them are cross-support patterns; i.e., the patterns contain items from both G_1 and G_3. The maximum correlation obtained from the cross-support patterns is 0.029, which is much lower than the maximum correlation obtained from frequent patterns involving items from the same group (which is as high as 1.0). Similar statement can be made about many other interestingness measures discussed in the previous section. This example shows that a large number of weakly correlated cross-support patterns can be generated when the support threshold is sufficiently low. Before presenting a methodology for eliminating such patterns, we formally define the concept of cross-support patterns.

Definition 6.9 (Cross-Support Pattern). A cross-support pattern is an itemset $X = \{i_1, i_2, \ldots, i_k\}$ whose support ratio

$$r(X) = \frac{\min \left[s(i_1), s(i_2), \ldots, s(i_k) \right]}{\max \left[s(i_1), s(i_2), \ldots, s(i_k) \right]}, \tag{6.13}$$

is less than a user-specified threshold h_c.

Example 6.4. Suppose the support for milk is 70%, while the support for sugar is 10% and caviar is 0.04%. Given $h_c = 0.01$, the frequent itemset {milk, sugar, caviar} is a cross-support pattern because its support ratio is

$$r = \frac{\min \left[0.7, 0.1, 0.0004 \right]}{\max \left[0.7, 0.1, 0.0004 \right]} = \frac{0.0004}{0.7} = 0.00058 < 0.01.$$

∎

Existing measures such as support and confidence may not be sufficient to eliminate cross-support patterns, as illustrated by the data set shown in Figure 6.30. Assuming that $h_c = 0.3$, the itemsets $\{p, q\}$, $\{p, r\}$, and $\{p, q, r\}$ are cross-support patterns because their support ratios, which are equal to 0.2, are less than the threshold h_c. Although we can apply a high support threshold, say, 20%, to eliminate the cross-support patterns, this may come at the expense of discarding other interesting patterns such as the strongly correlated itemset, $\{q, r\}$ that has support equal to 16.7%.

Confidence pruning also does not help because the confidence of the rules extracted from cross-support patterns can be very high. For example, the confidence for $\{q\} \longrightarrow \{p\}$ is 80% even though $\{p, q\}$ is a cross-support pattern. The fact that the cross-support pattern can produce a high-confidence rule should not come as a surprise because one of its items (p) appears very frequently in the data. Therefore, p is expected to appear in many of the transactions that contain q. Meanwhile, the rule $\{q\} \longrightarrow \{r\}$ also has high confidence even though $\{q, r\}$ is not a cross-support pattern. This example demonstrates the difficulty of using the confidence measure to distinguish between rules extracted from cross-support and non-cross-support patterns.

Returning to the previous example, notice that the rule $\{p\} \longrightarrow \{q\}$ has very low confidence because most of the transactions that contain p do not contain q. In contrast, the rule $\{r\} \longrightarrow \{q\}$, which is derived from the pattern $\{q, r\}$, has very high confidence. This observation suggests that cross-support patterns can be detected by examining the lowest confidence rule that can be extracted from a given itemset. The proof of this statement can be understood as follows.

p	q	r
0	1	1
1	1	1
1	1	1
1	1	1
1	1	1
1	0	0
1	0	0
1	0	0
1	0	0
1	0	0
1	0	0
1	0	0
1	0	0
1	0	0
1	0	0
1	0	0
1	0	0
1	0	0
1	0	0
1	0	0
1	0	0
1	0	0
1	0	0
1	0	0
1	0	0
0	0	0
0	0	0
0	0	0
0	0	0

Figure 6.30. A transaction data set containing three items, p, q, and r, where p is a high support item and q and r are low support items.

1. Recall the following anti-monotone property of confidence:

$$conf(\{i_1 i_2\} \longrightarrow \{i_3, i_4, \ldots, i_k\}) \leq conf(\{i_1 i_2 i_3\} \longrightarrow \{i_4, i_5, \ldots, i_k\}).$$

This property suggests that confidence never increases as we shift more items from the left- to the right-hand side of an association rule. Because of this property, the lowest confidence rule extracted from a frequent itemset contains only one item on its left-hand side. We denote the set of all rules with only one item on its left-hand side as R_1.

2. Given a frequent itemset $\{i_1, i_2, \ldots, i_k\}$, the rule

$$\{i_j\} \longrightarrow \{i_1, i_2, \ldots, i_{j-1}, i_{j+1}, \ldots, i_k\}$$

has the lowest confidence in R_1 if $s(i_j) = \max\big[s(i_1), s(i_2), \ldots, s(i_k)\big]$. This follows directly from the definition of confidence as the ratio between the rule's support and the support of the rule antecedent.

3. Summarizing the previous points, the lowest confidence attainable from a frequent itemset $\{i_1, i_2, \ldots, i_k\}$ is

$$\frac{s(\{i_1, i_2, \ldots, i_k\})}{\max \left[s(i_1), s(i_2), \ldots, s(i_k) \right]}.$$

This expression is also known as the **h-confidence** or **all-confidence** measure. Because of the anti-monotone property of support, the numerator of the h-confidence measure is bounded by the minimum support of any item that appears in the frequent itemset. In other words, the h-confidence of an itemset $X = \{i_1, i_2, \ldots, i_k\}$ must not exceed the following expression:

$$\text{h-confidence}(X) \leq \frac{\min \left[s(i_1), s(i_2), \ldots, s(i_k) \right]}{\max \left[s(i_1), s(i_2), \ldots, s(i_k) \right]}.$$

Note the equivalence between the upper bound of h-confidence and the support ratio (r) given in Equation 6.13. Because the support ratio for a cross-support pattern is always less than h_c, the h-confidence of the pattern is also guaranteed to be less than h_c.

Therefore, cross-support patterns can be eliminated by ensuring that the h-confidence values for the patterns exceed h_c. As a final note, it is worth mentioning that the advantages of using h-confidence go beyond eliminating cross-support patterns. The measure is also anti-monotone, i.e.,

$$\text{h-confidence}(\{i_1, i_2, \ldots, i_k\}) \geq \text{h-confidence}(\{i_1, i_2, \ldots, i_{k+1}\}),$$

and thus can be incorporated directly into the mining algorithm. Furthermore, h-confidence ensures that the items contained in an itemset are strongly associated with each other. For example, suppose the h-confidence of an itemset X is 80%. If one of the items in X is present in a transaction, there is at least an 80% chance that the rest of the items in X also belong to the same transaction. Such strongly associated patterns are called **hyperclique patterns**.

6.9   Bibliographic Notes

The association rule mining task was first introduced by Agrawal et al. in [228, 229] to discover interesting relationships among items in market basket transactions. Since its inception, extensive studies have been conducted to address the various conceptual, implementation, and application issues pertaining to the association analysis task. A summary of the various research activities in this area is shown in Figure 6.31.

Conceptual Issues

Research in conceptual issues is focused primarily on (1) developing a framework to describe the theoretical underpinnings of association analysis, (2) extending the formulation to handle new types of patterns, and (3) extending the formulation to incorporate attribute types beyond asymmetric binary data.

Following the pioneering work by Agrawal et al., there has been a vast amount of research on developing a theory for the association analysis problem. In [254], Gunopoulos et al. showed a relation between the problem of finding maximal frequent itemsets and the hypergraph transversal problem. An upper bound on the complexity of association analysis task was also derived. Zaki et al. [334, 336] and Pasquier et al. [294] have applied formal concept analysis to study the frequent itemset generation problem. The work by Zaki et al. have subsequently led them to introduce the notion of closed frequent itemsets [336]. Friedman et al. have studied the association analysis problem in the context of **bump hunting** in multidimensional space [252]. More specifically, they consider frequent itemset generation as the task of finding high probability density regions in multidimensional space.

Over the years, new types of patterns have been defined, such as profile association rules [225], cyclic association rules [290], fuzzy association rules [273], exception rules [316], negative association rules [238, 304], weighted association rules [240, 300], dependence rules [308], peculiar rules[340], inter-transaction association rules [250, 323], and partial classification rules [231, 285]. Other types of patterns include closed itemsets [294, 336], maximal itemsets [234], hyperclique patterns [330], support envelopes [314], emerging patterns [246], and contrast sets [233]. Association analysis has also been successfully applied to sequential [230, 312], spatial [266], and graph-based [268, 274, 293, 331, 335] data. The concept of cross-support pattern was first introduced by Hui et al. in [330]. An efficient algorithm (called Hyperclique Miner) that automatically eliminates cross-support patterns was also proposed by the authors.

Substantial research has been conducted to extend the original association rule formulation to nominal [311], ordinal [281], interval [284], and ratio [253, 255, 311, 325, 339] attributes. One of the key issues is how to define the support measure for these attributes. A methodology was proposed by Steinbach et al. [315] to extend the traditional notion of support to more general patterns and attribute types.

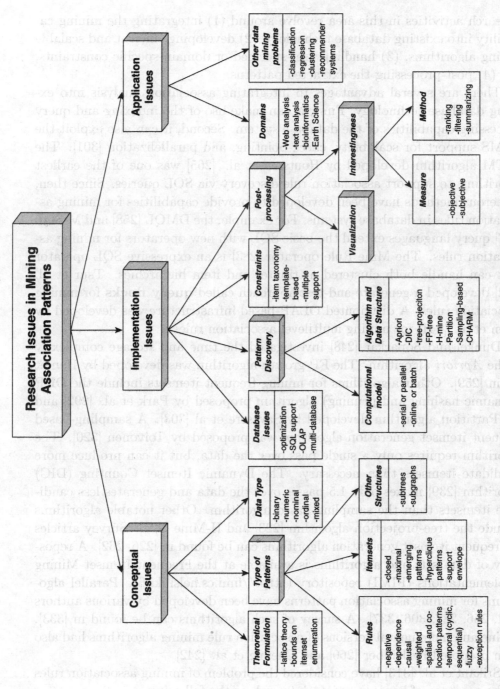

Figure 6.31. A summary of the various research activities in association analysis.

Implementation Issues

Research activities in this area revolve around (1) integrating the mining capability into existing database technology, (2) developing efficient and scalable mining algorithms, (3) handling user-specified or domain-specific constraints, and (4) post-processing the extracted patterns.

There are several advantages to integrating association analysis into existing database technology. First, it can make use of the indexing and query processing capabilities of the database system. Second, it can also exploit the DBMS support for scalability, check-pointing, and parallelization [301]. The SETM algorithm developed by Houtsma et al. [265] was one of the earliest algorithms to support association rule discovery via SQL queries. Since then, numerous methods have been developed to provide capabilities for mining association rules in database systems. For example, the DMQL [258] and M-SQL [267] query languages extend the basic SQL with new operators for mining association rules. The Mine Rule operator [283] is an expressive SQL operator that can handle both clustered attributes and item hierarchies. Tsur et al. [322] developed a generate-and-test approach called **query flocks** for mining association rules. A distributed OLAP-based infrastructure was developed by Chen et al. [241] for mining multilevel association rules.

Dunkel and Soparkar [248] investigated the time and storage complexity of the *Apriori* algorithm. The FP-growth algorithm was developed by Han et al. in [259]. Other algorithms for mining frequent itemsets include the DHP (dynamic hashing and pruning) algorithm proposed by Park et al. [292] and the Partition algorithm developed by Savasere et al [303]. A sampling-based frequent itemset generation algorithm was proposed by Toivonen [320]. The algorithm requires only a single pass over the data, but it can produce more candidate itemsets than necessary. The Dynamic Itemset Counting (DIC) algorithm [239] makes only 1.5 passes over the data and generates less candidate itemsets than the sampling-based algorithm. Other notable algorithms include the tree-projection algorithm [223] and H-Mine [295]. Survey articles on frequent itemset generation algorithms can be found in [226, 262]. A repository of data sets and algorithms is available at the Frequent Itemset Mining Implementations (FIMI) repository (http://fimi.cs.helsinki.fi). Parallel algorithms for mining association patterns have been developed by various authors [224, 256, 287, 306, 337]. A survey of such algorithms can be found in [333]. Online and incremental versions of association rule mining algorithms had also been proposed by Hidber [260] and Cheung et al. [242].

Srikant et al. [313] have considered the problem of mining association rules in the presence of boolean constraints such as the following:

(Cookies ∧ Milk) ∨ (descendents(Cookies) ∧ ¬ancestors(Wheat Bread))

Given such a constraint, the algorithm looks for rules that contain both cookies and milk, or rules that contain the descendent items of cookies but not ancestor items of wheat bread. Singh et al. [310] and Ng et al. [288] had also developed alternative techniques for constrained-based association rule mining. Constraints can also be imposed on the support for different itemsets. This problem was investigated by Wang et al. [324], Liu et al. in [279], and Seno et al. [305].

One potential problem with association analysis is the large number of patterns that can be generated by current algorithms. To overcome this problem, methods to rank, summarize, and filter patterns have been developed. Toivonen et al. [321] proposed the idea of eliminating redundant rules using **structural rule covers** and to group the remaining rules using clustering. Liu et al. [280] applied the statistical chi-square test to prune spurious patterns and summarized the remaining patterns using a subset of the patterns called **direction setting rules**. The use of objective measures to filter patterns has been investigated by many authors, including Brin et al. [238], Bayardo and Agrawal [235], Aggarwal and Yu [227], and DuMouchel and Pregibon[247]. The properties for many of these measures were analyzed by Piatetsky-Shapiro [297], Kamber and Singhal [270], Hilderman and Hamilton [261], and Tan et al. [318]. The grade-gender example used to highlight the importance of the row and column scaling invariance property was heavily influenced by the discussion given in [286] by Mosteller. Meanwhile, the tea-coffee example illustrating the limitation of confidence was motivated by an example given in [238] by Brin et al. Because of the limitation of confidence, Brin et al. [238] had proposed the idea of using interest factor as a measure of interestingness. The all-confidence measure was proposed by Omiecinski [289]. Xiong et al. [330] introduced the cross-support property and showed that the all-confidence measure can be used to eliminate cross-support patterns. A key difficulty in using alternative objective measures besides support is their lack of a monotonicity property, which makes it difficult to incorporate the measures directly into the mining algorithms. Xiong et al. [328] have proposed an efficient method for mining correlations by introducing an upper bound function to the ϕ-coefficient. Although the measure is non-monotone, it has an upper bound expression that can be exploited for the efficient mining of strongly correlated itempairs.

Fabris and Freitas [249] have proposed a method for discovering interesting associations by detecting the occurrences of Simpson's paradox [309]. Megiddo and Srikant [282] described an approach for validating the extracted patterns using hypothesis testing methods. A resampling-based technique was also developed to avoid generating spurious patterns because of the multiple comparison problem. Bolton et al. [237] have applied the Benjamini-Hochberg [236] and Bonferroni correction methods to adjust the p-values of discovered patterns in market basket data. Alternative methods for handling the multiple comparison problem were suggested by Webb [326] and Zhang et al. [338].

Application of subjective measures to association analysis has been investigated by many authors. Silberschatz and Tuzhilin [307] presented two principles in which a rule can be considered interesting from a subjective point of view. The concept of unexpected condition rules was introduced by Liu et al. in [277]. Cooley et al. [243] analyzed the idea of combining soft belief sets using the Dempster-Shafer theory and applied this approach to identify contradictory and novel association patterns in Web data. Alternative approaches include using Bayesian networks [269] and neighborhood-based information [245] to identify subjectively interesting patterns.

Visualization also helps the user to quickly grasp the underlying structure of the discovered patterns. Many commercial data mining tools display the complete set of rules (which satisfy both support and confidence threshold criteria) as a two-dimensional plot, with each axis corresponding to the antecedent or consequent itemsets of the rule. Hofmann et al. [263] proposed using Mosaic plots and Double Decker plots to visualize association rules. This approach can visualize not only a particular rule, but also the overall contingency table between itemsets in the antecedent and consequent parts of the rule. Nevertheless, this technique assumes that the rule consequent consists of only a single attribute.

Application Issues

Association analysis has been applied to a variety of application domains such as Web mining [296, 317], document analysis [264], telecommunication alarm diagnosis [271], network intrusion detection [232, 244, 275], and bioinformatics [302, 327]. Applications of association and correlation pattern analysis to Earth Science studies have been investigated in [298, 299, 319].

Association patterns have also been applied to other learning problems such as classification [276, 278], regression [291], and clustering [257, 329, 332]. A comparison between classification and association rule mining was made by Freitas in his position paper [251]. The use of association patterns for clustering has been studied by many authors including Han et al.[257], Kosters et al. [272], Yang et al. [332] and Xiong et al. [329].

Bibliography

[223] R. C. Agarwal, C. C. Aggarwal, and V. V. V. Prasad. A Tree Projection Algorithm for Generation of Frequent Itemsets. *Journal of Parallel and Distributed Computing (Special Issue on High Performance Data Mining)*, 61(3):350–371, 2001.

[224] R. C. Agarwal and J. C. Shafer. Parallel Mining of Association Rules. *IEEE Transactions on Knowledge and Data Engineering*, 8(6):962–969, March 1998.

[225] C. C. Aggarwal, Z. Sun, and P. S. Yu. Online Generation of Profile Association Rules. In *Proc. of the 4th Intl. Conf. on Knowledge Discovery and Data Mining*, pages 129–133, New York, NY, August 1996.

[226] C. C. Aggarwal and P. S. Yu. Mining Large Itemsets for Association Rules. *Data Engineering Bulletin*, 21(1):23–31, March 1998.

[227] C. C. Aggarwal and P. S. Yu. Mining Associations with the Collective Strength Approach. *IEEE Trans. on Knowledge and Data Engineering*, 13(6):863–873, January/February 2001.

[228] R. Agrawal, T. Imielinski, and A. Swami. Database mining: A performance perspective. *IEEE Transactions on Knowledge and Data Engineering*, 5:914–925, 1993.

[229] R. Agrawal, T. Imielinski, and A. Swami. Mining association rules between sets of items in large databases. In *Proc. ACM SIGMOD Intl. Conf. Management of Data*, pages 207–216, Washington, DC, 1993.

[230] R. Agrawal and R. Srikant. Mining Sequential Patterns. In *Proc. of Intl. Conf. on Data Engineering*, pages 3–14, Taipei, Taiwan, 1995.

[231] K. Ali, S. Manganaris, and R. Srikant. Partial Classification using Association Rules. In *Proc. of the 3rd Intl. Conf. on Knowledge Discovery and Data Mining*, pages 115–118, Newport Beach, CA, August 1997.

[232] D. Barbará, J. Couto, S. Jajodia, and N. Wu. ADAM: A Testbed for Exploring the Use of Data Mining in Intrusion Detection. *SIGMOD Record*, 30(4):15–24, 2001.

[233] S. D. Bay and M. Pazzani. Detecting Group Differences: Mining Contrast Sets. *Data Mining and Knowledge Discovery*, 5(3):213–246, 2001.

[234] R. Bayardo. Efficiently Mining Long Patterns from Databases. In *Proc. of 1998 ACM-SIGMOD Intl. Conf. on Management of Data*, pages 85–93, Seattle, WA, June 1998.

[235] R. Bayardo and R. Agrawal. Mining the Most Interesting Rules. In *Proc. of the 5th Intl. Conf. on Knowledge Discovery and Data Mining*, pages 145–153, San Diego, CA, August 1999.

[236] Y. Benjamini and Y. Hochberg. Controlling the False Discovery Rate: A Practical and Powerful Approach to Multiple Testing. *Journal Royal Statistical Society B*, 57 (1):289–300, 1995.

[237] R. J. Bolton, D. J. Hand, and N. M. Adams. Determining Hit Rate in Pattern Search. In *Proc. of the ESF Exploratory Workshop on Pattern Detection and Discovery in Data Mining*, pages 36–48, London, UK, September 2002.

[238] S. Brin, R. Motwani, and C. Silverstein. Beyond market baskets: Generalizing association rules to correlations. In *Proc. ACM SIGMOD Intl. Conf. Management of Data*, pages 265–276, Tucson, AZ, 1997.

[239] S. Brin, R. Motwani, J. Ullman, and S. Tsur. Dynamic Itemset Counting and Implication Rules for market basket data. In *Proc. of 1997 ACM-SIGMOD Intl. Conf. on Management of Data*, pages 255–264, Tucson, AZ, June 1997.

[240] C. H. Cai, A. Fu, C. H. Cheng, and W. W. Kwong. Mining Association Rules with Weighted Items. In *Proc. of IEEE Intl. Database Engineering and Applications Symp.*, pages 68–77, Cardiff, Wales, 1998.

[241] Q. Chen, U. Dayal, and M. Hsu. A Distributed OLAP infrastructure for E-Commerce. In *Proc. of the 4th IFCIS Intl. Conf. on Cooperative Information Systems*, pages 209–220, Edinburgh, Scotland, 1999.

[242] D. C. Cheung, S. D. Lee, and B. Kao. A General Incremental Technique for Maintaining Discovered Association Rules. In *Proc. of the 5th Intl. Conf. on Database Systems for Advanced Applications*, pages 185–194, Melbourne, Australia, 1997.

[243] R. Cooley, P. N. Tan, and J. Srivastava. Discovery of Interesting Usage Patterns from Web Data. In M. Spiliopoulou and B. Masand, editors, *Advances in Web Usage Analysis and User Profiling*, volume 1836, pages 163–182. Lecture Notes in Computer Science, 2000.

[244] P. Dokas, L. Ertöz, V. Kumar, A. Lazarevic, J. Srivastava, and P. N. Tan. Data Mining for Network Intrusion Detection. In *Proc. NSF Workshop on Next Generation Data Mining*, Baltimore, MD, 2002.

[245] G. Dong and J. Li. Interestingness of discovered association rules in terms of neighborhood-based unexpectedness. In *Proc. of the 2nd Pacific-Asia Conf. on Knowledge Discovery and Data Mining*, pages 72–86, Melbourne, Australia, April 1998.

[246] G. Dong and J. Li. Efficient Mining of Emerging Patterns: Discovering Trends and Differences. In *Proc. of the 5th Intl. Conf. on Knowledge Discovery and Data Mining*, pages 43–52, San Diego, CA, August 1999.

[247] W. DuMouchel and D. Pregibon. Empirical Bayes Screening for Multi-Item Associations. In *Proc. of the 7th Intl. Conf. on Knowledge Discovery and Data Mining*, pages 67–76, San Francisco, CA, August 2001.

[248] B. Dunkel and N. Soparkar. Data Organization and Access for Efficient Data Mining. In *Proc. of the 15th Intl. Conf. on Data Engineering*, pages 522–529, Sydney, Australia, March 1999.

[249] C. C. Fabris and A. A. Freitas. Discovering surprising patterns by detecting occurrences of Simpson's paradox. In *Proc. of the 19th SGES Intl. Conf. on Knowledge-Based Systems and Applied Artificial Intelligence)*, pages 148–160, Cambridge, UK, December 1999.

[250] L. Feng, H. J. Lu, J. X. Yu, and J. Han. Mining inter-transaction associations with templates. In *Proc. of the 8th Intl. Conf. on Information and Knowledge Management*, pages 225–233, Kansas City, Missouri, Nov 1999.

[251] A. A. Freitas. Understanding the crucial differences between classification and discovery of association rules—a position paper. *SIGKDD Explorations*, 2(1):65–69, 2000.

[252] J. H. Friedman and N. I. Fisher. Bump hunting in high-dimensional data. *Statistics and Computing*, 9(2):123–143, April 1999.

[253] T. Fukuda, Y. Morimoto, S. Morishita, and T. Tokuyama. Mining Optimized Association Rules for Numeric Attributes. In *Proc. of the 15th Symp. on Principles of Database Systems*, pages 182–191, Montreal, Canada, June 1996.

[254] D. Gunopulos, R. Khardon, H. Mannila, and H. Toivonen. Data Mining, Hypergraph Transversals, and Machine Learning. In *Proc. of the 16th Symp. on Principles of Database Systems*, pages 209–216, Tucson, AZ, May 1997.

[255] E.-H. Han, G. Karypis, and V. Kumar. Min-Apriori: An Algorithm for Finding Association Rules in Data with Continuous Attributes. http://www.cs.umn.edu/~han, 1997.

[256] E.-H. Han, G. Karypis, and V. Kumar. Scalable Parallel Data Mining for Association Rules. In *Proc. of 1997 ACM-SIGMOD Intl. Conf. on Management of Data*, pages 277–288, Tucson, AZ, May 1997.

[257] E.-H. Han, G. Karypis, V. Kumar, and B. Mobasher. Clustering Based on Association Rule Hypergraphs. In *Proc. of the 1997 ACM SIGMOD Workshop on Research Issues in Data Mining and Knowledge Discovery*, Tucson, AZ, 1997.

[258] J. Han, Y. Fu, K. Koperski, W. Wang, and O. R. Zaïane. DMQL: A data mining query language for relational databases. In *Proc. of the 1996 ACM SIGMOD Workshop on Research Issues in Data Mining and Knowledge Discovery*, Montreal, Canada, June 1996.

[259] J. Han, J. Pei, and Y. Yin. Mining Frequent Patterns without Candidate Generation. In *Proc. ACM-SIGMOD Int. Conf. on Management of Data (SIGMOD'00)*, pages 1–12, Dallas, TX, May 2000.

[260] C. Hidber. Online Association Rule Mining. In *Proc. of 1999 ACM-SIGMOD Intl. Conf. on Management of Data*, pages 145–156, Philadelphia, PA, 1999.

[261] R. J. Hilderman and H. J. Hamilton. *Knowledge Discovery and Measures of Interest*. Kluwer Academic Publishers, 2001.

[262] J. Hipp, U. Guntzer, and G. Nakhaeizadeh. Algorithms for Association Rule Mining— A General Survey. *SigKDD Explorations*, 2(1):58–64, June 2000.

[263] H. Hofmann, A. P. J. M. Siebes, and A. F. X. Wilhelm. Visualizing Association Rules with Interactive Mosaic Plots. In *Proc. of the 6th Intl. Conf. on Knowledge Discovery and Data Mining*, pages 227–235, Boston, MA, August 2000.

[264] J. D. Holt and S. M. Chung. Efficient Mining of Association Rules in Text Databases. In *Proc. of the 8th Intl. Conf. on Information and Knowledge Management*, pages 234–242, Kansas City, Missouri, 1999.

[265] M. Houtsma and A. Swami. Set-oriented Mining for Association Rules in Relational Databases. In *Proc. of the 11th Intl. Conf. on Data Engineering*, pages 25–33, Taipei, Taiwan, 1995.

[266] Y. Huang, S. Shekhar, and H. Xiong. Discovering Co-location Patterns from Spatial Datasets: A General Approach. *IEEE Trans. on Knowledge and Data Engineering*, 16 (12):1472–1485, December 2004.

[267] T. Imielinski, A. Virmani, and A. Abdulghani. DataMine: Application Programming Interface and Query Language for Database Mining. In *Proc. of the 2nd Intl. Conf. on Knowledge Discovery and Data Mining*, pages 256–262, Portland, Oregon, 1996.

[268] A. Inokuchi, T. Washio, and H. Motoda. An Apriori-based Algorithm for Mining Frequent Substructures from Graph Data. In *Proc. of the 4th European Conf. of Principles and Practice of Knowledge Discovery in Databases*, pages 13–23, Lyon, France, 2000.

[269] S. Jaroszewicz and D. Simovici. Interestingness of Frequent Itemsets Using Bayesian Networks as Background Knowledge. In *Proc. of the 10th Intl. Conf. on Knowledge Discovery and Data Mining*, pages 178–186, Seattle, WA, August 2004.

[270] M. Kamber and R. Shinghal. Evaluating the Interestingness of Characteristic Rules. In *Proc. of the 2nd Intl. Conf. on Knowledge Discovery and Data Mining*, pages 263–266, Portland, Oregon, 1996.

[271] M. Klemettinen. *A Knowledge Discovery Methodology for Telecommunication Network Alarm Databases*. PhD thesis, University of Helsinki, 1999.

[272] W. A. Kosters, E. Marchiori, and A. Oerlemans. Mining Clusters with Association Rules. In *The 3rd Symp. on Intelligent Data Analysis (IDA99)*, pages 39–50, Amsterdam, August 1999.

[273] C. M. Kuok, A. Fu, and M. H. Wong. Mining Fuzzy Association Rules in Databases. *ACM SIGMOD Record*, 27(1):41–46, March 1998.

[274] M. Kuramochi and G. Karypis. Frequent Subgraph Discovery. In *Proc. of the 2001 IEEE Intl. Conf. on Data Mining*, pages 313–320, San Jose, CA, November 2001.

[275] W. Lee, S. J. Stolfo, and K. W. Mok. Adaptive Intrusion Detection: A Data Mining Approach. *Artificial Intelligence Review*, 14(6):533–567, 2000.

[276] W. Li, J. Han, and J. Pei. CMAR: Accurate and Efficient Classification Based on Multiple Class-association Rules. In *Proc. of the 2001 IEEE Intl. Conf. on Data Mining*, pages 369–376, San Jose, CA, 2001.

[277] B. Liu, W. Hsu, and S. Chen. Using General Impressions to Analyze Discovered Classification Rules. In *Proc. of the 3rd Intl. Conf. on Knowledge Discovery and Data Mining*, pages 31–36, Newport Beach, CA, August 1997.

[278] B. Liu, W. Hsu, and Y. Ma. Integrating Classification and Association Rule Mining. In *Proc. of the 4th Intl. Conf. on Knowledge Discovery and Data Mining*, pages 80–86, New York, NY, August 1998.

[279] B. Liu, W. Hsu, and Y. Ma. Mining association rules with multiple minimum supports. In *Proc. of the 5th Intl. Conf. on Knowledge Discovery and Data Mining*, pages 125–134, San Diego, CA, August 1999.

[280] B. Liu, W. Hsu, and Y. Ma. Pruning and Summarizing the Discovered Associations. In *Proc. of the 5th Intl. Conf. on Knowledge Discovery and Data Mining*, pages 125–134, San Diego, CA, August 1999.

[281] A. Marcus, J. I. Maletic, and K.-I. Lin. Ordinal association rules for error identification in data sets. In *Proc. of the 10th Intl. Conf. on Information and Knowledge Management*, pages 589–591, Atlanta, GA, October 2001.

[282] N. Megiddo and R. Srikant. Discovering Predictive Association Rules. In *Proc. of the 4th Intl. Conf. on Knowledge Discovery and Data Mining*, pages 274–278, New York, August 1998.

[283] R. Meo, G. Psaila, and S. Ceri. A New SQL-like Operator for Mining Association Rules. In *Proc. of the 22nd VLDB Conf.*, pages 122–133, Bombay, India, 1996.

[284] R. J. Miller and Y. Yang. Association Rules over Interval Data. In *Proc. of 1997 ACM-SIGMOD Intl. Conf. on Management of Data*, pages 452–461, Tucson, AZ, May 1997.

[285] Y. Morimoto, T. Fukuda, H. Matsuzawa, T. Tokuyama, and K. Yoda. Algorithms for mining association rules for binary segmentations of huge categorical databases. In *Proc. of the 24th VLDB Conf.*, pages 380–391, New York, August 1998.

[286] F. Mosteller. Association and Estimation in Contingency Tables. *Journal of the American Statistical Association*, 63:1–28, 1968.

[287] A. Mueller. Fast sequential and parallel algorithms for association rule mining: A comparison. Technical Report CS-TR-3515, University of Maryland, August 1995.

[288] R. T. Ng, L. V. S. Lakshmanan, J. Han, and A. Pang. Exploratory Mining and Pruning Optimizations of Constrained Association Rules. In *Proc. of 1998 ACM-SIGMOD Intl. Conf. on Management of Data*, pages 13–24, Seattle, WA, June 1998.

[289] E. Omiecinski. Alternative Interest Measures for Mining Associations in Databases. *IEEE Trans. on Knowledge and Data Engineering*, 15(1):57–69, January/February 2003.

[290] B. Ozden, S. Ramaswamy, and A. Silberschatz. Cyclic Association Rules. In *Proc. of the 14th Intl. Conf. on Data Eng.*, pages 412–421, Orlando, FL, February 1998.

[291] A. Ozgur, P. N. Tan, and V. Kumar. RBA: An Integrated Framework for Regression based on Association Rules. In *Proc. of the SIAM Intl. Conf. on Data Mining*, pages 210–221, Orlando, FL, April 2004.

[292] J. S. Park, M.-S. Chen, and P. S. Yu. An effective hash-based algorithm for mining association rules. *SIGMOD Record*, 25(2):175–186, 1995.

[293] S. Parthasarathy and M. Coatney. Efficient Discovery of Common Substructures in Macromolecules. In *Proc. of the 2002 IEEE Intl. Conf. on Data Mining*, pages 362–369, Maebashi City, Japan, December 2002.

[294] N. Pasquier, Y. Bastide, R. Taouil, and L. Lakhal. Discovering frequent closed itemsets for association rules. In *Proc. of the 7th Intl. Conf. on Database Theory (ICDT'99)*, pages 398–416, Jerusalem, Israel, January 1999.

[295] J. Pei, J. Han, H. J. Lu, S. Nishio, and S. Tang. H-Mine: Hyper-Structure Mining of Frequent Patterns in Large Databases. In *Proc. of the 2001 IEEE Intl. Conf. on Data Mining*, pages 441–448, San Jose, CA, November 2001.

[296] J. Pei, J. Han, B. Mortazavi-Asl, and H. Zhu. Mining Access Patterns Efficiently from Web Logs. In *Proc. of the 4th Pacific-Asia Conf. on Knowledge Discovery and Data Mining*, pages 396–407, Kyoto, Japan, April 2000.

[297] G. Piatetsky-Shapiro. Discovery, Analysis and Presentation of Strong Rules. In G. Piatetsky-Shapiro and W. Frawley, editors, *Knowledge Discovery in Databases*, pages 229–248. MIT Press, Cambridge, MA, 1991.

[298] C. Potter, S. Klooster, M. Steinbach, P. N. Tan, V. Kumar, S. Shekhar, and C. Carvalho. Understanding Global Teleconnections of Climate to Regional Model Estimates of Amazon Ecosystem Carbon Fluxes. *Global Change Biology*, 10(5):693–703, 2004.

[299] C. Potter, S. Klooster, M. Steinbach, P. N. Tan, V. Kumar, S. Shekhar, R. Myneni, and R. Nemani. Global Teleconnections of Ocean Climate to Terrestrial Carbon Flux. *J. Geophysical Research*, 108(D17), 2003.

[300] G. D. Ramkumar, S. Ranka, and S. Tsur. Weighted Association Rules: Model and Algorithm. http://www.cs.ucla.edu/~czdemo/tsur/, 1997.

[301] S. Sarawagi, S. Thomas, and R. Agrawal. Integrating Mining with Relational Database Systems: Alternatives and Implications. In *Proc. of 1998 ACM-SIGMOD Intl. Conf. on Management of Data*, pages 343–354, Seattle, WA, 1998.

[302] K. Satou, G. Shibayama, T. Ono, Y. Yamamura, E. Furuichi, S. Kuhara, and T. Takagi. Finding Association Rules on Heterogeneous Genome Data. In *Proc. of the Pacific Symp. on Biocomputing*, pages 397–408, Hawaii, January 1997.

[303] A. Savasere, E. Omiecinski, and S. Navathe. An efficient algorithm for mining association rules in large databases. In *Proc. of the 21st Int. Conf. on Very Large Databases (VLDB'95)*, pages 432–444, Zurich, Switzerland, September 1995.

[304] A. Savasere, E. Omiecinski, and S. Navathe. Mining for Strong Negative Associations in a Large Database of Customer Transactions. In *Proc. of the 14th Intl. Conf. on Data Engineering*, pages 494–502, Orlando, Florida, February 1998.

[305] M. Seno and G. Karypis. LPMiner: An Algorithm for Finding Frequent Itemsets Using Length-Decreasing Support Constraint. In *Proc. of the 2001 IEEE Intl. Conf. on Data Mining*, pages 505–512, San Jose, CA, November 2001.

[306] T. Shintani and M. Kitsuregawa. Hash based parallel algorithms for mining association rules. In *Proc of the 4th Intl. Conf. on Parallel and Distributed Info. Systems*, pages 19–30, Miami Beach, FL, December 1996.

[307] A. Silberschatz and A. Tuzhilin. What makes patterns interesting in knowledge discovery systems. *IEEE Trans. on Knowledge and Data Engineering*, 8(6):970–974, 1996.

[308] C. Silverstein, S. Brin, and R. Motwani. Beyond market baskets: Generalizing association rules to dependence rules. *Data Mining and Knowledge Discovery*, 2(1):39–68, 1998.

[309] E.-H. Simpson. The Interpretation of Interaction in Contingency Tables. *Journal of the Royal Statistical Society*, B(13):238–241, 1951.

[310] L. Singh, B. Chen, R. Haight, and P. Scheuermann. An Algorithm for Constrained Association Rule Mining in Semi-structured Data. In *Proc. of the 3rd Pacific-Asia Conf. on Knowledge Discovery and Data Mining*, pages 148–158, Beijing, China, April 1999.

[311] R. Srikant and R. Agrawal. Mining Quantitative Association Rules in Large Relational Tables. In *Proc. of 1996 ACM-SIGMOD Intl. Conf. on Management of Data*, pages 1–12, Montreal, Canada, 1996.

[312] R. Srikant and R. Agrawal. Mining Sequential Patterns: Generalizations and Performance Improvements. In *Proc. of the 5th Intl Conf. on Extending Database Technology (EDBT'96)*, pages 18–32, Avignon, France, 1996.

[313] R. Srikant, Q. Vu, and R. Agrawal. Mining Association Rules with Item Constraints. In *Proc. of the 3rd Intl. Conf. on Knowledge Discovery and Data Mining*, pages 67–73, Newport Beach, CA, August 1997.

[314] M. Steinbach, P. N. Tan, and V. Kumar. Support Envelopes: A Technique for Exploring the Structure of Association Patterns. In *Proc. of the 10th Intl. Conf. on Knowledge Discovery and Data Mining*, pages 296–305, Seattle, WA, August 2004.

[315] M. Steinbach, P. N. Tan, H. Xiong, and V. Kumar. Extending the Notion of Support. In *Proc. of the 10th Intl. Conf. on Knowledge Discovery and Data Mining*, pages 689–694, Seattle, WA, August 2004.

[316] E. Suzuki. Autonomous Discovery of Reliable Exception Rules. In *Proc. of the 3rd Intl. Conf. on Knowledge Discovery and Data Mining*, pages 259–262, Newport Beach, CA, August 1997.

[317] P. N. Tan and V. Kumar. Mining Association Patterns in Web Usage Data. In *Proc. of the Intl. Conf. on Advances in Infrastructure for e-Business, e-Education, e-Science and e-Medicine on the Internet*, L'Aquila, Italy, January 2002.

[318] P. N. Tan, V. Kumar, and J. Srivastava. Selecting the Right Interestingness Measure for Association Patterns. In *Proc. of the 8th Intl. Conf. on Knowledge Discovery and Data Mining*, pages 32–41, Edmonton, Canada, July 2002.

[319] P. N. Tan, M. Steinbach, V. Kumar, S. Klooster, C. Potter, and A. Torregrosa. Finding Spatio-Temporal Patterns in Earth Science Data. In *KDD 2001 Workshop on Temporal Data Mining*, San Francisco, CA, 2001.

[320] H. Toivonen. Sampling Large Databases for Association Rules. In *Proc. of the 22nd VLDB Conf.*, pages 134–145, Bombay, India, 1996.

[321] H. Toivonen, M. Klemettinen, P. Ronkainen, K. Hatonen, and H. Mannila. Pruning and Grouping Discovered Association Rules. In *ECML-95 Workshop on Statistics, Machine Learning and Knowledge Discovery in Databases*, pages 47 – 52, Heraklion, Greece, April 1995.

[322] S. Tsur, J. Ullman, S. Abiteboul, C. Clifton, R. Motwani, S. Nestorov, and A. Rosenthal. Query Flocks: A Generalization of Association Rule Mining. In *Proc. of 1998 ACM-SIGMOD Intl. Conf. on Management of Data*, pages 1–12, Seattle, WA, June 1998.

[323] A. Tung, H. J. Lu, J. Han, and L. Feng. Breaking the Barrier of Transactions: Mining Inter-Transaction Association Rules. In *Proc. of the 5th Intl. Conf. on Knowledge Discovery and Data Mining*, pages 297–301, San Diego, CA, August 1999.

[324] K. Wang, Y. He, and J. Han. Mining Frequent Itemsets Using Support Constraints. In *Proc. of the 26th VLDB Conf.*, pages 43–52, Cairo, Egypt, September 2000.

[325] K. Wang, S. H. Tay, and B. Liu. Interestingness-Based Interval Merger for Numeric Association Rules. In *Proc. of the 4th Intl. Conf. on Knowledge Discovery and Data Mining*, pages 121–128, New York, NY, August 1998.

[326] G. I. Webb. Preliminary investigations into statistically valid exploratory rule discovery. In *Proc. of the Australasian Data Mining Workshop (AusDM03)*, Canberra, Australia, December 2003.

[327] H. Xiong, X. He, C. Ding, Y. Zhang, V. Kumar, and S. R. Holbrook. Identification of Functional Modules in Protein Complexes via Hyperclique Pattern Discovery. In *Proc. of the Pacific Symposium on Biocomputing, (PSB 2005)*, Maui, January 2005.

[328] H. Xiong, S. Shekhar, P. N. Tan, and V. Kumar. Exploiting a Support-based Upper Bound of Pearson's Correlation Coefficient for Efficiently Identifying Strongly Correlated Pairs. In *Proc. of the 10th Intl. Conf. on Knowledge Discovery and Data Mining*, pages 334–343, Seattle, WA, August 2004.

[329] H. Xiong, M. Steinbach, P. N. Tan, and V. Kumar. HICAP: Hierarchial Clustering with Pattern Preservation. In *Proc. of the SIAM Intl. Conf. on Data Mining*, pages 279–290, Orlando, FL, April 2004.

[330] H. Xiong, P. N. Tan, and V. Kumar. Mining Strong Affinity Association Patterns in Data Sets with Skewed Support Distribution. In *Proc. of the 2003 IEEE Intl. Conf. on Data Mining*, pages 387–394, Melbourne, FL, 2003.

[331] X. Yan and J. Han. gSpan: Graph-based Substructure Pattern Mining. In *Proc. of the 2002 IEEE Intl. Conf. on Data Mining*, pages 721–724, Maebashi City, Japan, December 2002.

[332] C. Yang, U. M. Fayyad, and P. S. Bradley. Efficient discovery of error-tolerant frequent itemsets in high dimensions. In *Proc. of the 7th Intl. Conf. on Knowledge Discovery and Data Mining*, pages 194–203, San Francisco, CA, August 2001.

[333] M. J. Zaki. Parallel and Distributed Association Mining: A Survey. *IEEE Concurrency, special issue on Parallel Mechanisms for Data Mining*, 7(4):14–25, December 1999.

[334] M. J. Zaki. Generating Non-Redundant Association Rules. In *Proc. of the 6th Intl. Conf. on Knowledge Discovery and Data Mining*, pages 34–43, Boston, MA, August 2000.

[335] M. J. Zaki. Efficiently mining frequent trees in a forest. In *Proc. of the 8th Intl. Conf. on Knowledge Discovery and Data Mining*, pages 71–80, Edmonton, Canada, July 2002.

[336] M. J. Zaki and M. Orihara. Theoretical foundations of association rules. In *Proc. of the 1998 ACM SIGMOD Workshop on Research Issues in Data Mining and Knowledge Discovery*, Seattle, WA, June 1998.

[337] M. J. Zaki, S. Parthasarathy, M. Ogihara, and W. Li. New Algorithms for Fast Discovery of Association Rules. In *Proc. of the 3rd Intl. Conf. on Knowledge Discovery and Data Mining*, pages 283–286, Newport Beach, CA, August 1997.

[338] H. Zhang, B. Padmanabhan, and A. Tuzhilin. On the Discovery of Significant Statistical Quantitative Rules. In *Proc. of the 10th Intl. Conf. on Knowledge Discovery and Data Mining*, pages 374–383, Seattle, WA, August 2004.

[339] Z. Zhang, Y. Lu, and B. Zhang. An Effective Partioning-Combining Algorithm for Discovering Quantitative Association Rules. In *Proc. of the 1st Pacific-Asia Conf. on Knowledge Discovery and Data Mining*, Singapore, 1997.

[340] N. Zhong, Y. Y. Yao, and S. Ohsuga. Peculiarity Oriented Multi-database Mining. In *Proc. of the 3rd European Conf. of Principles and Practice of Knowledge Discovery in Databases*, pages 136–146, Prague, Czech Republic, 1999.

6.10   Exercises

1. For each of the following questions, provide an example of an association rule from the market basket domain that satisfies the following conditions. Also, describe whether such rules are subjectively interesting.

   (a) A rule that has high support and high confidence.

   (b) A rule that has reasonably high support but low confidence.

   (c) A rule that has low support and low confidence.

   (d) A rule that has low support and high confidence.

2. Consider the data set shown in Table 6.22.

Table 6.22. Example of market basket transactions.

Customer ID	Transaction ID	Items Bought
1	0001	$\{a, d, e\}$
1	0024	$\{a, b, c, e\}$
2	0012	$\{a, b, d, e\}$
2	0031	$\{a, c, d, e\}$
3	0015	$\{b, c, e\}$
3	0022	$\{b, d, e\}$
4	0029	$\{c, d\}$
4	0040	$\{a, b, c\}$
5	0033	$\{a, d, e\}$
5	0038	$\{a, b, e\}$

   (a) Compute the support for itemsets $\{e\}$, $\{b, d\}$, and $\{b, d, e\}$ by treating each transaction ID as a market basket.

   (b) Use the results in part (a) to compute the confidence for the association rules $\{b, d\} \longrightarrow \{e\}$ and $\{e\} \longrightarrow \{b, d\}$. Is confidence a symmetric measure?

   (c) Repeat part (a) by treating each customer ID as a market basket. Each item should be treated as a binary variable (1 if an item appears in at least one transaction bought by the customer, and 0 otherwise.)

   (d) Use the results in part (c) to compute the confidence for the association rules $\{b, d\} \longrightarrow \{e\}$ and $\{e\} \longrightarrow \{b, d\}$.

   (e) Suppose s_1 and c_1 are the support and confidence values of an association rule r when treating each transaction ID as a market basket. Also, let s_2 and c_2 be the support and confidence values of r when treating each customer ID as a market basket. Discuss whether there are any relationships between s_1 and s_2 or c_1 and c_2.

3. (a) What is the confidence for the rules $\emptyset \longrightarrow A$ and $A \longrightarrow \emptyset$?

   (b) Let c_1, c_2, and c_3 be the confidence values of the rules $\{p\} \longrightarrow \{q\}$, $\{p\} \longrightarrow \{q, r\}$, and $\{p, r\} \longrightarrow \{q\}$, respectively. If we assume that c_1, c_2, and c_3 have different values, what are the possible relationships that may exist among c_1, c_2, and c_3? Which rule has the lowest confidence?

   (c) Repeat the analysis in part (b) assuming that the rules have identical support. Which rule has the highest confidence?

   (d) Transitivity: Suppose the confidence of the rules $A \longrightarrow B$ and $B \longrightarrow C$ are larger than some threshold, $minconf$. Is it possible that $A \longrightarrow C$ has a confidence less than $minconf$?

4. For each of the following measures, determine whether it is monotone, anti-monotone, or non-monotone (i.e., neither monotone nor anti-monotone).

   Example: Support, $s = \frac{\sigma(X)}{|T|}$ is anti-monotone because $s(X) \geq s(Y)$ whenever $X \subset Y$.

   (a) A characteristic rule is a rule of the form $\{p\} \longrightarrow \{q_1, q_2, \ldots, q_n\}$, where the rule antecedent contains only a single item. An itemset of size k can produce up to k characteristic rules. Let ζ be the minimum confidence of all characteristic rules generated from a given itemset:

   $$\zeta(\{p_1, p_2, \ldots, p_k\}) = \min \left[c(\{p_1\} \longrightarrow \{p_2, p_3, \ldots, p_k\}), \ldots \right.$$
   $$\left. c(\{p_k\} \longrightarrow \{p_1, p_3 \ldots, p_{k-1}\}) \right]$$

   Is ζ monotone, anti-monotone, or non-monotone?

   (b) A discriminant rule is a rule of the form $\{p_1, p_2, \ldots, p_n\} \longrightarrow \{q\}$, where the rule consequent contains only a single item. An itemset of size k can produce up to k discriminant rules. Let η be the minimum confidence of all discriminant rules generated from a given itemset:

   $$\eta(\{p_1, p_2, \ldots, p_k\}) = \min \left[c(\{p_2, p_3, \ldots, p_k\} \longrightarrow \{p_1\}), \ldots \right.$$
   $$\left. c(\{p_1, p_2, \ldots p_{k-1}\} \longrightarrow \{p_k\}) \right]$$

   Is η monotone, anti-monotone, or non-monotone?

   (c) Repeat the analysis in parts (a) and (b) by replacing the min function with a max function.

5. Prove Equation 6.3. (Hint: First, count the number of ways to create an itemset that forms the left hand side of the rule. Next, for each size k itemset selected for the left-hand side, count the number of ways to choose the remaining $d - k$ items to form the right-hand side of the rule.)

Table 6.23. Market basket transactions.

Transaction ID	Items Bought
1	{Milk, Beer, Diapers}
2	{Bread, Butter, Milk}
3	{Milk, Diapers, Cookies}
4	{Bread, Butter, Cookies}
5	{Beer, Cookies, Diapers}
6	{Milk, Diapers, Bread, Butter}
7	{Bread, Butter, Diapers}
8	{Beer, Diapers}
9	{Milk, Diapers, Bread, Butter}
10	{Beer, Cookies}

6. Consider the market basket transactions shown in Table 6.23.

   (a) What is the maximum number of association rules that can be extracted from this data (including rules that have zero support)?

   (b) What is the maximum size of frequent itemsets that can be extracted (assuming $minsup > 0$)?

   (c) Write an expression for the maximum number of size-3 itemsets that can be derived from this data set.

   (d) Find an itemset (of size 2 or larger) that has the largest support.

   (e) Find a pair of items, a and b, such that the rules $\{a\} \longrightarrow \{b\}$ and $\{b\} \longrightarrow \{a\}$ have the same confidence.

7. Consider the following set of frequent 3-itemsets:

   $$\{1,2,3\}, \{1,2,4\}, \{1,2,5\}, \{1,3,4\}, \{1,3,5\}, \{2,3,4\}, \{2,3,5\}, \{3,4,5\}.$$

   Assume that there are only five items in the data set.

   (a) List all candidate 4-itemsets obtained by a candidate generation procedure using the $F_{k-1} \times F_1$ merging strategy.

   (b) List all candidate 4-itemsets obtained by the candidate generation procedure in *Apriori*.

   (c) List all candidate 4-itemsets that survive the candidate pruning step of the *Apriori* algorithm.

8. The *Apriori* algorithm uses a generate-and-count strategy for deriving frequent itemsets. Candidate itemsets of size $k + 1$ are created by joining a pair of frequent itemsets of size k (this is known as the candidate generation step). A candidate is discarded if any one of its subsets is found to be infrequent during the candidate pruning step. Suppose the *Apriori* algorithm is applied to the

Table 6.24. Example of market basket transactions.

Transaction ID	Items Bought
1	$\{a, b, d, e\}$
2	$\{b, c, d\}$
3	$\{a, b, d, e\}$
4	$\{a, c, d, e\}$
5	$\{b, c, d, e\}$
6	$\{b, d, e\}$
7	$\{c, d\}$
8	$\{a, b, c\}$
9	$\{a, d, e\}$
10	$\{b, d\}$

data set shown in Table 6.24 with $minsup = 30\%$, i.e., any itemset occurring in less than 3 transactions is considered to be infrequent.

(a) Draw an itemset lattice representing the data set given in Table 6.24. Label each node in the lattice with the following letter(s):

- **N**: If the itemset is not considered to be a candidate itemset by the *Apriori* algorithm. There are two reasons for an itemset not to be considered as a candidate itemset: (1) it is not generated at all during the candidate generation step, or (2) it is generated during the candidate generation step but is subsequently removed during the candidate pruning step because one of its subsets is found to be infrequent.

- **F**: If the candidate itemset is found to be frequent by the *Apriori* algorithm.

- **I**: If the candidate itemset is found to be infrequent after support counting.

(b) What is the percentage of frequent itemsets (with respect to all itemsets in the lattice)?

(c) What is the pruning ratio of the *Apriori* algorithm on this data set? (Pruning ratio is defined as the percentage of itemsets not considered to be a candidate because (1) they are not generated during candidate generation or (2) they are pruned during the candidate pruning step.)

(d) What is the false alarm rate (i.e, percentage of candidate itemsets that are found to be infrequent after performing support counting)?

9. The *Apriori* algorithm uses a hash tree data structure to efficiently count the support of candidate itemsets. Consider the hash tree for candidate 3-itemsets shown in Figure 6.32.

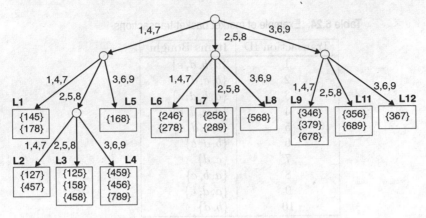

Figure 6.32. An example of a hash tree structure.

(a) Given a transaction that contains items $\{1, 3, 4, 5, 8\}$, which of the hash tree leaf nodes will be visited when finding the candidates of the transaction?

(b) Use the visited leaf nodes in part (b) to determine the candidate itemsets that are contained in the transaction $\{1, 3, 4, 5, 8\}$.

10. Consider the following set of candidate 3-itemsets:

$$\{1, 2, 3\}, \{1, 2, 6\}, \{1, 3, 4\}, \{2, 3, 4\}, \{2, 4, 5\}, \{3, 4, 6\}, \{4, 5, 6\}$$

(a) Construct a hash tree for the above candidate 3-itemsets. Assume the tree uses a hash function where all odd-numbered items are hashed to the left child of a node, while the even-numbered items are hashed to the right child. A candidate k-itemset is inserted into the tree by hashing on each successive item in the candidate and then following the appropriate branch of the tree according to the hash value. Once a leaf node is reached, the candidate is inserted based on one of the following conditions:

Condition 1: If the depth of the leaf node is equal to k (the root is assumed to be at depth 0), then the candidate is inserted regardless of the number of itemsets already stored at the node.

Condition 2: If the depth of the leaf node is less than k, then the candidate can be inserted as long as the number of itemsets stored at the node is less than $maxsize$. Assume $maxsize = 2$ for this question.

Condition 3: If the depth of the leaf node is less than k and the number of itemsets stored at the node is equal to $maxsize$, then the leaf node is converted into an internal node. New leaf nodes are created as children of the old leaf node. Candidate itemsets previously stored

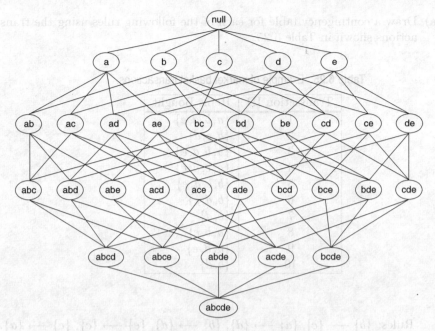

Figure 6.33. An itemset lattice

in the old leaf node are distributed to the children based on their hash values. The new candidate is also hashed to its appropriate leaf node.

(b) How many leaf nodes are there in the candidate hash tree? How many internal nodes are there?

(c) Consider a transaction that contains the following items: $\{1,2,3,5,6\}$. Using the hash tree constructed in part (a), which leaf nodes will be checked against the transaction? What are the candidate 3-itemsets contained in the transaction?

11. Given the lattice structure shown in Figure 6.33 and the transactions given in Table 6.24, label each node with the following letter(s):

- M if the node is a maximal frequent itemset,
- C if it is a closed frequent itemset,
- N if it is frequent but neither maximal nor closed, and
- I if it is infrequent.

Assume that the support threshold is equal to 30%.

12. The original association rule mining formulation uses the support and confidence measures to prune uninteresting rules.

(a) Draw a contingency table for each of the following rules using the transactions shown in Table 6.25.

Table 6.25. Example of market basket transactions.

Transaction ID	Items Bought
1	$\{a, b, d, e\}$
2	$\{b, c, d\}$
3	$\{a, b, d, e\}$
4	$\{a, c, d, e\}$
5	$\{b, c, d, e\}$
6	$\{b, d, e\}$
7	$\{c, d\}$
8	$\{a, b, c\}$
9	$\{a, d, e\}$
10	$\{b, d\}$

Rules: $\{b\} \longrightarrow \{c\}$, $\{a\} \longrightarrow \{d\}$, $\{b\} \longrightarrow \{d\}$, $\{e\} \longrightarrow \{c\}$, $\{c\} \longrightarrow \{a\}$.

(b) Use the contingency tables in part (a) to compute and rank the rules in decreasing order according to the following measures.

    i. Support.

    ii. Confidence.

    iii. Interest$(X \longrightarrow Y) = \frac{P(X,Y)}{P(X)} P(Y)$.

    iv. IS$(X \longrightarrow Y) = \frac{P(X,Y)}{\sqrt{P(X)P(Y)}}$.

    v. Klosgen$(X \longrightarrow Y) = \sqrt{P(X,Y)} \times (P(Y|X) - P(Y))$, where $P(Y|X) = \frac{P(X,Y)}{P(X)}$.

    vi. Odds ratio$(X \longrightarrow Y) = \frac{P(X,Y)P(\overline{X},\overline{Y})}{P(X,\overline{Y})P(\overline{X},Y)}$.

13. Given the rankings you had obtained in Exercise 12, compute the correlation between the rankings of confidence and the other five measures. Which measure is most highly correlated with confidence? Which measure is least correlated with confidence?

14. Answer the following questions using the data sets shown in Figure 6.34. Note that each data set contains 1000 items and 10,000 transactions. Dark cells indicate the presence of items and white cells indicate the absence of items. We will apply the *Apriori* algorithm to extract frequent itemsets with *minsup* = 10% (i.e., itemsets must be contained in at least 1000 transactions)?

    (a) Which data set(s) will produce the most number of frequent itemsets?

(b) Which data set(s) will produce the fewest number of frequent itemsets?

(c) Which data set(s) will produce the longest frequent itemset?

(d) Which data set(s) will produce frequent itemsets with highest maximum support?

(e) Which data set(s) will produce frequent itemsets containing items with wide-varying support levels (i.e., items with mixed support, ranging from less than 20% to more than 70%).

15. (a) Prove that the ϕ coefficient is equal to 1 if and only if $f_{11} = f_{1+} = f_{+1}$.

(b) Show that if A and B are independent, then $P(A, B) \times P(A, \overline{B}) = P(A, \overline{B}) \times P(\overline{A}, B)$.

(c) Show that Yule's Q and Y coefficients

$$Q = \left[\frac{f_{11} f_{00} - f_{10} f_{01}}{f_{11} f_{00} + f_{10} f_{01}} \right]$$

$$Y = \left[\frac{\sqrt{f_{11} f_{00}} - \sqrt{f_{10} f_{01}}}{\sqrt{f_{11} f_{00}} + \sqrt{f_{10} f_{01}}} \right]$$

are normalized versions of the odds ratio.

(d) Write a simplified expression for the value of each measure shown in Tables 6.11 and 6.12 when the variables are statistically independent.

16. Consider the interestingness measure, $M = \frac{P(B|A) - P(B)}{1 - P(B)}$, for an association rule $A \longrightarrow B$.

(a) What is the range of this measure? When does the measure attain its maximum and minimum values?

(b) How does M behave when $P(A, B)$ is increased while $P(A)$ and $P(B)$ remain unchanged?

(c) How does M behave when $P(A)$ is increased while $P(A, B)$ and $P(B)$ remain unchanged?

(d) How does M behave when $P(B)$ is increased while $P(A, B)$ and $P(A)$ remain unchanged?

(e) Is the measure symmetric under variable permutation?

(f) What is the value of the measure when A and B are statistically independent?

(g) Is the measure null-invariant?

(h) Does the measure remain invariant under row or column scaling operations?

(i) How does the measure behave under the inversion operation?

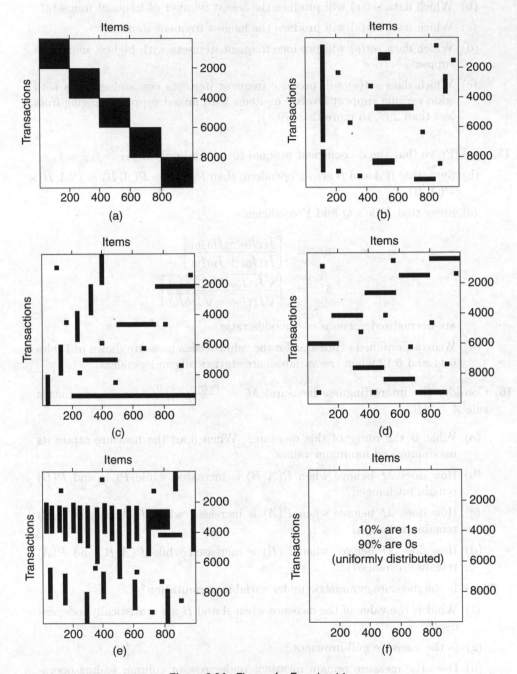

Figure 6.34. Figures for Exercise 14.

17. Suppose we have market basket data consisting of 100 transactions and 20 items. If the support for item a is 25%, the support for item b is 90% and the support for itemset $\{a, b\}$ is 20%. Let the support and confidence thresholds be 10% and 60%, respectively.

    (a) Compute the confidence of the association rule $\{a\} \rightarrow \{b\}$. Is the rule interesting according to the confidence measure?

    (b) Compute the interest measure for the association pattern $\{a, b\}$. Describe the nature of the relationship between item a and item b in terms of the interest measure.

    (c) What conclusions can you draw from the results of parts (a) and (b)?

    (d) Prove that if the confidence of the rule $\{a\} \longrightarrow \{b\}$ is less than the support of $\{b\}$, then:

        i. $c(\{\bar{a}\} \longrightarrow \{b\}) > c(\{\bar{a}\} \longrightarrow \{b\})$,
        ii. $c(\{\bar{a}\} \longrightarrow \{b\}) > s(\{b\})$,

        where $c(\cdot)$ denote the rule confidence and $s(\cdot)$ denote the support of an itemset.

18. Table 6.26 shows a $2 \times 2 \times 2$ contingency table for the binary variables A and B at different values of the control variable C.

Table 6.26. A Contingency Table.

			A	
			1	0
C = 0	B	1	0	15
		0	15	30
C = 1	B	1	5	0
		0	0	15

    (a) Compute the ϕ coefficient for A and B when $C = 0$, $C = 1$, and $C = 0$ or 1. Note that $\phi(\{A, B\}) = \frac{P(A,B) - P(A)P(B)}{\sqrt{P(A)P(B)(1-P(A))(1-P(B))}}$.

    (b) What conclusions can you draw from the above result?

19. Consider the contingency tables shown in Table 6.27.

    (a) For table I, compute support, the interest measure, and the ϕ correlation coefficient for the association pattern $\{A, B\}$. Also, compute the confidence of rules $A \rightarrow B$ and $B \rightarrow A$.

Table 6.27. Contingency tables for Exercise 19.

	B	$\overline{B}$
A	9	1
$\overline{A}$	1	89

	B	$\overline{B}$
A	89	1
$\overline{A}$	1	9

(a) Table I.   (b) Table II.

(b) For table II, compute support, the interest measure, and the ϕ correlation coefficient for the association pattern {A, B}. Also, compute the confidence of rules $A \rightarrow B$ and $B \rightarrow A$.

(c) What conclusions can you draw from the results of (a) and (b)?

20. Consider the relationship between customers who buy high-definition televisions and exercise machines as shown in Tables 6.19 and 6.20.

    (a) Compute the odds ratios for both tables.

    (b) Compute the ϕ-coefficient for both tables.

    (c) Compute the interest factor for both tables.

    For each of the measures given above, describe how the direction of association changes when data is pooled together instead of being stratified.

Association Analysis: Advanced Concepts

The association rule mining formulation described in the previous chapter assumes that the input data consists of binary attributes called items. The presence of an item in a transaction is also assumed to be more important than its absence. As a result, an item is treated as an asymmetric binary attribute and only frequent patterns are considered interesting.

This chapter extends the formulation to data sets with symmetric binary, categorical, and continuous attributes. The formulation will also be extended to incorporate more complex entities such as sequences and graphs. Although the overall structure of association analysis algorithms remains unchanged, certain aspects of the algorithms must be modified to handle the non-traditional entities.

7.1 Handling Categorical Attributes

There are many applications that contain symmetric binary and nominal attributes. The Internet survey data shown in Table 7.1 contains symmetric binary attributes such as Gender, Computer at Home, Chat Online, Shop Online, and Privacy Concerns; as well as nominal attributes such as Level of Education and State. Using association analysis, we may uncover interesting information about the characteristics of Internet users such as:

$$\{\text{Shop Online} = \text{Yes}\} \longrightarrow \{\text{Privacy Concerns} = \text{Yes}\}.$$

This rule suggests that most Internet users who shop online are concerned about their personal privacy.

From Chapter 7 of *Introduction to Data Mining*, First Edition. Pang-Ning Tan, Michael Steinbach, Vipin Kumar. Copyright © 2006 by Pearson Education, Inc. All rights reserved.

Table 7.1. Internet survey data with categorical attributes.

Gender	Level of Education	State	Computer at Home	Chat Online	Shop Online	Privacy Concerns
Female	Graduate	Illinois	Yes	Yes	Yes	Yes
Male	College	California	No	No	No	No
Male	Graduate	Michigan	Yes	Yes	Yes	Yes
Female	College	Virginia	No	No	Yes	Yes
Female	Graduate	California	Yes	No	No	Yes
Male	College	Minnesota	Yes	Yes	Yes	Yes
Male	College	Alaska	Yes	Yes	Yes	No
Male	High School	Oregon	Yes	No	No	No
Female	Graduate	Texas	No	Yes	No	No
...	...	...	...	...	...	...

To extract such patterns, the categorical and symmetric binary attributes are transformed into "items" first, so that existing association rule mining algorithms can be applied. This type of transformation can be performed by creating a new item for each distinct attribute-value pair. For example, the nominal attribute `Level of Education` can be replaced by three binary items: `Education = College`, `Education = Graduate`, and `Education = High School`. Similarly, symmetric binary attributes such as `Gender` can be converted into a pair of binary items, `Male` and `Female`. Table 7.2 shows the result of binarizing the Internet survey data.

Table 7.2. Internet survey data after binarizing categorical and symmetric binary attributes.

Male	Female	Education = Graduate	Education = College	...	Privacy = Yes	Privacy = No
0	1	1	0	...	1	0
1	0	0	1	...	0	1
1	0	1	0	...	1	0
0	1	0	1	...	1	0
0	1	1	0	...	1	0
1	0	0	1	...	1	0
1	0	0	1	...	0	1
1	0	0	0	...	0	1
0	1	1	0	...	0	1
...	...	...	...	...	...	...

There are several issues to consider when applying association analysis to the binarized data:

1. Some attribute values may not be frequent enough to be part of a frequent pattern. This problem is more evident for nominal attributes that have many possible values, e.g., state names. Lowering the support threshold does not help because it exponentially increases the number of frequent patterns found (many of which may be spurious) and makes the computation more expensive. A more practical solution is to group related attribute values into a small number of categories. For example, each state name can be replaced by its corresponding geographical region, such as Midwest, Pacific Northwest, Southwest, and East Coast. Another possibility is to aggregate the less frequent attribute values into a single category called Others, as shown in Figure 7.1.

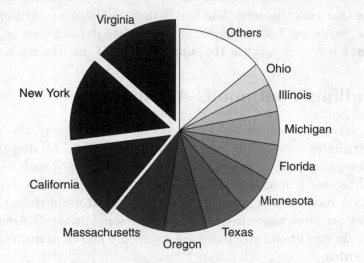

Figure 7.1. A pie chart with a merged category called Others.

2. Some attribute values may have considerably higher frequencies than others. For example, suppose 85% of the survey participants own a home computer. By creating a binary item for each attribute value that appears frequently in the data, we may potentially generate many redundant patterns, as illustrated by the following example:

$$\{\text{Computer at home = Yes, Shop Online = Yes}\}$$
$$\longrightarrow \{\text{Privacy Concerns = Yes}\}.$$

The rule is redundant because it is subsumed by the more general rule given at the beginning of this section. Because the high-frequency items correspond to the typical values of an attribute, they seldom carry any new information that can help us to better understand the pattern. It may therefore be useful to remove such items before applying standard association analysis algorithms. Another possibility is to apply the techniques presented in Section 6.8 for handling data sets with a wide range of support values.

3. Although the width of every transaction is the same as the number of attributes in the original data, the computation time may increase especially when many of the newly created items become frequent. This is because more time is needed to deal with the additional candidate itemsets generated by these items (see Exercise 1 on page 473). One way to reduce the computation time is to avoid generating candidate itemsets that contain more than one item from the same attribute. For example, we do not have to generate a candidate itemset such as {State = X, State = Y, ...} because the support count of the itemset is zero.

7.2   Handling Continuous Attributes

The Internet survey data described in the previous section may also contain continuous attributes such as the ones shown in Table 7.3. Mining the continuous attributes may reveal useful insights about the data such as "users whose annual income is more than \$120K belong to the 45–60 age group" or "users who have more than 3 email accounts and spend more than 15 hours online per week are often concerned about their personal privacy." Association rules that contain continuous attributes are commonly known as **quantitative association rules**.

This section describes the various methodologies for applying association analysis to continuous data. We will specifically discuss three types of methods: (1) discretization-based methods, (2) statistics-based methods, and (3) non-discretization methods. The quantitative association rules derived using these methods are quite different in nature.

7.2.1   Discretization-Based Methods

Discretization is the most common approach for handling continuous attributes. This approach groups the adjacent values of a continuous attribute into a finite number of intervals. For example, the Age attribute can be divided into the

Table 7.3. Internet survey data with continuous attributes.

Gender	...	Age	Annual Income	No. of Hours Spent Online per Week	No. of Email Accounts	Privacy Concern
Female	...	26	90K	20	4	Yes
Male	...	51	135K	10	2	No
Male	...	29	80K	10	3	Yes
Female	...	45	120K	15	3	Yes
Female	...	31	95K	20	5	Yes
Male	...	25	55K	25	5	Yes
Male	...	37	100K	10	1	No
Male	...	41	65K	8	2	No
Female	...	26	85K	12	1	No
...	...	...	...	...	...	...

following intervals:

$$\text{Age} \in [12, 16), \; \text{Age} \in [16, 20), \; \text{Age} \in [20, 24), \ldots, \text{Age} \in [56, 60),$$

where $[a, b)$ represents an interval that includes a but not b. Discretization can be performed using any of the techniques described in Section 2.3.6 (equal interval width, equal frequency, entropy-based, or clustering). The discrete intervals are then mapped into asymmetric binary attributes so that existing association analysis algorithms can be applied. Table 7.4 shows the Internet survey data after discretization and binarization.

Table 7.4. Internet survey data after binarizing categorical and continuous attributes.

Male	Female	...	Age < 13	Age ∈ [13, 21)	Age ∈ [21, 30)	...	Privacy = Yes	Privacy = No
0	1	...	0	0	1	...	1	0
1	0	...	0	0	0	...	0	1
1	0	...	0	0	1	...	1	0
0	1	...	0	0	0	...	1	0
0	1	...	0	0	0	...	1	0
1	0	...	0	0	1	...	1	0
1	0	...	0	0	0	...	0	1
1	0	...	0	0	0	...	0	1
0	1	...	0	0	1	...	0	1
...	...	...	...	...	...	...	...	...

Table 7.5. A breakdown of Internet users who participated in online chat according to their age group.

Age Group	Chat Online = Yes	Chat Online = No
[12, 16)	12	13
[16, 20)	11	2
[20, 24)	11	3
[24, 28)	12	13
[28, 32)	14	12
[32, 36)	15	12
[36, 40)	16	14
[40, 44)	16	14
[44, 48)	4	10
[48, 52)	5	11
[52, 56)	5	10
[56, 60)	4	11

A key parameter in attribute discretization is the number of intervals used to partition each attribute. This parameter is typically provided by the users and can be expressed in terms of the interval width (for the equal interval width approach), the average number of transactions per interval (for the equal frequency approach), or the number of desired clusters (for the clustering-based approach). The difficulty in determining the right number of intervals can be illustrated using the data set shown in Table 7.5, which summarizes the responses of 250 users who participated in the survey. There are two strong rules embedded in the data:

R_1:   Age $\in$ [16, 24) $\longrightarrow$ Chat Online = Yes (s = 8.8%, c = 81.5%).
R_2:   Age $\in$ [44, 60) $\longrightarrow$ Chat Online = No (s = 16.8%, c = 70%).

These rules suggest that most of the users from the age group of 16–24 often participate in online chatting, while those from the age group of 44–60 are less likely to chat online. In this example, we consider a rule to be interesting only if its support (s) exceeds 5% and its confidence (c) exceeds 65%. One of the problems encountered when discretizing the **Age** attribute is how to determine the interval width.

1. If the interval is too wide, then we may lose some patterns because of their lack of confidence. For example, when the interval width is 24 years, R_1 and R_2 are replaced by the following rules:

   R_1':   Age $\in$ [12, 36) $\longrightarrow$ Chat Online = Yes (s = 30%, c = 57.7%).
   R_2':   Age $\in$ [36, 60) $\longrightarrow$ Chat Online = No (s = 28%, c = 58.3%).

Despite their higher supports, the wider intervals have caused the confidence for both rules to drop below the minimum confidence threshold. As a result, both patterns are lost after discretization.

2. If the interval is too narrow, then we may lose some patterns because of their lack of support. For example, if the interval width is 4 years, then R_1 is broken up into the following two subrules:

$R_{11}^{(4)}$: Age $\in [16, 20) \longrightarrow$ Chat Online $=$ Yes (s=4.4%, c=84.6%).
$R_{12}^{(4)}$: Age $\in [20, 24) \longrightarrow$ Chat Online $=$ No (s=4.4%, c=78.6%).

Since the supports for the subrules are less than the minimum support threshold, R_1 is lost after discretization. Similarly, the rule R_2, which is broken up into four subrules, will also be lost because the support of each subrule is less than the minimum support threshold.

3. If the interval width is 8 years, then the rule R_2 is broken up into the following two subrules:

$R_{21}^{(8)}$: Age $\in [44, 52) \longrightarrow$ Chat Online $=$ No (s=8.4%, c=70%).
$R_{22}^{(8)}$: Age $\in [52, 60) \longrightarrow$ Chat Online $=$ No (s=8.4%, c=70%).

Since $R_{21}^{(8)}$ and $R_{22}^{(8)}$ have sufficient support and confidence, R_2 can be recovered by aggregating both subrules. Meanwhile, R_1 is broken up into the following two subrules:

$R_{11}^{(8)}$: Age $\in [12, 20) \longrightarrow$ Chat Online $=$ Yes (s=9.2%, c=60.5%).
$R_{12}^{(8)}$: Age $\in [20, 28) \longrightarrow$ Chat Online $=$ Yes (s=9.2%, c=60.0%).

Unlike R_2, we cannot recover the rule R_1 by aggregating the subrules because both subrules fail the confidence threshold.

One way to address these issues is to consider every possible grouping of adjacent intervals. For example, we can start with an interval width of 4 years and then merge the adjacent intervals into wider intervals, Age $\in [12, 16)$, Age $\in [12, 20)$, ..., Age $\in [12, 60)$, Age $\in [16, 20)$, Age $\in [16, 24)$, etc. This approach enables the detection of both R_1 and R_2 as strong rules. However, it also leads to the following computational issues:

1. **The computation becomes extremely expensive.** If the range is initially divided into k intervals, then $k(k-1)/2$ binary items must be

generated to represent all possible intervals. Furthermore, if an item corresponding to the interval [a,b) is frequent, then all other items corresponding to intervals that subsume [a,b) must be frequent too. This approach can therefore generate far too many candidate and frequent itemsets. To address these problems, a maximum support threshold can be applied to prevent the creation of items corresponding to very wide intervals and to reduce the number of itemsets.

2. **Many redundant rules are extracted.** For example, consider the following pair of rules:

$$R_3 : \{\text{Age} \in [16, 20), \text{Gender} = \text{Male}\} \longrightarrow \{\text{Chat Online} = \text{Yes}\},$$

$$R_4 : \{\text{Age} \in [16, 24), \text{Gender} = \text{Male}\} \longrightarrow \{\text{Chat Online} = \text{Yes}\}.$$

R_4 is a generalization of R_3 (and R_3 is a specialization of R_4) because R_4 has a wider interval for the Age attribute. If the confidence values for both rules are the same, then R_4 should be more interesting because it covers more examples—including those for R_3. R_3 is therefore a redundant rule.

7.2.2   Statistics-Based Methods

Quantitative association rules can be used to infer the statistical properties of a population. For example, suppose we are interested in finding the average age of certain groups of Internet users based on the data provided in Tables 7.1 and 7.3. Using the statistics-based method described in this section, quantitative association rules such as the following can be extracted:

$$\{\text{Annual Income} > \$100K, \text{Shop Online} = \text{Yes}\} \longrightarrow \text{Age: Mean} = 38.$$

The rule states that the average age of Internet users whose annual income exceeds \$100K and who shop online regularly is 38 years old.

Rule Generation

To generate the statistics-based quantitative association rules, the target attribute used to characterize interesting segments of the population must be specified. By withholding the target attribute, the remaining categorical and continuous attributes in the data are binarized using the methods described in the previous section. Existing algorithms such as *Apriori* or FP-growth are then applied to extract frequent itemsets from the binarized data. Each frequent itemset identifies an interesting segment of the population. The distribution of the target attribute in each segment can be summarized using descriptive statistics such as mean, median, variance, or absolute deviation. For example, the preceding rule is obtained by averaging the age of Internet users who support the frequent itemset {`Annual Income` > $100K, `Shop Online = Yes`}.

The number of quantitative association rules discovered using this method is the same as the number of extracted frequent itemsets. Because of the way the quantitative association rules are defined, the notion of confidence is not applicable to such rules. An alternative method for validating the quantitative association rules is presented next.

Rule Validation

A quantitative association rule is interesting only if the statistics computed from transactions covered by the rule are different than those computed from transactions not covered by the rule. For example, the rule given at the beginning of this section is interesting only if the average age of Internet users who do not support the frequent itemset {`Annual Income` > 100K, `Shop Online = Yes`} is significantly higher or lower than 38 years old. To determine whether the difference in their average ages is statistically significant, statistical hypothesis testing methods should be applied.

Consider the quantitative association rule, $A \longrightarrow t : \mu$, where A is a frequent itemset, t is the continuous target attribute, and μ is the average value of t among transactions covered by A. Furthermore, let μ' denote the average value of t among transactions not covered by A. The goal is to test whether the difference between μ and μ' is greater than some user-specified threshold, Δ. In statistical hypothesis testing, two opposite propositions, known as the null hypothesis and the alternative hypothesis, are given. A hypothesis test is performed to determine which of these two hypotheses should be accepted, based on evidence gathered from the data (see Appendix C).

In this case, assuming that $\mu < \mu'$, the null hypothesis is $H_0 : \mu' = \mu + \Delta$, while the alternative hypothesis is $H_1 : \mu' > \mu + \Delta$. To determine which hypothesis should be accepted, the following Z-statistic is computed:

$$Z = \frac{\mu' - \mu - \Delta}{\sqrt{\frac{s_1^2}{n_1} + \frac{s_2^2}{n_2}}}, \qquad (7.1)$$

where n_1 is the number of transactions supporting A, n_2 is the number of transactions not supporting A, s_1 is the standard deviation for t among transactions that support A, and s_2 is the standard deviation for t among transactions that do not support A. Under the null hypothesis, Z has a standard normal distribution with mean 0 and variance 1. The value of Z computed using Equation 7.1 is then compared against a critical value, Z_α, which is a threshold that depends on the desired confidence level. If $Z > Z_\alpha$, then the null hypothesis is rejected and we may conclude that the quantitative association rule is interesting. Otherwise, there is not enough evidence in the data to show that the difference in mean is statistically significant.

Example 7.1. Consider the quantitative association rule

$$\{Income > 100K, \; Shop \; Online = Yes\} \longrightarrow Age : \mu = 38.$$

Suppose there are 50 Internet users who supported the rule antecedent. The standard deviation of their ages is 3.5. On the other hand, the average age of the 200 users who do not support the rule antecedent is 30 and their standard deviation is 6.5. Assume that a quantitative association rule is considered interesting only if the difference between μ and μ' is more than 5 years. Using Equation 7.1 we obtain

$$Z = \frac{38 - 30 - 5}{\sqrt{\frac{3.5^2}{50} + \frac{6.5^2}{200}}} = 4.4414.$$

For a one-sided hypothesis test at a 95% confidence level, the critical value for rejecting the null hypothesis is 1.64. Since $Z > 1.64$, the null hypothesis can be rejected. We therefore conclude that the quantitative association rule is interesting because the difference between the average ages of users who support and do not support the rule antecedent is more than 5 years. ∎

7.2.3 Non-discretization Methods

There are certain applications in which analysts are more interested in finding associations among the continuous attributes, rather than associations among discrete intervals of the continuous attributes. For example, consider the problem of finding word associations in text documents, as shown in Table 7.6. Each entry in the document-word matrix represents the normalized frequency count of a word appearing in a given document. The data is normalized by dividing the frequency of each word by the sum of the word frequency across all documents. One reason for this normalization is to make sure that the resulting support value is a number between 0 and 1. However, a more

Table 7.6. Normalized document-word matrix.

Document	$word_1$	$word_2$	$word_3$	$word_4$	$word_5$	$word_6$
d_1	0.3	0.6	0	0	0	0.2
d_2	0.1	0.2	0	0	0	0.2
d_3	0.4	0.2	0.7	0	0	0.2
d_4	0.2	0	0.3	0	0	0.1
d_5	0	0	0	1.0	1.0	0.3

important reason is to ensure that the data is on the same scale so that sets of words that vary in the same way have similar support values.

In text mining, analysts are more interested in finding associations between words (e.g., data and mining) instead of associations between ranges of word frequencies (e.g., data $\in [1,4]$ and mining $\in [2,3]$). One way to do this is to transform the data into a 0/1 matrix, where the entry is 1 if the normalized frequency count exceeds some threshold t, and 0 otherwise. While this approach allows analysts to apply existing frequent itemset generation algorithms to the binarized data set, finding the right threshold for binarization can be quite tricky. If the threshold is set too high, it is possible to miss some interesting associations. Conversely, if the threshold is set too low, there is a potential for generating a large number of spurious associations.

This section presents another methodology for finding word associations known as min-*Apriori*. Analogous to traditional association analysis, an itemset is considered to be a collection of words, while its support measures the degree of association among the words. The support of an itemset can be computed based on the normalized frequency of its corresponding words. For example, consider the document d_1 shown in Table 7.6. The normalized frequencies for $word_1$ and $word_2$ in this document are 0.3 and 0.6, respectively. One might think that a reasonable approach to compute the association between both words is to take the average value of their normalized frequencies, i.e., $(0.3 + 0.6)/2 = 0.45$. The support of an itemset can then be computed by summing up the averaged normalized frequencies across all the documents:

$$s(\{word_1, word_2\}) = \frac{0.3 + 0.6}{2} + \frac{0.1 + 0.2}{2} + \frac{0.4 + 0.2}{2} + \frac{0.2 + 0}{2} = 1.$$

This result is by no means an accident. Because every word frequency is normalized to 1, averaging the normalized frequencies makes the support for every itemset equal to 1. All itemsets are therefore frequent using this approach, making it useless for identifying interesting patterns.

In min-*Apriori*, the association among words in a given document is obtained by taking the minimum value of their normalized frequencies, i.e., $\min(word_1, word_2) = \min(0.3, 0.6) = 0.3$. The support of an itemset is computed by aggregating its association over all the documents.

$$
\begin{aligned}
s(\{word_1, word_2\}) &= \min(0.3, 0.6) + \min(0.1, 0.2) + \min(0.4, 0.2) \\
&\quad + \min(0.2, 0) \\
&= 0.6.
\end{aligned}
$$

The support measure defined in min-*Apriori* has the following desired properties, which makes it suitable for finding word associations in documents:

1. Support increases monotonically as the normalized frequency of a word increases.

2. Support increases monotonically as the number of documents that contain the word increases.

3. Support has an anti-monotone property. For example, consider a pair of itemsets $\{A, B\}$ and $\{A, B, C\}$. Since $\min(\{A, B\}) \geq \min(\{A, B, C\})$, $s(\{A, B\}) \geq s(\{A, B, C\})$. Therefore, support decreases monotonically as the number of words in an itemset increases.

The standard *Apriori* algorithm can be modified to find associations among words using the new support definition.

7.3   Handling a Concept Hierarchy

A concept hierarchy is a multilevel organization of the various entities or concepts defined in a particular domain. For example, in market basket analysis, a concept hierarchy has the form of an item taxonomy describing the "is-a" relationships among items sold at a grocery store—e.g., milk is a kind of food and DVD is a kind of home electronics equipment (see Figure 7.2). Concept hierarchies are often defined according to domain knowledge or based on a standard classification scheme defined by certain organizations (e.g., the Library of Congress classification scheme is used to organize library materials based on their subject categories).

A concept hierarchy can be represented using a **directed acyclic graph**, as shown in Figure 7.2. If there is an edge in the graph from a node p to another node c, we call p the **parent** of c and c the **child** of p. For example,

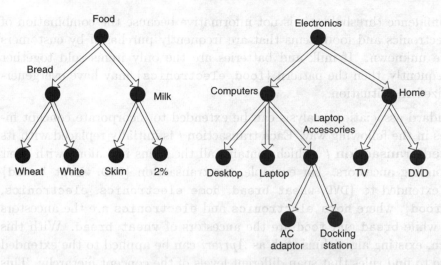

Figure 7.2. Example of an item taxonomy.

milk is the parent of skim milk because there is a directed edge from the node milk to the node skim milk. $\hat{X}$ is called an **ancestor** of X (and X a **descendent** of $\hat{X}$) if there is a path from node $\hat{X}$ to node X in the directed acyclic graph. In the diagram shown in Figure 7.2, food is an ancestor of skim milk and AC adaptor is a descendent of electronics.

The main advantages of incorporating concept hierarchies into association analysis are as follows:

1. Items at the lower levels of a hierarchy may not have enough support to appear in any frequent itemsets. For example, although the sale of AC adaptors and docking stations may be low, the sale of laptop accessories, which is their parent node in the concept hierarchy, may be high. Unless the concept hierarchy is used, there is a potential to miss interesting patterns involving the laptop accessories.

2. Rules found at the lower levels of a concept hierarchy tend to be overly specific and may not be as interesting as rules at the higher levels. For example, staple items such as milk and bread tend to produce many low-level rules such as skim milk ⟶ wheat bread, 2% milk ⟶ wheat bread, and skim milk ⟶ white bread. Using a concept hierarchy, they can be summarized into a single rule, milk ⟶ bread. Considering only items residing at the top level of their hierarchies may not be good enough because such rules may not be of any practical use. For example, although the rule electronics ⟶ food may satisfy the support and

confidence thresholds, it is not informative because the combination of electronics and food items that are frequently purchased by customers are unknown. If milk and batteries are the only items sold together frequently, then the pattern {food, electronics} may have overgeneralized the situation.

Standard association analysis can be extended to incorporate concept hierarchies in the following way. Each transaction t is initially replaced with its **extended transaction** t', which contains all the items in t along with their corresponding ancestors. For example, the transaction {DVD, wheat bread} can be extended to {DVD, wheat bread, home electronics, electronics, bread, food}, where home electronics and electronics are the ancestors of DVD, while bread and food are the ancestors of wheat bread. With this approach, existing algorithms such as *Apriori* can be applied to the extended database to find rules that span different levels of the concept hierarchy. This approach has several obvious limitations:

1. Items residing at the higher levels tend to have higher support counts than those residing at the lower levels of a concept hierarchy. As a result, if the support threshold is set too high, then only patterns involving the high-level items are extracted. On the other hand, if the threshold is set too low, then the algorithm generates far too many patterns (most of which may be spurious) and becomes computationally inefficient.

2. Introduction of a concept hierarchy tends to increase the computation time of association analysis algorithms because of the larger number of items and wider transactions. The number of candidate patterns and frequent patterns generated by these algorithms may also grow exponentially with wider transactions.

3. Introduction of a concept hierarchy may produce redundant rules. A rule $X \longrightarrow Y$ is redundant if there exists a more general rule $\hat{X} \longrightarrow \hat{Y}$, where $\hat{X}$ is an ancestor of X, $\hat{Y}$ is an ancestor of Y, and both rules have very similar confidence. For example, suppose {bread} $\longrightarrow$ {milk}, {white bread} $\longrightarrow$ {2% milk}, {wheat bread} $\longrightarrow$ {2% milk}, {white bread} $\longrightarrow$ {skim milk}, and {wheat bread} $\longrightarrow$ {skim milk} have very similar confidence. The rules involving items from the lower level of the hierarchy are considered redundant because they can be summarized by a rule involving the ancestor items. An itemset such as {skim milk, milk, food} is also redundant because food and milk are ancestors of skim milk. Fortunately, it is easy to eliminate such redundant itemsets during frequent itemset generation, given the knowledge of the hierarchy.

Sequence Database:

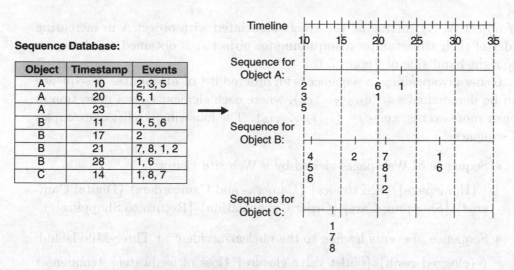

Object	Timestamp	Events
A	10	2, 3, 5
A	20	6, 1
A	23	1
B	11	4, 5, 6
B	17	2
B	21	7, 8, 1, 2
B	28	1, 6
C	14	1, 8, 7

Figure 7.3. Example of a sequence database.

7.4   Sequential Patterns

Market basket data often contains temporal information about when an item was purchased by customers. Such information can be used to piece together the sequence of transactions made by a customer over a certain period of time. Similarly, event-based data collected from scientific experiments or the monitoring of physical systems such as telecommunications networks, computer networks, and wireless sensor networks, have an inherent sequential nature to them. This means that an ordinal relation, usually based on temporal or spatial precedence, exists among events occurring in such data. However, the concepts of association patterns discussed so far emphasize only co-occurrence relationships and disregard the sequential information of the data. The latter information may be valuable for identifying recurring features of a dynamic system or predicting future occurrences of certain events. This section presents the basic concept of sequential patterns and the algorithms developed to discover them.

7.4.1   Problem Formulation

The input to the problem of discovering sequential patterns is a sequence data set, which is shown on the left-hand side of Figure 7.3. Each row records the occurrences of events associated with a particular object at a given time. For example, the first row contains the set of events occurring at timestamp $t = 10$

for object A. By sorting all the events associated with object A in increasing order of their timestamps, a **sequence** for object A is obtained, as shown on the right-hand side of Figure 7.3.

Generally speaking, a sequence is an ordered list of **elements**. A sequence can be denoted as $s = \langle e_1 e_2 e_3 \ldots e_n \rangle$, where each element e_j is a collection of one or more events, i.e., $e_j = \{i_1, i_2, \ldots, i_k\}$. The following is a list of examples of sequences:

- Sequence of Web pages viewed by a Web site visitor:

  $\langle$ {Homepage} {Electronics} {Cameras and Camcorders} {Digital Cameras} {Shopping Cart} {Order Confirmation} {Return to Shopping} $\rangle$

- Sequence of events leading to the nuclear accident at Three-Mile Island:

  $\langle$ {clogged resin} {outlet valve closure} {loss of feedwater} {condenser polisher outlet valve shut} {booster pumps trip} {main waterpump trips} {main turbine trips} {reactor pressure increases} $\rangle$

- Sequence of classes taken by a computer science major:

  $\langle$ {Algorithms and Data Structures, Introduction to Operating Systems} {Database Systems, Computer Architecture} {Computer Networks, Software Engineering} {Computer Graphics, Parallel Programming} $\rangle$

A sequence can be characterized by its length and the number of occurring events. The length of a sequence corresponds to the number of elements present in the sequence, while a k-sequence is a sequence that contains k events. The Web sequence in the previous example contains 7 elements and 7 events; the event sequence at Three-Mile Island contains 8 elements and 8 events; and the class sequence contains 4 elements and 8 events.

Figure 7.4 provides examples of sequences, elements, and events defined for a variety of application domains. Except for the last row, the ordinal attribute associated with each of the first three domains corresponds to calendar time. For the last row, the ordinal attribute corresponds to the location of the bases (A, C, G, T) in the gene sequence. Although the discussion on sequential patterns is primarily focused on temporal events, it can be extended to the case where the events have spatial ordering.

Subsequences

A sequence t is a **subsequence** of another sequence s if each ordered element in t is a subset of an ordered element in s. Formally, the sequence $t = \langle t_1 t_2 \ldots t_m \rangle$

Sequence Database	Sequence	Element (Transaction)	Event (Item)
Customer	Purchase history of a given customer	A set of items bought by a customer at time t	Books, diary products, CDs, etc
Web Data	Browsing activity of a particular Web visitor	The collection of files viewed by a Web visitor after a single mouse click	Home page, index page, contact info, etc
Event data	History of events generated by a given sensor	Events triggered by a sensor at time t	Types of alarms generated by sensors
Genome sequences	DNA sequence of a particular species	An element of the DNA sequence	Bases A,T,G,C

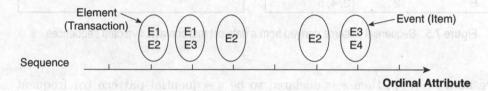

Figure 7.4. Examples of elements and events in sequence data sets.

is a subsequence of $s = \langle s_1 s_2 \ldots s_n \rangle$ if there exist integers $1 \leq j_1 < j_2 < \cdots < j_m \leq n$ such that $t_1 \subseteq s_{j_1}, t_2 \subseteq s_{j_2}, \ldots, t_m \subseteq s_{j_m}$. If t is a subsequence of s, then we say that t is **contained** in s. The following table gives examples illustrating the idea of subsequences for various sequences.

Sequence, s	Sequence, t	Is t a subsequence of s?
<{2,4} {3,5,6} {8} >	< {2} {3,6} {8} >	Yes
<{2,4} {3,5,6} {8} >	< {2} {8} >	Yes
<{1,2} {3,4} >	< {1} {2} >	No
<{2,4} {2,4} {2,5} >	< {2} {4} >	Yes

7.4.2   Sequential Pattern Discovery

Let D be a data set that contains one or more **data sequences**. The term data sequence refers to an ordered list of events associated with a single data object. For example, the data set shown in Figure 7.3 contains three data sequences, one for each object A, B, and C.

The support of a sequence s is the fraction of all data sequences that contain s. If the support for s is greater than or equal to a user-specified

Object	Timestamp	Events
A	1	1, 2, 4
A	2	2, 3
A	3	5
B	1	1, 2
B	2	2, 3, 4
C	1	1, 2
C	2	2, 3, 4
C	3	2, 4, 5
D	1	2
D	2	3, 4
D	3	4, 5
E	1	1, 3
E	2	2, 4, 5

Minsup = 50%

Examples of Sequential Patterns:

<{1,2}>	s=60%
<{2,3}>	s=60%
<{2,4}>	s=80%
<{3} {5}>	s=80%
<{1} {2}>	s=80%
<{2} {2}>	s=60%
<{1} {2,3}>	s=60%
<{2} {2,3}>	s=60%
<{1,2} {2,3}>	s=60%

Figure 7.5. Sequential patterns derived from a data set that contains five data sequences.

threshold *minsup*, then *s* is declared to be a sequential pattern (or frequent sequence).

Definition 7.1 (Sequential Pattern Discovery). Given a sequence data set D and a user-specified minimum support threshold *minsup*, the task of sequential pattern discovery is to find all sequences with support $\geq$ *minsup*.

Figure 7.5 illustrates an example of a data set that contains five data sequences. The support for the sequence $<\{1\}\{2\}>$ is equal to 80% because it occurs in four of the five data sequences (every object except for D). Assuming that the minimum support threshold is 50%, any sequence that appears in at least three data sequences is considered to be a sequential pattern. Examples of sequential patterns extracted from the given data set include $<\{1\}\{2\}>$, $<\{1,2\}>$, $<\{2,3\}>$, $<\{1,2\}\{2,3\}>$, etc.

Sequential pattern discovery is a computationally challenging task because there are exponentially many sequences contained in a given data sequence. For example, the data sequence $<\{a,b\}\ \{c,d,e\}\ \{f\}\ \{g,h,i\}>$ contains sequences such as $<\{a\}\ \{c,d\}\ \{f\}\ \{g\}>$, $<\{c,d,e\}>$, $<\{b\}\ \{g\}>$, etc. It can be easily shown that the total number of k-sequences present in a data sequence with n events is $\binom{n}{k}$. A data sequence with nine events therefore contains

$$\binom{9}{1} + \binom{9}{2} + \ldots + \binom{9}{9} = 2^9 - 1 = 511$$

distinct sequences.

A brute-force approach for generating sequential patterns is to enumerate all possible sequences and count their respective supports. Given a collection of n events, candidate 1-sequences are generated first, followed by candidate 2-sequences, candidate 3-sequences, and so on:

1-sequences: $< i_1 >, < i_2 >, \ldots, < i_n >$

2-sequences: $< \{i_1, i_2\} >, < \{i_1, i_3\} >, \ldots, < \{i_{n-1}, i_n\} >,$
$< \{i_1\}\{i_1\} >, < \{i_1\}\{i_2\} >, \ldots, < \{i_{n-1}\}\{i_n\} >$

3-sequences: $< \{i_1, i_2, i_3\} >, < \{i_1, i_2, i_4\} >, \ldots, < \{i_1, i_2\}\{i_1\} >, \ldots,$
$< \{i_1\}\{i_1, i_2\} >, \ldots, < \{i_1\}\{i_1\}\{i_1\} >, \ldots, < \{i_n\}\{i_n\}\{i_n\} >$

Notice that the number of candidate sequences is substantially larger than the number of candidate itemsets. There are two reasons for the additional number of candidates:

1. An item can appear at most once in an itemset, but an event can appear more than once in a sequence. Given a pair of items, i_1 and i_2, only one candidate 2-itemset, $\{i_1, i_2\}$, can be generated. On the other hand, there are many candidate 2-sequences, such as $< \{i_1, i_2\} >$, $< \{i_1\}\{i_2\} >$, $< \{i_2\}\{i_1\} >$, and $< \{i_1, i_1\} >$, that can be generated.

2. Order matters in sequences, but not for itemsets. For example, $\{1, 2\}$ and $\{2, 1\}$ refers to the same itemset, whereas $< \{i_1\}\{i_2\} >$ and $< \{i_2\}\{i_1\} >$ correspond to different sequences, and thus must be generated separately.

The *Apriori* principle holds for sequential data because any data sequence that contains a particular k-sequence must also contain all of its $(k-1)$-subsequences. An *Apriori*-like algorithm can be developed to extract sequential patterns from a sequence data set. The basic structure of the algorithm is shown in Algorithm 7.1.

Notice that the structure of the algorithm is almost identical to Algorithm 6.1 presented in the previous chapter. The algorithm would iteratively generate new candidate k-sequences, prune candidates whose $(k-1)$-sequences are infrequent, and then count the supports of the remaining candidates to identify the sequential patterns. The detailed aspects of these steps are given next.

Candidate Generation A pair of frequent $(k-1)$-sequences are merged to produce a candidate k-sequence. To avoid generating duplicate candidates, recall that the traditional *Apriori* algorithm merges a pair of frequent k-itemsets only if their first $k-1$ items are identical. A similar approach can be used

Algorithm 7.1 *Apriori*-like algorithm for sequential pattern discovery.

1: $k = 1$.
2: $F_k = \{\, i \mid i \in I \wedge \frac{\sigma(\{i\})}{N} \geq minsup \,\}$.   {Find all frequent 1-subsequences.}
3: **repeat**
4:      $k = k + 1$.
5:      $C_k = \text{apriori-gen}(F_{k-1})$.   {Generate candidate k-subsequences.}
6:      **for** each data sequence $t \in T$ **do**
7:          $C_t = \text{subsequence}(C_k, t)$.   {Identify all candidates contained in t.}
8:          **for** each candidate k-subsequence $c \in C_t$ **do**
9:              $\sigma(c) = \sigma(c) + 1$.   {Increment the support count.}
10:         **end for**
11:     **end for**
12:     $F_k = \{\, c \mid c \in C_k \wedge \frac{\sigma(c)}{N} \geq minsup \,\}$.   {Extract the frequent k-subsequences.}
13: **until** $F_k = \emptyset$
14: Answer $= \bigcup F_k$.

for sequences. The criteria for merging sequences are stated in the form of the following procedure.

Sequence Merging Procedure

A sequence $s^{(1)}$ is merged with another sequence $s^{(2)}$ only if the subsequence obtained by dropping the first event in $s^{(1)}$ is identical to the subsequence obtained by dropping the last event in $s^{(2)}$. The resulting candidate is the sequence $s^{(1)}$, concatenated with the last event from $s^{(2)}$. The last event from $s^{(2)}$ can either be merged into the same element as the last event in $s^{(1)}$ or different elements depending on the following conditions:

1. If the last two events in $s^{(2)}$ belong to the same element, then the last event in $s^{(2)}$ is part of the last element in $s^{(1)}$ in the merged sequence.

2. If the last two events in $s^{(2)}$ belong to different elements, then the last event in $s^{(2)}$ becomes a separate element appended to the end of $s^{(1)}$ in the merged sequence.

Figure 7.6 illustrates examples of candidate 4-sequences obtained by merging pairs of frequent 3-sequences. The first candidate $\langle \{1\}\{2\}\{3\}\{4\} \rangle$ is obtained by merging $\langle (1)(2)(3) \rangle$ with $\langle (2)(3)(4) \rangle$. Since events 3 and 4 belong to different elements of the second sequence, they also belong to separate elements in the merged sequence. On the other hand, merging $\langle \{1\}\{5\}\{3\} \rangle$ with $\langle \{5\}\{3,4\} \rangle$ produces the candidate 4-sequence $\langle \{1\}\{5\}\{3,4\} \rangle$. In this case,

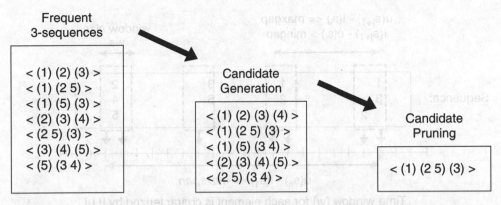

Figure 7.6. Example of the candidate generation and pruning steps of a sequential pattern mining algorithm.

since events 3 and 4 belong to the same element of the second sequence, they are combined into the same element in the merged sequence. Finally, the sequences $\langle\{1\}\{2\}\{3\}\rangle$ and $\langle\{1\}\{2,5\}\rangle$ do not have to be merged because removing the first event from the first sequence does not give the same subsequence as removing the last event from the second sequence. Although $\langle\{1\}\{2,5\}\{3\}\rangle$ is a viable candidate, it is generated by merging a different pair of sequences, $\langle\{1\}\{2,5\}\rangle$ and $\langle\{2,5\}\{3\}\rangle$. This example shows that the sequence merging procedure is complete; i.e., it will not miss any viable candidate, while at the same time, it avoids generating duplicate candidate sequences.

Candidate Pruning   A candidate k-sequence is pruned if at least one of its $(k-1)$-sequences is infrequent. For example, suppose $\langle\{1\}\{2\}\{3\}\{4\}\rangle$ is a candidate 4-sequence. We need to check whether $\langle\{1\}\{2\}\{4\}\rangle$ and $\langle\{1\}\{3\}\{4\}\rangle$ are frequent 3-sequences. Since both are infrequent, the candidate $\langle\{1\}\{2\}\{3\}\{4\}\rangle$ can be eliminated. Readers should be able to verify that the only candidate 4-sequence that survives the candidate pruning step in Figure 7.6 is $\langle\{1\}\{2\,5\}\{3\}\rangle$.

Support Counting   During support counting, the algorithm will enumerate all candidate k-sequences belonging to a particular data sequence. The support of these candidates will be incremented. After counting their supports, the algorithm may identify the frequent k-sequences and may discard all candidates whose support counts are less than the *minsup* threshold.

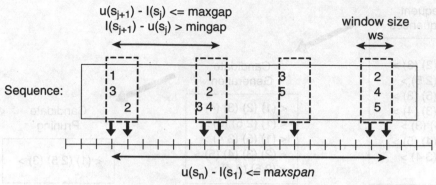

Figure 7.7. Timing constraints of a sequential pattern.

7.4.3 Timing Constraints

This section presents a sequential pattern formulation where timing constraints are imposed on the events and elements of a pattern. To motivate the need for timing constraints, consider the following sequence of courses taken by two students who enrolled in a data mining class:

Student A: ⟨ {Statistics} {Database Systems} {Data Mining} ⟩.
Student B: ⟨ {Database Systems} {Statistics} {Data Mining} ⟩.

The sequential pattern of interest is ⟨ {Statistics, Database Systems} {Data Mining} ⟩, which means that students who are enrolled in the data mining class must have previously taken a course in statistics and database systems. Clearly, the pattern is supported by both students even though they do not take statistics and database systems at the same time. In contrast, a student who took a statistics course ten years earlier should not be considered as supporting the pattern because the time gap between the courses is too long. Because the formulation presented in the previous section does not incorporate these timing constraints, a new sequential pattern definition is needed.

Figure 7.7 illustrates some of the timing constraints that can be imposed on a pattern. The definition of these constraints and the impact they have on sequential pattern discovery algorithms will be discussed in the next sections. Note that each element of the sequential pattern is associated with a time window $[l, u]$, where l is the earliest occurrence of an event within the time window and u is the latest occurrence of an event within the time window.

The maxspan Constraint

The *maxspan* constraint specifies the maximum allowed time difference between the latest and the earliest occurrences of events in the entire sequence. For example, suppose the following data sequences contain events that occur at consecutive time stamps $(1, 2, 3, \ldots)$. Assuming that $maxspan = 3$, the following table contains sequential patterns that are supported and not supported by a given data sequence.

Data Sequence, s	Sequential Pattern, t	Does s support t?
$<\{1,3\} \{3,4\} \{4\} \{5\} \{6,7\} \{8\} >$	$< \{3\} \{4\} >$	Yes
$<\{1,3\} \{3,4\} \{4\} \{5\} \{6,7\} \{8\} >$	$< \{3\} \{6\} >$	Yes
$<\{1,3\} \{3,4\} \{4\} \{5\} \{6,7\} \{8\} >$	$< \{1,3\} \{6\} >$	No

In general, the longer the *maxspan*, the more likely it is to detect a pattern in a data sequence. However, a longer *maxspan* can also capture spurious patterns because it increases the chance for two unrelated events to be temporally related. In addition, the pattern may involve events that are already obsolete.

The *maxspan* constraint affects the support counting step of sequential pattern discovery algorithms. As shown in the preceding examples, some data sequences no longer support a candidate pattern when the *maxspan* constraint is imposed. If we simply apply Algorithm 7.1, the support counts for some patterns may be overestimated. To avoid this problem, the algorithm must be modified to ignore cases where the interval between the first and last occurrences of events in a given pattern is greater than *maxspan*.

The mingap and maxgap Constraints

Timing constraints can also be specified to restrict the time difference between two consecutive elements of a sequence. If the maximum time difference (*maxgap*) is one week, then events in one element must occur within a week's time of the events occurring in the previous element. If the minimum time difference (*mingap*) is zero, then events in one element must occur immediately after the events occurring in the previous element. The following table shows examples of patterns that pass or fail the *maxgap* and *mingap* constraints, assuming that $maxgap = 3$ and $mingap = 1$.

Data Sequence, s	Sequential Pattern, t	*maxgap*	*mingap*
$<\{1,3\} \{3,4\} \{4\} \{5\} \{6,7\} \{8\} >$	$< \{3\} \{6\} >$	Pass	Pass
$<\{1,3\} \{3,4\} \{4\} \{5\} \{6,7\} \{8\} >$	$< \{6\} \{8\} >$	Pass	Fail
$<\{1,3\} \{3,4\} \{4\} \{5\} \{6,7\} \{8\} >$	$< \{1,3\} \{6\} >$	Fail	Pass
$<\{1,3\} \{3,4\} \{4\} \{5\} \{6,7\} \{8\} >$	$< \{1\} \{3\} \{8\} >$	Fail	Fail

As with *maxspan*, these constraints will affect the support counting step of sequential pattern discovery algorithms because some data sequences no longer support a candidate pattern when *mingap* and *maxgap* constraints are present. These algorithms must be modified to ensure that the timing constraints are not violated when counting the support of a pattern. Otherwise, some infrequent sequences may mistakenly be declared as frequent patterns.

A side effect of using the *maxgap* constraint is that the *Apriori* principle might be violated. To illustrate this, consider the data set shown in Figure 7.5. Without *mingap* or *maxgap* constraints, the support for $\langle\{2\}\{5\}\rangle$ and $\langle\{2\}\{3\}\{5\}\rangle$ are both equal to 60%. However, if *mingap* = 0 and *maxgap* = 1, then the support for $\langle\{2\}\{5\}\rangle$ reduces to 40%, while the support for $\langle\{2\}\{3\}\{5\}\rangle$ is still 60%. In other words, support has increased when the number of events in a sequence increases—which contradicts the *Apriori* principle. The violation occurs because the object D does not support the pattern $\langle\{2\}\{5\}\rangle$ since the time gap between events 2 and 5 is greater than *maxgap*. This problem can be avoided by using the concept of a contiguous subsequence.

Definition 7.2 (Contiguous Subsequence). A sequence s is a contiguous subsequence of $w = \langle e_1 e_2 \ldots e_k \rangle$ if any one of the following conditions hold:

1. s is obtained from w after deleting an event from either e_1 or e_k,

2. s is obtained from w after deleting an event from any element $e_i \in w$ that contains at least two events, or

3. s is a contiguous subsequence of t and t is a contiguous subsequence of w.

The following examples illustrate the concept of a contiguous subsequence:

Data Sequence, s	Sequential Pattern, t	Is t a contiguous subsequence of s?
<{1} {2,3}>	< {1} {2} >	Yes
<{1,2} {2} {3} >	< {1} {2} >	Yes
<{3,4} {1,2} {2,3} {4} >	< {1} {2} >	Yes
<{1} {3} {2} >	< {1} {2} >	No
<{1,2} {1} {3} {2} >	< {1} {2} >	No

Using the concept of contiguous subsequences, the *Apriori* principle can be modified to handle *maxgap* constraints in the following way.

Definition 7.3 (Modified *Apriori* Principle). If a k-sequence is frequent, then all of its contiguous $k - 1$-subsequences must also be frequent.

The modified *Apriori* principle can be applied to the sequential pattern discovery algorithm with minor modifications. During candidate pruning, not all k-sequences need to be verified since some of them may violate the *maxgap* constraint. For example, if *maxgap* = 1, it is not necessary to check whether the subsequence $\langle\{1\}\{2,3\}\{5\}\rangle$ of the candidate $\langle\{1\}\{2,3\}\{4\}\{5\}\rangle$ is frequent since the time difference between elements $\{2,3\}$ and $\{5\}$ is greater than one time unit. Instead, only the contiguous subsequences of $\langle\{1\}\{2,3\}\{4\}\{5\}\rangle$ need to be examined. These subsequences include $\langle\{1\}\{2,3\}\{4\}\rangle$, $\langle\{2,3\}\{4\}\{5\}\rangle$, $\langle\{1\}\{2\}\{4\}\{5\}\rangle$, and $\langle\{1\}\{3\}\{4\}\{5\}\rangle$.

The Window Size Constraint

Finally, events within an element s_j do not have to occur at the same time. A **window size** threshold (ws) can be defined to specify the maximum allowed time difference between the latest and earliest occurrences of events in any element of a sequential pattern. A window size of 0 means all events in the same element of a pattern must occur simultaneously.

The following example uses $ws = 2$ to determine whether a data sequence supports a given sequence (assuming *mingap* = 0, *maxgap* = 3, and *maxspan* = ∞).

Data Sequence, s	Sequential Pattern, t	Does s support t?
<{1,3} {3,4} {4} {5} {6,7} {8} >	< {3,4} {5} >	Yes
<{1,3} {3,4} {4} {5} {6,7} {8} >	< {4,6} {8} >	Yes
<{1,3} {3,4} {4} {5} {6,7} {8} >	< {3, 4, 6} {8} >	No
<{1,3} {3,4} {4} {5} {6,7} {8} >	< {1,3,4} {6,7,8} >	No

In the last example, although the pattern $\langle\{1,3,4\}\{6,7,8\}\rangle$ satisfies the window size constraint, it violates the *maxgap* constraint because the maximum time difference between events in the two elements is 5 units. The window size constraint also affects the support counting step of sequential pattern discovery algorithms. If Algorithm 7.1 is applied without imposing the window size constraint, the support counts for some of the candidate patterns might be underestimated, and thus some interesting patterns may be lost.

7.4.4   Alternative Counting Schemes

There are several methods available for counting the support of a candidate k-sequence from a database of sequences. For illustrative purposes, consider the problem of counting the support for sequence $\langle\{p\}\{q\}\rangle$, as shown in Figure 7.8. Assume that $ws = 0$, *mingap* = 0, *maxgap* = 1, and *maxspan* = 2.

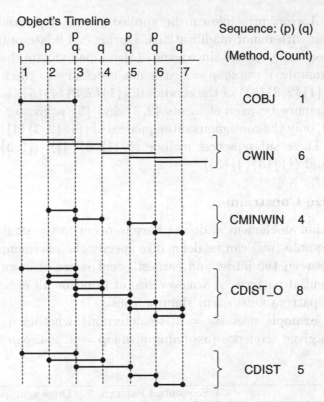

Figure 7.8. Comparing different support counting methods.

- **COBJ**: One occurrence per object.
  This method looks for at least one occurrence of a given sequence in an object's timeline. In Figure 7.8, even though the sequence $\langle (p)(q) \rangle$ appears several times in the object's timeline, it is counted only once—with p occurring at $t = 1$ and q occuring at $t = 3$.

- **CWIN**: One occurrence per sliding window.
  In this approach, a sliding time window of fixed length ($maxspan$) is moved across an object's timeline, one unit at a time. The support count is incremented each time the sequence is encountered in the sliding window. In Figure 7.8, the sequence $\langle \{p\}\{q\} \rangle$ is observed six times using this method.

- **CMINWIN**: Number of minimal windows of occurrence.
  A minimal window of occurrence is the smallest window in which the sequence occurs given the timing constraints. In other words, a minimal

window is the time interval such that the sequence occurs in that time interval, but it does not occur in any of the proper subintervals of it. This definition can be considered as a restrictive version of CWIN, because its effect is to shrink and collapse some of the windows that are counted by CWIN. For example, sequence $\langle\{p\}\{q\}\rangle$ has four minimal window occurrences: (1) the pair (p: $t = 2$, q: $t = 3$), (2) the pair (p: $t = 3$, q: $t = 4$), (3) the pair (p: $t = 5$, q: $t = 6$), and (4) the pair (p: $t = 6$, q: $t = 7$). The occurrence of event p at $t = 1$ and event q at $t = 3$ is not a minimal window occurrence because it contains a smaller window with (p: $t = 2$, q: $t = 3$), which is indeed a minimal window of occurrence.

- **CDIST_O**: Distinct occurrences with possibility of event-timestamp overlap.
  A distinct occurrence of a sequence is defined to be the set of event-timestamp pairs such that there has to be at least one new event-timestamp pair that is different from a previously counted occurrence. Counting all such distinct occurrences results in the CDIST_O method. If the occurrence time of events p and q is denoted as a tuple $(t(p), t(q))$, then this method yields eight distinct occurrences of sequence $\langle\{p\}\{q\}\rangle$ at times (1,3), (2,3), (2,4), (3,4), (3,5), (5,6), (5,7), and (6,7).

- **CDIST**: Distinct occurrences with no event-timestamp overlap allowed. In CDIST_O above, two occurrences of a sequence were allowed to have overlapping event-timestamp pairs, e.g., the overlap between (1,3) and (2,3). In the CDIST method, no overlap is allowed. Effectively, when an event-timestamp pair is considered for counting, it is marked as used and is never used again for subsequent counting of the same sequence. As an example, there are five distinct, non-overlapping occurrences of the sequence $\langle\{p\}\{q\}\rangle$ in the diagram shown in Figure 7.8. These occurrences happen at times (1,3), (2,4), (3,5), (5,6), and (6,7). Observe that these occurrences are subsets of the occurrences observed in CDIST_O.

One final point regarding the counting methods is the need to determine the baseline for computing the support measure. For frequent itemset mining, the baseline is given by the total number of transactions. For sequential pattern mining, the baseline depends on the counting method used. For the COBJ method, the total number of objects in the input data can be used as the baseline. For the CWIN and CMINWIN methods, the baseline is given by the sum of the number of time windows possible in all objects. For methods such as CDIST and CDIST_O, the baseline is given by the sum of the number of distinct timestamps present in the input data of each object.

7.5　Subgraph Patterns

This section describes the application of association analysis methods to more complex entities beyond itemsets and sequences. Examples include chemical compounds, 3-D protein structures, network topologies, and tree structured XML documents. These entities can be modeled using a graph representation, as shown in Table 7.7.

Table 7.7. Graph representation of entities in various application domains.

Application	Graphs	Vertices	Edges
Web mining	Web browsing patterns	Web pages	Hyperlink between pages
Computational chemistry	Structure of chemical compounds	Atoms or ions	Bond between atoms or ions
Network computing	Computer networks	Computers and servers	Interconnection between machines
Semantic Web	Collection of XML documents	XML elements	Parent-child relationship between elements
Bioinformatics	Protein structures	Amino acids	Contact residue

A useful data mining task to perform on this type of data is to derive a set of common substructures among the collection of graphs. Such a task is known as **frequent subgraph mining**. A potential application of frequent subgraph mining can be seen in the context of computational chemistry. Each year, new chemical compounds are designed for the development of pharmaceutical drugs, pesticides, fertilizers, etc. Although the structure of a compound is known to play a major role in determining its chemical properties, it is difficult to establish their exact relationship. Frequent subgraph mining can aid this undertaking by identifying the substructures commonly associated with certain properties of known compounds. Such information can help scientists to develop new chemical compounds that have certain desired properties.

This section presents a methodology for applying association analysis to graph-based data. The section begins with a review of some of the basic graph-related concepts and definitions. The frequent subgraph mining problem is then introduced, followed by a description of how the traditional *Apriori* algorithm can be extended to discover such patterns.

7.5.1   Graphs and Subgraphs

A graph is a data structure that can be used to represent the relationships among a set of entities. Mathematically, a graph is composed of a vertex set V and a set of edges E connecting between pairs of vertices. Each edge is denoted by a vertex pair (v_i, v_j), where $v_i, v_j \in V$. A label $l(v_i)$ can be assigned to each vertex v_i representing the name of an entity. Similarly each edge (v_i, v_j) can also be associated with a label $l(v_i, v_j)$ describing the relationship between a pair of entities. Table 7.7 shows the vertices and edges associated with different types of graphs. For example, in a Web graph, the vertices correspond to Web pages and the edges represent the hyperlinks between Web pages.

Definition 7.4 (Subgraph). A graph $G' = (V', E')$ is a subgraph of another graph $G = (V, E)$ if its vertex set V' is a subset of V and its edge set E' is a subset of E. The subgraph relationship is denoted as $G' \subseteq_S G$.

Figure 7.9 shows a graph that contains 6 vertices and 11 edges along with one of its possible subgraphs. The subgraph, which is shown in Figure 7.9(b), contains only 4 of the 6 vertices and 4 of the 11 edges in the original graph.

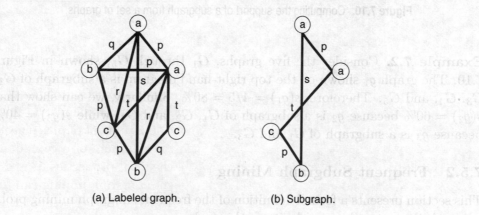

(a) Labeled graph.   (b) Subgraph.

Figure 7.9. Example of a subgraph.

Definition 7.5 (Support). Given a collection of graphs $\mathcal{G}$, the support for a subgraph g is defined as the fraction of all graphs that contain g as its subgraph, i.e.:

$$s(g) = \frac{|\{G_i | g \subseteq_S G_i, \ G_i \in \mathcal{G}\}|}{|\mathcal{G}|}. \tag{7.2}$$

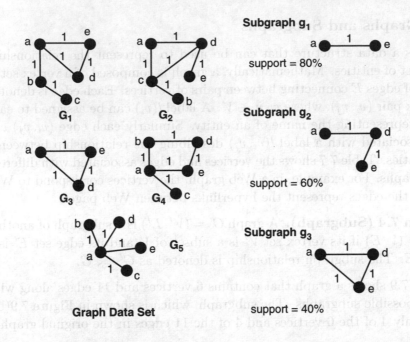

Figure 7.10. Computing the support of a subgraph from a set of graphs.

Example 7.2. Consider the five graphs, G_1 through G_5, shown in Figure 7.10. The graph g_1 shown on the top right-hand diagram is a subgraph of G_1, G_3, G_4, and G_5. Therefore, $s(g_1) = 4/5 = 80\%$. Similarly, we can show that $s(g_2) = 60\%$ because g_2 is a subgraph of G_1, G_2, and G_3, while $s(g_3) = 40\%$ because g_3 is a subgraph of G_1 and G_3. ∎

7.5.2 Frequent Subgraph Mining

This section presents a formal definition of the frequent subgraph mining problem and illustrates the complexity of this task.

Definition 7.6 (Frequent Subgraph Mining). Given a set of graphs $\mathcal{G}$ and a support threshold, *minsup*, the goal of frequent subgraph mining is to find all subgraphs g such that $s(g) \geq minsup$.

While this formulation is generally applicable to any type of graph, the discussion presented in this chapter focuses primarily on **undirected, connected** graphs. The definitions of these graphs are given below:

1. A graph is connected if there exists a path between every pair of vertices in the graph, in which a path is a sequence of vertices $< v_1 v_2 \ldots v_k >$

such that there is an edge connecting between every pair of adjacent vertices (v_i, v_{i+1}) in the sequence.

2. A graph is undirected if it contains only undirected edges. An edge (v_i, v_j) is undirected if it is indistinguishable from (v_j, v_i).

Methods for handling other types of subgraphs (directed or disconnected) are left as an exercise to the readers (see Exercise 15 on page 482).

Mining frequent subgraphs is a computationally expensive task because of the exponential scale of the search space. To illustrate the complexity of this task, consider a data set that contains d entities. In frequent itemset mining, each entity is an item and the size of the search space to be explored is 2^d, which is the number of candidate itemsets that can be generated. In frequent subgraph mining, each entity is a vertex and can have up to $d - 1$ edges to other vertices. Assuming that the vertex labels are unique, the total number of subgraphs is

$$\sum_{i=1}^{d} \binom{d}{i} \times 2^{i(i-1)/2},$$

where $\binom{d}{i}$ is the number of ways to choose i vertices to form a subgraph and $2^{i(i-1)/2}$ is the maximum number of edges between vertices. Table 7.8 compares the number of itemsets and subgraphs for different values of d.

Table 7.8. A comparison between number of itemsets and subgraphs for different dimensionality, d.

Number of entities, d	1	2	3	4	5	6	7	8
Number of itemsets	2	4	8	16	32	64	128	256
Number of subgraphs	2	5	18	113	1,450	40,069	2,350,602	28,619,2513

The number of candidate subgraphs is actually much smaller because the numbers given in Table 7.8 include subgraphs that are disconnected. Disconnected subgraphs are usually ignored because they are not as interesting as connected subgraphs.

A brute-force method for doing this is to generate all connected subgraphs as candidates and count their respective supports. For example, consider the graphs shown in Figure 7.11(a). Assuming that the vertex labels are chosen from the set $\{a, b\}$ and the edge labels are chosen from the set $\{p, q\}$, the list of connected subgraphs with one vertex up to three vertices is shown in Figure 7.11(b). The number of candidate subgraphs is considerably larger than the

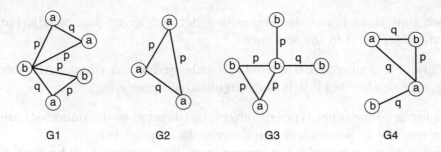

(a) Example of a graph data set.

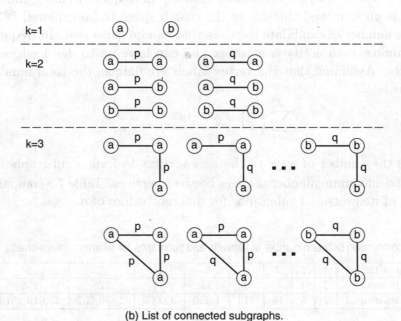

(b) List of connected subgraphs.

Figure 7.11. Brute-force method for mining frequent subgraphs.

number of candidate itemsets in traditional association rule mining for the following reasons:

1. An item can appear at most once in an itemset, whereas a vertex label can appear more than once in a graph.

2. The same pair of vertex labels can have multiple choices of edge labels.

Given the large number of candidate subgraphs, a brute-force method may break down even for moderately sized graphs.

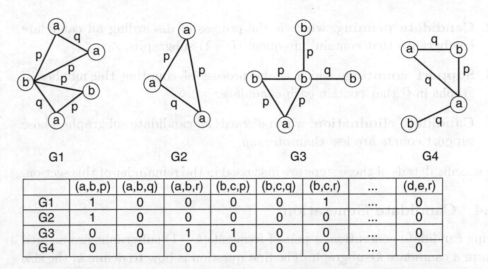

	(a,b,p)	(a,b,q)	(a,b,r)	(b,c,p)	(b,c,q)	(b,c,r)	...	(d,e,r)
G1	1	0	0	0	0	1	...	0
G2	1	0	0	0	0	0	...	0
G3	0	0	1	1	0	0	...	0
G4	0	0	0	0	0	0	...	0

Figure 7.12. Mapping a collection of graph structures into market basket transactions.

7.5.3   *Apriori*-like Method

This section examines how an *Apriori*-like algorithm can be developed for finding frequent subgraphs.

Data Transformation

One possible approach is to transform each graph into a transaction-like format so that existing algorithms such as *Apriori* can be applied. Figure 7.12 illustrates how to transform a collection of graphs into its equivalent market basket representation. In this representation, each combination of edge label $l(e)$ with its corresponding vertex labels, $(l(v_i), l(v_j))$, is mapped into an "item." The width of the "transaction" is given by the number of edges in the graph. Despite its simplicity, this approach works only if every edge in a graph has a unique combination of vertex and edge labels. Otherwise, such graphs cannot be accurately modeled using this representation.

General Structure of the Frequent Subgraph Mining Algorithm

An *Apriori*-like algorithm for mining frequent subgraphs consists of the following steps:

1. **Candidate generation**, which is the process of merging pairs of frequent $(k-1)$-subgraphs to obtain a candidate k-subgraph.

2. **Candidate pruning**, which is the process of discarding all candidate k-subgraphs that contain infrequent $(k-1)$-subgraphs.

3. **Support counting**, which is the process of counting the number of graphs in $\mathcal{G}$ that contain each candidate.

4. **Candidate elimination**, which discards all candidate subgraphs whose support counts are less than *minsup*.

The specific details of these steps are discussed in the remainder of this section.

7.5.4   Candidate Generation

During candidate generation, a pair of frequent $(k-1)$-subgraphs are merged to form a candidate k-subgraph. The first question is how to define k, the size of a subgraph. In the example shown in Figure 7.11, k refers to the number of vertices in the graph. This approach of iteratively expanding a subgraph by adding an extra vertex is known as **vertex growing**. Alternatively, k may refer to the number of edges in the graph. This approach of adding an extra edge to the existing subgraphs is known as **edge growing**.

To avoid generating duplicate candidates, we may impose an additional condition for merging, that the two $(k-1)$-subgraphs must share a common $(k-2)$-subgraph. The common $(k-2)$-subgraph is known as their **core**. Below, we briefly describe the candidate generation procedure for both vertex-growing and edge-growing strategies.

Candidate Generation via Vertex Growing

Vertex growing is the process of generating a new candidate by adding a new vertex into an existing frequent subgraph. Before describing this approach, let us first consider the adjacency matrix representation of a graph. Each entry $M(i, j)$ in the matrix contains either the label of the edge connecting between the vertices v_i and v_j, or zero, if there is no edge between them. The vertex-growing approach can be viewed as the process of generating a $k \times k$ adjacency matrix by combining a pair of $(k-1) \times (k-1)$ adjacency matrices, as illustrated in Figure 7.13. $G1$ and $G2$ are two graphs whose adjacency matrices are given by $M(G1)$ and $M(G2)$, respectively. The core for the graphs is indicated by dashed lines in the diagram. The procedure for generating candidate subgraphs via vertex growing is presented next.

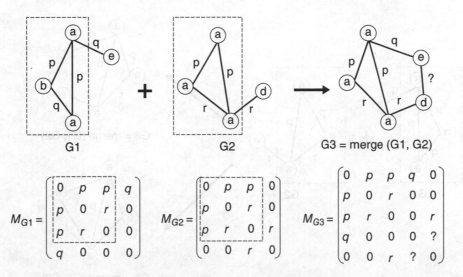

Figure 7.13. Vertex-growing strategy.

Subgraph Merging Procedure via Vertex Growing

An adjacency matrix $M^{(1)}$ is merged with another matrix $M^{(2)}$ if the submatrices obtained by removing the last row and last column of $M^{(1)}$ and $M^{(2)}$ are identical to each other. The resulting matrix is the matrix $M^{(1)}$, appended with the last row and last column of matrix $M^{(2)}$. The remaining entries of the new matrix are either zero or replaced by all valid edge labels connecting the pair of vertices.

The resulting graph contains one or two edges more than the original graphs. In Figure 7.13, both $G1$ and $G2$ contain four vertices and four edges. After merging, the resulting graph $G3$ has five vertices. The number of edges in $G3$ depends on whether the vertices d and e are connected. If d and e are disconnected, then $G3$ has five edges and the corresponding matrix entry for (d, e) is zero. Otherwise, $G3$ has six edges and the matrix entry for (d, e) corresponds to the label for the newly created edge. Since the edge label is unknown, we need to consider all possible edge labels for (d, e), thus increasing the number of candidate subgraphs substantially.

Candidate Generation via Edge Growing

Edge growing inserts a new edge to an existing frequent subgraph during candidate generation. Unlike vertex growing, the resulting subgraph does not

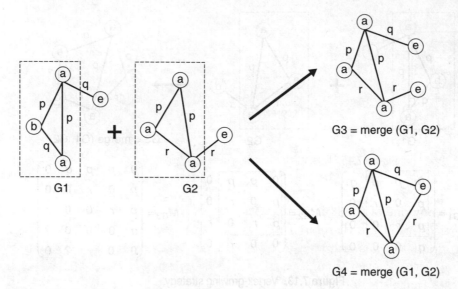

Figure 7.14. Edge-growing strategy.

necessarily increase the number of vertices in the original graphs. Figure 7.14 shows two possible candidate subgraphs obtained by merging $G1$ and $G2$ via the edge-growing strategy. The first candidate subgraph, $G3$, has one extra vertex, while the second candidate subgraph, $G4$, has the same number of vertices as the original graphs. The core for the graphs is indicated by dashed lines in the diagram.

The procedure for generating candidate subgraphs via edge growing can be summarized as follows.

Subgraph Merging Procedure via Edge Growing

A frequent subgraph $g^{(1)}$ is merged with another frequent subgraph $g^{(2)}$ only if the subgraph obtained by removing an edge from $g^{(1)}$ is topologically equivalent to the subgraph obtained by removing an edge from $g^{(2)}$. After merging, the resulting candidate is the subgraph $g^{(1)}$, appended with the extra edge from $g^{(2)}$.

The graphs to be merged may contain several vertices that are **topologically equivalent** to each other. To illustrate the concept of topologically equivalent vertices, consider the graphs shown in Figure 7.15. The graph $G1$ contains four vertices with identical vertex labels, "a." If a new edge is at-

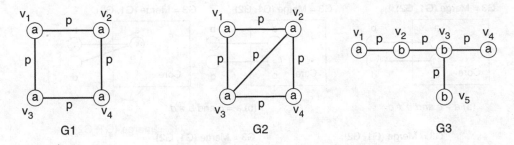

Figure 7.15. Illustration of topologically equivalent vertices.

tached to any one of the four vertices, the resulting graph will look the same. The vertices in $G1$ are therefore topologically equivalent to each other.

The graph $G2$ has two pairs of topologically equivalent vertices, v_1 with v_4 and v_2 with v_3, even though the vertex and edge labels are identical. It is easy to see that v_1 is not topologically equivalent to v_2 because the number of edges incident on the vertices is different. Therefore, attaching a new edge to v_1 results in a different graph than attaching the same edge to v_2. Meanwhile, the graph $G3$ does not have any topologically equivalent vertices. While v_1 and v_4 have the same vertex labels and number of incident edges, attaching a new edge to v_1 results in a different graph than attaching the same edge to v_4.

The notion of topologically equivalent vertices can help us understand why multiple candidate subgraphs can be generated during edge growing. Consider the $(k - 1)$-subgraphs $G1$ and $G2$ shown in Figure 7.16. To simplify the notation, their core, which contains $k - 2$ common edges between the two graphs, is drawn as a rectangular box. The remaining edge in $G1$ that is not included in the core is shown as a dangling edge connecting the vertices a and b. Similarly, the remaining edge in $G2$ that is not part of the core is shown as a dangling edge connecting vertices c and d. Although the cores for $G1$ and $G2$ are identical, a and c may or may not be topologically equivalent to each

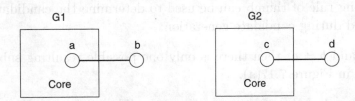

Figure 7.16. General approach for merging a pair of subgraphs via edge growing.

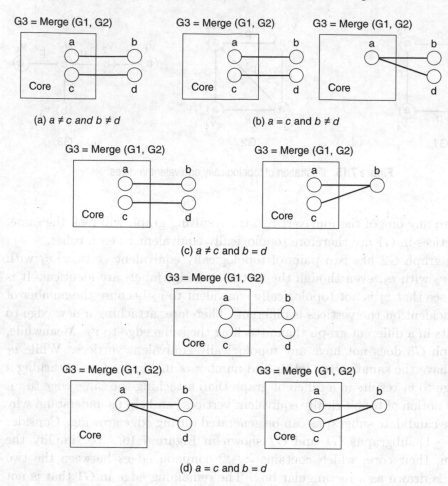

Figure 7.17. Candidate subgraphs generated via edge growing.

other. If a and c are topologically equivalent, we denote them as $a = c$. For vertices outside the core, we denote them as $b = d$ if their labels are identical.

The following rule of thumb can be used to determine the candidate subgraphs obtained during candidate generation:

1. If $a \neq c$ and $b \neq d$, then there is only one possible resulting subgraph, as shown in Figure 7.17(a).

2. If $a = c$ but $b \neq d$, then there are two possible resulting subgraphs, as shown in Figure 7.17(b).

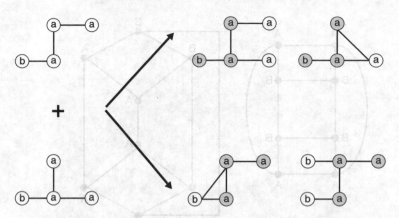

Figure 7.18. Multiplicity of candidates during candidate generation.

3. If $a \neq c$ but $b = d$, then there are two possible resulting subgraphs, as shown in Figure 7.17(c).

4. If $a = c$ and $b = d$, then there are three possible resulting subgraphs, as shown in Figure 7.17(d).

Multiple candidate subgraphs can also be generated when there is more than one core associated with the pair of $(k-1)$-subgraphs, as shown in Figure 7.18. The shaded vertices correspond to those vertices whose edges form a core during the merging operation. Each core may lead to a different set of candidate subgraphs. In principle, if a pair of frequent $(k-1)$-subgraphs is merged, there can be at most $k-2$ cores, each of which is obtained by removing an edge from one of the merged graphs. Although the edge-growing procedure can produce multiple candidate subgraphs, the number of candidate subgraphs tends to be smaller than those produced by the vertex-growing strategy.

7.5.5   Candidate Pruning

After the candidate k-subgraphs are generated, the candidates whose $(k-1)$-subgraphs are infrequent need to be pruned. The pruning step can be performed by successively removing an edge from the candidate k-subgraph and checking whether the corresponding $(k-1)$-subgraph is connected and frequent. If not, the candidate k-subgraph can be discarded.

To check whether the $(k-1)$-subgraph is frequent, it should be matched against other frequent $(k-1)$-subgraphs. Determining whether two graphs are topologically equivalent (or isomorphic) is known as the **graph isomorphism** problem. To illustrate the difficulty of solving the graph isomorphism problem,

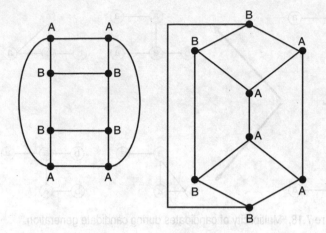

Figure 7.19. Graph isomorphism

consider the two graphs shown in Figure 7.19. Even though both graphs look different, they are actually isomorphic to each other because there is a one-to-one mapping between vertices in both graphs.

Handling Graph Isomorphism

A standard approach for handling the graph isomorphism problem is to map each graph into a unique string representation known as its **code** or **canonical label**. A canonical label has the property that if two graphs are isomorphic, then their codes must be the same. This property allows us to test for graph isomorphism by comparing the canonical labels of the graphs.

The first step toward constructing the canonical label of a graph is to find an adjacency matrix representation for the graph. Figure 7.20 shows an

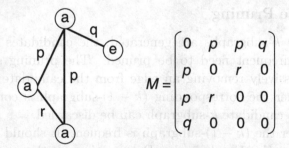

Figure 7.20. Adjacency matrix representation of a graph.

example of such a matrix for the given graph. In principle, a graph can have more than one adjacency matrix representation because there are multiple ways to order the vertices in the adjacency matrix. In the example shown in Figure 7.20, the first row and column correspond to the vertex a that has 3 edges, the second row and column correspond to another vertex a that has 2 edges, and so on. To derive all the adjacency matrix representations for a graph, we need to consider all possible permutations of rows (and their corresponding columns) of the matrix.

Mathematically, each permutation corresponds to a multiplication of the initial adjacency matrix with a corresponding permutation matrix, as illustrated in the following example.

Example 7.3. Consider the following matrix:

$$M = \begin{pmatrix} 1 & 2 & 3 & 4 \\ 5 & 6 & 7 & 8 \\ 9 & 10 & 11 & 12 \\ 13 & 14 & 15 & 16 \end{pmatrix}$$

The following permutation matrix can be used to exchange the first row (and column) with the third row (and column) of M:

$$P_{13} = \begin{pmatrix} 0 & 0 & 1 & 0 \\ 0 & 1 & 0 & 0 \\ 1 & 0 & 0 & 0 \\ 0 & 0 & 0 & 1 \end{pmatrix},$$

where P_{13} is obtained by swapping the first and third row of the identity matrix. To exchange the first and third rows (and columns), the permutation matrix is multiplied with M:

$$M' = P_{13}^T \times M \times P_{13} = \begin{pmatrix} 11 & 10 & 9 & 12 \\ 7 & 6 & 5 & 8 \\ 3 & 2 & 1 & 4 \\ 15 & 14 & 13 & 16 \end{pmatrix}.$$

Note that multiplying M from the right with P_{13} exchanges the first and third columns of M, while multiplying M from the left with P_{13}^T exchanges the first and third rows of M. If all three matrices are multiplied, this will produce a matrix M' whose first and third rows and columns have been swapped. ∎

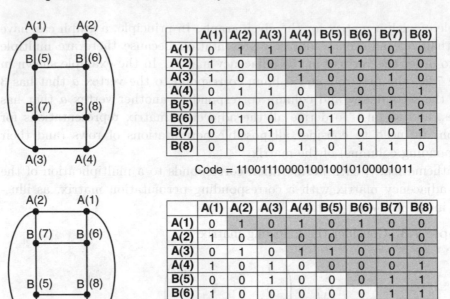

Figure 7.21. String representation of adjacency matrices.

The second step is to determine the string representation for each adjacency matrix. Since the adjacency matrix is symmetric, it is sufficient to construct the string representation based on the upper triangular part of the matrix. In the example shown in Figure 7.21, the code is obtained by concatenating the entries of the upper triangular matrix in a column-wise fashion. The final step is to compare all the string representations of the graph and choose the one that has the lowest (or highest) lexicographic value.

The preceding approach seems expensive because it requires us to examine all possible adjacency matrices of a graph and to compute each of their string representation in order to find the canonical label. More specifically, there are $k!$ permutations that must be considered for every graph that contains k vertices. Some of the methods developed to reduce the complexity of this task include caching the previously computed canonical label (so that we do not have to recompute it again when performing an isomorphism test on the same graph) and reducing the number of permutations needed to determine the canonical label by incorporating additional information such as vertex labels and the degree of a vertex. The latter approach is beyond the scope of this book, but interested readers may consult the bibliographic notes at the end of this chapter.

7.5.6 Support Counting

Support counting is also a potentially costly operation because all the candidate subgraphs contained in each graph $G \in \mathcal{G}$ must be determined. One way to speed up this operation is to maintain a list of graph IDs associated with each frequent $(k-1)$-subgraph. Whenever a new candidate k-subgraph is generated by merging a pair of frequent $(k-1)$-subgraphs, their corresponding lists of graph IDs are intersected. Finally, the subgraph isomorphism tests are performed on the graphs in the intersected list to determine whether they contain a particular candidate subgraph.

7.6 Infrequent Patterns

The association analysis formulation described so far is based on the premise that the presence of an item in a transaction is more important than its absence. As a consequence, patterns that are rarely found in a database are often considered to be uninteresting and are eliminated using the support measure. Such patterns are known as infrequent patterns.

Definition 7.7 (Infrequent Pattern). An infrequent pattern is an itemset or a rule whose support is less than the *minsup* threshold.

Although a vast majority of infrequent patterns are uninteresting, some of them might be useful to the analysts, particularly those that correspond to negative correlations in the data. For example, the sale of DVDs and VCRs together is low because any customer who buys a DVD will most likely not buy a VCR, and vice versa. Such negative-correlated patterns are useful to help identify **competing items**, which are items that can be substituted for one another. Examples of competing items include tea versus coffee, butter versus margarine, regular versus diet soda, and desktop versus laptop computers.

Some infrequent patterns may also suggest the occurrence of interesting rare events or exceptional situations in the data. For example, if {Fire = Yes} is frequent but {Fire = Yes, Alarm = On} is infrequent, then the latter is an interesting infrequent pattern because it may indicate faulty alarm systems. To detect such unusual situations, the expected support of a pattern must be determined, so that, if a pattern turns out to have a considerably lower support than expected, it is declared as an interesting infrequent pattern.

Mining infrequent patterns is a challenging endeavor because there is an enormous number of such patterns that can be derived from a given data set. More specifically, the key issues in mining infrequent patterns are: (1) how to identify interesting infrequent patterns, and (2) how to efficiently discover them in large data sets. To get a different perspective on various types of interesting infrequent patterns, two related concepts—negative patterns and negatively correlated patterns—are introduced in Sections 7.6.1 and 7.6.2, respectively. The relationships among these patterns are elucidated in Section 7.6.3. Finally, two classes of techniques developed for mining interesting infrequent patterns are presented in Sections 7.6.5 and 7.6.6.

7.6.1 Negative Patterns

Let $I = \{i_1, i_2, \ldots, i_d\}$ be a set of items. A **negative item**, $\overline{i_k}$, denotes the absence of item i_k from a given transaction. For example, $\overline{\texttt{coffee}}$ is a negative item whose value is 1 if a transaction does not contain `coffee`.

Definition 7.8 (Negative Itemset). A negative itemset X is an itemset that has the following properties: (1) $X = A \cup \overline{B}$, where A is a set of positive items, $\overline{B}$ is a set of negative items, $|\overline{B}| \geq 1$, and (2) $s(X) \geq minsup$.

Definition 7.9 (Negative Association Rule). A negative association rule is an association rule that has the following properties: (1) the rule is extracted from a negative itemset, (2) the support of the rule is greater than or equal to $minsup$, and (3) the confidence of the rule is greater than or equal to minconf.

The negative itemsets and negative association rules are collectively known as **negative patterns** throughout this chapter. An example of a negative association rule is `tea` $\longrightarrow$ $\overline{\texttt{coffee}}$, which may suggest that people who drink tea tend to not drink coffee.

7.6.2 Negatively Correlated Patterns

Section 6.7.1 on page 371 described how correlation analysis can be used to analyze the relationship between a pair of categorical variables. Measures such as interest factor (Equation 6.5) and the ϕ-coefficient (Equation 6.8) were shown to be useful for discovering itemsets that are positively correlated. This section extends the discussion to negatively correlated patterns.

Let $X = \{x_1, x_2, \ldots, x_k\}$ denote a k-itemset and $P(X)$ denote the probability that a transaction contains X. In association analysis, the probability is often estimated using the itemset support, $s(X)$.

Definition 7.10 (Negatively Correlated Itemset). An itemset X is negatively correlated if

$$s(X) < \prod_{j=1}^{k} s(x_j) = s(x_1) \times s(x_2) \times \ldots \times s(x_k), \qquad (7.3)$$

where $s(x_j)$ is the support of an item x_j.

The right-hand side of the preceding expression, $\prod_{j=1}^{k} s(x_j)$, represents an estimate of the probability that all the items in X are statistically independent. Definition 7.10 suggests that an itemset is negatively correlated if its support is below the expected support computed using the statistical independence assumption. The smaller $s(X)$, the more negatively correlated is the pattern.

Definition 7.11 (Negatively Correlated Association Rule). An association rule $X \longrightarrow Y$ is negatively correlated if

$$s(X \cup Y) < s(X)s(Y), \qquad (7.4)$$

where X and Y are disjoint itemsets; i.e., $X \cup Y = \emptyset$.

The preceding definition provides only a partial condition for negative correlation between items in X and items in Y. A full condition for negative correlation can be stated as follows:

$$s(X \cup Y) < \prod_{i} s(x_i) \prod_{j} s(y_j), \qquad (7.5)$$

where $x_i \in X$ and $y_j \in Y$. Because the items in X (and in Y) are often positively correlated, it is more practical to use the partial condition to define a negatively correlated association rule instead of the full condition. For example, although the rule

{eyeglass, lens cleaner} $\longrightarrow$ {contact lens, saline solution}

is negatively correlated according to Inequality 7.4, eyeglass is positively correlated with lens cleaner and contact lens is positively correlated with saline solution. If Inequality 7.5 is applied instead, such a rule could be missed because it may not satisfy the full condition for negative correlation.

The condition for negative correlation can also be expressed in terms of the support for positive and negative itemsets. Let $\overline{X}$ and $\overline{Y}$ denote the corresponding negative itemsets for X and Y, respectively. Since

$$s(X \cup Y) - s(X)s(Y)$$

$$= s(X \cup Y) - \left[s(X \cup Y) + s(X \cup \overline{Y})\right]\left[s(X \cup Y) + s(\overline{X} \cup Y)\right]$$

$$= s(X \cup Y)\left[1 - s(X \cup Y) - s(X \cup \overline{Y}) - s(\overline{X} \cup Y)\right] - s(X \cup \overline{Y})s(\overline{X} \cup Y)$$

$$= s(X \cup Y)s(\overline{X} \cup \overline{Y}) - s(X \cup \overline{Y})s(\overline{X} \cup Y),$$

the condition for negative correlation can be stated as follows:

$$s(X \cup Y)s(\overline{X} \cup \overline{Y}) < s(X \cup \overline{Y})s(\overline{X} \cup Y). \qquad (7.6)$$

The negatively correlated itemsets and association rules are known as **negatively correlated patterns** throughout this chapter.

7.6.3 Comparisons among Infrequent Patterns, Negative Patterns, and Negatively Correlated Patterns

Infrequent patterns, negative patterns, and negatively correlated patterns are three closely related concepts. Although infrequent patterns and negatively correlated patterns refer only to itemsets or rules that contain positive items, while negative patterns refer to itemsets or rules that contain both positive and negative items, there are certain commonalities among these concepts, as illustrated in Figure 7.22.

First, note that many infrequent patterns have corresponding negative patterns. To understand why this is the case, consider the contingency table shown in Table 7.9. If $X \cup Y$ is infrequent, then it is likely to have a corresponding negative itemset unless *minsup* is too high. For example, assuming that $minsup \le 0.25$, if $X \cup Y$ is infrequent, then the support for at least one of the following itemsets, $X \cup \overline{Y}$, $\overline{X} \cup Y$, or $\overline{X} \cup \overline{Y}$, must be higher than *minsup* since the sum of the supports in a contingency table is 1.

Second, note that many negatively correlated patterns also have corresponding negative patterns. Consider the contingency table shown in Table 7.9 and the condition for negative correlation stated in Inequality 7.6. If X and Y have strong negative correlation, then

$$s(X \cup \overline{Y}) \times s(\overline{X} \cup Y) \gg s(X \cup Y) \times s(\overline{X} \cup \overline{Y}).$$

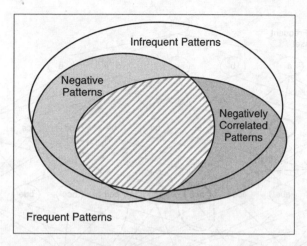

Figure 7.22. Comparisons among infrequent patterns, negative patterns, and negatively correlated patterns.

Table 7.9. A two-way contingency table for the association rule $X \longrightarrow Y$.

	Y	$\overline{Y}$	
X	$s(X \cup Y)$	$s(X \cup \overline{Y})$	$s(X)$
$\overline{X}$	$s(\overline{X} \cup Y)$	$s(\overline{X} \cup \overline{Y})$	$s(\overline{X})$
	$s(Y)$	$s(\overline{Y})$	1

Therefore, either $X \cup \overline{Y}$ or $\overline{X} \cup Y$, or both, must have relatively high support when X and Y are negatively correlated. These itemsets correspond to the negative patterns.

Finally, because the lower the support of $X \cup Y$, the more negatively correlated is the pattern, negatively correlated patterns that are infrequent tend to be more interesting than negatively correlated patterns that are frequent. The infrequent, negatively correlated patterns are illustrated by the overlapping region in Figure 7.22 between both types of patterns.

7.6.4   Techniques for Mining Interesting Infrequent Patterns

In principle, infrequent itemsets are given by all itemsets that are not extracted by standard frequent itemset generation algorithms such as *Apriori* and FP-

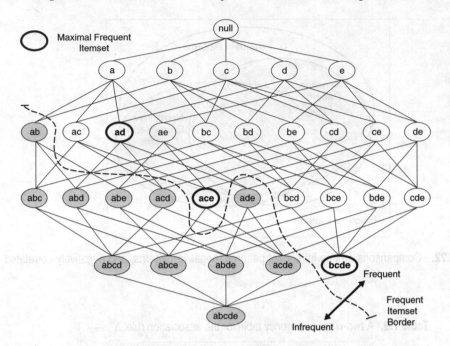

Figure 7.23. Frequent and infrequent itemsets.

growth. These itemsets correspond to those located below the frequent itemset border shown in Figure 7.23.

Since the number of infrequent patterns can be exponentially large, especially for sparse, high-dimensional data, techniques developed for mining infrequent patterns focus on finding only interesting infrequent patterns. An example of such patterns includes the negatively correlated patterns discussed in Section 7.6.2. These patterns are obtained by eliminating all infrequent itemsets that fail the negative correlation condition provided in Inequality 7.3. This approach can be computationally intensive because the supports for all infrequent itemsets must be computed in order to determine whether they are negatively correlated. Unlike the support measure used for mining frequent itemsets, correlation-based measures used for mining negatively correlated itemsets do not possess an anti-monotone property that can be exploited for pruning the exponential search space. Although an efficient solution remains elusive, several innovative methods have been developed, as mentioned in the bibliographic notes provided at the end of this chapter.

The remainder of this chapter presents two classes of techniques for mining interesting infrequent patterns. Section 7.6.5 describes methods for mining

TID	Items
1	{A,B}
2	{A,B,C}
3	{C}
4	{B,C}
5	{B,D}

Original Transactions

TID	A	$\overline{A}$	B	B	C	$\overline{C}$	D	D
1	1	0	1	0	0	1	0	1
2	1	0	1	0	1	0	0	1
3	0	1	0	1	1	0	0	1
4	0	1	1	0	1	0	0	1
5	0	1	1	0	0	1	1	0

Transactions with Negative Items

Figure 7.24. Augmenting a data set with negative items.

negative patterns in data, while Section 7.6.6 describes methods for finding interesting infrequent patterns based on support expectation.

7.6.5 Techniques Based on Mining Negative Patterns

The first class of techniques developed for mining infrequent patterns treats every item as a symmetric binary variable. Using the approach described in Section 7.1, the transaction data can be binarized by augmenting it with negative items. Figure 7.24 shows an example of transforming the original data into transactions having both positive and negative items. By applying existing frequent itemset generation algorithms such as *Apriori* on the augmented transactions, all the negative itemsets can be derived.

Such an approach is feasible only if a few variables are treated as symmetric binary (i.e., we look for negative patterns involving the negation of only a small number of items). If every item must be treated as symmetric binary, the problem becomes computationally intractable due to the following reasons.

1. The number of items doubles when every item is augmented with its corresponding negative item. Instead of exploring an itemset lattice of size 2^d, where d is the number of items in the original data set, the lattice becomes considerably larger, as shown in Exercise 21 on page 485.

2. Support-based pruning is no longer effective when negative items are augmented. For each variable x, either x or $\overline{x}$ has support greater than or equal to 50%. Hence, even if the support threshold is as high as 50%, half of the items will remain frequent. For lower thresholds, many more items and possibly itemsets containing them will be frequent. The support-based pruning strategy employed by *Apriori* is effective only

when the support for most itemsets is low; otherwise, the number of frequent itemsets grows exponentially.

3. The width of each transaction increases when negative items are augmented. Suppose there are d items available in the original data set. For sparse data sets such as market basket transactions, the width of each transaction tends to be much smaller than d. As a result, the maximum size of a frequent itemset, which is bounded by the maximum transaction width, w_{max}, tends to be relatively small. When negative items are included, the width of the transactions increases to d because an item is either present in the transaction or absent from the transaction, but not both. Since the maximum transaction width has grown from w_{max} to d, this will increase the number of frequent itemsets exponentially. As a result, many existing algorithms tend to break down when they are applied to the extended data set.

The previous brute-force approach is computationally expensive because it forces us to determine the support for a large number of positive and negative patterns. Instead of augmenting the data set with negative items, another approach is to determine the support of the negative itemsets based on the support of their corresponding positive items. For example, the support for $\{p, \overline{q}, \overline{r}\}$ can be computed in the following way:

$$s(\{p, \overline{q}, \overline{r}\}) = s(\{p\}) - s(\{p, q\}) - s(\{p, r\}) + s(\{p, q, r\}).$$

More generally, the support for any itemset $X \cup \overline{Y}$ can be obtained as follows:

$$s(X \cup \overline{Y}) = s(X) + \sum_{i=1}^{n} \sum_{Z \subset Y, |Z|=i} \{(-1)^i \times s(X \cup Z)\}. \qquad (7.7)$$

To apply Equation 7.7, $s(X \cup Z)$ must be determined for every Z that is a subset of Y. The support for any combination of X and Z that exceeds the *minsup* threshold can be found using the *Apriori* algorithm. For all other combinations, the supports must be determined explicitly, e.g., by scanning the entire set of transactions. Another possible approach is to either ignore the support for any infrequent itemset $X \cup Z$ or to approximate it with the *minsup* threshold.

Several optimization strategies are available to further improve the performance of the mining algorithms. First, the number of variables considered as symmetric binary can be restricted. More specifically, a negative item $\overline{y}$ is considered interesting only if y is a frequent item. The rationale for this strategy is that rare items tend to produce a large number of infrequent patterns and many of which are uninteresting. By restricting the set $\overline{Y}$ given in Equation 7.7 to variables whose positive items are frequent, the number of candidate negative itemsets considered by the mining algorithm can be substantially reduced. Another strategy is to restrict the type of negative patterns. For example, the algorithm may consider only a negative pattern $X \cup \overline{Y}$ if it contains at least one positive item (i.e., $|X| \geq 1$). The rationale for this strategy is that if the data set contains very few positive items with support greater than 50%, then most of the negative patterns of the form $\overline{X} \cup \overline{Y}$ will become frequent, thus degrading the performance of the mining algorithm.

7.6.6 Techniques Based on Support Expectation

Another class of techniques considers an infrequent pattern to be interesting only if its actual support is considerably smaller than its expected support. For negatively correlated patterns, the expected support is computed based on the statistical independence assumption. This section describes two alternative approaches for determining the expected support of a pattern using (1) a concept hierarchy and (2) a neighborhood-based approach known as **indirect association**.

Support Expectation Based on Concept Hierarchy

Objective measures alone may not be sufficient to eliminate uninteresting infrequent patterns. For example, suppose `bread` and `laptop computer` are frequent items. Even though the itemset {`bread`, `laptop computer`} is infrequent and perhaps negatively correlated, it is not interesting because their lack of support seems obvious to domain experts. Therefore, a subjective approach for determining expected support is needed to avoid generating such infrequent patterns.

In the preceding example, `bread` and `laptop computer` belong to two completely different product categories, which is why it is not surprising to find that their support is low. This example also illustrates the advantage of using domain knowledge to prune uninteresting patterns. For market basket data, the domain knowledge can be inferred from a concept hierarchy such as the one shown in Figure 7.25. The basic assumption of this approach is that items from the same product family are expected to have similar types of interaction with other items. For example, since `ham` and `bacon` belong to the

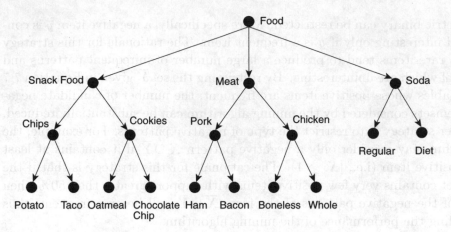

Figure 7.25. Example of a concept hierarchy.

same product family, we expect the association between ham and chips to be somewhat similar to the association between bacon and chips. If the actual support for any one of these pairs is less than their expected support, then the infrequent pattern is interesting.

To illustrate how to compute the expected support, consider the diagram shown in Figure 7.26. Suppose the itemset $\{C, G\}$ is frequent. Let $s(\cdot)$ denote the actual support of a pattern and $\epsilon(\cdot)$ denote its expected support. The expected support for any children or siblings of C and G can be computed using the formula shown below.

$$\epsilon(s(E, J)) = s(C, G) \times \frac{s(E)}{s(C)} \times \frac{s(J)}{s(G)} \tag{7.8}$$

$$\epsilon(s(C, J)) = s(C, G) \times \frac{s(J)}{s(G)} \tag{7.9}$$

$$\epsilon(s(C, H)) = s(C, G) \times \frac{s(H)}{s(G)} \tag{7.10}$$

For example, if soda and snack food are frequent, then the expected support between diet soda and chips can be computed using Equation 7.8 because these items are children of soda and snack food, respectively. If the actual support for diet soda and chips is considerably lower than their expected value, then diet soda and chips form an interesting infrequent pattern.

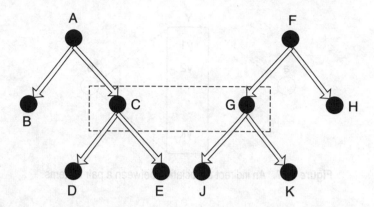

Figure 7.26. Mining interesting negative patterns using a concept hierarchy.

Support Expectation Based on Indirect Association

Consider a pair of items, (a, b), that are rarely bought together by customers. If a and b are unrelated items, such as bread and DVD player, then their support is expected to be low. On the other hand, if a and b are related items, then their support is expected to be high. The expected support was previously computed using a concept hierarchy. This section presents an approach for determining the expected support between a pair of items by looking at other items commonly purchased together with these two items.

For example, suppose customers who buy a sleeping bag also tend to buy other camping equipment, whereas those who buy a desktop computer also tend to buy other computer accessories such as an optical mouse or a printer. Assuming there is no other item frequently bought together with both a sleeping bag and a desktop computer, the support for these unrelated items is expected to be low. On the other hand, suppose diet and regular soda are often bought together with chips and cookies. Even without using a concept hierarchy, both items are expected to be somewhat related and their support should be high. Because their actual support is low, diet and regular soda form an interesting infrequent pattern. Such patterns are known as **indirect association** patterns.

A high-level illustration of indirect association is shown in Figure 7.27. Items a and b correspond to diet soda and regular soda, while Y, which is known as the **mediator set**, contains items such as chips and cookies. A formal definition of indirect association is presented next.

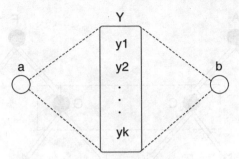

Figure 7.27. An indirect association between a pair of items.

Definition 7.12 (Indirect Association). A pair of items a, b is indirectly associated via a mediator set Y if the following conditions hold:

1. $s(\{a, b\}) < t_s$ (Itempair support condition).

2. $\exists Y \neq \emptyset$ such that:

    (a) $s(\{a\} \cup Y) \geq t_f$ and $s(\{b\} \cup Y) \geq t_f$ (Mediator support condition).

    (b) $d(\{a\}, Y) \geq t_d, d(\{b\}, Y) \geq t_d$, where $d(X, Z)$ is an objective measure of the association between X and Z (Mediator dependence condition).

Note that the mediator support and dependence conditions are used to ensure that items in Y form a close neighborhood to both a and b. Some of the dependence measures that can be used include interest, cosine or IS, Jaccard, and other measures previously described in Section 6.7.1 on page 371.

Indirect association has many potential applications. In the market basket domain, a and b may refer to competing items such as **desktop** and **laptop** **computers**. In text mining, indirect association can be used to identify synonyms, antonyms, or words that are used in different contexts. For example, given a collection of documents, the word **data** may be indirectly associated with **gold** via the mediator **mining**. This pattern suggests that the word **mining** can be used in two different contexts—data mining versus gold mining.

Indirect associations can be generated in the following way. First, the set of frequent itemsets is generated using standard algorithms such as *Apriori* or FP-growth. Each pair of frequent k-itemsets are then merged to obtain a candidate indirect association (a, b, Y), where a and b are a pair of items and Y is their common mediator. For example, if $\{p, q, r\}$ and $\{p, q, s\}$ are

---

Algorithm 7.2 Algorithm for mining indirect associations.

1: Generate F_k, the set of frequent itemsets.
2: **for** $k = 2$ to $k_{\max}$ **do**
3:     $C_k = \{(a, b, Y) | \{a\} \cup Y \in F_k, \{b\} \cup Y \in F_k, a \neq b\}$
4:     **for** each candidate $(a, b, Y) \in C_k$ **do**
5:         **if** $s(\{a, b\}) < t_s \wedge d(\{a\}, Y) \geq t_d \wedge d(\{b\}, Y) \geq t_d$ **then**
6:             $I_k = I_k \cup \{(a, b, Y)\}$
7:         **end if**
8:     **end for**
9: **end for**
10: Result $= \bigcup I_k$.

---

frequent 3-itemsets, then the candidate indirect association $(r, s, \{p, q\})$ is obtained by merging the pair of frequent itemsets. Once the candidates have been generated, it is necessary to verify that they satisfy the itempair support and mediator dependence conditions provided in Definition 7.12. However, the mediator support condition does not have to be verified because the candidate indirect association is obtained by merging a pair of frequent itemsets. A summary of the algorithm is shown in Algorithm 7.2.

7.7 Bibliographic Notes

The problem of mining association rules from categorical and continuous data was introduced by Srikant and Agrawal in [363]. Their strategy was to binarize the categorical attributes and to apply equal-frequency discretization to the continuous attributes. A **partial completeness** measure was also proposed to determine the amount of information loss as a result of discretization. This measure was then used to determine the number of discrete intervals needed to ensure that the amount of information loss can be kept at a certain desired level. Following this work, numerous other formulations have been proposed for mining quantitative association rules. The statistics-based approach was developed by Aumann and Lindell [343] to identify segments of the population who exhibit interesting behavior characterized by some quantitative attributes. This formulation was later extended by other authors including Webb [368] and Zhang et al. [372]. The min-*Apriori* algorithm was developed by Han et al. [349] for finding association rules in continuous data without discretization. The problem of mining association rules in continuous data has also been investigated by numerous other researchers including Fukuda et al. [347], Lent et al. [355], Wang et al. [367], and Miller and Yang [357].

The method described in Section 7.3 for handling concept hierarchy using extended transactions was developed by Srikant and Agrawal [362]. An alternative algorithm was proposed by Han and Fu [350], where frequent itemsets are generated one level at a time. More specifically, their algorithm initially generates all the frequent 1-itemsets at the top level of the concept hierarchy. The set of frequent 1-itemsets is denoted as $L(1,1)$. Using the frequent 1-itemsets in $L(1,1)$, the algorithm proceeds to generate all frequent 2-itemsets at level 1, $L(1,2)$. This procedure is repeated until all the frequent itemsets involving items from the highest level of the hierarchy, $L(1,k)$ $(k > 1)$, are extracted. The algorithm then continues to extract frequent itemsets at the next level of the hierarchy, $L(2,1)$, based on the frequent itemsets in $L(1,1)$. The procedure is repeated until it terminates at the lowest level of the concept hierarchy requested by the user.

The sequential pattern formulation and algorithm described in Section 7.4 was proposed by Agrawal and Srikant in [341, 364]. Similarly, Mannila et al. [356] introduced the concept of frequent episode, which is useful for mining sequential patterns from a long stream of events. Another formulation of sequential pattern mining based on regular expressions was proposed by Garofalakis et al. in [348]. Joshi et al. have attempted to reconcile the differences between various sequential pattern formulations [352]. The result was a universal formulation of sequential pattern with the different counting schemes described in Section 7.4.4. Alternative algorithms for mining sequential patterns were also proposed by Pei et al. [359], Ayres et al. [344], Cheng et al. [346], and Seno et al. [361].

The frequent subgraph mining problem was initially introduced by Inokuchi et al. in [351]. They used a vertex-growing approach for generating frequent induced subgraphs from a graph data set. The edge-growing strategy was developed by Kuramochi and Karypis in [353], where they also presented an *Apriori*-like algorithm called FSG that addresses issues such as multiplicity of candidates, canonical labeling, and vertex invariant schemes. Another frequent subgraph mining algorithm known as gSpan was developed by Yan and Han in [370]. The authors proposed using a minimum DFS code for encoding the various subgraphs. Other variants of the frequent subgraph mining problems were proposed by Zaki in [371], Parthasarathy and Coatney in [358], and Kuramochi and Karypis in [354].

The problem of mining infrequent patterns has been investigated by many authors. Savasere et al. [360] examined the problem of mining negative association rules using a concept hierarchy. Tan et al. [365] proposed the idea of mining indirect associations for sequential and non-sequential data. Efficient algorithms for mining negative patterns have also been proposed by Boulicaut et al. [345], Teng et al. [366], Wu et al. [369], and Antonie and Zaïane [342].

Bibliography

[341] R. Agrawal and R. Srikant. Mining Sequential Patterns. In *Proc. of Intl. Conf. on Data Engineering*, pages 3–14, Taipei, Taiwan, 1995.

[342] M.-L. Antonie and O. R. Zaïane. Mining Positive and Negative Association Rules: An Approach for Confined Rules. In *Proc. of the 8th European Conf. of Principles and Practice of Knowledge Discovery in Databases*, pages 27–38, Pisa, Italy, September 2004.

[343] Y. Aumann and Y. Lindell. A Statistical Theory for Quantitative Association Rules. In *KDD99*, pages 261–270, San Diego, CA, August 1999.

[344] J. Ayres, J. Flannick, J. Gehrke, and T. Yiu. Sequential Pattern mining using a bitmap representation. In *Proc. of the 8th Intl. Conf. on Knowledge Discovery and Data Mining*, pages 429–435, Edmonton, Canada, July 2002.

[345] J.-F. Boulicaut, A. Bykowski, and B. Jeudy. Towards the Tractable Discovery of Association Rules with Negations. In *Proc. of the 4th Intl. Conf on Flexible Query Answering Systems FQAS'00*, pages 425–434, Warsaw, Poland, October 2000.

[346] H. Cheng, X. Yan, and J. Han. IncSpan: incremental mining of sequential patterns in large database. In *Proc. of the 10th Intl. Conf. on Knowledge Discovery and Data Mining*, pages 527–532, Seattle, WA, August 2004.

[347] T. Fukuda, Y. Morimoto, S. Morishita, and T. Tokuyama. Mining Optimized Association Rules for Numeric Attributes. In *Proc. of the 15th Symp. on Principles of Database Systems*, pages 182–191, Montreal, Canada, June 1996.

[348] M. N. Garofalakis, R. Rastogi, and K. Shim. SPIRIT: Sequential Pattern Mining with Regular Expression Constraints. In *Proc. of the 25th VLDB Conf.*, pages 223–234, Edinburgh, Scotland, 1999.

[349] E.-H. Han, G. Karypis, and V. Kumar. Min-Apriori: An Algorithm for Finding Association Rules in Data with Continuous Attributes. http://www.cs.umn.edu/~han, 1997.

[350] J. Han and Y. Fu. Mining Multiple-Level Association Rules in Large Databases. *IEEE Trans. on Knowledge and Data Engineering*, 11(5):798–804, 1999.

[351] A. Inokuchi, T. Washio, and H. Motoda. An Apriori-based Algorithm for Mining Frequent Substructures from Graph Data. In *Proc. of the 4th European Conf. of Principles and Practice of Knowledge Discovery in Databases*, pages 13–23, Lyon, France, 2000.

[352] M. V. Joshi, G. Karypis, and V. Kumar. A Universal Formulation of Sequential Patterns. In *Proc. of the KDD'2001 workshop on Temporal Data Mining*, San Francisco, CA, August 2001.

[353] M. Kuramochi and G. Karypis. Frequent Subgraph Discovery. In *Proc. of the 2001 IEEE Intl. Conf. on Data Mining*, pages 313–320, San Jose, CA, November 2001.

[354] M. Kuramochi and G. Karypis. Discovering Frequent Geometric Subgraphs. In *Proc. of the 2002 IEEE Intl. Conf. on Data Mining*, pages 258–265, Maebashi City, Japan, December 2002.

[355] B. Lent, A. Swami, and J. Widom. Clustering Association Rules. In *Proc. of the 13th Intl. Conf. on Data Engineering*, pages 220–231, Birmingham, U.K, April 1997.

[356] H. Mannila, H. Toivonen, and A. I. Verkamo. Discovery of Frequent Episodes in Event Sequences. *Data Mining and Knowledge Discovery*, 1(3):259–289, November 1997.

[357] R. J. Miller and Y. Yang. Association Rules over Interval Data. In *Proc. of 1997 ACM-SIGMOD Intl. Conf. on Management of Data*, pages 452–461, Tucson, AZ, May 1997.

[358] S. Parthasarathy and M. Coatney. Efficient Discovery of Common Substructures in Macromolecules. In *Proc. of the 2002 IEEE Intl. Conf. on Data Mining*, pages 362–369, Maebashi City, Japan, December 2002.

[359] J. Pei, J. Han, B. Mortazavi-Asl, Q. Chen, U. Dayal, and M. Hsu. PrefixSpan: Mining Sequential Patterns efficiently by prefix-projected pattern growth. In *Proc of the 17th Intl. Conf. on Data Engineering*, Heidelberg, Germany, April 2001.

[360] A. Savasere, E. Omiecinski, and S. Navathe. Mining for Strong Negative Associations in a Large Database of Customer Transactions. In *Proc. of the 14th Intl. Conf. on Data Engineering*, pages 494–502, Orlando, Florida, February 1998.

[361] M. Seno and G. Karypis. SLPMiner: An Algorithm for Finding Frequent Sequential Patterns Using Length-Decreasing Support Constraint. In *Proc. of the 2002 IEEE Intl. Conf. on Data Mining*, pages 418–425, Maebashi City, Japan, December 2002.

[362] R. Srikant and R. Agrawal. Mining Generalized Association Rules. In *Proc. of the 21st VLDB Conf.*, pages 407–419, Zurich, Switzerland, 1995.

[363] R. Srikant and R. Agrawal. Mining Quantitative Association Rules in Large Relational Tables. In *Proc. of 1996 ACM-SIGMOD Intl. Conf. on Management of Data*, pages 1–12, Montreal, Canada, 1996.

[364] R. Srikant and R. Agrawal. Mining Sequential Patterns: Generalizations and Performance Improvements. In *Proc. of the 5th Intl Conf. on Extending Database Technology (EDBT'96)*, pages 18–32, Avignon, France, 1996.

[365] P. N. Tan, V. Kumar, and J. Srivastava. Indirect Association: Mining Higher Order Dependencies in Data. In *Proc. of the 4th European Conf. of Principles and Practice of Knowledge Discovery in Databases*, pages 632–637, Lyon, France, 2000.

[366] W. G. Teng, M. J. Hsieh, and M.-S. Chen. On the Mining of Substitution Rules for Statistically Dependent Items. In *Proc. of the 2002 IEEE Intl. Conf. on Data Mining*, pages 442–449, Maebashi City, Japan, December 2002.

[367] K. Wang, S. H. Tay, and B. Liu. Interestingness-Based Interval Merger for Numeric Association Rules. In *Proc. of the 4th Intl. Conf. on Knowledge Discovery and Data Mining*, pages 121–128, New York, NY, August 1998.

[368] G. I. Webb. Discovering associations with numeric variables. In *Proc. of the 7th Intl. Conf. on Knowledge Discovery and Data Mining*, pages 383–388, San Francisco, CA, August 2001.

[369] X. Wu, C. Zhang, and S. Zhang. Mining Both Positive and Negative Association Rules. *ACM Trans. on Information Systems*, 22(3):381–405, 2004.

[370] X. Yan and J. Han. gSpan: Graph-based Substructure Pattern Mining. In *Proc. of the 2002 IEEE Intl. Conf. on Data Mining*, pages 721–724, Maebashi City, Japan, December 2002.

[371] M. J. Zaki. Efficiently mining frequent trees in a forest. In *Proc. of the 8th Intl. Conf. on Knowledge Discovery and Data Mining*, pages 71–80, Edmonton, Canada, July 2002.

[372] H. Zhang, B. Padmanabhan, and A. Tuzhilin. On the Discovery of Significant Statistical Quantitative Rules. In *Proc. of the 10th Intl. Conf. on Knowledge Discovery and Data Mining*, pages 374–383, Seattle, WA, August 2004.

7.8 Exercises

1. Consider the traffic accident data set shown in Table 7.10.

Table 7.10. Traffic accident data set.

Weather Condition	Driver's Condition	Traffic Violation	Seat Belt	Crash Severity
Good	Alcohol-impaired	Exceed speed limit	No	Major
Bad	Sober	None	Yes	Minor
Good	Sober	Disobey stop sign	Yes	Minor
Good	Sober	Exceed speed limit	Yes	Major
Bad	Sober	Disobey traffic signal	No	Major
Good	Alcohol-impaired	Disobey stop sign	Yes	Minor
Bad	Alcohol-impaired	None	Yes	Major
Good	Sober	Disobey traffic signal	Yes	Major
Good	Alcohol-impaired	None	No	Major
Bad	Sober	Disobey traffic signal	No	Major
Good	Alcohol-impaired	Exceed speed limit	Yes	Major
Bad	Sober	Disobey stop sign	Yes	Minor

(a) Show a binarized version of the data set.

(b) What is the maximum width of each transaction in the binarized data?

(c) Assuming that support threshold is 30%, how many candidate and frequent itemsets will be generated?

(d) Create a data set that contains only the following asymmetric binary attributes: (Weather = Bad, Driver's condition = Alcohol-impaired, Traffic violation = Yes, Seat Belt = No, Crash Severity = Major). For Traffic violation, only None has a value of 0. The rest of the attribute values are assigned to 1. Assuming that support threshold is 30%, how many candidate and frequent itemsets will be generated?

(e) Compare the number of candidate and frequent itemsets generated in parts (c) and (d).

2. (a) Consider the data set shown in Table 7.11. Suppose we apply the following discretization strategies to the continuous attributes of the data set.

   D1: Partition the range of each continuous attribute into 3 equal-sized bins.

   D2: Partition the range of each continuous attribute into 3 bins; where each bin contains an equal number of transactions

Table 7.11. Data set for Exercise 2.

TID	Temperature	Pressure	Alarm 1	Alarm 2	Alarm 3
1	95	1105	0	0	1
2	85	1040	1	1	0
3	103	1090	1	1	1
4	97	1084	1	0	0
5	80	1038	0	1	1
6	100	1080	1	1	0
7	83	1025	1	0	1
8	86	1030	1	0	0
9	101	1100	1	1	1

For each strategy, answer the following questions:

   i. Construct a binarized version of the data set.

  ii. Derive all the frequent itemsets having support $\geq 30\%$.

(b) The continuous attribute can also be discretized using a clustering approach.

   i. Plot a graph of temperature versus pressure for the data points shown in Table 7.11.

  ii. How many natural clusters do you observe from the graph? Assign a label (C_1, C_2, etc.) to each cluster in the graph.

  iii. What type of clustering algorithm do you think can be used to identify the clusters? State your reasons clearly.

  iv. Replace the temperature and pressure attributes in Table 7.11 with asymmetric binary attributes C_1, C_2, etc. Construct a transaction matrix using the new attributes (along with attributes Alarm1, Alarm2, and Alarm3).

   v. Derive all the frequent itemsets having support $\geq 30\%$ from the binarized data.

3. Consider the data set shown in Table 7.12. The first attribute is continuous, while the remaining two attributes are asymmetric binary. A rule is considered to be strong if its support exceeds 15% and its confidence exceeds 60%. The data given in Table 7.12 supports the following two strong rules:

  (i) $\{(1 \leq A \leq 2), B = 1\} \rightarrow \{C = 1\}$

  (ii) $\{(5 \leq A \leq 8), B = 1\} \rightarrow \{C = 1\}$

(a) Compute the support and confidence for both rules.

(b) To find the rules using the traditional *Apriori* algorithm, we need to discretize the continuous attribute A. Suppose we apply the equal width

Table 7.12. Data set for Exercise 3.

A	B	C
1	1	1
2	1	1
3	1	0
4	1	0
5	1	1
6	0	1
7	0	0
8	1	1
9	0	0
10	0	0
11	0	0
12	0	1

binning approach to discretize the data, with *bin-width* = 2, 3, 4. For each *bin-width*, state whether the above two rules are discovered by the *Apriori* algorithm. (Note that the rules may not be in the same exact form as before because it may contain wider or narrower intervals for A.) For each rule that corresponds to one of the above two rules, compute its support and confidence.

(c) Comment on the effectiveness of using the equal width approach for classifying the above data set. Is there a *bin*-width that allows you to find both rules satisfactorily? If not, what alternative approach can you take to ensure that you will find both rules?

4. Consider the data set shown in Table 7.13.

Table 7.13. Data set for Exercise 4.

Age (A)	Number of Hours Online per Week (B)				
	0 – 5	5 – 10	10 – 20	20 – 30	30 – 40
10 – 15	2	3	5	3	2
15 – 25	2	5	10	10	3
25 – 35	10	15	5	3	2
35 – 50	4	6	5	3	2

(a) For each combination of rules given below, specify the rule that has the highest confidence.

i. $15 < A < 25 \longrightarrow 10 < B < 20$, $10 < A < 25 \longrightarrow 10 < B < 20$, and $15 < A < 35 \longrightarrow 10 < B < 20$.

    ii. $15 < A < 25 \longrightarrow 10 < B < 20$, $15 < A < 25 \longrightarrow 5 < B < 20$, and $15 < A < 25 \longrightarrow 5 < B < 30$.

    iii. $15 < A < 25 \longrightarrow 10 < B < 20$ and $10 < A < 35 \longrightarrow 5 < B < 30$.

(b) Suppose we are interested in finding the average number of hours spent online per week by Internet users between the age of 15 and 35. Write the corresponding statistics-based association rule to characterize the segment of users. To compute the average number of hours spent online, approximate each interval by its midpoint value (e.g., use $B = 7.5$ to represent the interval $5 < B < 10$).

(c) Test whether the quantitative association rule given in part (b) is statistically significant by comparing its mean against the average number of hours spent online by other users who do not belong to the age group.

5. For the data set with the attributes given below, describe how you would convert it into a binary transaction data set appropriate for association analysis. Specifically, indicate for each attribute in the original data set

(a) how many binary attributes it would correspond to in the transaction data set,

(b) how the values of the original attribute would be mapped to values of the binary attributes, and

(c) if there is any hierarchical structure in the data values of an attribute that could be useful for grouping the data into fewer binary attributes.

The following is a list of attributes for the data set along with their possible values. Assume that all attributes are collected on a per-student basis:

- **Year** : Freshman, Sophomore, Junior, Senior, Graduate:Masters, Graduate:PhD, Professional

- **Zip code** : zip code for the home address of a U.S. student, zip code for the local address of a non-U.S. student

- **College** : Agriculture, Architecture, Continuing Education, Education, Liberal Arts, Engineering, Natural Sciences, Business, Law, Medical, Dentistry, Pharmacy, Nursing, Veterinary Medicine

- **On Campus** : 1 if the student lives on campus, 0 otherwise

- Each of the following is a separate attribute that has a value of 1 if the person speaks the language and a value of 0, otherwise.

    – Arabic

    – Bengali

    – Chinese Mandarin

    – English

    – Portuguese

  – Russian

  – Spanish

6. Consider the data set shown in Table 7.14. Suppose we are interested in extracting the following association rule:

$$\{\alpha_1 \leq \text{Age} \leq \alpha_2, \text{Play Piano} = \text{Yes}\} \longrightarrow \{\text{Enjoy Classical Music} = \text{Yes}\}$$

Table 7.14. Data set for Exercise 6.

Age	Play Piano	Enjoy Classical Music
9	Yes	Yes
11	Yes	Yes
14	Yes	No
17	Yes	No
19	Yes	Yes
21	No	No
25	No	No
29	Yes	Yes
33	No	No
39	No	Yes
41	No	No
47	No	Yes

To handle the continuous attribute, we apply the equal-frequency approach with 3, 4, and 6 intervals. Categorical attributes are handled by introducing as many new asymmetric binary attributes as the number of categorical values. Assume that the support threshold is 10% and the confidence threshold is 70%.

 (a) Suppose we discretize the Age attribute into 3 equal-frequency intervals. Find a pair of values for α_1 and α_2 that satisfy the minimum support and minimum confidence requirements.

 (b) Repeat part (a) by discretizing the Age attribute into 4 equal-frequency intervals. Compare the extracted rules against the ones you had obtained in part (a).

 (c) Repeat part (a) by discretizing the Age attribute into 6 equal-frequency intervals. Compare the extracted rules against the ones you had obtained in part (a).

 (d) From the results in part (a), (b), and (c), discuss how the choice of discretization intervals will affect the rules extracted by association rule mining algorithms.

7. Consider the transactions shown in Table 7.15, with an item taxonomy given in Figure 7.25.

Table 7.15. Example of market basket transactions.

Transaction ID	Items Bought
1	Chips, Cookies, Regular Soda, Ham
2	Chips, Ham, Boneless Chicken, Diet Soda
3	Ham, Bacon, Whole Chicken, Regular Soda
4	Chips, Ham, Boneless Chicken, Diet Soda
5	Chips, Bacon, Boneless Chicken
6	Chips, Ham, Bacon, Whole Chicken, Regular Soda
7	Chips, Cookies, Boneless Chicken, Diet Soda

(a) What are the main challenges of mining association rules with item taxonomy?

(b) Consider the approach where each transaction t is replaced by an extended transaction t' that contains all the items in t as well as their respective ancestors. For example, the transaction $t = \{$ Chips, Cookies$\}$ will be replaced by $t' = \{$Chips, Cookies, Snack Food, Food$\}$. Use this approach to derive all frequent itemsets (up to size 4) with support $\geq 70\%$.

(c) Consider an alternative approach where the frequent itemsets are generated one level at a time. Initially, all the frequent itemsets involving items at the highest level of the hierarchy are generated. Next, we use the frequent itemsets discovered at the higher level of the hierarchy to generate candidate itemsets involving items at the lower levels of the hierarchy. For example, we generate the candidate itemset $\{$Chips, Diet Soda$\}$ only if $\{$Snack Food, Soda$\}$ is frequent. Use this approach to derive all frequent itemsets (up to size 4) with support $\geq 70\%$.

(d) Compare the frequent itemsets found in parts (b) and (c). Comment on the efficiency and completeness of the algorithms.

8. The following questions examine how the support and confidence of an association rule may vary in the presence of a concept hierarchy.

(a) Consider an item x in a given concept hierarchy. Let $\bar{x}_1, \bar{x}_2, \ldots, \bar{x}_k$ denote the k children of x in the concept hierarchy. Show that $s(x) \leq \sum_{i=1}^{k} s(\bar{x}_i)$, where $s(\cdot)$ is the support of an item. Under what conditions will the inequality become an equality?

(b) Let p and q denote a pair of items, while $\hat{p}$ and $\hat{q}$ are their corresponding parents in the concept hierarchy. If $s(\{p,q\}) > minsup$, which of the following itemsets are guaranteed to be frequent? (i) $s(\{\hat{p}, q\})$, (ii) $s(\{p, \hat{q}\})$, and (iii) $s(\{\hat{p}, \hat{q}\})$.

(c) Consider the association rule $\{p\} \longrightarrow \{q\}$. Suppose the confidence of the rule exceeds $minconf$. Which of the following rules are guaranteed to have confidence higher than $minconf$? (i) $\{p\} \longrightarrow \{\hat{q}\}$, (ii) $\{\hat{p}\} \longrightarrow \{q\}$, and (iii) $\{\hat{p}\} \longrightarrow \{\hat{q}\}$.

9. (a) List all the 4-subsequences contained in the following data sequence:

    $$< \{1,3\} \ \{2\} \ \{2,3\} \ \{4\} >,$$

    assuming no timing constraints.

    (b) List all the 3-element subsequences contained in the data sequence for part (a) assuming that no timing constraints are imposed.

    (c) List all the 4-subsequences contained in the data sequence for part (a) (assuming the timing constraints are flexible).

    (d) List all the 3-element subsequences contained in the data sequence for part (a) (assuming the timing constraints are flexible).

10. Find all the frequent subsequences with support $\geq 50\%$ given the sequence database shown in Table 7.16. Assume that there are no timing constraints imposed on the sequences.

Table 7.16. Example of event sequences generated by various sensors.

Sensor	Timestamp	Events
S1	1	A, B
	2	C
	3	D, E
	4	C
S2	1	A, B
	2	C, D
	3	E
S3	1	B
	2	A
	3	B
	4	D, E
S4	1	C
	2	D, E
	3	C
	4	E
S5	1	B
	2	A
	3	B, C
	4	A, D

11. (a) For each of the sequences $w = < e_1 e_2 \ldots e_i \ldots e_{i+1} \ldots e_{last} >$ given below, determine whether they are subsequences of the sequence

$$< \{1, 2, 3\}\{2, 4\}\{2, 4, 5\}\{3, 5\}\{6\} >$$

subjected to the following timing constraints:

mingap $= 0$ (interval between last event in e_i and first event in e_{i+1} is > 0)

maxgap $= 3$ (interval between first event in e_i and last event in e_{i+1} is ≤ 3)

maxspan $= 5$ (interval between first event in e_1 and last event in e_{last} is ≤ 5)

$ws = 1$ (time between first and last events in e_i is ≤ 1)

- $w = < \{1\}\{2\}\{3\} >$
- $w = < \{1, 2, 3, 4\}\{5, 6\} >$
- $w = < \{2, 4\}\{2, 4\}\{6\} >$
- $w = < \{1\}\{2, 4\}\{6\} >$
- $w = < \{1, 2\}\{3, 4\}\{5, 6\} >$

(b) Determine whether each of the subsequences w given in the previous question are contiguous subsequences of the following sequences s.

- $s = < \{1, 2, 3, 4, 5, 6\}\{1, 2, 3, 4, 5, 6\}\{1, 2, 3, 4, 5, 6\} >$
- $s = < \{1, 2, 3, 4\}\{1, 2, 3, 4, 5, 6\}\{3, 4, 5, 6\} >$
- $s = < \{1, 2\}\{1, 2, 3, 4\}\{3, 4, 5, 6\}\{5, 6\} >$
- $s = < \{1, 2, 3\}\{2, 3, 4, 5\}\{4, 5, 6\} >$

12. For each of the sequence $w = \langle e_1, \ldots, e_{last} \rangle$ below, determine whether they are subsequences of the following data sequence:

$$\langle \{A, B\}\{C, D\}\{A, B\}\{C, D\}\{A, B\}\{C, D\} \rangle$$

subjected to the following timing constraints:

mingap $= 0$ (interval between last event in e_i and first event in e_{i+1} is > 0)

maxgap $= 2$ (interval between first event in e_i and last event in e_{i+1} is ≤ 2)

maxspan $= 6$ (interval between first event in e_1 and last event in e_{last} is ≤ 6)

$ws = 1$ (time between first and last events in e_i is ≤ 1)

(a) $w = \langle \{A\}\{B\}\{C\}\{D\} \rangle$

(b) $w = \langle \{A\}\{B, C, D\}\{A\} \rangle$

(c) $w = \langle \{A\}\{B, C, D\}\{A\} \rangle$

(d) $w = \langle \{B, C\}\{A, D\}\{B, C\} \rangle$

(e) $w = \langle\{A,B,C,D\}\{A,B,C,D\}\rangle$

13. Consider the following frequent 3-sequences:

    $< \{1,2,3\} >$, $< \{1,2\}\{3\} >$, $< \{1\}\{2,3\} >$, $< \{1,2\}\{4\} >$,
    $< \{1,3\}\{4\} >$, $< \{1,2,4\} >$, $< \{2,3\}\{3\} >$, $< \{2,3\}\{4\} >$,
    $< \{2\}\{3\}\{3\} >$, and $< \{2\}\{3\}\{4\} >$.

    (a) List all the candidate 4-sequences produced by the candidate generation step of the GSP algorithm.

    (b) List all the candidate 4-sequences pruned during the candidate pruning step of the GSP algorithm (assuming no timing constraints).

    (c) List all the candidate 4-sequences pruned during the candidate pruning step of the GSP algorithm (assuming $maxgap = 1$).

14. Consider the data sequence shown in Table 7.17 for a given object. Count the number of occurrences for the sequence $\langle\{p\}\{q\}\{r\}\rangle$ according to the following counting methods:

    (a) COBJ (one occurrence per object).

    (b) CWIN (one occurrence per sliding window).

    (c) CMINWIN (number of minimal windows of occurrence).

    (d) CDIST_O (distinct occurrences with possibility of event-timestamp overlap).

    (e) CDIST (distinct occurrences with no event timestamp overlap allowed).

Table 7.17. Example of event sequence data for Exercise 14.

Timestamp	Events
1	p, q
2	r
3	s
4	p, q
5	r, s
6	p
7	q, r
8	q, s
9	p
10	q, r, s

15. Describe the types of modifications necessary to adapt the frequent subgraph mining algorithm to handle:

    (a) Directed graphs

    (b) Unlabeled graphs

    (c) Acyclic graphs

    (d) Disconnected graphs

    For each type of graph given above, describe which step of the algorithm will be affected (candidate generation, candidate pruning, and support counting), and any further optimization that can help improve the efficiency of the algorithm.

16. Draw all candidate subgraphs obtained from joining the pair of graphs shown in Figure 7.28. Assume the edge-growing method is used to expand the subgraphs.

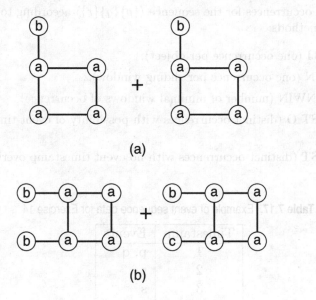

Figure 7.28. Graphs for Exercise 16.

17. Draw all the candidate subgraphs obtained by joining the pair of graphs shown in Figure 7.29. Assume the edge-growing method is used to expand the subgraphs.

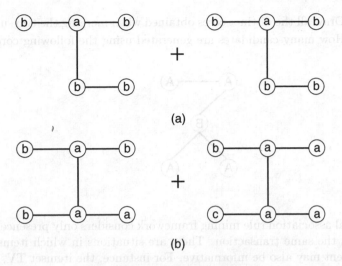

Figure 7.29. Graphs for Exercise 17.

18. (a) If support is defined in terms of induced subgraph relationship, show that the confidence of the rule $g_1 \longrightarrow g_2$ can be greater than 1 if g_1 and g_2 are allowed to have overlapping vertex sets.

    (b) What is the time complexity needed to determine the canonical label of a graph that contains $|V|$ vertices?

    (c) The core of a subgraph can have multiple automorphisms. This will increase the number of candidate subgraphs obtained after merging two frequent subgraphs that share the same core. Determine the maximum number of candidate subgraphs obtained due to automorphism of a core of size k.

    (d) Two frequent subgraphs of size k may share multiple cores. Determine the maximum number of cores that can be shared by the two frequent subgraphs.

19. (a) Consider a graph mining algorithm that uses the edge-growing method to join the two undirected and unweighted subgraphs shown in Figure 19a.

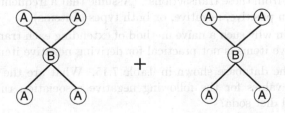

i. Draw all the distinct cores obtained when merging the two subgraphs.

ii. How many candidates are generated using the following core?

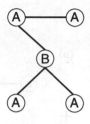

20. The original association rule mining framework considers only presence of items together in the same transaction. There are situations in which itemsets that are infrequent may also be informative. For instance, the itemset TV, DVD, ¬ VCR suggests that many customers who buy TVs and DVDs do not buy VCRs.

In this problem, you are asked to extend the association rule framework to negative itemsets (i.e., itemsets that contain both presence and absence of items). We will use the negation symbol (¬) to refer to absence of items.

(a) A naïve way for deriving negative itemsets is to extend each transaction to include absence of items as shown in Table 7.18.

Table 7.18. Example of numeric data set.

TID	TV	¬TV	DVD	¬DVD	VCR	¬VCR	...
1	1	0	0	1	0	1	...
2	1	0	0	1	0	1	...

i. Suppose the transaction database contains 1000 distinct items. What is the total number of positive itemsets that can be generated from these items? (Note: A positive itemset does not contain any negated items).

ii. What is the maximum number of frequent itemsets that can be generated from these transactions? (Assume that a frequent itemset may contain positive, negative, or both types of items)

iii. Explain why such a naïve method of extending each transaction with negative items is not practical for deriving negative itemsets.

(b) Consider the database shown in Table 7.15. What are the support and confidence values for the following negative association rules involving regular and diet soda?

i. ¬Regular ⟶ Diet.

      ii. Regular $\longrightarrow$ $\neg$Diet.

      iii. $\neg$Diet $\longrightarrow$ Regular.

      iv. Diet $\longrightarrow$ $\neg$Regular.

21. Suppose we would like to extract positive and negative itemsets from a data set that contains d items.

  (a) Consider an approach where we introduce a new variable to represent each negative item. With this approach, the number of items grows from d to $2d$. What is the total size of the itemset lattice, assuming that an itemset may contain both positive and negative items of the same variable?

  (b) Assume that an itemset must contain positive or negative items of different variables. For example, the itemset $\{a, \bar{a}, b, \bar{c}\}$ is invalid because it contains both positive and negative items for variable a. What is the total size of the itemset lattice?

22. For each type of pattern defined below, determine whether the support measure is monotone, anti-monotone, or non-monotone (i.e., neither monotone nor anti-monotone) with respect to increasing itemset size.

  (a) Itemsets that contain both positive and negative items such as $\{a, b, \bar{c}, \bar{d}\}$. Is the support measure monotone, anti-monotone, or non-monotone when applied to such patterns?

  (b) Boolean logical patterns such as $\{(a \lor b \lor c), d, e\}$, which may contain both disjunctions and conjunctions of items. Is the support measure monotone, anti-monotone, or non-monotone when applied to such patterns?

23. Many association analysis algorithms rely on an *Apriori*-like approach for finding frequent patterns. The overall structure of the algorithm is given below.

Algorithm 7.3 *Apriori*-like algorithm.

1: $k = 1$.
2: $F_k = \{ i \mid i \in I \land \frac{\sigma(\{i\})}{N} \geq minsup \}$.   {Find frequent 1-patterns.}
3: **repeat**
4:    $k = k + 1$.
5:    $C_k = \text{genCandidate}(F_{k-1})$.   {Candidate Generation}
6:    $C_k = \text{pruneCandidate}(C_k, F_{k-1})$.   {Candidate Pruning}
7:    $C_k = \text{count}(C_k, D)$.   {Support Counting}
8:    $F_k = \{ c \mid c \in C_k \land \frac{\sigma(c)}{N} \geq minsup \}$.   {Extract frequent patterns}
9: **until** $F_k = \emptyset$
10: Answer $= \bigcup F_k$.

Suppose we are interested in finding boolean logical rules such as

$$\{a \vee b\} \longrightarrow \{c, d\},$$

which may contain both disjunctions and conjunctions of items. The corresponding itemset can be written as $\{(a \vee b), c, d\}$.

(a) Does the *Apriori* principle still hold for such itemsets?

(b) How should the candidate generation step be modified to find such patterns?

(c) How should the candidate pruning step be modified to find such patterns?

(d) How should the support counting step be modified to find such patterns?

8

Cluster Analysis: Basic Concepts and Algorithms

Cluster analysis divides data into groups (clusters) that are meaningful, useful, or both. If meaningful groups are the goal, then the clusters should capture the natural structure of the data. In some cases, however, cluster analysis is only a useful starting point for other purposes, such as data summarization. Whether for understanding or utility, cluster analysis has long played an important role in a wide variety of fields: psychology and other social sciences, biology, statistics, pattern recognition, information retrieval, machine learning, and data mining.

There have been many applications of cluster analysis to practical problems. We provide some specific examples, organized by whether the purpose of the clustering is understanding or utility.

Clustering for Understanding Classes, or conceptually meaningful groups of objects that share common characteristics, play an important role in how people analyze and describe the world. Indeed, human beings are skilled at dividing objects into groups (clustering) and assigning particular objects to these groups (classification). For example, even relatively young children can quickly label the objects in a photograph as buildings, vehicles, people, animals, plants, etc. In the context of understanding data, clusters are potential classes and cluster analysis is the study of techniques for automatically finding classes. The following are some examples:

From Chapter 8 of *Introduction to Data Mining*, First Edition. Pang-Ning Tan, Michael Steinbach, Vipin Kumar.

- **Biology.** Biologists have spent many years creating a taxonomy (hierarchical classification) of all living things: kingdom, phylum, class, order, family, genus, and species. Thus, it is perhaps not surprising that much of the early work in cluster analysis sought to create a discipline of mathematical taxonomy that could automatically find such classification structures. More recently, biologists have applied clustering to analyze the large amounts of genetic information that are now available. For example, clustering has been used to find groups of genes that have similar functions.

- **Information Retrieval.** The World Wide Web consists of billions of Web pages, and the results of a query to a search engine can return thousands of pages. Clustering can be used to group these search results into a small number of clusters, each of which captures a particular aspect of the query. For instance, a query of "movie" might return Web pages grouped into categories such as reviews, trailers, stars, and theaters. Each category (cluster) can be broken into subcategories (subclusters), producing a hierarchical structure that further assists a user's exploration of the query results.

- **Climate.** Understanding the Earth's climate requires finding patterns in the atmosphere and ocean. To that end, cluster analysis has been applied to find patterns in the atmospheric pressure of polar regions and areas of the ocean that have a significant impact on land climate.

- **Psychology and Medicine.** An illness or condition frequently has a number of variations, and cluster analysis can be used to identify these different subcategories. For example, clustering has been used to identify different types of depression. Cluster analysis can also be used to detect patterns in the spatial or temporal distribution of a disease.

- **Business.** Businesses collect large amounts of information on current and potential customers. Clustering can be used to segment customers into a small number of groups for additional analysis and marketing activities.

Clustering for Utility Cluster analysis provides an abstraction from individual data objects to the clusters in which those data objects reside. Additionally, some clustering techniques characterize each cluster in terms of a cluster prototype; i.e., a data object that is representative of the other objects in the cluster. These cluster prototypes can be used as the basis for a number of data analysis or data processing techniques. Therefore, in the context of utility, cluster analysis is the study of techniques for finding the most representative cluster prototypes.

- **Summarization.** Many data analysis techniques, such as regression or PCA, have a time or space complexity of $O(m^2)$ or higher (where m is the number of objects), and thus, are not practical for large data sets. However, instead of applying the algorithm to the entire data set, it can be applied to a reduced data set consisting only of cluster prototypes. Depending on the type of analysis, the number of prototypes, and the accuracy with which the prototypes represent the data, the results can be comparable to those that would have been obtained if all the data could have been used.

- **Compression.** Cluster prototypes can also be used for data compression. In particular, a table is created that consists of the prototypes for each cluster; i.e., each prototype is assigned an integer value that is its position (index) in the table. Each object is represented by the index of the prototype associated with its cluster. This type of compression is known as **vector quantization** and is often applied to image, sound, and video data, where (1) many of the data objects are highly similar to one another, (2) some loss of information is acceptable, and (3) a substantial reduction in the data size is desired.

- **Efficiently Finding Nearest Neighbors.** Finding nearest neighbors can require computing the pairwise distance between all points. Often clusters and their cluster prototypes can be found much more efficiently. If objects are relatively close to the prototype of their cluster, then we can use the prototypes to reduce the number of distance computations that are necessary to find the nearest neighbors of an object. Intuitively, if two cluster prototypes are far apart, then the objects in the corresponding clusters cannot be nearest neighbors of each other. Consequently, to find an object's nearest neighbors it is only necessary to compute the distance to objects in nearby clusters, where the nearness of two clusters is measured by the distance between their prototypes. This idea is made more precise in Exercise 25 on page 94.

This chapter provides an introduction to cluster analysis. We begin with a high-level overview of clustering, including a discussion of the various approaches to dividing objects into sets of clusters and the different types of clusters. We then describe three specific clustering techniques that represent broad categories of algorithms and illustrate a variety of concepts: K-means, agglomerative hierarchical clustering, and DBSCAN. The final section of this chapter is devoted to cluster validity—methods for evaluating the goodness of the clusters produced by a clustering algorithm. More advanced clustering concepts and algorithms will be discussed in Chapter 9. Whenever possible, we discuss the strengths and weaknesses of different schemes. In addition, the bibliographic notes provide references to relevant books and papers that explore cluster analysis in greater depth.

8.1   Overview

Before discussing specific clustering techniques, we provide some necessary background. First, we further define cluster analysis, illustrating why it is difficult and explaining its relationship to other techniques that group data. Then we explore two important topics: (1) different ways to group a set of objects into a set of clusters, and (2) types of clusters.

8.1.1   What Is Cluster Analysis?

Cluster analysis groups data objects based only on information found in the data that describes the objects and their relationships. The goal is that the objects within a group be similar (or related) to one another and different from (or unrelated to) the objects in other groups. The greater the similarity (or homogeneity) within a group and the greater the difference between groups, the better or more distinct the clustering.

In many applications, the notion of a cluster is not well defined. To better understand the difficulty of deciding what constitutes a cluster, consider Figure 8.1, which shows twenty points and three different ways of dividing them into clusters. The shapes of the markers indicate cluster membership. Figures 8.1(b) and 8.1(d) divide the data into two and six parts, respectively. However, the apparent division of each of the two larger clusters into three subclusters may simply be an artifact of the human visual system. Also, it may not be unreasonable to say that the points form four clusters, as shown in Figure 8.1(c). This figure illustrates that the definition of a cluster is imprecise and that the best definition depends on the nature of data and the desired results.

Cluster analysis is related to other techniques that are used to divide data objects into groups. For instance, clustering can be regarded as a form of classification in that it creates a labeling of objects with class (cluster) labels. However, it derives these labels only from the data. In contrast, classification

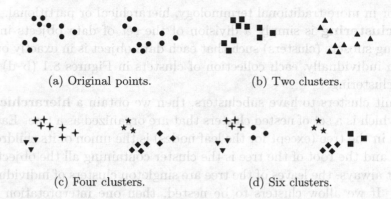

(a) Original points.   (b) Two clusters.

(c) Four clusters.   (d) Six clusters.

Figure 8.1. Different ways of clustering the same set of points.

in the sense of Chapter 4 is **supervised classification**; i.e., new, unlabeled objects are assigned a class label using a model developed from objects with known class labels. For this reason, cluster analysis is sometimes referred to as **unsupervised classification**. When the term classification is used without any qualification within data mining, it typically refers to supervised classification.

Also, while the terms **segmentation** and **partitioning** are sometimes used as synonyms for clustering, these terms are frequently used for approaches outside the traditional bounds of cluster analysis. For example, the term partitioning is often used in connection with techniques that divide graphs into subgraphs and that are not strongly connected to clustering. Segmentation often refers to the division of data into groups using simple techniques; e.g., an image can be split into segments based only on pixel intensity and color, or people can be divided into groups based on their income. Nonetheless, some work in graph partitioning and in image and market segmentation is related to cluster analysis.

8.1.2 Different Types of Clusterings

An entire collection of clusters is commonly referred to as a **clustering**, and in this section, we distinguish various types of clusterings: hierarchical (nested) versus partitional (unnested), exclusive versus overlapping versus fuzzy, and complete versus partial.

Hierarchical versus Partitional The most commonly discussed distinction among different types of clusterings is whether the set of clusters is nested or unnested, or in more traditional terminology, hierarchical or partitional. A **partitional clustering** is simply a division of the set of data objects into non-overlapping subsets (clusters) such that each data object is in exactly one subset. Taken individually, each collection of clusters in Figures 8.1 (b–d) is a partitional clustering.

If we permit clusters to have subclusters, then we obtain a **hierarchical clustering**, which is a set of nested clusters that are organized as a tree. Each node (cluster) in the tree (except for the leaf nodes) is the union of its children (subclusters), and the root of the tree is the cluster containing all the objects. Often, but not always, the leaves of the tree are singleton clusters of individual data objects. If we allow clusters to be nested, then one interpretation of Figure 8.1(a) is that it has two subclusters (Figure 8.1(b)), each of which, in turn, has three subclusters (Figure 8.1(d)). The clusters shown in Figures 8.1 (a–d), when taken in that order, also form a hierarchical (nested) clustering with, respectively, 1, 2, 4, and 6 clusters on each level. Finally, note that a hierarchical clustering can be viewed as a sequence of partitional clusterings and a partitional clustering can be obtained by taking any member of that sequence; i.e., by cutting the hierarchical tree at a particular level.

Exclusive versus Overlapping versus Fuzzy   The clusterings shown in Figure 8.1 are all **exclusive**, as they assign each object to a single cluster. There are many situations in which a point could reasonably be placed in more than one cluster, and these situations are better addressed by non-exclusive clustering. In the most general sense, an **overlapping** or **non-exclusive clustering** is used to reflect the fact that an object can *simultaneously* belong to more than one group (class). For instance, a person at a university can be both an enrolled student and an employee of the university. A non-exclusive clustering is also often used when, for example, an object is "between" two or more clusters and could reasonably be assigned to any of these clusters. Imagine a point halfway between two of the clusters of Figure 8.1. Rather than make a somewhat arbitrary assignment of the object to a single cluster, it is placed in all of the "equally good" clusters.

In a **fuzzy clustering**, every object belongs to every cluster with a membership weight that is between 0 (absolutely doesn't belong) and 1 (absolutely belongs). In other words, clusters are treated as fuzzy sets. (Mathematically, a fuzzy set is one in which an object belongs to any set with a weight that is between 0 and 1. In fuzzy clustering, we often impose the additional constraint that the sum of the weights for each object must equal 1.) Similarly, probabilistic clustering techniques compute the probability with which each point belongs to each cluster, and these probabilities must also sum to 1. Because the membership weights or probabilities for any object sum to 1, a fuzzy or probabilistic clustering does not address true multiclass situations, such as the case of a student employee, where an object belongs to multiple classes. Instead, these approaches are most appropriate for avoiding the arbitrariness of assigning an object to only one cluster when it may be close to several. In practice, a fuzzy or probabilistic clustering is often converted to an exclusive clustering by assigning each object to the cluster in which its membership weight or probability is highest.

Complete versus Partial A **complete clustering** assigns every object to a cluster, whereas a **partial clustering** does not. The motivation for a partial clustering is that some objects in a data set may not belong to well-defined groups. Many times objects in the data set may represent noise, outliers, or "uninteresting background." For example, some newspaper stories may share a common theme, such as global warming, while other stories are more generic or one-of-a-kind. Thus, to find the important topics in last month's stories, we may want to search only for clusters of documents that are tightly related by a common theme. In other cases, a complete clustering of the objects is desired. For example, an application that uses clustering to organize documents for browsing needs to guarantee that all documents can be browsed.

8.1.3 Different Types of Clusters

Clustering aims to find useful groups of objects (clusters), where usefulness is defined by the goals of the data analysis. Not surprisingly, there are several different notions of a cluster that prove useful in practice. In order to visually illustrate the differences among these types of clusters, we use two-dimensional points, as shown in Figure 8.2, as our data objects. We stress, however, that the types of clusters described here are equally valid for other kinds of data.

Well-Separated A cluster is a set of objects in which each object is closer (or more similar) to every other object in the cluster than to any object not in the cluster. Sometimes a threshold is used to specify that all the objects in a cluster must be sufficiently close (or similar) to one another. This idealistic definition of a cluster is satisfied only when the data contains natural clusters that are quite far from each other. Figure 8.2(a) gives an example of well-separated clusters that consists of two groups of points in a two-dimensional space. The distance between any two points in different groups is larger than the distance between any two points within a group. Well-separated clusters do not need to be globular, but can have any shape.

Prototype-Based   A cluster is a set of objects in which each object is closer (more similar) to the prototype that defines the cluster than to the prototype of any other cluster. For data with continuous attributes, the prototype of a cluster is often a centroid, i.e., the average (mean) of all the points in the cluster. When a centroid is not meaningful, such as when the data has categorical attributes, the prototype is often a medoid, i.e., the most representative point of a cluster. For many types of data, the prototype can be regarded as the most central point, and in such instances, we commonly refer to prototype-based clusters as **center-based clusters**. Not surprisingly, such clusters tend to be globular. Figure 8.2(b) shows an example of center-based clusters.

Graph-Based   If the data is represented as a graph, where the nodes are objects and the links represent connections among objects (see Section 2.1.2), then a cluster can be defined as a **connected component**; i.e., a group of objects that are connected to one another, but that have no connection to objects outside the group. An important example of graph-based clusters are **contiguity-based clusters**, where two objects are connected only if they are within a specified distance of each other. This implies that each object in a contiguity-based cluster is closer to some other object in the cluster than to any point in a different cluster. Figure 8.2(c) shows an example of such clusters for two-dimensional points. This definition of a cluster is useful when clusters are irregular or intertwined, but can have trouble when noise is present since, as illustrated by the two spherical clusters of Figure 8.2(c), a small bridge of points can merge two distinct clusters.

Other types of graph-based clusters are also possible. One such approach (Section 8.3.2) defines a cluster as a **clique**; i.e., a set of nodes in a graph that are completely connected to each other. Specifically, if we add connections between objects in the order of their distance from one another, a cluster is formed when a set of objects forms a clique. Like prototype-based clusters, such clusters tend to be globular.

Density-Based   A cluster is a dense region of objects that is surrounded by a region of low density. Figure 8.2(d) shows some density-based clusters for data created by adding noise to the data of Figure 8.2(c). The two circular clusters are not merged, as in Figure 8.2(c), because the bridge between them fades into the noise. Likewise, the curve that is present in Figure 8.2(c) also fades into the noise and does not form a cluster in Figure 8.2(d). A density-based definition of a cluster is often employed when the clusters are irregular or intertwined, and when noise and outliers are present. By contrast, a contiguity-based definition of a cluster would not work well for the data of Figure 8.2(d) since the noise would tend to form bridges between clusters.

Shared-Property (Conceptual Clusters)   More generally, we can define a cluster as a set of objects that share some property. This definition encompasses all the previous definitions of a cluster; e.g., objects in a center-based cluster share the property that they are all closest to the same centroid or medoid. However, the shared-property approach also includes new types of clusters. Consider the clusters shown in Figure 8.2(e). A triangular area (cluster) is adjacent to a rectangular one, and there are two intertwined circles (clusters). In both cases, a clustering algorithm would need a very specific concept of a cluster to successfully detect these clusters. The process of finding such clusters is called conceptual clustering. However, too sophisticated a notion of a cluster would take us into the area of pattern recognition, and thus, we only consider simpler types of clusters in this book.

Road Map

In this chapter, we use the following three simple, but important techniques to introduce many of the concepts involved in cluster analysis.

- **K-means**. This is a prototype-based, partitional clustering technique that attempts to find a user-specified number of clusters (K), which are represented by their centroids.

- **Agglomerative Hierarchical Clustering.** This clustering approach refers to a collection of closely related clustering techniques that produce a hierarchical clustering by starting with each point as a singleton cluster and then repeatedly merging the two closest clusters until a single, all-encompassing cluster remains. Some of these techniques have a natural interpretation in terms of graph-based clustering, while others have an interpretation in terms of a prototype-based approach.

- **DBSCAN**. This is a density-based clustering algorithm that produces a partitional clustering, in which the number of clusters is automatically determined by the algorithm. Points in low-density regions are classified as noise and omitted; thus, DBSCAN does not produce a complete clustering.

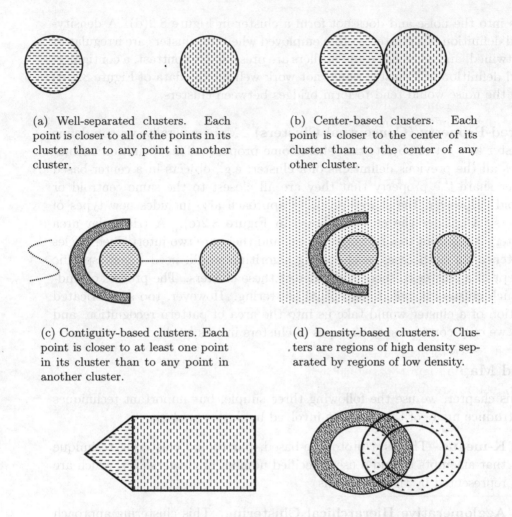

(a) Well-separated clusters. Each point is closer to all of the points in its cluster than to any point in another cluster.

(b) Center-based clusters. Each point is closer to the center of its cluster than to the center of any other cluster.

(c) Contiguity-based clusters. Each point is closer to at least one point in its cluster than to any point in another cluster.

(d) Density-based clusters. Clusters are regions of high density separated by regions of low density.

(e) Conceptual clusters. Points in a cluster share some general property that derives from the entire set of points. (Points in the intersection of the circles belong to both.)

Figure 8.2. Different types of clusters as illustrated by sets of two-dimensional points.

8.2 K-means

Prototype-based clustering techniques create a one-level partitioning of the data objects. There are a number of such techniques, but two of the most prominent are K-means and K-medoid. K-means defines a prototype in terms of a centroid, which is usually the mean of a group of points, and is typically applied to objects in a continuous n-dimensional space. K-medoid defines a prototype in terms of a medoid, which is the most representative point for a group of points, and can be applied to a wide range of data since it requires only a proximity measure for a pair of objects. While a centroid almost never corresponds to an actual data point, a medoid, by its definition, must be an actual data point. In this section, we will focus solely on K-means, which is one of the oldest and most widely used clustering algorithms.

8.2.1   The Basic K-means Algorithm

The K-means clustering technique is simple, and we begin with a description of the basic algorithm. We first choose K initial centroids, where K is a user-specified parameter, namely, the number of clusters desired. Each point is then assigned to the closest centroid, and each collection of points assigned to a centroid is a cluster. The centroid of each cluster is then updated based on the points assigned to the cluster. We repeat the assignment and update steps until no point changes clusters, or equivalently, until the centroids remain the same.

K-means is formally described by Algorithm 8.1. The operation of K-means is illustrated in Figure 8.3, which shows how, starting from three centroids, the final clusters are found in four assignment-update steps. In these and other figures displaying K-means clustering, each subfigure shows (1) the centroids at the start of the iteration and (2) the assignment of the points to those centroids. The centroids are indicated by the "+" symbol; all points belonging to the same cluster have the same marker shape.

Algorithm 8.1 Basic K-means algorithm.

1: Select K points as initial centroids.
2: **repeat**
3:     Form K clusters by assigning each point to its closest centroid.
4:     Recompute the centroid of each cluster.
5: **until** Centroids do not change.

In the first step, shown in Figure 8.3(a), points are assigned to the initial centroids, which are all in the larger group of points. For this example, we use the mean as the centroid. After points are assigned to a centroid, the centroid is then updated. Again, the figure for each step shows the centroid at the beginning of the step and the assignment of points to those centroids. In the second step, points are assigned to the updated centroids, and the centroids

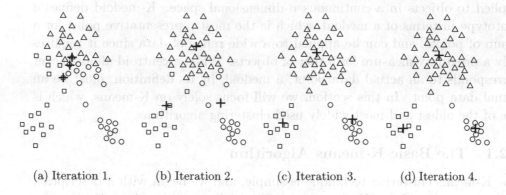

(a) Iteration 1.   (b) Iteration 2.   (c) Iteration 3.   (d) Iteration 4.

Figure 8.3. Using the K-means algorithm to find three clusters in sample data.

are updated again. In steps 2, 3, and 4, which are shown in Figures 8.3 (b), (c), and (d), respectively, two of the centroids move to the two small groups of points at the bottom of the figures. When the K-means algorithm terminates in Figure 8.3(d), because no more changes occur, the centroids have identified the natural groupings of points.

For some combinations of proximity functions and types of centroids, K-means always converges to a solution; i.e., K-means reaches a state in which no points are shifting from one cluster to another, and hence, the centroids don't change. Because most of the convergence occurs in the early steps, however, the condition on line 5 of Algorithm 8.1 is often replaced by a weaker condition, e.g., repeat until only 1% of the points change clusters.

We consider each of the steps in the basic K-means algorithm in more detail and then provide an analysis of the algorithm's space and time complexity.

Assigning Points to the Closest Centroid

To assign a point to the closest centroid, we need a proximity measure that quantifies the notion of "closest" for the specific data under consideration. Euclidean (L_2) distance is often used for data points in Euclidean space, while cosine similarity is more appropriate for documents. However, there may be several types of proximity measures that are appropriate for a given type of data. For example, Manhattan (L_1) distance can be used for Euclidean data, while the Jaccard measure is often employed for documents.

Usually, the similarity measures used for K-means are relatively simple since the algorithm repeatedly calculates the similarity of each point to each centroid. In some cases, however, such as when the data is in low-dimensional

Table 8.1. Table of notation.

Symbol	Description
$\mathbf{x}$	An object.
C_i	The ith cluster.
$\mathbf{c}_i$	The centroid of cluster C_i.
$\mathbf{c}$	The centroid of all points.
m_i	The number of objects in the ith cluster.
m	The number of objects in the data set.
K	The number of clusters.

Euclidean space, it is possible to avoid computing many of the similarities, thus significantly speeding up the K-means algorithm. Bisecting K-means (described in Section 8.2.3) is another approach that speeds up K-means by reducing the number of similarities computed.

Centroids and Objective Functions

Step 4 of the K-means algorithm was stated rather generally as "recompute the centroid of each cluster," since the centroid can vary, depending on the proximity measure for the data and the goal of the clustering. The goal of the clustering is typically expressed by an objective function that depends on the proximities of the points to one another or to the cluster centroids; e.g., minimize the squared distance of each point to its closest centroid. We illustrate this with two examples. However, the key point is this: once we have specified a proximity measure and an objective function, the centroid that we should choose can often be determined mathematically. We provide mathematical details in Section 8.2.6, and provide a non-mathematical discussion of this observation here.

Data in Euclidean Space Consider data whose proximity measure is Euclidean distance. For our objective function, which measures the quality of a clustering, we use the **sum of the squared error (SSE)**, which is also known as scatter. In other words, we calculate the error of each data point, i.e., its Euclidean distance to the closest centroid, and then compute the total sum of the squared errors. Given two different sets of clusters that are produced by two different runs of K-means, we prefer the one with the smallest squared error since this means that the prototypes (centroids) of this clustering are a better representation of the points in their cluster. Using the notation in Table 8.1, the SSE is formally defined as follows:

$$\text{SSE} = \sum_{i=1}^{K} \sum_{x \in C_i} dist(c_i, x)^2 \tag{8.1}$$

where $dist$ is the standard Euclidean (L_2) distance between two objects in Euclidean space.

Given these assumptions, it can be shown (see Section 8.2.6) that the centroid that minimizes the SSE of the cluster is the mean. Using the notation in Table 8.1, the centroid (mean) of the ith cluster is defined by Equation 8.2.

$$c_i = \frac{1}{m_i} \sum_{x \in C_i} x \tag{8.2}$$

To illustrate, the centroid of a cluster containing the three two-dimensional points, (1,1), (2,3), and (6,2), is $((1+2+6)/3, ((1+3+2)/3) = (3,2)$.

Steps 3 and 4 of the K-means algorithm directly attempt to minimize the SSE (or more generally, the objective function). Step 3 forms clusters by assigning points to their nearest centroid, which minimizes the SSE for the given set of centroids. Step 4 recomputes the centroids so as to further minimize the SSE. However, the actions of K-means in Steps 3 and 4 are only guaranteed to find a local minimum with respect to the SSE since they are based on optimizing the SSE for specific choices of the centroids and clusters, rather than for all possible choices. We will later see an example in which this leads to a suboptimal clustering.

Document Data   To illustrate that K-means is not restricted to data in Euclidean space, we consider document data and the cosine similarity measure. Here we assume that the document data is represented as a document-term matrix as described on page 31. Our objective is to maximize the similarity of the documents in a cluster to the cluster centroid; this quantity is known as the **cohesion** of the cluster. For this objective it can be shown that the cluster centroid is, as for Euclidean data, the mean. The analogous quantity to the total SSE is the total cohesion, which is given by Equation 8.3.

$$\text{Total Cohesion} = \sum_{i=1}^{K} \sum_{x \in C_i} cosine(x, c_i) \tag{8.3}$$

The General Case   There are a number of choices for the proximity function, centroid, and objective function that can be used in the basic K-means

Table 8.2. K-means: Common choices for proximity, centroids, and objective functions.

Proximity Function	Centroid	Objective Function
Manhattan (L_1)	median	Minimize sum of the L_1 distance of an object to its cluster centroid
Squared Euclidean (L_2^2)	mean	Minimize sum of the squared L_2 distance of an object to its cluster centroid
cosine	mean	Maximize sum of the cosine similarity of an object to its cluster centroid
Bregman divergence	mean	Minimize sum of the Bregman divergence of an object to its cluster centroid

algorithm and that are guaranteed to converge. Table 8.2 shows some possible choices, including the two that we have just discussed. Notice that for Manhattan (L_1) distance and the objective of minimizing the sum of the distances, the appropriate centroid is the median of the points in a cluster.

The last entry in the table, Bregman divergence (Section 2.4.5), is actually a class of proximity measures that includes the squared Euclidean distance, L_2^2, the Mahalanobis distance, and cosine similarity. The importance of Bregman divergence functions is that any such function can be used as the basis of a K-means style clustering algorithm with the mean as the centroid. Specifically, if we use a Bregman divergence as our proximity function, then the resulting clustering algorithm has the usual properties of K-means with respect to convergence, local minima, etc. Furthermore, the properties of such a clustering algorithm can be developed for all possible Bregman divergences. Indeed, K-means algorithms that use cosine similarity or squared Euclidean distance are particular instances of a general clustering algorithm based on Bregman divergences.

For the rest our K-means discussion, we use two-dimensional data since it is easy to explain K-means and its properties for this type of data. But, as suggested by the last few paragraphs, K-means is a very general clustering algorithm and can be used with a wide variety of data types, such as documents and time series.

Choosing Initial Centroids

When random initialization of centroids is used, different runs of K-means typically produce different total SSEs. We illustrate this with the set of two-dimensional points shown in Figure 8.3, which has three natural clusters of points. Figure 8.4(a) shows a clustering solution that is the global minimum of

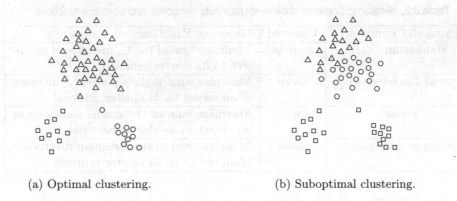

(a) Optimal clustering.   (b) Suboptimal clustering.

Figure 8.4. Three optimal and non-optimal clusters.

the SSE for three clusters, while Figure 8.4(b) shows a suboptimal clustering that is only a local minimum.

Choosing the proper initial centroids is the key step of the basic K-means procedure. A common approach is to choose the initial centroids randomly, but the resulting clusters are often poor.

Example 8.1 (Poor Initial Centroids). Randomly selected initial centroids may be poor. We provide an example of this using the same data set used in Figures 8.3 and 8.4. Figures 8.3 and 8.5 show the clusters that result from two particular choices of initial centroids. (For both figures, the positions of the cluster centroids in the various iterations are indicated by crosses.) In Figure 8.3, even though all the initial centroids are from one natural cluster, the minimum SSE clustering is still found. In Figure 8.5, however, even though the initial centroids seem to be better distributed, we obtain a suboptimal clustering, with higher squared error.   ∎

Example 8.2 (Limits of Random Initialization). One technique that is commonly used to address the problem of choosing initial centroids is to perform multiple runs, each with a different set of randomly chosen initial centroids, and then select the set of clusters with the minimum SSE. While simple, this strategy may not work very well, depending on the data set and the number of clusters sought. We demonstrate this using the sample data set shown in Figure 8.6(a). The data consists of two pairs of clusters, where the clusters in each (top-bottom) pair are closer to each other than to the clusters in the other pair. Figure 8.6 (b–d) shows that if we start with two initial centroids per pair of clusters, then even when both centroids are in a single

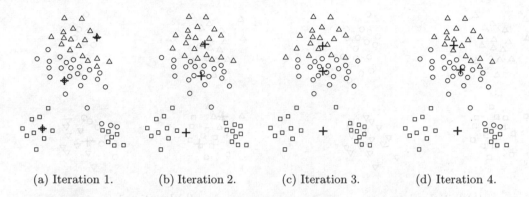

Figure 8.5. Poor starting centroids for K-means.

cluster, the centroids will redistribute themselves so that the "true" clusters are found. However, Figure 8.7 shows that if a pair of clusters has only one initial centroid and the other pair has three, then two of the true clusters will be combined and one true cluster will be split.

Note that an optimal clustering will be obtained as long as two initial centroids fall anywhere in a pair of clusters, since the centroids will redistribute themselves, one to each cluster. Unfortunately, as the number of clusters becomes larger, it is increasingly likely that at least one pair of clusters will have only one initial centroid. (See Exercise 4 on page 559.) In this case, because the pairs of clusters are farther apart than clusters within a pair, the K-means algorithm will not redistribute the centroids between pairs of clusters, and thus, only a local minimum will be achieved. ∎

Because of the problems with using randomly selected initial centroids, which even repeated runs may not overcome, other techniques are often employed for initialization. One effective approach is to take a sample of points and cluster them using a hierarchical clustering technique. K clusters are extracted from the hierarchical clustering, and the centroids of those clusters are used as the initial centroids. This approach often works well, but is practical only if (1) the sample is relatively small, e.g., a few hundred to a few thousand (hierarchical clustering is expensive), and (2) K is relatively small compared to the sample size.

The following procedure is another approach to selecting initial centroids. Select the first point at random or take the centroid of all points. Then, for each successive initial centroid, select the point that is farthest from any of the initial centroids already selected. In this way, we obtain a set of initial

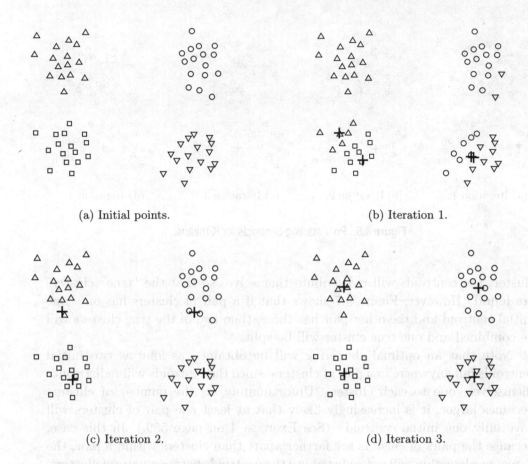

(a) Initial points.

(b) Iteration 1.

(c) Iteration 2.

(d) Iteration 3.

Figure 8.6. Two pairs of clusters with a pair of initial centroids within each pair of clusters.

centroids that is guaranteed to be not only randomly selected but also well separated. Unfortunately, such an approach can select outliers, rather than points in dense regions (clusters). Also, it is expensive to compute the farthest point from the current set of initial centroids. To overcome these problems, this approach is often applied to a sample of the points. Since outliers are rare, they tend not to show up in a random sample. In contrast, points from every dense region are likely to be included unless the sample size is very small. Also, the computation involved in finding the initial centroids is greatly reduced because the sample size is typically much smaller than the number of points.

Later on, we will discuss two other approaches that are useful for producing better-quality (lower SSE) clusterings: using a variant of K-means that

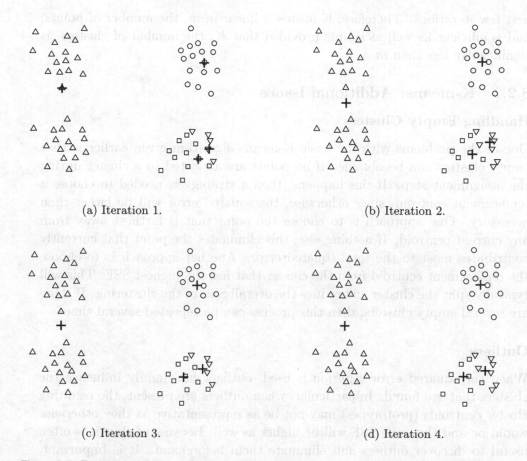

(a) Iteration 1.

(b) Iteration 2.

(c) Iteration 3.

(d) Iteration 4.

Figure 8.7. Two pairs of clusters with more or fewer than two initial centroids within a pair of clusters.

is less susceptible to initialization problems (bisecting K-means) and using postprocessing to "fixup" the set of clusters produced.

Time and Space Complexity

The space requirements for K-means are modest because only the data points and centroids are stored. Specifically, the storage required is $O((m + K)n)$, where m is the number of points and n is the number of attributes. The time requirements for K-means are also modest—basically linear in the number of data points. In particular, the time required is $O(I * K * m * n)$, where I is the number of iterations required for convergence. As mentioned, I is often small and can usually be safely bounded, as most changes typically occur in the first few iterations. Therefore, K-means is linear in m, the number of points, and is efficient as well as simple provided that K, the number of clusters, is significantly less than m.

8.2.2   K-means: Additional Issues

Handling Empty Clusters

One of the problems with the basic K-means algorithm given earlier is that empty clusters can be obtained if no points are allocated to a cluster during the assignment step. If this happens, then a strategy is needed to choose a replacement centroid, since otherwise, the squared error will be larger than necessary. One approach is to choose the point that is farthest away from any current centroid. If nothing else, this eliminates the point that currently contributes most to the total squared error. Another approach is to choose the replacement centroid from the cluster that has the highest SSE. This will typically split the cluster and reduce the overall SSE of the clustering. If there are several empty clusters, then this process can be repeated several times.

Outliers

When the squared error criterion is used, outliers can unduly influence the clusters that are found. In particular, when outliers are present, the resulting cluster centroids (prototypes) may not be as representative as they otherwise would be and thus, the SSE will be higher as well. Because of this, it is often useful to discover outliers and eliminate them beforehand. It is important, however, to appreciate that there are certain clustering applications for which outliers should not be eliminated. When clustering is used for data compression, every point must be clustered, and in some cases, such as financial analysis, apparent outliers, e.g., unusually profitable customers, can be the most interesting points.

An obvious issue is how to identify outliers. A number of techniques for identifying outliers will be discussed in Chapter 10. If we use approaches that remove outliers before clustering, we avoid clustering points that will not cluster well. Alternatively, outliers can also be identified in a postprocessing step. For instance, we can keep track of the SSE contributed by each point, and eliminate those points with unusually high contributions, especially over multiple runs. Also, we may want to eliminate small clusters since they frequently represent groups of outliers.

Reducing the SSE with Postprocessing

An obvious way to reduce the SSE is to find more clusters, i.e., to use a larger K. However, in many cases, we would like to improve the SSE, but don't want to increase the number of clusters. This is often possible because K-means typically converges to a local minimum. Various techniques are used to "fix up" the resulting clusters in order to produce a clustering that has lower SSE. The strategy is to focus on individual clusters since the total SSE is simply the sum of the SSE contributed by each cluster. (We will use the terminology *total SSE* and *cluster SSE*, respectively, to avoid any potential confusion.) We can change the total SSE by performing various operations on the clusters, such as splitting or merging clusters. One commonly used approach is to use alternate cluster splitting and merging phases. During a splitting phase, clusters are divided, while during a merging phase, clusters are combined. In this way, it is often possible to escape local SSE minima and still produce a clustering solution with the desired number of clusters. The following are some techniques used in the splitting and merging phases.

Two strategies that decrease the total SSE by increasing the number of clusters are the following:

Split a cluster: The cluster with the largest SSE is usually chosen, but we could also split the cluster with the largest standard deviation for one particular attribute.

Introduce a new cluster centroid: Often the point that is farthest from any cluster center is chosen. We can easily determine this if we keep track of the SSE contributed by each point. Another approach is to choose randomly from all points or from the points with the highest SSE.

Two strategies that decrease the number of clusters, while trying to minimize the increase in total SSE, are the following:

Disperse a cluster: This is accomplished by removing the centroid that corresponds to the cluster and reassigning the points to other clusters. Ideally, the cluster that is dispersed should be the one that increases the total SSE the least.

Merge two clusters: The clusters with the closest centroids are typically chosen, although another, perhaps better, approach is to merge the two clusters that result in the smallest increase in total SSE. These two merging strategies are the same ones that are used in the hierarchical clustering techniques known as the centroid method and Ward's method, respectively. Both methods are discussed in Section 8.3.

Updating Centroids Incrementally

Instead of updating cluster centroids after all points have been assigned to a cluster, the centroids can be updated incrementally, after each assignment of a point to a cluster. Notice that this requires either zero or two updates to cluster centroids at each step, since a point either moves to a new cluster (two updates) or stays in its current cluster (zero updates). Using an incremental update strategy guarantees that empty clusters are not produced since all clusters start with a single point, and if a cluster ever has only one point, then that point will always be reassigned to the same cluster.

In addition, if incremental updating is used, the relative weight of the point being added may be adjusted; e.g., the weight of points is often decreased as the clustering proceeds. While this can result in better accuracy and faster convergence, it can be difficult to make a good choice for the relative weight, especially in a wide variety of situations. These update issues are similar to those involved in updating weights for artificial neural networks.

Yet another benefit of incremental updates has to do with using objectives other than "minimize SSE." Suppose that we are given an arbitrary objective function to measure the goodness of a set of clusters. When we process an individual point, we can compute the value of the objective function for each possible cluster assignment, and then choose the one that optimizes the objective. Specific examples of alternative objective functions are given in Section 8.5.2.

On the negative side, updating centroids incrementally introduces an order dependency. In other words, the clusters produced may depend on the order in which the points are processed. Although this can be addressed by randomizing the order in which the points are processed, the basic K-means approach of updating the centroids after all points have been assigned to clusters has no order dependency. Also, incremental updates are slightly more expensive. However, K-means converges rather quickly, and therefore, the number of points switching clusters quickly becomes relatively small.

8.2.3 Bisecting K-means

The bisecting K-means algorithm is a straightforward extension of the basic K-means algorithm that is based on a simple idea: to obtain K clusters, split the set of all points into two clusters, select one of these clusters to split, and so on, until K clusters have been produced. The details of bisecting K-means are given by Algorithm 8.2.

Algorithm 8.2 Bisecting K-means algorithm.
1: Initialize the list of clusters to contain the cluster consisting of all points.
2: **repeat**
3:    Remove a cluster from the list of clusters.
4:    {Perform several "trial" bisections of the chosen cluster.}
5:    **for** $i = 1$ to *number of trials* **do**
6:      Bisect the selected cluster using basic K-means.
7:    **end for**
8:    Select the two clusters from the bisection with the lowest total SSE.
9:    Add these two clusters to the list of clusters.
10: **until** Until the list of clusters contains K clusters.

There are a number of different ways to choose which cluster to split. We can choose the largest cluster at each step, choose the one with the largest SSE, or use a criterion based on both size and SSE. Different choices result in different clusters.

We often refine the resulting clusters by using their centroids as the initial centroids for the basic K-means algorithm. This is necessary because, although the K-means algorithm is guaranteed to find a clustering that represents a local minimum with respect to the SSE, in bisecting K-means we are using the K-means algorithm "locally," i.e., to bisect individual clusters. Therefore, the final set of clusters does not represent a clustering that is a local minimum with respect to the total SSE.

Example 8.3 (Bisecting K-means and Initialization). To illustrate that bisecting K-means is less susceptible to initialization problems, we show, in Figure 8.8, how bisecting K-means finds four clusters in the data set originally shown in Figure 8.6(a). In iteration 1, two pairs of clusters are found; in iteration 2, the rightmost pair of clusters is split; and in iteration 3, the leftmost pair of clusters is split. Bisecting K-means has less trouble with initialization because it performs several trial bisections and takes the one with the lowest SSE, and because there are only two centroids at each step. ∎

Finally, by recording the sequence of clusterings produced as K-means bisects clusters, we can also use bisecting K-means to produce a hierarchical clustering.

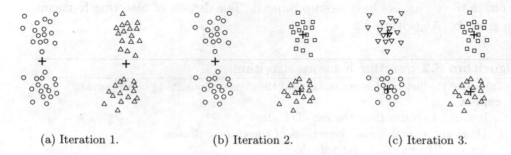

(a) Iteration 1.   (b) Iteration 2.   (c) Iteration 3.

Figure 8.8. Bisecting K-means on the four clusters example.

8.2.4 K-means and Different Types of Clusters

K-means and its variations have a number of limitations with respect to finding different types of clusters. In particular, K-means has difficulty detecting the "natural" clusters, when clusters have non-spherical shapes or widely different sizes or densities. This is illustrated by Figures 8.9, 8.10, and 8.11. In Figure 8.9, K-means cannot find the three natural clusters because one of the clusters is much larger than the other two, and hence, the larger cluster is broken, while one of the smaller clusters is combined with a portion of the larger cluster. In Figure 8.10, K-means fails to find the three natural clusters because the two smaller clusters are much denser than the larger cluster. Finally, in Figure 8.11, K-means finds two clusters that mix portions of the two natural clusters because the shape of the natural clusters is not globular.

The difficulty in these three situations is that the K-means objective function is a mismatch for the kinds of clusters we are trying to find since it is minimized by globular clusters of equal size and density or by clusters that are well separated. However, these limitations can be overcome, in some sense, if the user is willing to accept a clustering that breaks the natural clusters into a number of subclusters. Figure 8.12 shows what happens to the three previous data sets if we find six clusters instead of two or three. Each smaller cluster is pure in the sense that it contains only points from one of the natural clusters.

8.2.5 Strengths and Weaknesses

K-means is simple and can be used for a wide variety of data types. It is also quite efficient, even though multiple runs are often performed. Some variants, including bisecting K-means, are even more efficient, and are less susceptible to initialization problems. K-means is not suitable for all types of data,

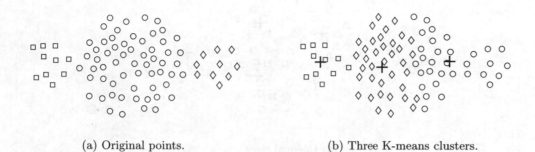

(a) Original points.　　　　　　(b) Three K-means clusters.

Figure 8.9. K-means with clusters of different size.

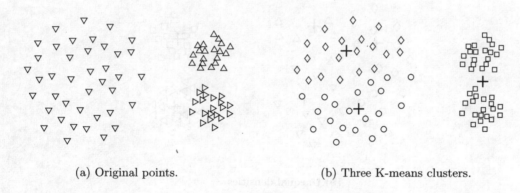

(a) Original points.　　　　　　(b) Three K-means clusters.

Figure 8.10. K-means with clusters of different density.

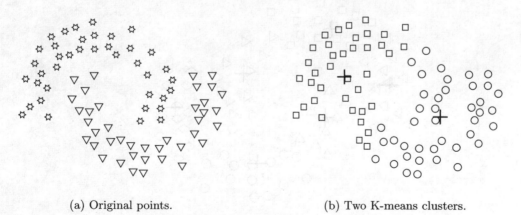

(a) Original points.　　　　　　(b) Two K-means clusters.

Figure 8.11. K-means with non-globular clusters.

(a) Unequal sizes.

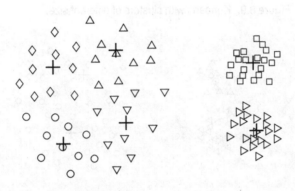

(b) Unequal densities.

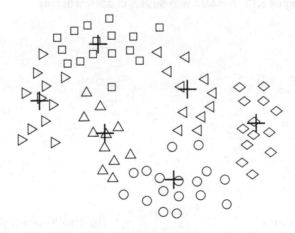

(c) Non-spherical shapes.

Figure 8.12. Using K-means to find clusters that are subclusters of the natural clusters.

however. It cannot handle non-globular clusters or clusters of different sizes and densities, although it can typically find pure subclusters if a large enough number of clusters is specified. K-means also has trouble clustering data that contains outliers. Outlier detection and removal can help significantly in such situations. Finally, K-means is restricted to data for which there is a notion of a center (centroid). A related technique, K-medoid clustering, does not have this restriction, but is more expensive.

8.2.6   K-means as an Optimization Problem

Here, we delve into the mathematics behind K-means. This section, which can be skipped without loss of continuity, requires knowledge of calculus through partial derivatives. Familiarity with optimization techniques, especially those based on gradient descent, may also be helpful.

As mentioned earlier, given an objective function such as "minimize SSE," clustering can be treated as an optimization problem. One way to solve this problem—to find a global optimum—is to enumerate all possible ways of dividing the points into clusters and then choose the set of clusters that best satisfies the objective function, e.g., that minimizes the total SSE. Of course, this exhaustive strategy is computationally infeasible and as a result, a more practical approach is needed, even if such an approach finds solutions that are not guaranteed to be optimal. One technique, which is known as **gradient descent**, is based on picking an initial solution and then repeating the following two steps: compute the change to the solution that best optimizes the objective function and then update the solution.

We assume that the data is one-dimensional, i.e., $dist(x, y) = (x - y)^2$. This does not change anything essential, but greatly simplifies the notation.

Derivation of K-means as an Algorithm to Minimize the SSE

In this section, we show how the centroid for the K-means algorithm can be mathematically derived when the proximity function is Euclidean distance and the objective is to minimize the SSE. Specifically, we investigate how we can best update a cluster centroid so that the cluster SSE is minimized. In mathematical terms, we seek to minimize Equation 8.1, which we repeat here, specialized for one-dimensional data.

$$\text{SSE} = \sum_{i=1}^{K} \sum_{x \in C_i} (c_i - x)^2 \tag{8.4}$$

Here, C_i is the ith cluster, x is a point in C_i, and c_i is the mean of the ith cluster. See Table 8.1 for a complete list of notation.

We can solve for the kth centroid c_k, which minimizes Equation 8.4, by differentiating the SSE, setting it equal to 0, and solving, as indicated below.

$$
\frac{\partial}{\partial c_k}\text{SSE} = \frac{\partial}{\partial c_k}\sum_{i=1}^{K}\sum_{x \in C_i}(c_i - x)^2
$$

$$
= \sum_{i=1}^{K}\sum_{x \in C_i}\frac{\partial}{\partial c_k}(c_i - x)^2
$$

$$
= \sum_{x \in C_k} 2 * (c_k - x_k) = 0
$$

$$
\sum_{x \in C_k} 2 * (c_k - x_k) = 0 \Rightarrow m_k c_k = \sum_{x \in C_k} x_k \Rightarrow c_k = \frac{1}{m_k}\sum_{x \in C_k} x_k
$$

Thus, as previously indicated, the best centroid for minimizing the SSE of a cluster is the mean of the points in the cluster.

Derivation of K-means for SAE

To demonstrate that the K-means algorithm can be applied to a variety of different objective functions, we consider how to partition the data into K clusters such that the sum of the Manhattan (L_1) distances of points from the center of their clusters is minimized. We are seeking to minimize the sum of the L_1 absolute errors (SAE) as given by the following equation, where $dist_{L_1}$ is the L_1 distance. Again, for notational simplicity, we use one-dimensional data, i.e., $dist_{L_1} = |c_i - x|$.

$$
\text{SAE} = \sum_{i=1}^{K}\sum_{x \in C_i} dist_{L_1}(c_i, x) \tag{8.5}
$$

We can solve for the kth centroid c_k, which minimizes Equation 8.5, by differentiating the SAE, setting it equal to 0, and solving.

$$\frac{\partial}{\partial c_k}\text{SAE} = \frac{\partial}{\partial c_k}\sum_{i=1}^{K}\sum_{x \in C_i}|c_i - x|$$

$$= \sum_{i=1}^{K}\sum_{x \in C_i}\frac{\partial}{\partial c_k}|c_i - x|$$

$$= \sum_{x \in C_k}\frac{\partial}{\partial c_k}|c_k - x| = 0$$

$$\sum_{x \in C_k}\frac{\partial}{\partial c_k}|c_k - x| = 0 \Rightarrow \sum_{x \in C_k}sign(x - c_k) = 0$$

If we solve for c_k, we find that $c_k = median\{x \in C_k\}$, the median of the points in the cluster. The median of a group of points is straightforward to compute and less susceptible to distortion by outliers.

8.3   Agglomerative Hierarchical Clustering

Hierarchical clustering techniques are a second important category of clustering methods. As with K-means, these approaches are relatively old compared to many clustering algorithms, but they still enjoy widespread use. There are two basic approaches for generating a hierarchical clustering:

Agglomerative: Start with the points as individual clusters and, at each step, merge the closest pair of clusters. This requires defining a notion of cluster proximity.

Divisive: Start with one, all-inclusive cluster and, at each step, split a cluster until only singleton clusters of individual points remain. In this case, we need to decide which cluster to split at each step and how to do the splitting.

Agglomerative hierarchical clustering techniques are by far the most common, and, in this section, we will focus exclusively on these methods. A divisive hierarchical clustering technique is described in Section 9.4.2.

A hierarchical clustering is often displayed graphically using a tree-like diagram called a **dendrogram**, which displays both the cluster-subcluster

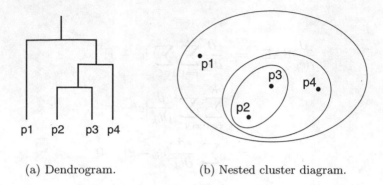

|(a) Dendrogram.|(b) Nested cluster diagram.|

Figure 8.13. A hierarchical clustering of four points shown as a dendrogram and as nested clusters.

relationships and the order in which the clusters were merged (agglomerative view) or split (divisive view). For sets of two-dimensional points, such as those that we will use as examples, a hierarchical clustering can also be graphically represented using a nested cluster diagram. Figure 8.13 shows an example of these two types of figures for a set of four two-dimensional points. These points were clustered using the single-link technique that is described in Section 8.3.2.

8.3.1   Basic Agglomerative Hierarchical Clustering Algorithm

Many agglomerative hierarchical clustering techniques are variations on a single approach: starting with individual points as clusters, successively merge the two closest clusters until only one cluster remains. This approach is expressed more formally in Algorithm 8.3.

Algorithm 8.3 Basic agglomerative hierarchical clustering algorithm.

1: Compute the proximity matrix, if necessary.
2: **repeat**
3:    Merge the closest two clusters.
4:    Update the proximity matrix to reflect the proximity between the new cluster and the original clusters.
5: **until** Only one cluster remains.

Defining Proximity between Clusters

The key operation of Algorithm 8.3 is the computation of the proximity between two clusters, and it is the definition of cluster proximity that differentiates the various agglomerative hierarchical techniques that we will discuss. Cluster proximity is typically defined with a particular type of cluster in mind—see Section 8.1.2. For example, many agglomerative hierarchical clustering techniques, such as MIN, MAX, and Group Average, come from a graph-based view of clusters. **MIN** defines cluster proximity as the proximity between the closest two points that are in different clusters, or using graph terms, the shortest edge between two nodes in different subsets of nodes. This yields contiguity-based clusters as shown in Figure 8.2(c). Alternatively, **MAX** takes the proximity between the farthest two points in different clusters to be the cluster proximity, or using graph terms, the longest edge between two nodes in different subsets of nodes. (If our proximities are distances, then the names, MIN and MAX, are short and suggestive. For similarities, however, where higher values indicate closer points, the names seem reversed. For that reason, we usually prefer to use the alternative names, **single link** and **complete link**, respectively.) Another graph-based approach, the **group average** technique, defines cluster proximity to be the average pairwise proximities (average length of edges) of all pairs of points from different clusters. Figure 8.14 illustrates these three approaches.

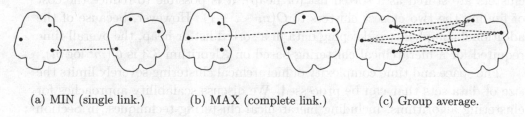

(a) MIN (single link.)   (b) MAX (complete link.)   (c) Group average.

Figure 8.14. Graph-based definitions of cluster proximity

If, instead, we take a prototype-based view, in which each cluster is represented by a centroid, different definitions of cluster proximity are more natural. When using centroids, the cluster proximity is commonly defined as the proximity between cluster centroids. An alternative technique, **Ward's** method, also assumes that a cluster is represented by its centroid, but it measures the proximity between two clusters in terms of the increase in the SSE that results from merging the two clusters. Like K-means, Ward's method attempts to minimize the sum of the squared distances of points from their cluster centroids.

Time and Space Complexity

The basic agglomerative hierarchical clustering algorithm just presented uses a proximity matrix. This requires the storage of $\frac{1}{2}m^2$ proximities (assuming the proximity matrix is symmetric) where m is the number of data points. The space needed to keep track of the clusters is proportional to the number of clusters, which is $m-1$, excluding singleton clusters. Hence, the total space complexity is $O(m^2)$.

The analysis of the basic agglomerative hierarchical clustering algorithm is also straightforward with respect to computational complexity. $O(m^2)$ time is required to compute the proximity matrix. After that step, there are $m-1$ iterations involving steps 3 and 4 because there are m clusters at the start and two clusters are merged during each iteration. If performed as a linear search of the proximity matrix, then for the ith iteration, step 3 requires $O((m-i+1)^2)$ time, which is proportional to the current number of clusters squared. Step 4 only requires $O(m-i+1)$ time to update the proximity matrix after the merger of two clusters. (A cluster merger affects only $O(m-i+1)$ proximities for the techniques that we consider.) Without modification, this would yield a time complexity of $O(m^3)$. If the distances from each cluster to all other clusters are stored as a sorted list (or heap), it is possible to reduce the cost of finding the two closest clusters to $O(m-i+1)$. However, because of the additional complexity of keeping data in a sorted list or heap, the overall time required for a hierarchical clustering based on Algorithm 8.3 is $O(m^2 \log m)$.

The space and time complexity of hierarchical clustering severely limits the size of data sets that can be processed. We discuss scalability approaches for clustering algorithms, including hierarchical clustering techniques, in Section 9.5.

8.3.2   Specific Techniques

Sample Data

To illustrate the behavior of the various hierarchical clustering algorithms, we shall use sample data that consists of 6 two-dimensional points, which are shown in Figure 8.15. The x and y coordinates of the points and the Euclidean distances between them are shown in Tables 8.3 and 8.4, respectively.

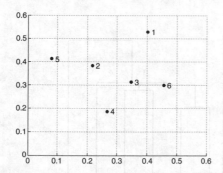

Figure 8.15. Set of 6 two-dimensional points.

Table 8.3. xy coordinates of 6 points.

Point	x Coordinate	y Coordinate
p1	0.40	0.53
p2	0.22	0.38
p3	0.35	0.32
p4	0.26	0.19
p5	0.08	0.41
p6	0.45	0.30

	p1	p2	p3	p4	p5	p6
p1	0.00	0.24	0.22	0.37	0.34	0.23
p2	0.24	0.00	0.15	0.20	0.14	0.25
p3	0.22	0.15	0.00	0.15	0.28	0.11
p4	0.37	0.20	0.15	0.00	0.29	0.22
p5	0.34	0.14	0.28	0.29	0.00	0.39
p6	0.23	0.25	0.11	0.22	0.39	0.00

Table 8.4. Euclidean distance matrix for 6 points.

Single Link or MIN

For the single link or MIN version of hierarchical clustering, the proximity of two clusters is defined as the minimum of the distance (maximum of the similarity) between any two points in the two different clusters. Using graph terminology, if you start with all points as singleton clusters and add links between points one at a time, shortest links first, then these single links combine the points into clusters. The single link technique is good at handling non-elliptical shapes, but is sensitive to noise and outliers.

Example 8.4 (Single Link). Figure 8.16 shows the result of applying the single link technique to our example data set of six points. Figure 8.16(a) shows the nested clusters as a sequence of nested ellipses, where the numbers associated with the ellipses indicate the order of the clustering. Figure 8.16(b) shows the same information, but as a dendrogram. The height at which two clusters are merged in the dendrogram reflects the distance of the two clusters. For instance, from Table 8.4, we see that the distance between points 3 and 6

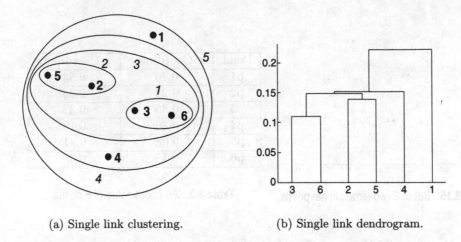

(a) Single link clustering.   (b) Single link dendrogram.

Figure 8.16. Single link clustering of the six points shown in Figure 8.15.

is 0.11, and that is the height at which they are joined into one cluster in the dendrogram. As another example, the distance between clusters $\{3, 6\}$ and $\{2, 5\}$ is given by

$$
\begin{aligned}
dist(\{3, 6\}, \{2, 5\}) &= \min(dist(3, 2), dist(6, 2), dist(3, 5), dist(6, 5)) \\
&= \min(0.15, 0.25, 0.28, 0.39) \\
&= 0.15.
\end{aligned}
$$

Complete Link or MAX or CLIQUE

For the complete link or MAX version of hierarchical clustering, the proximity of two clusters is defined as the maximum of the distance (minimum of the similarity) between any two points in the two different clusters. Using graph terminology, if you start with all points as singleton clusters and add links between points one at a time, shortest links first, then a group of points is not a cluster until all the points in it are completely linked, i.e., form a *clique*. Complete link is less susceptible to noise and outliers, but it can break large clusters and it favors globular shapes.

Example 8.5 (Complete Link). Figure 8.17 shows the results of applying MAX to the sample data set of six points. As with single link, points 3 and 6

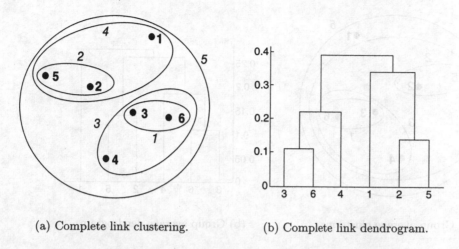

(a) Complete link clustering.   (b) Complete link dendrogram.

Figure 8.17. Complete link clustering of the six points shown in Figure 8.15.

are merged first. However, $\{3, 6\}$ is merged with $\{4\}$, instead of $\{2, 5\}$ or $\{1\}$ because

$$
\begin{aligned}
dist(\{3,6\}, \{4\}) &= \max(dist(3,4), dist(6,4)) \\
&= \max(0.15, 0.22) \\
&= 0.22. \\
dist(\{3,6\}, \{2,5\}) &= \max(dist(3,2), dist(6,2), dist(3,5), dist(6,5)) \\
&= \max(0.15, 0.25, 0.28, 0.39) \\
&= 0.39. \\
dist(\{3,6\}, \{1\}) &= \max(dist(3,1), dist(6,1)) \\
&= \max(0.22, 0.23) \\
&= 0.23.
\end{aligned}
$$

$\blacksquare$

Group Average

For the group average version of hierarchical clustering, the proximity of two clusters is defined as the average pairwise proximity among all pairs of points in the different clusters. This is an intermediate approach between the single and complete link approaches. Thus, for group average, the cluster proxim-

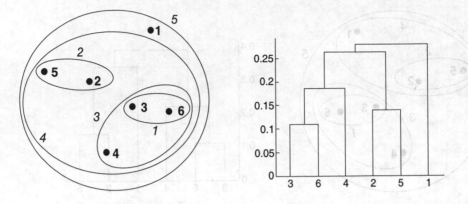

(a) Group average clustering.   (b) Group average dendrogram.

Figure 8.18. Group average clustering of the six points shown in Figure 8.15.

ity $proximity(C_i, C_j)$ of clusters C_i and C_j, which are of size m_i and m_j, respectively, is expressed by the following equation:

$$proximity(C_i, C_j) = \frac{\sum_{\substack{\mathbf{x} \in C_i \\ \mathbf{y} \in C_j}} proximity(\mathbf{x}, \mathbf{y})}{m_i * m_j}. \tag{8.6}$$

Example 8.6 (Group Average). Figure 8.18 shows the results of applying the group average approach to the sample data set of six points. To illustrate how group average works, we calculate the distance between some clusters.

$$
\begin{aligned}
dist(\{3, 6, 4\}, \{1\}) &= (0.22 + 0.37 + 0.23)/(3 * 1) \\
&= 0.28 \\
dist(\{2, 5\}, \{1\}) &= (0.2357 + 0.3421)/(2 * 1) \\
&= 0.2889 \\
dist(\{3, 6, 4\}, \{2, 5\}) &= (0.15 + 0.28 + 0.25 + 0.39 + 0.20 + 0.29)/(6 * 2) \\
&= 0.26
\end{aligned}
$$

Because $dist(\{3, 6, 4\}, \{2, 5\})$ is smaller than $dist(\{3, 6, 4\}, \{1\})$ and $dist(\{2, 5\}, \{1\})$, clusters $\{3, 6, 4\}$ and $\{2, 5\}$ are merged at the fourth stage. ■

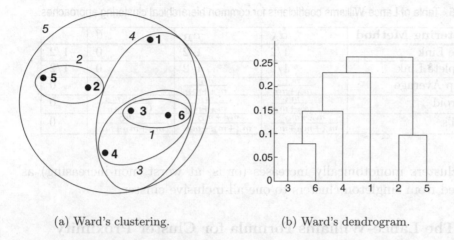

| (a) Ward's clustering. | (b) Ward's dendrogram. |

Figure 8.19. Ward's clustering of the six points shown in Figure 8.15.

Ward's Method and Centroid Methods

For Ward's method, the proximity between two clusters is defined as the increase in the squared error that results when two clusters are merged. Thus, this method uses the same objective function as K-means clustering. While it may seem that this feature makes Ward's method somewhat distinct from other hierarchical techniques, it can be shown mathematically that Ward's method is very similar to the group average method when the proximity between two points is taken to be the square of the distance between them.

Example 8.7 (Ward's Method). Figure 8.19 shows the results of applying Ward's method to the sample data set of six points. The clustering that is produced is different from those produced by single link, complete link, and group average. ∎

Centroid methods calculate the proximity between two clusters by calculating the distance between the centroids of clusters. These techniques may seem similar to K-means, but as we have remarked, Ward's method is the correct hierarchical analog.

Centroid methods also have a characteristic—often considered bad—that is not possessed by the other hierarchical clustering techniques that we have discussed: the possibility of **inversions**. Specifically, two clusters that are merged may be more similar (less distant) than the pair of clusters that were merged in a previous step. For the other methods, the distance between

Table 8.5. Table of Lance-Williams coefficients for common hierarchical clustering approaches.

Clustering Method	α_A	α_B	β	γ
Single Link	$1/2$	$1/2$	0	$-1/2$
Complete Link	$1/2$	$1/2$	0	$1/2$
Group Average	$\frac{m_A}{m_A+m_B}$	$\frac{m_B}{m_A+m_B}$	0	0
Centroid	$\frac{m_A}{m_A+m_B}$	$\frac{m_B}{m_A+m_B}$	$\frac{-m_A m_B}{(m_A+m_B)^2}$	0
Ward's	$\frac{m_A+m_Q}{m_A+m_B+m_Q}$	$\frac{m_B+m_Q}{m_A+m_B+m_Q}$	$\frac{-m_Q}{m_A+m_B+m_Q}$	0

merged clusters monotonically increases (or is, at worst, non-increasing) as we proceed from singleton clusters to one all-inclusive cluster.

8.3.3   The Lance-Williams Formula for Cluster Proximity

Any of the cluster proximities that we have discussed in this section can be viewed as a choice of different parameters (in the Lance-Williams formula shown below in Equation 8.7) for the proximity between clusters Q and R, where R is formed by merging clusters A and B. In this equation, $p(.,.)$ is a proximity function, while m_A, m_B, and m_Q are the number of points in clusters A, B, and Q, respectively. In other words, after we merge clusters A and B to form cluster R, the proximity of the new cluster, R, to an existing cluster, Q, is a linear function of the proximities of Q with respect to the original clusters A and B. Table 8.5 shows the values of these coefficients for the techniques that we have discussed.

$$p(R,Q) = \alpha_A\, p(A,Q) + \alpha_B\, p(B,Q) + \beta\, p(A,B) + \gamma\, |p(A,Q) - p(B,Q)| \quad (8.7)$$

Any hierarchical clustering technique that can be expressed using the Lance-Williams formula does not need to keep the original data points. Instead, the proximity matrix is updated as clustering occurs. While a general formula is appealing, especially for implementation, it is easier to understand the different hierarchical methods by looking directly at the definition of cluster proximity that each method uses.

8.3.4   Key Issues in Hierarchical Clustering

Lack of a Global Objective Function

We previously mentioned that agglomerative hierarchical clustering cannot be viewed as globally optimizing an objective function. Instead, agglomerative hierarchical clustering techniques use various criteria to decide locally, at each step, which clusters should be merged (or split for divisive approaches). This approach yields clustering algorithms that avoid the difficulty of attempting to solve a hard combinatorial optimization problem. (It can be shown that the general clustering problem for an objective function such as "minimize SSE" is computationally infeasible.) Furthermore, such approaches do not have problems with local minima or difficulties in choosing initial points. Of course, the time complexity of $O(m^2 \log m)$ and the space complexity of $O(m^2)$ are prohibitive in many cases.

Ability to Handle Different Cluster Sizes

One aspect of agglomerative hierarchical clustering that we have not yet discussed is how to treat the relative sizes of the pairs of clusters that are merged. (This discussion applies only to cluster proximity schemes that involve sums, such as centroid, Ward's, and group average.) There are two approaches: **weighted**, which treats all clusters equally, and **unweighted**, which takes the number of points in each cluster into account. Note that the terminology of weighted or unweighted refers to the data points, not the clusters. In other words, treating clusters of unequal size equally gives different weights to the points in different clusters, while taking the cluster size into account gives points in different clusters the same weight.

We will illustrate this using the group average technique discussed in Section 8.3.2, which is the unweighted version of the group average technique. In the clustering literature, the full name of this approach is the Unweighted Pair Group Method using Arithmetic averages (UPGMA). In Table 8.5, which gives the formula for updating cluster similarity, the coefficients for UPGMA involve the size of each of the clusters that were merged: $\alpha_A = \frac{m_A}{m_A+m_B}, \alpha_B = \frac{m_B}{m_A+m_B}, \beta = 0, \gamma = 0$. For the weighted version of group average—known as WPGMA—the coefficients are constants: $\alpha_A = 1/2, \alpha_B = 1/2, \beta = 0, \gamma = 0$. In general, unweighted approaches are preferred unless there is reason to believe that individual points should have different weights; e.g., perhaps classes of objects have been unevenly sampled.

Merging Decisions Are Final

Agglomerative hierarchical clustering algorithms tend to make good local decisions about combining two clusters since they can use information about the pairwise similarity of all points. However, once a decision is made to merge two clusters, it cannot be undone at a later time. This approach prevents a local optimization criterion from becoming a global optimization criterion.

For example, although the "minimize squared error" criterion from K-means is used in deciding which clusters to merge in Ward's method, the clusters at each level do not represent local minima with respect to the total SSE. Indeed, the clusters are not even stable, in the sense that a point in one cluster may be closer to the centroid of some other cluster than it is to the centroid of its current cluster. Nonetheless, Ward's method is often used as a robust method of initializing a K-means clustering, indicating that a local "minimize squared error" objective function does have a connection to a global "minimize squared error" objective function.

There are some techniques that attempt to overcome the limitation that merges are final. One approach attempts to fix up the hierarchical clustering by moving branches of the tree around so as to improve a global objective function. Another approach uses a partitional clustering technique such as K-means to create many small clusters, and then performs hierarchical clustering using these small clusters as the starting point.

8.3.5   Strengths and Weaknesses

The strengths and weakness of specific agglomerative hierarchical clustering algorithms were discussed above. More generally, such algorithms are typically used because the underlying application, e.g., creation of a taxonomy, requires a hierarchy. Also, there have been some studies that suggest that these algorithms can produce better-quality clusters. However, agglomerative hierarchical clustering algorithms are expensive in terms of their computational and storage requirements. The fact that all merges are final can also cause trouble for noisy, high-dimensional data, such as document data. In turn, these two problems can be addressed to some degree by first partially clustering the data using another technique, such as K-means.

8.4   DBSCAN

Density-based clustering locates regions of high density that are separated from one another by regions of low density. DBSCAN is a simple and effective density-based clustering algorithm that illustrates a number of important concepts that are important for any density-based clustering approach. In this section, we focus solely on DBSCAN after first considering the key notion of density. Other algorithms for finding density-based clusters are described in the next chapter.

8.4.1 Traditional Density: Center-Based Approach

Although there are not as many approaches for defining density as there are for defining similarity, there are several distinct methods. In this section we discuss the center-based approach on which DBSCAN is based. Other definitions of density will be presented in Chapter 9.

In the center-based approach, density is estimated for a particular point in the data set by counting the number of points within a specified radius, *Eps*, of that point. This includes the point itself. This technique is graphically illustrated by Figure 8.20. The number of points within a radius of *Eps* of point *A* is 7, including *A* itself.

This method is simple to implement, but the density of any point will depend on the specified radius. For instance, if the radius is large enough, then all points will have a density of m, the number of points in the data set. Likewise, if the radius is too small, then all points will have a density of 1. An approach for deciding on the appropriate radius for low-dimensional data is given in the next section in the context of our discussion of DBSCAN.

Classification of Points According to Center-Based Density

The center-based approach to density allows us to classify a point as being (1) in the interior of a dense region (a core point), (2) on the edge of a dense region (a border point), or (3) in a sparsely occupied region (a noise or background point). Figure 8.21 graphically illustrates the concepts of core, border, and noise points using a collection of two-dimensional points. The following text provides a more precise description.

Core points: These points are in the interior of a density-based cluster. A point is a core point if the number of points within a given neighborhood around the point as determined by the distance function and a user-specified distance parameter, *Eps*, exceeds a certain threshold, *MinPts*, which is also a user-specified parameter. In Figure 8.21, point *A* is a core point, for the indicated radius (*Eps*) if *MinPts* $\leq$ 7.

Border points: A border point is not a core point, but falls within the neighborhood of a core point. In Figure 8.21, point *B* is a border point. A border point can fall within the neighborhoods of several core points.

Noise points: A noise point is any point that is neither a core point nor a border point. In Figure 8.21, point *C* is a noise point.

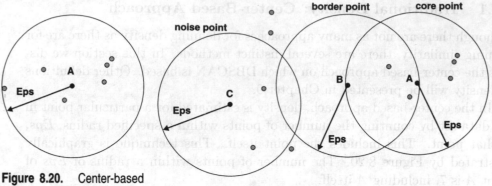

Figure 8.20. Center-based density.

Figure 8.21. Core, border, and noise points.

8.4.2   The DBSCAN Algorithm

Given the previous definitions of core points, border points, and noise points, the DBSCAN algorithm can be informally described as follows. Any two core points that are close enough—within a distance *Eps* of one another—are put in the same cluster. Likewise, any border point that is close enough to a core point is put in the same cluster as the core point. (Ties may need to be resolved if a border point is close to core points from different clusters.) Noise points are discarded. The formal details are given in Algorithm 8.4. This algorithm uses the same concepts and finds the same clusters as the original DBSCAN, but is optimized for simplicity, not efficiency.

Algorithm 8.4 DBSCAN algorithm.

1: Label all points as core, border, or noise points.
2: Eliminate noise points.
3: Put an edge between all core points that are within *Eps* of each other.
4: Make each group of connected core points into a separate cluster.
5: Assign each border point to one of the clusters of its associated core points.

Time and Space Complexity

The basic time complexity of the DBSCAN algorithm is $O(m \times$ time to find points in the *Eps*-neighborhood), where m is the number of points. In the worst case, this complexity is $O(m^2)$. However, in low-dimensional spaces, there are data structures, such as kd-trees, that allow efficient retrieval of all points within a given distance of a specified point, and the time complexity can be as low as $O(m \log m)$. The space requirement of DBSCAN, even for high-dimensional data, is $O(m)$ because it is only necessary to keep a small amount of data for each point, i.e., the cluster label and the identification of each point as a core, border, or noise point.

Selection of DBSCAN Parameters

There is, of course, the issue of how to determine the parameters Eps and $MinPts$. The basic approach is to look at the behavior of the distance from a point to its kth nearest neighbor, which we will call the k-dist. For points that belong to some cluster, the value of k-dist will be small if k is not larger than the cluster size. Note that there will be some variation, depending on the density of the cluster and the random distribution of points, but on average, the range of variation will not be huge if the cluster densities are not radically different. However, for points that are not in a cluster, such as noise points, the k-dist will be relatively large. Therefore, if we compute the k-dist for all the data points for some k, sort them in increasing order, and then plot the sorted values, we expect to see a sharp change at the value of k-dist that corresponds to a suitable value of Eps. If we select this distance as the Eps parameter and take the value of k as the $MinPts$ parameter, then points for which k-dist is less than Eps will be labeled as core points, while other points will be labeled as noise or border points.

Figure 8.22 shows a sample data set, while the k-dist graph for the data is given in Figure 8.23. The value of Eps that is determined in this way depends on k, but does not change dramatically as k changes. If the value of k is too small, then even a small number of closely spaced points that are noise or outliers will be incorrectly labeled as clusters. If the value of k is too large, then small clusters (of size less than k) are likely to be labeled as noise. The original DBSCAN algorithm used a value of $k = 4$, which appears to be a reasonable value for most two-dimensional data sets.

Clusters of Varying Density

DBSCAN can have trouble with density if the density of clusters varies widely. Consider Figure 8.24, which shows four clusters embedded in noise. The density of the clusters and noise regions is indicated by their darkness. The noise around the pair of denser clusters, A and B, has the same density as clusters C and D. If the Eps threshold is low enough that DBSCAN finds C and D as clusters, then A and B and the points surrounding them will become a single

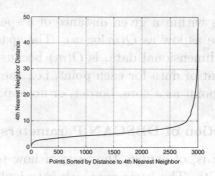

Figure 8.22. Sample data.

Figure 8.23. K-dist plot for sample data.

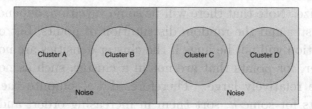

Figure 8.24. Four clusters embedded in noise.

cluster. If the *Eps* threshold is high enough that DBSCAN finds *A* and *B* as separate clusters, and the points surrounding them are marked as noise, then *C* and *D* and the points surrounding them will also be marked as noise.

An Example

To illustrate the use of DBSCAN, we show the clusters that it finds in the relatively complicated two-dimensional data set shown in Figure 8.22. This data set consists of 3000 two-dimensional points. The *Eps* threshold for this data was found by plotting the sorted distances of the fourth nearest neighbor of each point (Figure 8.23) and identifying the value at which there is a sharp increase. We selected *Eps* = 10, which corresponds to the knee of the curve. The clusters found by DBSCAN using these parameters, i.e., *MinPts* = 4 and *Eps* = 10, are shown in Figure 8.25(a). The core points, border points, and noise points are displayed in Figure 8.25(b).

8.4.3 Strengths and Weaknesses

Because DBSCAN uses a density-based definition of a cluster, it is relatively resistant to noise and can handle clusters of arbitrary shapes and sizes. Thus,

(a) Clusters found by DBSCAN.

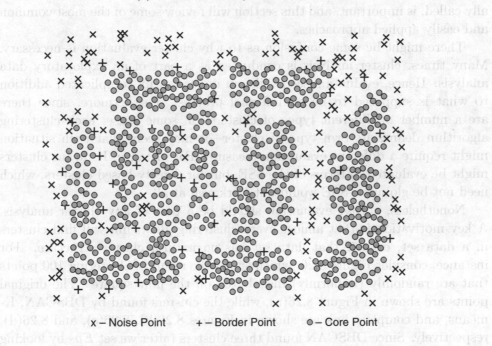

x – Noise Point   + – Border Point   ● – Core Point

(b) Core, border, and noise points.

Figure 8.25. DBSCAN clustering of 3000 two-dimensional points.

DBSCAN can find many clusters that could not be found using K-means, such as those in Figure 8.22. As indicated previously, however, DBSCAN has trouble when the clusters have widely varying densities. It also has trouble with high-dimensional data because density is more difficult to define for such data. One possible approach to dealing with such issues is given in Section 9.4.8. Finally, DBSCAN can be expensive when the computation of nearest neighbors requires computing all pairwise proximities, as is usually the case for high-dimensional data.

8.5   Cluster Evaluation

In supervised classification, the evaluation of the resulting classification model is an integral part of the process of developing a classification model, and there are well-accepted evaluation measures and procedures, e.g., accuracy and cross-validation, respectively. However, because of its very nature, cluster evaluation is not a well-developed or commonly used part of cluster analysis. Nonetheless, cluster evaluation, or **cluster validation** as it is more traditionally called, is important, and this section will review some of the most common and easily applied approaches.

There might be some confusion as to why cluster evaluation is necessary. Many times, cluster analysis is conducted as a part of an exploratory data analysis. Hence, evaluation seems like an unnecessarily complicated addition to what is supposed to be an informal process. Furthermore, since there are a number of different types of clusters—in some sense, each clustering algorithm defines its own type of cluster—it may seem that each situation might require a different evaluation measure. For instance, K-means clusters might be evaluated in terms of the SSE, but for density-based clusters, which need not be globular, SSE would not work well at all.

Nonetheless, cluster evaluation should be a part of any cluster analysis. A key motivation is that almost every clustering algorithm will find clusters in a data set, even if that data set has no natural cluster structure. For instance, consider Figure 8.26, which shows the result of clustering 100 points that are randomly (uniformly) distributed on the unit square. The original points are shown in Figure 8.26(a), while the clusters found by DBSCAN, K-means, and complete link are shown in Figures 8.26(b), 8.26(c), and 8.26(d), respectively. Since DBSCAN found three clusters (after we set *Eps* by looking at the distances of the fourth nearest neighbors), we set K-means and complete link to find three clusters as well. (In Figure 8.26(b) the noise is shown by the small markers.) However, the clusters do not look compelling for any of the three methods. In higher dimensions, such problems cannot be so easily detected.

8.5.1 Overview

Being able to distinguish whether there is non-random structure in the data is just one important aspect of cluster validation. The following is a list of several important issues for cluster validation.

1. Determining the **clustering tendency** of a set of data, i.e., distinguishing whether non-random structure actually exists in the data.

2. Determining the correct number of clusters.

3. Evaluating how well the results of a cluster analysis fit the data *without* reference to external information.

4. Comparing the results of a cluster analysis to externally known results, such as externally provided class labels.

5. Comparing two sets of clusters to determine which is better.

Notice that items 1, 2, and 3 do not make use of any external information—they are unsupervised techniques—while item 4 requires external information. Item 5 can be performed in either a supervised or an unsupervised manner. A further distinction can be made with respect to items 3, 4, and 5: Do we want to evaluate the entire clustering or just individual clusters?

While it is possible to develop various numerical measures to assess the different aspects of cluster validity mentioned above, there are a number of challenges. First, a measure of cluster validity may be quite limited in the scope of its applicability. For example, most work on measures of clustering tendency has been done for two- or three-dimensional spatial data. Second, we need a framework to interpret any measure. If we obtain a value of 10 for a measure that evaluates how well cluster labels match externally provided class labels, does this value represent a good, fair, or poor match? The goodness of a match often can be measured by looking at the statistical distribution of this value, i.e., how likely it is that such a value occurs by chance. Finally, if a measure is too complicated to apply or to understand, then few will use it.

The evaluation measures, or indices, that are applied to judge various aspects of cluster validity are traditionally classified into the following three types.

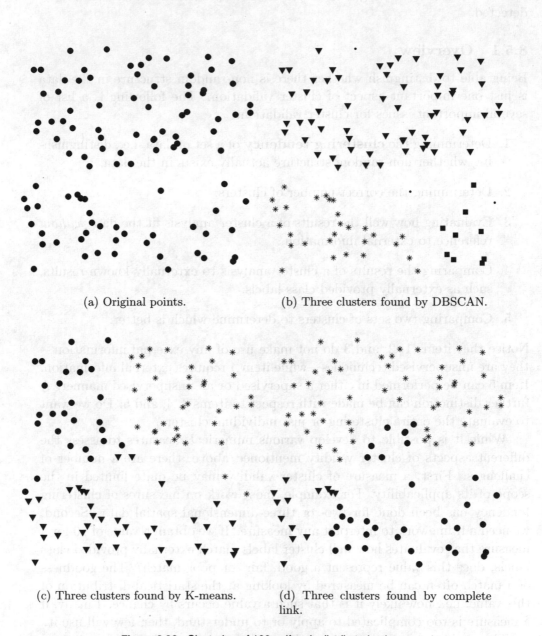

(a) Original points. (b) Three clusters found by DBSCAN.

(c) Three clusters found by K-means. (d) Three clusters found by complete link.

Figure 8.26. Clustering of 100 uniformly distributed points.

Unsupervised. Measures the goodness of a clustering structure without respect to external information. An example of this is the SSE. Unsupervised measures of cluster validity are often further divided into two classes: measures of **cluster cohesion** (compactness, tightness), which determine how closely related the objects in a cluster are, and measures of **cluster separation** (isolation), which determine how distinct or well-separated a cluster is from other clusters. Unsupervised measures are often called **internal indices** because they use only information present in the data set.

Supervised. Measures the extent to which the clustering structure discovered by a clustering algorithm matches some external structure. An example of a supervised index is entropy, which measures how well cluster labels match externally supplied class labels. Supervised measures are often called **external indices** because they use information not present in the data set.

Relative. Compares different clusterings or clusters. A relative cluster evaluation measure is a supervised or unsupervised evaluation measure that is used for the purpose of comparison. Thus, relative measures are not actually a separate type of cluster evaluation measure, but are instead a specific use of such measures. As an example, two K-means clusterings can be compared using either the SSE or entropy.

In the remainder of this section, we provide specific details concerning cluster validity. We first describe topics related to unsupervised cluster evaluation, beginning with (1) measures based on cohesion and separation, and (2) two techniques based on the proximity matrix. Since these approaches are useful only for partitional sets of clusters, we also describe the popular cophenetic correlation coefficient, which can be used for the unsupervised evaluation of a hierarchical clustering. We end our discussion of unsupervised evaluation with brief discussions about finding the correct number of clusters and evaluating clustering tendency. We then consider supervised approaches to cluster validity, such as entropy, purity, and the Jaccard measure. We conclude this section with a short discussion of how to interpret the values of (unsupervised or supervised) validity measures.

8.5.2   Unsupervised Cluster Evaluation Using Cohesion and Separation

Many internal measures of cluster validity for partitional clustering schemes are based on the notions of cohesion or separation. In this section, we use cluster validity measures for prototype- and graph-based clustering techniques to explore these notions in some detail. In the process, we will also see some interesting relationships between prototype- and graph-based clustering.

In general, we can consider expressing overall cluster validity for a set of K clusters as a weighted sum of the validity of individual clusters,

$$overall\ validity = \sum_{i=1}^{K} w_i\ validity(C_i). \tag{8.8}$$

The *validity* function can be cohesion, separation, or some combination of these quantities. The weights will vary depending on the cluster validity measure. In some cases, the weights are simply 1 or the size of the cluster, while in other cases they reflect a more complicated property, such as the square root of the cohesion. See Table 8.6. If the validity function is cohesion, then higher values are better. If it is separation, then lower values are better.

Graph-Based View of Cohesion and Separation

For graph-based clusters, the cohesion of a cluster can be defined as the sum of the weights of the links in the proximity graph that connect points within the cluster. See Figure 8.27(a). (Recall that the proximity graph has data objects as nodes, a link between each pair of data objects, and a weight assigned to each link that is the proximity between the two data objects connected by the link.) Likewise, the separation between two clusters can be measured by the sum of the weights of the links from points in one cluster to points in the other cluster. This is illustrated in Figure 8.27(b).

Mathematically, cohesion and separation for a graph-based cluster can be expressed using Equations 8.9 and 8.10, respectively. The *proximity* function can be a similarity, a dissimilarity, or a simple function of these quantities.

$$cohesion(C_i) \quad = \quad \sum_{\substack{\mathbf{x} \in C_i \\ \mathbf{y} \in C_i}} proximity(\mathbf{x}, \mathbf{y}) \tag{8.9}$$

$$separation(C_i, C_j) \quad = \quad \sum_{\substack{\mathbf{x} \in C_i \\ \mathbf{y} \in C_j}} proximity(\mathbf{x}, \mathbf{y}) \tag{8.10}$$

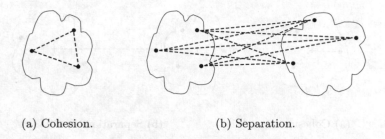

(a) Cohesion.   (b) Separation.

Figure 8.27. Graph-based view of cluster cohesion and separation.

Prototype-Based View of Cohesion and Separation

For prototype-based clusters, the cohesion of a cluster can be defined as the sum of the proximities with respect to the prototype (centroid or medoid) of the cluster. Similarly, the separation between two clusters can be measured by the proximity of the two cluster prototypes. This is illustrated in Figure 8.28, where the centroid of a cluster is indicated by a "+".

Cohesion for a prototype-based cluster is given in Equation 8.11, while two measures for separation are given in Equations 8.12 and 8.13, respectively, where c_i is the prototype (centroid) of cluster C_i and c is the overall prototype (centroid). There are two measures for separation because, as we will see shortly, the separation of cluster prototypes from an overall prototype is sometimes directly related to the separation of cluster prototypes from one another. Note that Equation 8.11 is the cluster SSE if we let proximity be the squared Euclidean distance.

$$cohesion(C_i) = \sum_{\mathbf{x} \in C_i} proximity(\mathbf{x}, \mathbf{c}_i) \tag{8.11}$$

$$separation(C_i, C_j) = proximity(\mathbf{c}_i, \mathbf{c}_j) \tag{8.12}$$

$$separation(C_i) = proximity(\mathbf{c}_i, \mathbf{c}) \tag{8.13}$$

Overall Measures of Cohesion and Separation

The previous definitions of cluster cohesion and separation gave us some simple and well-defined measures of cluster validity that can be combined into an overall measure of cluster validity by using a weighted sum, as indicated

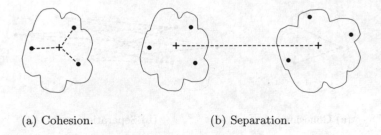

(a) Cohesion.   (b) Separation.

Figure 8.28. Prototype-based view of cluster cohesion and separation.

in Equation 8.8. However, we need to decide what weights to use. Not surprisingly, the weights used can vary widely, although typically they are some measure of cluster size.

Table 8.6 provides examples of validity measures based on cohesion and separation. $\mathcal{I}_1$ is a measure of cohesion in terms of the pairwise proximity of objects in the cluster divided by the cluster size. $\mathcal{I}_2$ is a measure of cohesion based on the sum of the proximities of objects in the cluster to the cluster centroid. $\mathcal{E}_1$ is a measure of separation defined as the proximity of a cluster centroid to the overall centroid multiplied by the number of objects in the cluster. $\mathcal{G}_1$, which is a measure based on both cohesion and separation, is the sum of the pairwise proximity of all objects in the cluster with all objects outside the cluster—the total weight of the edges of the proximity graph that must be cut to separate the cluster from all other clusters—divided by the sum of the pairwise proximity of objects in the cluster.

Table 8.6. Table of graph-based cluster evaluation measures.

Name	Cluster Measure	Cluster Weight	Type
$\mathcal{I}_1$	$\sum_{\substack{\mathbf{x} \in C_i \\ \mathbf{y} \in C_i}} proximity(\mathbf{x}, \mathbf{y})$	$\frac{1}{m_i}$	graph-based cohesion
$\mathcal{I}_2$	$\sum_{\mathbf{x} \in C_i} proximity(\mathbf{x}, \mathbf{c}_i)$	1	prototype-based cohesion
$\mathcal{E}_1$	$proximity(\mathbf{c}_i, \mathbf{c})$	m_i	prototype-based separation
$\mathcal{G}_1$	$\sum_{\substack{j=1 \\ j \neq i}}^{k} \sum_{\substack{\mathbf{x} \in C_i \\ \mathbf{y} \in C_j}} proximity(\mathbf{x}, \mathbf{y})$	$\dfrac{1}{\sum_{\substack{\mathbf{x} \in C_i \\ \mathbf{y} \in C_i}} proximity(\mathbf{x}, \mathbf{y})}$	graph-based separation and cohesion

Note that any unsupervised measure of cluster validity potentially can be used as an objective function for a clustering algorithm and vice versa. The CLUstering TOolkit (CLUTO) (see the bibliographic notes) uses the cluster evaluation measures described in Table 8.6, as well as some other evaluation measures not mentioned here, to drive the clustering process. It does this by using an algorithm that is similar to the incremental K-means algorithm discussed in Section 8.2.2. Specifically, each point is assigned to the cluster that produces the best value for the cluster evaluation function. The cluster evaluation measure $\mathcal{I}_2$ corresponds to traditional K-means and produces clusters that have good SSE values. The other measures produce clusters that are not as good with respect to SSE, but that are more optimal with respect to the specified cluster validity measure.

Relationship between Prototype-Based Cohesion and Graph-Based Cohesion

While the graph-based and prototype-based approaches to measuring the cohesion and separation of a cluster seem distinct, for some proximity measures they are equivalent. For instance, for the SSE and points in Euclidean space, it can be shown (Equation 8.14) that the average pairwise distance between the points in a cluster is equivalent to the SSE of the cluster. See Exercise 27 on page 566.

$$\text{Cluster SSE} = \sum_{\mathbf{x} \in C_i} dist(\mathbf{c}_i, \mathbf{x})^2 = \frac{1}{2m_i} \sum_{\mathbf{x} \in C_i} \sum_{\mathbf{y} \in C_i} dist(\mathbf{x}, \mathbf{y})^2 \qquad (8.14)$$

Two Approaches to Prototype-Based Separation

When proximity is measured by Euclidean distance, the traditional measure of separation between clusters is the between group sum of squares (SSB), which is the sum of the squared distance of a cluster centroid, $\mathbf{c}_i$, to the overall mean, $\mathbf{c}$, of all the data points. By summing the SSB over all clusters, we obtain the total SSB, which is given by Equation 8.15, where $\mathbf{c}_i$ is the mean of the ith cluster and $\mathbf{c}$ is the overall mean. The higher the total SSB of a clustering, the more separated the clusters are from one another.

$$\text{Total SSB} = \sum_{i=1}^{K} m_i \, dist(\mathbf{c}_i, \mathbf{c})^2 \qquad (8.15)$$

It is straightforward to show that the total SSB is directly related to the pairwise distances between the centroids. In particular, if the cluster sizes are equal, i.e., $m_i = m/K$, then this relationship takes the simple form given by Equation 8.16. (See Exercise 28 on page 566.) It is this type of equivalence that motivates the definition of prototype separation in terms of both Equations 8.12 and 8.13.

$$\text{Total SSB} = \frac{1}{2K} \sum_{i=1}^{K} \sum_{j=1}^{K} \frac{m}{K} \, dist(\mathbf{c}_i, \mathbf{c}_j)^2 \qquad (8.16)$$

Relationship between Cohesion and Separation

In some cases, there is also a strong relationship between cohesion and separation. Specifically, it is possible to show that the sum of the total SSE and the total SSB is a constant; i.e., that it is equal to the total sum of squares (TSS), which is the sum of squares of the distance of each point to the overall mean of the data. The importance of this result is that minimizing SSE (cohesion) is equivalent to maximizing SSB (separation).

We provide the proof of this fact below, since the approach illustrates techniques that are also applicable to proving the relationships stated in the last two sections. To simplify the notation, we assume that the data is one-dimensional, i.e., $dist(x, y) = (x-y)^2$. Also, we use the fact that the cross-term $\sum_{i=1}^{K} \sum_{x \in C_i} (x - c_i)(c - c_i)$ is 0. (See Exercise 29 on page 566.)

$$
\begin{aligned}
\text{TSS} &= \sum_{i=1}^{K} \sum_{x \in C_i} (x - c)^2 \\
&= \sum_{i=1}^{K} \sum_{x \in C_i} ((x - c_i) - (c - c_i))^2 \\
&= \sum_{i=1}^{K} \sum_{x \in C_i} (x - c_i)^2 - 2 \sum_{i=1}^{K} \sum_{x \in C_i} (x - c_i)(c - c_i) + \sum_{i=1}^{K} \sum_{x \in C_i} (c - c_i)^2 \\
&= \sum_{i=1}^{K} \sum_{x \in C_i} (x - c_i)^2 + \sum_{i=1}^{K} \sum_{x \in C_i} (c - c_i)^2 \\
&= \sum_{i=1}^{K} \sum_{x \in C_i} (x - c_i)^2 + \sum_{i=1}^{K} |C_i| (c - c_i)^2 \\
&= \text{SSE} + \text{SSB}
\end{aligned}
$$

Evaluating Individual Clusters and Objects

So far, we have focused on using cohesion and separation in the overall evaluation of a group of clusters. Many of these measures of cluster validity also can be used to evaluate individual clusters and objects. For example, we can rank individual clusters according to their specific value of cluster validity, i.e., cluster cohesion or separation. A cluster that has a high value of cohesion may be considered better than a cluster that has a lower value. This information often can be used to improve the quality of a clustering. If, for example, a cluster is not very cohesive, then we may want to split it into several subclusters. On the other hand, if two clusters are relatively cohesive, but not well separated, we may want to merge them into a single cluster.

We can also evaluate the objects within a cluster in terms of their contribution to the overall cohesion or separation of the cluster. Objects that contribute more to the cohesion and separation are near the "interior" of the cluster. Those objects for which the opposite is true are probably near the "edge" of the cluster. In the following section, we consider a cluster evaluation measure that uses an approach based on these ideas to evaluate points, clusters, and the entire set of clusters.

The Silhouette Coefficient

The popular method of silhouette coefficients combines both cohesion and separation. The following steps explain how to compute the silhouette coefficient for an individual point, a process that consists of the following three steps. We use distances, but an analogous approach can be used for similarities.

1. For the ith object, calculate its average distance to all other objects in its cluster. Call this value a_i.

2. For the ith object and any cluster not containing the object, calculate the object's average distance to all the objects in the given cluster. Find the minimum such value with respect to all clusters; call this value b_i.

3. For the ith object, the silhouette coefficient is $s_i = (b_i - a_i)/\max(a_i, b_i)$.

The value of the silhouette coefficient can vary between -1 and 1. A negative value is undesirable because this corresponds to a case in which a_i, the average distance to points in the cluster, is greater than b_i, the minimum average distance to points in another cluster. We want the silhouette coefficient to be positive ($a_i < b_i$), and for a_i to be as close to 0 as possible, since the coefficient assumes its maximum value of 1 when $a_i = 0$.

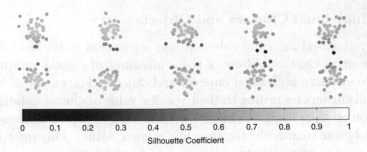

Figure 8.29. Silhouette coefficients for points in ten clusters.

We can compute the average silhouette coefficient of a cluster by simply taking the average of the silhouette coefficients of points belonging to the cluster. An overall measure of the goodness of a clustering can be obtained by computing the average silhouette coefficient of all points.

Example 8.8 (Silhouette Coefficient). Figure 8.29 shows a plot of the silhouette coefficients for points in 10 clusters. Darker shades indicate lower silhouette coefficients. ■

8.5.3   Unsupervised Cluster Evaluation Using the Proximity Matrix

In this section, we examine a couple of unsupervised approaches for assessing cluster validity that are based on the proximity matrix. The first compares an actual and idealized proximity matrix, while the second uses visualization.

Measuring Cluster Validity via Correlation

If we are given the similarity matrix for a data set and the cluster labels from a cluster analysis of the data set, then we can evaluate the "goodness" of the clustering by looking at the correlation between the similarity matrix and an ideal version of the similarity matrix based on the cluster labels. (With minor changes, the following applies to proximity matrices, but for simplicity, we discuss only similarity matrices.) More specifically, an ideal cluster is one whose points have a similarity of 1 to all points in the cluster, and a similarity of 0 to all points in other clusters. Thus, if we sort the rows and columns of the similarity matrix so that all objects belonging to the same class are together, then an ideal similarity matrix has a **block diagonal** structure. In other words, the similarity is non-zero, i.e., 1, inside the blocks of the similarity matrix whose entries represent intra-cluster similarity, and 0 elsewhere. The ideal similarity matrix is constructed by creating a matrix that has one row and one column for each data point—just like an actual similarity matrix—and assigning a 1 to an entry if the associated pair of points belongs to the same cluster. All other entries are 0.

High correlation between the ideal and actual similarity matrices indicates that the points that belong to the same cluster are close to each other, while low correlation indicates the opposite. (Since the actual and ideal similarity matrices are symmetric, the correlation is calculated only among the $n(n-1)/2$ entries below or above the diagonal of the matrices.) Consequently, this is not a good measure for many density- or contiguity-based clusters, because they are not globular and may be closely intertwined with other clusters.

Example 8.9 (Correlation of Actual and Ideal Similarity Matrices). To illustrate this measure, we calculated the correlation between the ideal and actual similarity matrices for the K-means clusters shown in Figure 8.26(c) (random data) and Figure 8.30(a) (data with three well-separated clusters). The correlations were 0.5810 and 0.9235, respectively, which reflects the expected result that the clusters found by K-means in the random data are worse than the clusters found by K-means in data with well-separated clusters. ∎

Judging a Clustering Visually by Its Similarity Matrix

The previous technique suggests a more general, qualitative approach to judging a set of clusters: Order the similarity matrix with respect to cluster labels and then plot it. In theory, if we have well-separated clusters, then the similarity matrix should be roughly block-diagonal. If not, then the patterns displayed in the similarity matrix can reveal the relationships between clusters. Again, all of this can be applied to dissimilarity matrices, but for simplicity, we will only discuss similarity matrices.

Example 8.10 (Visualizing a Similarity Matrix). Consider the points in Figure 8.30(a), which form three well-separated clusters. If we use K-means to group these points into three clusters, then we should have no trouble finding these clusters since they are well-separated. The separation of these clusters is illustrated by the reordered similarity matrix shown in Figure 8.30(b). (For uniformity, we have transformed the distances into similarities using the formula $s = 1 - (d - min\_d)/(max\_d - min\_d)$.) Figure 8.31 shows the reordered similarity matrices for clusters found in the random data set of Figure 8.26 by DBSCAN, K-means, and complete link.

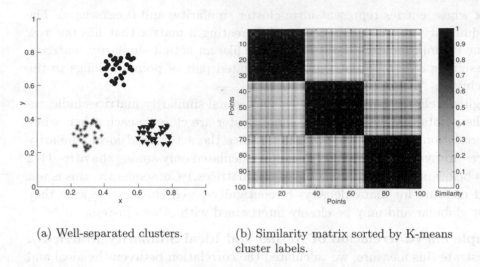

(a) Well-separated clusters.   (b) Similarity matrix sorted by K-means cluster labels.

Figure 8.30. Similarity matrix for well-separated clusters.

The well-separated clusters in Figure 8.30 show a very strong, block-diagonal pattern in the reordered similarity matrix. However, there are also weak block diagonal patterns—see Figure 8.31—in the reordered similarity matrices of the clusterings found by K-means, DBSCAN, and complete link in the random data. Just as people can find patterns in clouds, data mining algorithms can find clusters in random data. While it is entertaining to find patterns in clouds, it is pointless and perhaps embarrassing to find clusters in noise.   ∎

This approach may seem hopelessly expensive for large data sets, since the computation of the proximity matrix takes $O(m^2)$ time, where m is the number of objects, but with sampling, this method can still be used. We can take a sample of data points from each cluster, compute the similarity between these points, and plot the result. It may be necessary to oversample small clusters and undersample large ones to obtain an adequate representation of all clusters.

8.5.4   Unsupervised Evaluation of Hierarchical Clustering

The previous approaches to cluster evaluation are intended for partitional clusterings. Here we discuss the cophenetic correlation, a popular evaluation measure for hierarchical clusterings. The **cophenetic distance** between two objects is the proximity at which an agglomerative hierarchical clustering tech-

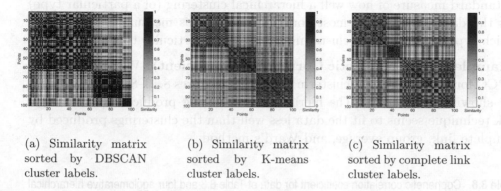

(a) Similarity matrix sorted by DBSCAN cluster labels.

(b) Similarity matrix sorted by K-means cluster labels.

(c) Similarity matrix sorted by complete link cluster labels.

Figure 8.31. Similarity matrices for clusters from random data.

nique puts the objects in the same cluster for the first time. For example, if at some point in the agglomerative hierarchical clustering process, the smallest distance between the two clusters that are merged is 0.1, then all points in one cluster have a cophenetic distance of 0.1 with respect to the points in the other cluster. In a cophenetic distance matrix, the entries are the cophenetic distances between each pair of objects. The cophenetic distance is different for each hierarchical clustering of a set of points.

Example 8.11 (Cophenetic Distance Matrix). Table 8.7 shows the cophentic distance matrix for the single link clustering shown in Figure 8.16. (The data for this figure consists of the 6 two-dimensional points given in Table 8.3.)

Table 8.7. Cophenetic distance matrix for single link and data in table 8.3

Point	P1	P2	P3	P4	P5	P6
P1	0	0.222	0.222	0.222	0.222	0.222
P2	0.222	0	0.148	0.151	0.139	0.148
P3	0.222	0.148	0	0.151	0.148	0.110
P4	0.222	0.151	0.151	0	0.151	0.151
P5	0.222	0.139	0.148	0.151	0	0.148
P6	0.222	0.148	0.110	0.151	0.148	0

The **CoPhenetic Correlation Coefficient** (CPCC) is the correlation between the entries of this matrix and the original dissimilarity matrix and is a standard measure of how well a hierarchical clustering (of a particular type) fits the data. One of the most common uses of this measure is to evaluate which type of hierarchical clustering is best for a particular type of data.

Example 8.12 (Cophenetic Correlation Coefficient). We calculated the CPCC for the hierarchical clusterings shown in Figures 8.16–8.19.These values are shown in Table 8.8. The hierarchical clustering produced by the single link technique seems to fit the data less well than the clusterings produced by complete link, group average, and Ward's method.

Table 8.8. Cophenetic correlation coefficient for data of Table 8.3 and four agglomerative hierarchical clustering techniques.

Technique	CPCC
Single Link	0.44
Complete Link	0.63
Group Average	0.66
Ward's	0.64

8.5.5   Determining the Correct Number of Clusters

Various unsupervised cluster evaluation measures can be used to approximately determine the correct or natural number of clusters.

Example 8.13 (Number of Clusters). The data set of Figure 8.29 has 10 natural clusters. Figure 8.32 shows a plot of the SSE versus the number of clusters for a (bisecting) K-means clustering of the data set, while Figure 8.33 shows the average silhouette coefficient versus the number of clusters for the same data. There is a distinct knee in the SSE and a distinct peak in the silhouette coefficient when the number of clusters is equal to 10. ∎

Thus, we can try to find the natural number of clusters in a data set by looking for the number of clusters at which there is a knee, peak, or dip in the plot of the evaluation measure when it is plotted against the number of clusters. Of course, such an approach does not always work well. Clusters may be considerably more intertwined or overlapping than those shown in Figure 8.29. Also, the data may consist of nested clusters. Actually, the clusters in Figure 8.29 are somewhat nested; i.e., there are 5 pairs of clusters since the clusters are closer top to bottom than they are left to right. There is a knee that indicates this in the SSE curve, but the silhouette coefficient curve is not

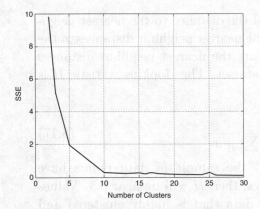

Figure 8.32. SSE versus number of clusters for the data of Figure 8.29.

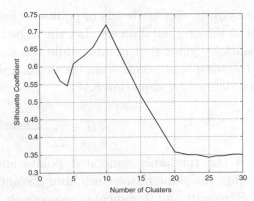

Figure 8.33. Average silhouette coefficient versus number of clusters for the data of Figure 8.29.

as clear. In summary, while caution is needed, the technique we have just described can provide insight into the number of clusters in the data.

8.5.6   Clustering Tendency

One obvious way to determine if a data set has clusters is to try to cluster it. However, almost all clustering algorithms will dutifully find clusters when given data. To address this issue, we could evaluate the resulting clusters and only claim that a data set has clusters if at least some of the clusters are of good quality. However, this approach does not address the fact the clusters in the data can be of a different type than those sought by our clustering algorithm. To handle this additional problem, we could use multiple algorithms and again evaluate the quality of the resulting clusters. If the clusters are uniformly poor, then this may indeed indicate that there are no clusters in the data.

Alternatively, and this is the focus of measures of clustering tendency, we can try to evaluate whether a data set has clusters without clustering. The most common approach, especially for data in Euclidean space, has been to use statistical tests for spatial randomness. Unfortunately, choosing the correct model, estimating the parameters, and evaluating the statistical significance of the hypothesis that the data is non-random can be quite challenging. Nonetheless, many approaches have been developed, most of them for points in low-dimensional Euclidean space.

Example 8.14 (Hopkins Statistic). For this approach, we generate p points that are randomly distributed across the data space and also sample p actual data points. For both sets of points we find the distance to the nearest neighbor in the original data set. Let the u_i be the nearest neighbor distances of the artificially generated points, while the w_i are the nearest neighbor distances of the sample of points from the original data set. The Hopkins statistic H is then defined by Equation 8.17.

$$H = \frac{\sum_{i=1}^{p} w_i}{\sum_{i=1}^{p} u_i + \sum_{i=1}^{p} w_i} \tag{8.17}$$

If the randomly generated points and the sample of data points have roughly the same nearest neighbor distances, then H will be near 0.5. Values of H near 0 and 1 indicate, respectively, data that is highly clustered and data that is regularly distributed in the data space. To give an example, the Hopkins statistic for the data of Figure 8.26 was computed for $p = 20$ and 100 different trials. The average value of H was 0.56 with a standard deviation of 0.03. The same experiment was performed for the well-separated points of Figure 8.30. The average value of H was 0.95 with a standard deviation of 0.006. ■

8.5.7 Supervised Measures of Cluster Validity

When we have external information about data, it is typically in the form of externally derived class labels for the data objects. In such cases, the usual procedure is to measure the degree of correspondence between the cluster labels and the class labels. But why is this of interest? After all, if we have the class labels, then what is the point in performing a cluster analysis? Motivations for such an analysis are the comparison of clustering techniques with the "ground truth" or the evaluation of the extent to which a manual classification process can be automatically produced by cluster analysis.

We consider two different kinds of approaches. The first set of techniques use measures from classification, such as entropy, purity, and the F-measure. These measures evaluate the extent to which a cluster contains objects of a single class. The second group of methods is related to the similarity measures for binary data, such as the Jaccard measure that we saw in Chapter 2. These approaches measure the extent to which two objects that are in the same class are in the same cluster and vice versa. For convenience, we will refer to these two types of measures as **classification-oriented** and **similarity-oriented**, respectively.

Classification-Oriented Measures of Cluster Validity

There are a number of measures—entropy, purity, precision, recall, and the F-measure—that are commonly used to evaluate the performance of a classification model. In the case of classification, we measure the degree to which predicted class labels correspond to actual class labels, but for the measures just mentioned, nothing fundamental is changed by using cluster labels instead of predicted class labels. Next, we quickly review the definitions of these measures, which were discussed in Chapter 4.

Entropy: The degree to which each cluster consists of objects of a single class. For each cluster, the class distribution of the data is calculated first, i.e., for cluster j we compute p_{ij}, the probability that a member of cluster i belongs to class j as $p_{ij} = m_{ij}/m_i$, where m_i is the number of objects in cluster i and m_{ij} is the number of objects of class j in cluster i. Using this class distribution, the entropy of each cluster i is calculated using the standard formula, $e_i = -\sum_{j=1}^{L} p_{ij} \log_2 p_{ij}$, where L is the number of classes. The total entropy for a set of clusters is calculated as the sum of the entropies of each cluster weighted by the size of each cluster, i.e., $e = \sum_{i=1}^{K} \frac{m_i}{m} e_i$, where K is the number of clusters and m is the total number of data points.

Purity: Another measure of the extent to which a cluster contains objects of a single class. Using the previous terminology, the purity of cluster i is $p_i = \max_j p_{ij}$, the overall purity of a clustering is $purity = \sum_{i=1}^{K} \frac{m_i}{m} p_i$.

Precision: The fraction of a cluster that consists of objects of a specified class. The precision of cluster i with respect to class j is $precision(i, j) = p_{ij}$.

Recall: The extent to which a cluster contains all objects of a specified class. The recall of cluster i with respect to class j is $recall(i, j) = m_{ij}/m_j$, where m_j is the number of objects in class j.

F-measure A combination of both precision and recall that measures the extent to which a cluster contains *only* objects of a particular class and *all* objects of that class. The F-measure of cluster i with respect to class j is $F(i, j) = (2 \times precision(i, j) \times recall(i, j))/(precision(i, j) + recall(i, j))$.

Example 8.15 (Supervised Evaluation Measures). We present an example to illustrate these measures. Specifically, we use K-means with the cosine similarity measure to cluster 3204 newspaper articles from the *Los Angeles*

Table 8.9. K-means clustering results for the *LA Times* document data set.

Cluster	Enter-tainment	Financial	Foreign	Metro	National	Sports	Entropy	Purity
1	3	5	40	506	96	27	1.2270	0.7474
2	4	7	280	29	39	2	1.1472	0.7756
3	1	1	1	7	4	671	0.1813	0.9796
4	10	162	3	119	73	2	1.7487	0.4390
5	331	22	5	70	13	23	1.3976	0.7134
6	5	358	12	212	48	13	1.5523	0.5525
Total	354	555	341	943	273	738	1.1450	0.7203

Times. These articles come from six different classes: Entertainment, Financial, Foreign, Metro, National, and Sports. Table 8.9 shows the results of a K-means clustering to find six clusters. The first column indicates the cluster, while the next six columns together form the confusion matrix; i.e., these columns indicate how the documents of each category are distributed among the clusters. The last two columns are the entropy and purity of each cluster, respectively.

Ideally, each cluster will contain documents from only one class. In reality, each cluster contains documents from many classes. Nevertheless, many clusters contain documents primarily from just one class. In particular, cluster 3, which contains mostly documents from the Sports section, is exceptionally good, both in terms of purity and entropy. The purity and entropy of the other clusters is not as good, but can typically be greatly improved if the data is partitioned into a larger number of clusters.

Precision, recall, and the F-measure can be calculated for each cluster. To give a concrete example, we consider cluster 1 and the Metro class of Table 8.9. The precision is $506/677 = 0.75$, recall is $506/943 = 0.26$, and hence, the F value is 0.39. In contrast, the F value for cluster 3 and Sports is 0.94.   ∎

Similarity-Oriented Measures of Cluster Validity

The measures that we discuss in this section are all based on the premise that any two objects that are in the same cluster should be in the same class and vice versa. We can view this approach to cluster validity as involving the comparison of two matrices: (1) the **ideal cluster similarity matrix** discussed previously, which has a 1 in the ij^{th} entry if two objects, i and j, are in the same cluster and 0, otherwise, and (2) an **ideal class similarity matrix** defined with respect to class labels, which has a 1 in the ij^{th} entry if two objects, i and j, belong to the same class, and a 0 otherwise. As before, we can take the correlation of these two matrices as the measure of cluster validity. This measure is known as the Γ statistic in clustering validation literature.

Example 8.16 (Correlation between Cluster and Class Matrices). To demonstrate this idea more concretely, we give an example involving five data points, p_1, p_2, p_3, p_4, p_5, two clusters, $C_1 = \{p_1, p_2, p_3\}$ and $C_2 = \{p_4, p_5\}$, and two classes, $L_1 = \{p_1, p_2\}$ and $L2 = \{p_3, p_4, p_5\}$. The ideal cluster and class similarity matrices are given in Tables 8.10 and 8.11. The correlation between the entries of these two matrices is 0.359.

Table 8.10. Ideal cluster similarity matrix.

Point	p1	p2	p3	p4	p5
p1	1	1	1	0	0
p2	1	1	1	0	0
p3	1	1	1	0	0
p4	0	0	0	1	1
p5	0	0	0	1	1

Table 8.11. Ideal class similarity matrix.

Point	p1	p2	p3	p4	p5
p1	1	1	0	0	0
p2	1	1	0	0	0
p3	0	0	1	1	1
p4	0	0	1	1	1
p5	0	0	1	1	1

More generally, we can use any of the measures for binary similarity that we saw in Section 2.4.5. (For example, we can convert these two matrices into binary vectors by appending the rows.) We repeat the definitions of the four quantities used to define those similarity measures, but modify our descriptive text to fit the current context. Specifically, we need to compute the following four quantities for all pairs of distinct objects. (There are $m(m-1)/2$ such pairs, if m is the number of objects.)

f_{00} = number of pairs of objects having a different class and a different cluster
f_{01} = number of pairs of objects having a different class and the same cluster
f_{10} = number of pairs of objects having the same class and a different cluster
f_{11} = number of pairs of objects having the same class and the same cluster

In particular, the simple matching coefficient, which is known as the Rand statistic in this context, and the Jaccard coefficient are two of the most frequently used cluster validity measures.

$$\text{Rand statistic} = \frac{f_{00} + f_{11}}{f_{00} + f_{01} + f_{10} + f_{11}} \qquad (8.18)$$

$$\text{Jaccard coefficient} = \frac{f_{11}}{f_{01} + f_{10} + f_{11}} \qquad (8.19)$$

Example 8.17 (Rand and Jaccard Measures). Based on these formulas, we can readily compute the Rand statistic and Jaccard coefficient for the example based on Tables 8.10 and 8.11. Noting that $f_{00} = 4$, $f_{01} = 2$, $f_{10} = 2$, and $f_{11} = 2$, the Rand statistic $= (2 + 4)/10 = 0.6$ and the Jaccard coefficient $= 2/(2+2+2) = 0.33$. ∎

We also note that the four quantities, f_{00}, f_{01}, f_{10}, and f_{11}, define a *contingency* table as shown in Table 8.12.

Table 8.12. Two-way contingency table for determining whether pairs of objects are in the same class and same cluster.

	Same Cluster	Different Cluster
Same Class	f_{11}	f_{10}
Different Class	f_{01}	f_{00}

Previously, in the context of association analysis—see Section 6.7.1—we presented an extensive discussion of measures of association that can be used for this type of contingency table. (Compare Table 8.12 with Table 6.7.) Those measures can also be applied to cluster validity.

Cluster Validity for Hierarchical Clusterings

So far in this section, we have discussed supervised measures of cluster validity only for partitional clusterings. Supervised evaluation of a hierarchical clustering is more difficult for a variety of reasons, including the fact that a preexisting hierarchical structure often does not exist. Here, we will give an example of an approach for evaluating a hierarchical clustering in terms of a (flat) set of class labels, which are more likely to be available than a preexisting hierarchical structure.

The key idea of this approach is to evaluate whether a hierarchical clustering contains, for each class, at least one cluster that is relatively pure and includes most of the objects of that class. To evaluate a hierarchical clustering with respect to this goal, we compute, for each class, the F-measure for each cluster in the cluster hierarchy. For each class, we take the maximum F-measure attained for any cluster. Finally, we calculate an overall F-measure for the hierarchical clustering by computing the weighted average of all per-class F-measures, where the weights are based on the class sizes. More formally, this hierarchical F-measure is defined as follows:

$$F = \sum_j \frac{m_j}{m} \max_i F(i, j)$$

where the maximum is taken over all clusters i at all levels, m_j is the number of objects in class j, and m is the total number of objects.

8.5.8 Assessing the Significance of Cluster Validity Measures

Cluster validity measures are intended to help us measure the goodness of the clusters that we have obtained. Indeed, they typically give us a single number as a measure of that goodness. However, we are then faced with the problem of interpreting the significance of this number, a task that may be even more difficult.

The minimum and maximum values of cluster evaluation measures may provide some guidance in many cases. For instance, by definition, a purity of 0 is bad, while a purity of 1 is good, at least if we trust our class labels and want our cluster structure to reflect the class structure. Likewise, an entropy of 0 is good, as is an SSE of 0.

Sometimes, however, there may not be a minimum or maximum value, or the scale of the data may affect the interpretation. Also, even if there are minimum and maximum values with obvious interpretations, intermediate values still need to be interpreted. In some cases, we can use an absolute standard. If, for example, we are clustering for utility, we may be willing to tolerate only a certain level of error in the approximation of our points by a cluster centroid.

But if this is not the case, then we must do something else. A common approach is to interpret the value of our validity measure in statistical terms. Specifically, we attempt to judge how likely it is that our observed value may be achieved by random chance. The value is good if it is unusual; i.e., if it is unlikely to be the result of random chance. The motivation for this approach is that we are only interested in clusters that reflect non-random structure in the data, and such structures should generate unusually high (low) values of our cluster validity measure, at least if the validity measures are designed to reflect the presence of strong cluster structure.

Example 8.18 (Significance of SSE). To show how this works, we present an example based on K-means and the SSE. Suppose that we want a measure of how good the well-separated clusters of Figure 8.30 are with respect to random data. We generate many random sets of 100 points having the same range as

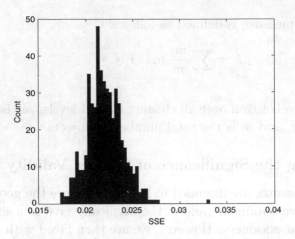

Figure 8.34. Histogram of SSE for 500 random data sets.

the points in the three clusters, find three clusters in each data set using K-means, and accumulate the distribution of SSE values for these clusterings. By using this distribution of the SSE values, we can then estimate the probability of the SSE value for the original clusters. Figure 8.34 shows the histogram of the SSE from 500 random runs. The lowest SSE shown in Figure 8.34 is 0.0173. For the three clusters of Figure 8.30, the SSE is 0.0050. We could therefore conservatively claim that there is less than a 1% chance that a clustering such as that of Figure 8.30 could occur by chance.

To conclude, we stress that there is more to cluster evaluation—supervised or unsupervised—than obtaining a numerical measure of cluster validity. Unless this value has a natural interpretation based on the definition of the measure, we need to interpret this value in some way. If our cluster evaluation measure is defined such that lower values indicate stronger clusters, then we can use statistics to evaluate whether the value we have obtained is unusually low, provided we have a distribution for the evaluation measure. We have presented an example of how to find such a distribution, but there is considerably more to this topic, and we refer the reader to the bibliographic notes for more pointers.

Finally, even when an evaluation measure is used as a relative measure, i.e., to compare two clusterings, we still need to assess the significance in the difference between the evaluation measures of the two clusterings. Although one value will almost always be better than another, it can be difficult to determine if the difference is significant. Note that there are two aspects to this significance: whether the difference is statistically significant (repeatable) and whether the magnitude of the difference is meaningful with respect to the application. Many would not regard a difference of 0.1% as significant, even if it is consistently reproducible.

8.6   Bibliographic Notes

Discussion in this chapter has been most heavily influenced by the books on cluster analysis written by Jain and Dubes [396], Anderberg [374], and Kaufman and Rousseeuw [400]. Additional clustering books that may also be of interest include those by Aldenderfer and Blashfield [373], Everitt et al. [388], Hartigan [394], Mirkin [405], Murtagh [407], Romesburg [409], and Späth [413]. A more statistically oriented approach to clustering is given by the pattern recognition book of Duda et al. [385], the machine learning book of Mitchell [406], and the book on statistical learning by Hastie et al. [395]. A general survey of clustering is given by Jain et al. [397], while a survey of spatial data mining techniques is provided by Han et al. [393]. Behrkin [379] provides a survey of clustering techniques for data mining. A good source of references to clustering outside of the data mining field is the article by Arabie and Hubert [376]. A paper by Kleinberg [401] provides a discussion of some of the trade-offs that clustering algorithms make and proves that it is impossible to for a clustering algorithm to simultaneously possess three simple properties.

The K-means algorithm has a long history, but is still the subject of current research. The original K-means algorithm was proposed by MacQueen [403]. The ISODATA algorithm by Ball and Hall [377] was an early, but sophisticated version of K-means that employed various pre- and postprocessing techniques to improve on the basic algorithm. The K-means algorithm and many of its variations are described in detail in the books by Anderberg [374] and Jain and Dubes [396]. The bisecting K-means algorithm discussed in this chapter was described in a paper by Steinbach et al. [414], and an implementation of this and other clustering approaches is freely available for academic use in the CLUTO (CLUstering TOolkit) package created by Karypis [382]. Boley [380] has created a divisive partitioning clustering algorithm (PDDP) based on finding the first principal direction (component) of the data, and Savaresi and Boley [411] have explored its relationship to bisecting K-means. Recent variations of K-means are a new incremental version of K-means (Dhillon et al. [383]), X-means (Pelleg and Moore [408]), and K-harmonic means (Zhang et al [416]). Hamerly and Elkan [392] discuss some clustering algorithms that produce better results than K-means. While some of the previously mentioned approaches address the initialization problem of K-means in some manner, other approaches to improving K-means initialization can also be found in the work of Bradley and Fayyad [381]. Dhillon and Modha [384] present a generalization of K-means, called spherical K-means, that works with commonly used similarity functions. A general framework for K-means clustering that uses dissimilarity functions based on Bregman divergences was constructed by Banerjee et al. [378].

Hierarchical clustering techniques also have a long history. Much of the initial activity was in the area of taxonomy and is covered in books by Jardine and Sibson [398] and Sneath and Sokal [412]. General-purpose discussions of hierarchical clustering are also available in most of the clustering books mentioned above. Agglomerative hierarchical clustering is the focus of most work in the area of hierarchical clustering, but divisive approaches have also received some attention. For example, Zahn [415] describes a divisive hierarchical technique that uses the minimum spanning tree of a graph. While both divisive and agglomerative approaches typically take the view that merging (splitting) decisions are final, there has been some work by Fisher [389] and Karypis et al. [399] to overcome these limitations.

Ester et al. proposed DBSCAN [387], which was later generalized to the GDBSCAN algorithm by Sander et al. [410] in order to handle more general types of data and distance measures, such as polygons whose closeness is measured by the degree of intersection. An incremental version of DBSCAN was developed by Kriegel et al. [386]. One interesting outgrowth of DBSCAN is OPTICS (Ordering Points To Identify the Clustering Structure) (Ankerst et al. [375]), which allows the visualization of cluster structure and can also be used for hierarchical clustering.

An authoritative discussion of cluster validity, which strongly influenced the discussion in this chapter, is provided in Chapter 4 of Jain and Dubes' clustering book [396]. More recent reviews of cluster validity are those of Halkidi et al. [390, 391] and Milligan [404]. Silhouette coefficients are described in Kaufman and Rousseeuw's clustering book [400]. The source of the cohesion and separation measures in Table 8.6 is a paper by Zhao and Karypis [417], which also contains a discussion of entropy, purity, and the hierarchical F-measure. The original source of the hierarchical F-measure is an article by Larsen and Aone [402].

Bibliography

[373] M. S. Aldenderfer and R. K. Blashfield. *Cluster Analysis*. Sage Publications, Los Angeles, 1985.

[374] M. R. Anderberg. *Cluster Analysis for Applications*. Academic Press, New York, December 1973.

Bibliography

[375] M. Ankerst, M. M. Breunig, H.-P. Kriegel, and J. Sander. OPTICS: Ordering Points To Identify the Clustering Structure. In *Proc. of 1999 ACM-SIGMOD Intl. Conf. on Management of Data*, pages 49–60, Philadelphia, Pennsylvania, June 1999. ACM Press.

[376] P. Arabie, L. Hubert, and G. D. Soete. An overview of combinatorial data analysis. In P. Arabie, L. Hubert, and G. D. Soete, editors, *Clustering and Classification*, pages 188–217. World Scientific, Singapore, January 1996.

[377] G. Ball and D. Hall. A Clustering Technique for Summarizing Multivariate Data. *Behavior Science*, 12:153–155, March 1967.

[378] A. Banerjee, S. Merugu, I. S. Dhillon, and J. Ghosh. Clustering with Bregman Divergences. In *Proc. of the 2004 SIAM Intl. Conf. on Data Mining*, pages 234–245, Lake Buena Vista, FL, April 2004.

[379] P. Berkhin. Survey Of Clustering Data Mining Techniques. Technical report, Accrue Software, San Jose, CA, 2002.

[380] D. Boley. Principal Direction Divisive Partitioning. *Data Mining and Knowledge Discovery*, 2(4):325–344, 1998.

[381] P. S. Bradley and U. M. Fayyad. Refining Initial Points for K-Means Clustering. In *Proc. of the 15th Intl. Conf. on Machine Learning*, pages 91–99, Madison, WI, July 1998. Morgan Kaufmann Publishers Inc.

[382] CLUTO 2.1.1: Software for Clustering High-Dimensional Datasets. /www.cs.umn.edu/~karypis, November 2003.

[383] I. S. Dhillon, Y. Guan, and J. Kogan. Iterative Clustering of High Dimensional Text Data Augmented by Local Search. In *Proc. of the 2002 IEEE Intl. Conf. on Data Mining*, pages 131–138. IEEE Computer Society, 2002.

[384] I. S. Dhillon and D. S. Modha. Concept Decompositions for Large Sparse Text Data Using Clustering. *Machine Learning*, 42(1/2):143–175, 2001.

[385] R. O. Duda, P. E. Hart, and D. G. Stork. *Pattern Classification*. John Wiley & Sons, Inc., New York, second edition, 2001.

[386] M. Ester, H.-P. Kriegel, J. Sander, M. Wimmer, and X. Xu. Incremental Clustering for Mining in a Data Warehousing Environment. In *Proc. of the 24th VLDB Conf.*, pages 323–333, New York City, August 1998. Morgan Kaufmann.

[387] M. Ester, H.-P. Kriegel, J. Sander, and X. Xu. A Density-Based Algorithm for Discovering Clusters in Large Spatial Databases with Noise. In *Proc. of the 2nd Intl. Conf. on Knowledge Discovery and Data Mining*, pages 226–231, Portland, Oregon, August 1996. AAAI Press.

[388] B. S. Everitt, S. Landau, and M. Leese. *Cluster Analysis*. Arnold Publishers, London, fourth edition, May 2001.

[389] D. Fisher. Iterative Optimization and Simplification of Hierarchical Clusterings. *Journal of Artificial Intelligence Research*, 4:147–179, 1996.

[390] M. Halkidi, Y. Batistakis, and M. Vazirgiannis. Cluster validity methods: part I. *SIGMOD Record (ACM Special Interest Group on Management of Data)*, 31(2):40–45, June 2002.

[391] M. Halkidi, Y. Batistakis, and M. Vazirgiannis. Clustering validity checking methods: part II. *SIGMOD Record (ACM Special Interest Group on Management of Data)*, 31 (3):19–27, Sept. 2002.

[392] G. Hamerly and C. Elkan. Alternatives to the k-means algorithm that find better clusterings. In *Proc. of the 11th Intl. Conf. on Information and Knowledge Management*, pages 600–607, McLean, Virginia, 2002. ACM Press.

[393] J. Han, M. Kamber, and A. Tung. Spatial Clustering Methods in Data Mining: A review. In H. J. Miller and J. Han, editors, *Geographic Data Mining and Knowledge Discovery*, pages 188–217. Taylor and Francis, London, December 2001.

[394] J. Hartigan. *Clustering Algorithms*. Wiley, New York, 1975.

[395] T. Hastie, R. Tibshirani, and J. H. Friedman. *The Elements of Statistical Learning: Data Mining, Inference, Prediction*. Springer, New York, 2001.

[396] A. K. Jain and R. C. Dubes. *Algorithms for Clustering Data*. Prentice Hall Advanced Reference Series. Prentice Hall, March 1988. Book available online at http://www.cse.msu.edu/~jain/Clustering_Jain_Dubes.pdf.

[397] A. K. Jain, M. N. Murty, and P. J. Flynn. Data clustering: A review. *ACM Computing Surveys*, 31(3):264–323, September 1999.

[398] N. Jardine and R. Sibson. *Mathematical Taxonomy*. Wiley, New York, 1971.

[399] G. Karypis, E.-H. Han, and V. Kumar. Multilevel Refinement for Hierarchical Clustering. Technical Report TR 99-020, University of Minnesota, Minneapolis, MN, 1999.

[400] L. Kaufman and P. J. Rousseeuw. *Finding Groups in Data: An Introduction to Cluster Analysis*. Wiley Series in Probability and Statistics. John Wiley and Sons, New York, November 1990.

[401] J. M. Kleinberg. An Impossibility Theorem for Clustering. In *Proc. of the 16th Annual Conf. on Neural Information Processing Systems*, December, 9–14 2002.

[402] B. Larsen and C. Aone. Fast and Effective Text Mining Using Linear-Time Document Clustering. In *Proc. of the 5th Intl. Conf. on Knowledge Discovery and Data Mining*, pages 16–22, San Diego, California, 1999. ACM Press.

[403] J. MacQueen. Some methods for classification and analysis of multivariate observations. In *Proc. of the 5th Berkeley Symp. on Mathematical Statistics and Probability*, pages 281–297. University of California Press, 1967.

[404] G. W. Milligan. Clustering Validation: Results and Implications for Applied Analyses. In P. Arabie, L. Hubert, and G. D. Soete, editors, *Clustering and Classification*, pages 345–375. World Scientific, Singapore, January 1996.

[405] B. Mirkin. *Mathematical Classification and Clustering*, volume 11 of *Nonconvex Optimization and Its Applications*. Kluwer Academic Publishers, August 1996.

[406] T. Mitchell. *Machine Learning*. McGraw-Hill, Boston, MA, 1997.

[407] F. Murtagh. *Multidimensional Clustering Algorithms*. Physica-Verlag, Heidelberg and Vienna, 1985.

[408] D. Pelleg and A. W. Moore. X-means: Extending K-means with Efficient Estimation of the Number of Clusters. In *Proc. of the 17th Intl. Conf. on Machine Learning*, pages 727–734. Morgan Kaufmann, San Francisco, CA, 2000.

[409] C. Romesburg. *Cluster Analysis for Researchers*. Life Time Learning, Belmont, CA, 1984.

[410] J. Sander, M. Ester, H.-P. Kriegel, and X. Xu. Density-Based Clustering in Spatial Databases: The Algorithm GDBSCAN and its Applications. *Data Mining and Knowledge Discovery*, 2(2):169–194, 1998.

[411] S. M. Savaresi and D. Boley. A comparative analysis on the bisecting K-means and the PDDP clustering algorithms. *Intelligent Data Analysis*, 8(4):345–362, 2004.

[412] P. H. A. Sneath and R. R. Sokal. *Numerical Taxonomy*. Freeman, San Francisco, 1971.

[413] H. Späth. *Cluster Analysis Algorithms for Data Reduction and Classification of Objects*, volume 4 of *Computers and Their Application*. Ellis Horwood Publishers, Chichester, 1980. ISBN 0-85312-141-9.

[414] M. Steinbach, G. Karypis, and V. Kumar. A Comparison of Document Clustering Techniques. In *Proc. of KDD Workshop on Text Mining, Proc. of the 6th Intl. Conf. on Knowledge Discovery and Data Mining*, Boston, MA, August 2000.

[415] C. T. Zahn. Graph-Theoretical Methods for Detecting and Describing Gestalt Clusters. *IEEE Transactions on Computers*, C-20(1):68–86, Jan. 1971.

[416] B. Zhang, M. Hsu, and U. Dayal. K-Harmonic Means—A Data Clustering Algorithm. Technical Report HPL-1999-124, Hewlett Packard Laboratories, Oct. 29 1999.

[417] Y. Zhao and G. Karypis. Empirical and theoretical comparisons of selected criterion functions for document clustering. *Machine Learning*, 55(3):311–331, 2004.

8.7 Exercises

1. Consider a data set consisting of 2^{20} data vectors, where each vector has 32 components and each component is a 4-byte value. Suppose that vector quantization is used for compression and that 2^{16} prototype vectors are used. How many bytes of storage does that data set take before and after compression and what is the compression ratio?

2. Find all well-separated clusters in the set of points shown in Figure 8.35.

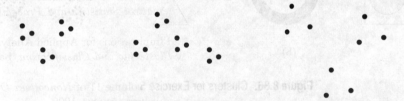

Figure 8.35. Points for Exercise 2.

3. Many partitional clustering algorithms that automatically determine the number of clusters claim that this is an advantage. List two situations in which this is not the case.

4. Given K equally sized clusters, the probability that a randomly chosen initial centroid will come from any given cluster is $1/K$, but the probability that each cluster will have exactly one initial centroid is much lower. (It should be clear that having one initial centroid in each cluster is a good starting situation for K-means.) In general, if there are K clusters and each cluster has n points, then the probability, p, of selecting in a sample of size K one initial centroid from each cluster is given by Equation 8.20. (This assumes sampling with replacement.) From this formula we can calculate, for example, that the chance of having one initial centroid from each of four clusters is $4!/4^4 = 0.0938$.

$$p = \frac{\text{number of ways to select one centroid from each cluster}}{\text{number of ways to select } K \text{ centroids}} = \frac{K!n^K}{(Kn)^K} = \frac{K!}{K^K} \quad (8.20)$$

(a) Plot the probability of obtaining one point from each cluster in a sample of size K for values of K between 2 and 100.

(b) For K clusters, $K = 10, 100$, and 1000, find the probability that a sample of size $2K$ contains at least one point from each cluster. You can use either mathematical methods or statistical simulation to determine the answer.

5. Identify the clusters in Figure 8.36 using the center-, contiguity-, and density-based definitions. Also indicate the number of clusters for each case and give a brief indication of your reasoning. Note that darkness or the number of dots indicates density. If it helps, assume center-based means K-means, contiguity-based means single link, and density-based means DBSCAN.

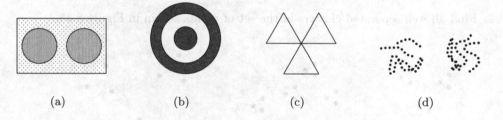

(a)   (b)   (c)   (d)

Figure 8.36. Clusters for Exercise 5.

6. For the following sets of two-dimensional points, (1) provide a sketch of how they would be split into clusters by K-means for the given number of clusters and (2) indicate approximately where the resulting centroids would be. Assume that we are using the squared error objective function. If you think that there is more than one possible solution, then please indicate whether each solution is a global or local minimum. Note that the label of each diagram in Figure 8.37 matches the corresponding part of this question, e.g., Figure 8.37(a) goes with part (a).

(a) $K = 2$. Assuming that the points are uniformly distributed in the circle, how many possible ways are there (in theory) to partition the points into two clusters? What can you say about the positions of the two centroids? (Again, you don't need to provide exact centroid locations, just a qualitative description.)

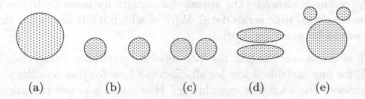

(a) (b) (c) (d) (e)

Figure 8.37. Diagrams for Exercise 6.

(b) $K = 3$. The distance between the edges of the circles is slightly greater than the radii of the circles.

(c) $K = 3$. The distance between the edges of the circles is much less than the radii of the circles.

(d) $K = 2$.

(e) $K = 3$. Hint: Use the symmetry of the situation and remember that we are looking for a rough sketch of what the result would be.

7. Suppose that for a data set

   - there are m points and K clusters,
   - half the points and clusters are in "more dense" regions,
   - half the points and clusters are in "less dense" regions, and
   - the two regions are well-separated from each other.

   For the given data set, which of the following should occur in order to minimize the squared error when finding K clusters:

   (a) Centroids should be equally distributed between more dense and less dense regions.

   (b) More centroids should be allocated to the less dense region.

   (c) More centroids should be allocated to the denser region.

   Note: Do not get distracted by special cases or bring in factors other than density. However, if you feel the true answer is different from any given above, justify your response.

8. Consider the mean of a cluster of objects from a binary transaction data set. What are the minimum and maximum values of the components of the mean? What is the interpretation of components of the cluster mean? Which components most accurately characterize the objects in the cluster?

9. Give an example of a data set consisting of three natural clusters, for which (almost always) K-means would likely find the correct clusters, but bisecting K-means would not.

10. Would the cosine measure be the appropriate similarity measure to use with K-means clustering for time series data? Why or why not? If not, what similarity measure would be more appropriate?

11. Total SSE is the sum of the SSE for each separate attribute. What does it mean if the SSE for one variable is low for all clusters? Low for just one cluster? High for all clusters? High for just one cluster? How could you use the per variable SSE information to improve your clustering?

12. The leader algorithm (Hartigan [394]) represents each cluster using a point, known as a *leader*, and assigns each point to the cluster corresponding to the closest leader, unless this distance is above a user-specified threshold. In that case, the point becomes the leader of a new cluster.

    (a) What are the advantages and disadvantages of the leader algorithm as compared to K-means?

    (b) Suggest ways in which the leader algorithm might be improved.

13. The Voronoi diagram for a set of K points in the plane is a partition of all the points of the plane into K regions, such that every point (of the plane) is assigned to the closest point among the K specified points. (See Figure 8.38.) What is the relationship between Voronoi diagrams and K-means clusters? What do Voronoi diagrams tell us about the possible shapes of K-means clusters?

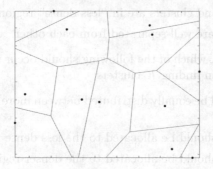

Figure 8.38. Voronoi diagram for Exercise 13.

14. You are given a data set with 100 records and are asked to cluster the data. You use K-means to cluster the data, but for all values of K, $1 \leq K \leq 100$, the K-means algorithm returns only one non-empty cluster. You then apply an incremental version of K-means, but obtain exactly the same result. How is this possible? How would single link or DBSCAN handle such data?

15. Traditional agglomerative hierarchical clustering routines merge two clusters at each step. Does it seem likely that such an approach accurately captures the

(nested) cluster structure of a set of data points? If not, explain how you might postprocess the data to obtain a more accurate view of the cluster structure.

16. Use the similarity matrix in Table 8.13 to perform single and complete link hierarchical clustering. Show your results by drawing a dendrogram. The dendrogram should clearly show the order in which the points are merged.

Table 8.13. Similarity matrix for Exercise 16.

	p1	p2	p3	p4	p5
p1	1.00	0.10	0.41	0.55	0.35
p2	0.10	1.00	0.64	0.47	0.98
p3	0.41	0.64	1.00	0.44	0.85
p4	0.55	0.47	0.44	1.00	0.76
p5	0.35	0.98	0.85	0.76	1.00

17. Hierarchical clustering is sometimes used to generate K clusters, $K > 1$ by taking the clusters at the Kth level of the dendrogram. (Root is at level 1.) By looking at the clusters produced in this way, we can evaluate the behavior of hierarchical clustering on different types of data and clusters, and also compare hierarchical approaches to K-means.

The following is a set of one-dimensional points: $\{6, 12, 18, 24, 30, 42, 48\}$.

(a) For each of the following sets of initial centroids, create two clusters by assigning each point to the nearest centroid, and then calculate the total squared error for each set of two clusters. Show both the clusters and the total squared error for each set of centroids.

    i. $\{18, 45\}$

    ii. $\{15, 40\}$

(b) Do both sets of centroids represent stable solutions; i.e., if the K-means algorithm was run on this set of points using the given centroids as the starting centroids, would there be any change in the clusters generated?

(c) What are the two clusters produced by single link?

(d) Which technique, K-means or single link, seems to produce the "most natural" clustering in this situation? (For K-means, take the clustering with the lowest squared error.)

(e) What definition(s) of clustering does this natural clustering correspond to? (Well-separated, center-based, contiguous, or density.)

(f) What well-known characteristic of the K-means algorithm explains the previous behavior?

18. Suppose we find K clusters using Ward's method, bisecting K-means, and ordinary K-means. Which of these solutions represents a local or global minimum? Explain.

19. Hierarchical clustering algorithms require $O(m^2 \log(m))$ time, and consequently, are impractical to use directly on larger data sets. One possible technique for reducing the time required is to sample the data set. For example, if K clusters are desired and $\sqrt{m}$ points are sampled from the m points, then a hierarchical clustering algorithm will produce a hierarchical clustering in roughly $O(m)$ time. K clusters can be extracted from this hierarchical clustering by taking the clusters on the Kth level of the dendrogram. The remaining points can then be assigned to a cluster in linear time, by using various strategies. To give a specific example, the centroids of the K clusters can be computed, and then each of the $m - \sqrt{m}$ remaining points can be assigned to the cluster associated with the closest centroid.

For each of the following types of data or clusters, discuss briefly if (1) sampling will cause problems for this approach and (2) what those problems are. Assume that the sampling technique randomly chooses points from the total set of m points and that any unmentioned characteristics of the data or clusters are as optimal as possible. In other words, focus only on problems caused by the particular characteristic mentioned. Finally, assume that K is very much less than m.

(a) Data with very different sized clusters.

(b) High-dimensional data.

(c) Data with outliers, i.e., atypical points.

(d) Data with highly irregular regions.

(e) Data with globular clusters.

(f) Data with widely different densities.

(g) Data with a small percentage of noise points.

(h) Non-Euclidean data.

(i) Euclidean data.

(j) Data with many and mixed attribute types.

20. Consider the following four faces shown in Figure 8.39. Again, darkness or number of dots represents density. Lines are used only to distinguish regions and do not represent points.

(a) For each figure, could you use single link to find the patterns represented by the nose, eyes, and mouth? Explain.

(b) For each figure, could you use K-means to find the patterns represented by the nose, eyes, and mouth? Explain.

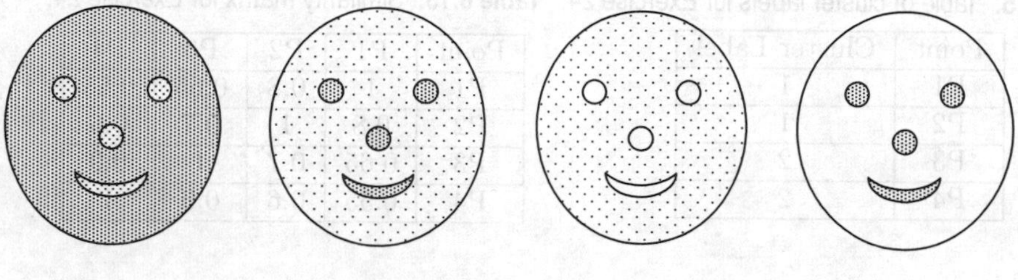

(a) (b) (c) (d)

Figure 8.39. Figure for Exercise 20.

(c) What limitation does clustering have in detecting all the patterns formed by the points in Figure 8.39(c)?

21. Compute the entropy and purity for the confusion matrix in Table 8.14.

Table 8.14. Confusion matrix for Exercise 21.

Cluster	Entertainment	Financial	Foreign	Metro	National	Sports	Total
#1	1	1	0	11	4	676	693
#2	27	89	333	827	253	33	1562
#3	326	465	8	105	16	29	949
Total	354	555	341	943	273	738	3204

22. You are given two sets of 100 points that fall within the unit square. One set of points is arranged so that the points are uniformly spaced. The other set of points is generated from a uniform distribution over the unit square.
    (a) Is there a difference between the two sets of points?
    (b) If so, which set of points will typically have a smaller SSE for K=10 clusters?
    (c) What will be the behavior of DBSCAN on the uniform data set? The random data set?

23. Using the data in Exercise 24, compute the silhouette coefficient for each point, each of the two clusters, and the overall clustering.

24. Given the set of cluster labels and similarity matrix shown in Tables 8.15 and 8.16, respectively, compute the correlation between the similarity matrix and the ideal similarity matrix, i.e., the matrix whose ij^{th} entry is 1 if two objects belong to the same cluster, and 0 otherwise.

Table 8.15. Table of cluster labels for Exercise 24.   **Table 8.16.** Similarity matrix for Exercise 24.

Point	Cluster Label
P1	1
P2	1
P3	2
P4	2

Point	P1	P2	P3	P4
P1	1	0.8	0.65	0.55
P2	0.8	1	0.7	0.6
P3	0.65	0.7	1	0.9
P4	0.55	0.6	0.9	1

25. Compute the hierarchical F-measure for the eight objects {p1, p2, p3, p4, p5, p6, p7, p8} and hierarchical clustering shown in Figure 8.40. Class A contains points p1, p2, and p3, while p4, p5, p6, p7, and p8 belong to class B.

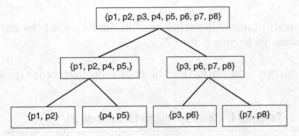

Figure 8.40. Hierarchical clustering for Exercise 25.

26. Compute the cophenetic correlation coefficient for the hierarchical clusterings in Exercise 16. (You will need to convert the similarities into dissimilarities.)

27. Prove Equation 8.14.

28. Prove Equation 8.16.

29. Prove that $\sum_{i=1}^{K} \sum_{x \in C_i} (x - m_i)(m - m_i) = 0$. This fact was used in the proof that TSS = SSE + SSB in Section 8.5.2.

30. Clusters of documents can be summarized by finding the top terms (words) for the documents in the cluster, e.g., by taking the most frequent k terms, where k is a constant, say 10, or by taking all terms that occur more frequently than a specified threshold. Suppose that K-means is used to find clusters of both documents and words for a document data set.

    (a) How might a set of term clusters defined by the top terms in a document cluster differ from the word clusters found by clustering the terms with K-means?

    (b) How could term clustering be used to define clusters of documents?

31. We can represent a data set as a collection of object nodes and a collection of attribute nodes, where there is a link between each object and each attribute,

and where the weight of that link is the value of the object for that attribute. For sparse data, if the value is 0, the link is omitted. Bipartite clustering attempts to partition this graph into disjoint clusters, where each cluster consists of a set of object nodes and a set of attribute nodes. The objective is to maximize the weight of links between the object and attribute nodes of a cluster, while minimizing the weight of links between object and attribute links in different clusters. This type of clustering is also known as **co-clustering** since the objects and attributes are clustered at the same time.

(a) How is bipartite clustering (co-clustering) different from clustering the sets of objects and attributes separately?

(b) Are there any cases in which these approaches yield the same clusters?

(c) What are the strengths and weaknesses of co-clustering as compared to ordinary clustering?

32. In Figure 8.41, match the similarity matrices, which are sorted according to cluster labels, with the sets of points. Differences in shading and marker shape distinguish between clusters, and each set of points contains 100 points and three clusters. In the set of points labeled 2, there are three very tight, equal-sized clusters.

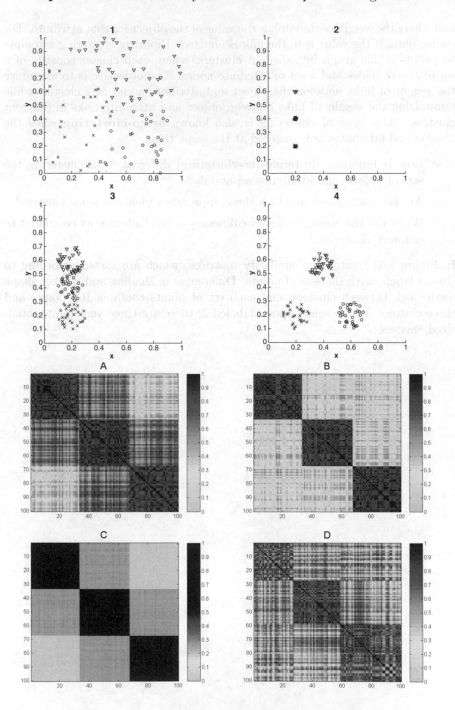

Figure 8.41. Points and similarity matrices for Exercise 32.

9

Cluster Analysis: Additional Issues and Algorithms

A large number of clustering algorithms have been developed in a variety of domains for different types of applications. None of these algorithms is suitable for all types of data, clusters, and applications. In fact, it seems that there is always room for a new clustering algorithm that is more efficient or better suited to a particular type of data, cluster, or application. Instead, we can only claim that we have techniques that work well in some situations. The reason is that, in many cases, what constitutes a good set of clusters is open to subjective interpretation. Furthermore, when an objective measure is employed to give a precise definition of a cluster, the problem of finding the optimal clustering is often computationally infeasible.

This chapter focuses on important issues in cluster analysis and explores the concepts and approaches that have been developed to address them. We begin with a discussion of the key issues of cluster analysis, namely, the characteristics of data, clusters, and algorithms that strongly impact clustering. These issues are important for understanding, describing, and comparing clustering techniques, and provide the basis for deciding which technique to use in a specific situation. For example, many clustering algorithms have a time or space complexity of $O(m^2)$ (m being the number of objects) and thus, are not suitable for large data sets. We then discuss additional clustering techniques. For each technique, we describe the algorithm, including the issues it addresses and the methods that it uses to address them. We conclude this chapter by providing some general guidelines for selecting a clustering algorithm for a given application.

9.1 Characteristics of Data, Clusters, and Clustering Algorithms

This section explores issues related to the characteristics of data, clusters, and algorithms that are important for a broad understanding of cluster analysis. Some of these issues represent challenges, such as handling noise and outliers. Other issues involve a desired feature of an algorithm, such as an ability to produce the same result regardless of the order in which the data objects are processed. The discussion in this section, along with the discussion of different types of clusterings in Section 8.1.2 and different types of clusters in Section 8.1.3, identifies a number of "dimensions" that can be used to describe and compare various clustering algorithms and the clustering results that they produce. To illustrate this, we begin this section with an example that compares two clustering algorithms that were described in the previous chapter, DBSCAN and K-means. This is followed by a more detailed description of the characteristics of data, clusters, and algorithms that impact cluster analysis.

9.1.1 Example: Comparing K-means and DBSCAN

To simplify the comparison, we assume that that there are no ties in distances for either K-means or DBSCAN and that DBSCAN always assigns a border point that is associated with several core points to the closest core point.

- Both DBSCAN and K-means are partitional clustering algorithms that assign each object to a single cluster, but K-means typically clusters all the objects, while DBSCAN discards objects that it classifies as noise.

- K-means uses a prototype-based notion of a cluster; DBSCAN uses a density-based concept.

- DBSCAN can handle clusters of different sizes and shapes and is not strongly affected by noise or outliers. K-means has difficulty with non-globular clusters and clusters of different sizes. Both algorithms can perform poorly when clusters have widely differing densities.

- K-means can only be used for data that has a well-defined centroid, such as a mean or median. DBSCAN requires that its definition of density, which is based on the traditional Euclidean notion of density, be meaningful for the data.

- K-means can be applied to sparse, high-dimensional data, such as document data. DBSCAN typically performs poorly for such data because the traditional Euclidean definition of density does not work well for high-dimensional data.

- The original versions of K-means and DBSCAN were designed for Euclidean data, but both have been extended to handle other types of data.

- DBSCAN makes no assumption about the distribution of the data. The basic K-means algorithm is equivalent to a statistical clustering approach (mixture models) that assumes all clusters come from spherical Gaussian distributions with different means but the same covariance matrix. See Section 9.2.2.

- DBSCAN and K-means both look for clusters using all attributes, that is, they do not look for clusters that may involve only a subset of the attributes.

- K-means can find clusters that are not well separated, even if they overlap (see Figure 8.2(b)), but DBSCAN merges clusters that overlap.

- The K-means algorithm has a time complexity of $O(m)$, while DBSCAN takes $O(m^2)$ time, except for special cases such as low-dimensional Euclidean data.

- DBSCAN produces the same set of clusters from one run to another, while K-means, which is typically used with random initialization of centroids, does not.

- DBSCAN automatically determines the number of clusters; for K-means, the number of clusters needs to be specified as a parameter. However, DBSCAN has two other parameters that must be specified, *Eps* and *MinPts*.

- K-means clustering can be viewed as an optimization problem; i.e., minimize the sum of the squared error of each point to its closest centroid, and as a specific case of a statistical clustering approach (mixture models). DBSCAN is not based on any formal model.

9.1.2 Data Characteristics

The following are some characteristics of data that can strongly affect cluster analysis.

High Dimensionality   In high-dimensional data sets, the traditional Euclidean notion of density, which is the number of points per unit volume, becomes meaningless. To see this, consider that as the number of dimensions increases, the volume increases rapidly, and unless the number of points grows exponentially with the number of dimensions, the density tends to 0. (Volume is exponential in the number of dimensions. For instance, a hypersphere with radius, r, and dimension, d, has volume proportional to r^d.) Also, proximity tends to become more uniform in high-dimensional spaces. Another way to view this fact is that there are more dimensions (attributes) that contribute to the proximity between two points and this tends to make the proximity more uniform. Since most clustering techniques are based on proximity or density, they can often have difficulty with high-dimensional data. One approach to addressing such problems is to employ dimensionality reduction techniques. Another approach, as discussed in Sections 9.4.5 and 9.4.7, is to redefine the notions of proximity and density.

Size   Many clustering algorithms that work well for small or medium-size data sets are unable to handle larger data sets. This is addressed further in the discussion of the characteristics of clustering algorithms—scalability is one such characteristic—and in Section 9.5, which discusses scalable clustering algorithms.

Sparseness   Sparse data often consists of asymmetric attributes, where zero values are not as important as non-zero values. Therefore, similarity measures appropriate for asymmetric attributes are commonly used. However, other, related issues also arise. For example, are the magnitudes of non-zero entries important, or do they distort the clustering? In other words, does the clustering work best when there are only two values, 0 and 1?

Noise and Outliers   An atypical point (outlier) can often severely degrade the performance of clustering algorithms, especially algorithms such as K-means that are prototype-based. On the other hand, noise can cause techniques, such as single link, to join clusters that should not be joined. In some cases, algorithms for removing noise and outliers are applied before a clustering algorithm is used. Alternatively, some algorithms can detect points that represent noise and outliers during the clustering process and then delete them or otherwise eliminate their negative effects. In the previous chapter, for instance, we saw that DBSCAN automatically classifies low-density points as noise and removes them from the clustering process. Chameleon (Section

9.4.4), SNN density-based clustering (Section 9.4.8), and CURE (Section 9.5.3) are three of the algorithms in this chapter that explicitly deal with noise and outliers during the clustering process.

Type of Attributes and Data Set   As discussed in Chapter 2, data sets can be of various types, such as structured, graph, or ordered, while attributes can be categorical (nominal or ordinal) or quantitative (interval or ratio), and are binary, discrete, or continuous. Different proximity and density measures are appropriate for different types of data. In some situations, data may need to be discretized or binarized so that a desired proximity measure or clustering algorithm can be used. Another complication occurs when attributes are of widely differing types, e.g., continuous and nominal. In such cases, proximity and density are more difficult to define and often more ad hoc. Finally, special data structures and algorithms may be needed to handle certain types of data efficiently.

Scale   Different attributes, e.g., height and weight, may be measured on different scales. These differences can strongly affect the distance or similarity between two objects and, consequently, the results of a cluster analysis. Consider clustering a group of people based on their heights, which are measured in meters, and their weights, which are measured in kilograms. If we use Euclidean distance as our proximity measure, then height will have little impact and people will be clustered mostly based on the weight attribute. If, however, we standardize each attribute by subtracting off its mean and dividing by its standard deviation, then we will have eliminated effects due to the difference in scale. More generally, normalization techniques, such as those discussed in Section 2.3.7, are typically used to handle these issues.

Mathematical Properties of the Data Space   Some clustering techniques calculate the mean of a collection of points or use other mathematical operations that only make sense in Euclidean space or in other specific data spaces. Other algorithms require that the definition of density be meaningful for the data.

9.1.3 Cluster Characteristics

The different types of clusters, such as prototype-, graph-, and density-based, were described earlier in Section 8.1.3. Here, we describe other important characteristics of clusters.

Data Distribution   Some clustering techniques assume a particular type of distribution for the data. More specifically, they often assume that data can be modeled as arising from a mixture of distributions, where each cluster corresponds to a distribution. Clustering based on mixture models is discussed in Section 9.2.2.

Shape   Some clusters are regularly shaped, e.g., rectangular or globular, but in general, clusters can be of arbitrary shape. Techniques such as DBSCAN and single link can handle clusters of arbitrary shape, but prototype-based schemes and some hierarchical techniques, such as complete link and group average, cannot. Chameleon (Section 9.4.4) and CURE (Section 9.5.3) are examples of techniques that were specifically designed to address this problem.

Differing Sizes   Many clustering methods, such as K-means, don't work well when clusters have different sizes. (See Section 8.2.4.) This topic is discussed further in Section 9.6.

Differing Densities   Clusters that have widely varying density can cause problems for methods such as DBSCAN and K-means. The SNN density-based clustering technique presented in Section 9.4.8 addresses this issue.

Poorly Separated Clusters   When clusters touch or overlap, some clustering techniques combine clusters that should be kept separate. Even techniques that find distinct clusters arbitrarily assign points to one cluster or another. Fuzzy clustering, which is described in Section 9.2.1, is one technique for dealing with data that does not form well-separated clusters.

Relationships among Clusters   In most clustering techniques, there is no explicit consideration of the relationships between clusters, such as their relative position. Self-organizing maps (SOM), which are described in Section 9.2.3, are a clustering technique that directly considers the relationships between clusters during the clustering process. Specifically, the assignment of a point to one cluster affects the definitions of nearby clusters.

Subspace Clusters   Clusters may only exist in a subset of dimensions (attributes), and the clusters determined using one set of dimensions may be quite different from the clusters determined by using another set. While this issue can arise with as few as two dimensions, it becomes more acute as dimensionality increases, since the number of possible subsets of dimensions is exponential in the total number of dimensions. For that reason, it is not feasible to simply look for clusters in all possible subsets of dimensions unless the number of dimensions is relatively low.

One approach is to apply feature selection, which was discussed in Section 2.3.4. However, this approach assumes that there is only one subset of dimensions in which the clusters exist. In reality, clusters can exist in many distinct subspaces (sets of dimensions), some of which overlap. Section 9.3.2 considers techniques that address the general problem of subspace clustering, i.e., of finding both clusters and the dimensions they span.

9.1.4   General Characteristics of Clustering Algorithms

Clustering algorithms are quite varied. We provide a general discussion of important characteristics of clustering algorithms here, and make more specific comments during our discussion of particular techniques.

Order Dependence   For some algorithms, the quality and number of clusters produced can vary, perhaps dramatically, depending on the order in which the data is processed. While it would seem desirable to avoid such algorithms, sometimes the order dependence is relatively minor or the algorithm may have other desirable characteristics. SOM (Section 9.2.3) is an example of an algorithm that is order dependent.

Nondeterminism   Clustering algorithms, such as K-means, are not order-dependent, but they produce different results for each run since they rely on an initialization step that requires a random choice. Because the quality of the clusters can vary from one run to another, multiple runs can be necessary.

Scalability   It is not unusual for a data set to contain millions of objects, and the clustering algorithms used for such data sets should have linear or near-linear time and space complexity. Even algorithms that have a complexity of $O(m^2)$ are not practical for large data sets. Furthermore, clustering techniques for data sets cannot always assume that all the data will fit in main memory or that data elements can be randomly accessed. Such algorithms are infeasible for large data sets. Section 9.5 is devoted to the issue of scalability.

Parameter Selection   Most clustering algorithms have one or more parameters that need to be set by the user. It can be difficult to choose the proper values; thus, the attitude is usually, "the fewer parameters, the better." Choosing parameter values becomes even more challenging if a small change in the parameters drastically changes the clustering results. Finally, unless a procedure (which may involve user input) is provided for determining parameter values, a user of the algorithm is reduced to using trial and error to find suitable parameter values.

Perhaps the most well-known parameter selection problem is that of "choosing the right number of clusters" for partitional clustering algorithms, such as K-means. One possible approach to that issue is given in Section 8.5.5, while references to others are provided in the bibliographic notes.

Transforming the Clustering Problem to Another Domain   One approach taken by some clustering techniques is to map the clustering problem to a problem in a different domain. Graph-based clustering, for instance, maps the task of finding clusters to the task of partitioning a proximity graph into connected components.

Treating Clustering as an Optimization Problem   Clustering is often viewed as an optimization problem: divide the points into clusters in a way that maximizes the goodness of the resulting set of clusters as measured by a user-specified objective function. For example, the K-means clustering algorithm (Section 8.2) tries to find the set of clusters that minimizes the sum of the squared distance of each point from its closest cluster centroid. In theory, such problems can be solved by enumerating all possible sets of clusters and selecting the one with the best value of the objective function, but this exhaustive approach is computationally infeasible. For this reason, many clustering techniques are based on heuristic approaches that produce good, but not optimal clusterings. Another approach is to use objective functions on a greedy or local basis. In particular, the hierarchical clustering techniques discussed in Section 8.3 proceed by making locally optimal (greedy) decisions at each step of the clustering process.

Road Map

We arrange our discussion of clustering algorithms in a manner similar to that of the previous chapter, grouping techniques primarily according to whether they are prototype-based, density-based, or graph-based. There is, however, a separate discussion for scalable clustering techniques. We conclude this chapter with a discussion of how to choose a clustering algorithm.

9.2   Prototype-Based Clustering

In prototype-based clustering, a cluster is a set of objects in which any object is closer to the prototype that defines the cluster than to the prototype of any other cluster. Section 8.2 described K-means, a simple prototype-based clustering algorithm that uses the centroid of the objects in a cluster as the prototype of the cluster. This section discusses clustering approaches that expand on the concept of prototype-based clustering in one or more ways, as discussed next:

- Objects are allowed to belong to more than one cluster. More specifically, an object belongs to every cluster with some weight. Such an approach addresses the fact that some objects are equally close to several cluster prototypes.

- A cluster is modeled as a statistical distribution, i.e., objects are generated by a random process from a statistical distribution that is characterized by a number of statistical parameters, such as the mean and variance. This viewpoint generalizes the notion of a prototype and enables the use of well-established statistical techniques.

- Clusters are constrained to have fixed relationships. Most commonly, these relationships are constraints that specify neighborhood relationships; i.e., the degree to which two clusters are neighbors of each other. Constraining the relationships among clusters can simplify the interpretation and visualization of the data.

We consider three specific clustering algorithms to illustrate these extensions of prototype-based clustering. Fuzzy c-means uses concepts from the field of fuzzy logic and fuzzy set theory to propose a clustering scheme, which is much like K-means, but which does not require a hard assignment of a point to only one cluster. Mixture model clustering takes the approach that a set of clusters can be modeled as a mixture of distributions, one for each cluster. The clustering scheme based on Self-Organizing Maps (SOM) performs clustering within a framework that requires clusters to have a prespecified relationship to one another, e.g., a two-dimensional grid structure.

9.2.1   Fuzzy Clustering

If data objects are distributed in well-separated groups, then a crisp classification of the objects into disjoint clusters seems like an ideal approach. However, in most cases, the objects in a data set cannot be partitioned into well-separated clusters, and there will be a certain arbitrariness in assigning an object to a particular cluster. Consider an object that lies near the boundary of two clusters, but is slightly closer to one of them. In many such cases, it might be more appropriate to assign a weight to each object and each cluster that indicates the degree to which the object belongs to the cluster. Mathematically, w_{ij} is the weight with which object $\mathbf{x}_i$ belongs to cluster C_j.

As shown in the next section, probabilistic approaches can also provide such weights. While probabilistic approaches are useful in many situations, there are times when it is difficult to determine an appropriate statistical model. In such cases, non-probabilistic clustering techniques are needed to provide similar capabilities. Fuzzy clustering techniques are based on fuzzy set theory and provide a natural technique for producing a clustering in which membership weights (the w_{ij}) have a natural (but not probabilistic) interpretation. This section describes the general approach of fuzzy clustering and provides a specific example in terms of fuzzy c-means (fuzzy K-means).

Fuzzy Sets

Lotfi Zadeh introduced **fuzzy set theory** and **fuzzy logic** in 1965 as a way of dealing with imprecision and uncertainty. Briefly, fuzzy set theory allows an object to belong to a set with a degree of membership between 0 and 1, while fuzzy logic allows a statement to be true with a degree of certainty between 0 and 1. Traditional set theory and logic are special cases of their fuzzy counterparts that restrict the degree of set membership or the degree of certainty to be either 0 or 1. Fuzzy concepts have been applied to many different areas, including control systems, pattern recognition, and data analysis (classification and clustering).

Consider the following example of fuzzy logic. The degree of truth of the statement "It is cloudy" can be defined to be the percentage of cloud cover in the sky, e.g., if the sky is 50% covered by clouds, then we would assign "It is cloudy" a degree of truth of 0.5. If we have two sets, "cloudy days" and "non-cloudy days," then we can similarly assign each day a degree of membership in the two sets. Thus, if a day were 25% cloudy, it would have a 25% degree of membership in "cloudy days" and a 75% degree of membership in "non-cloudy days."

Fuzzy Clusters

Assume that we have a set of data points $\mathcal{X} = \{\mathbf{x}_1, \ldots, \mathbf{x}_m\}$, where each point, $\mathbf{x}_i$, is an n-dimensional point, i.e., $\mathbf{x}_i = (x_{i1}, \ldots, x_{in})$. A collection of fuzzy clusters, $C_1, C_2, \ldots, C_k$ is a subset of all possible fuzzy subsets of $\mathcal{X}$. (This simply means that the membership weights (degrees), w_{ij}, have been assigned values between 0 and 1 for each point, $\mathbf{x}_i$, and each cluster, C_j.) However, we also want to impose the following reasonable conditions on the clusters in order to ensure that the clusters form what is called a **fuzzy psuedo-partition**.

1. All the weights for a given point, $\mathbf{x}_i$, add up to 1.

$$\sum_{j=1}^{k} w_{ij} = 1$$

2. Each cluster, C_j, contains, with non-zero weight, at least one point, but does not contain, with a weight of one, all of the points.

$$0 < \sum_{i=1}^{m} w_{ij} < m$$

Fuzzy c-means

While there are many types of fuzzy clustering—indeed, many data analysis algorithms can be "fuzzified"—we only consider the fuzzy version of K-means, which is called fuzzy c-means. In the clustering literature, the version of K-means that does not use incremental updates of cluster centroids is sometimes referred to as **c-means**, and this was the term adapted by the fuzzy community for the fuzzy version of K-means. The fuzzy c-means algorithm, also sometimes known as FCM, is given by Algorithm 9.1.

Algorithm 9.1 Basic fuzzy c-means algorithm.

1: Select an initial fuzzy pseudo-partition, i.e., assign values to all the w_{ij}.
2: **repeat**
3:    Compute the centroid of each cluster using the fuzzy pseudo-partition.
4:    Recompute the fuzzy pseudo-partition, i.e., the w_{ij}.
5: **until** The centroids don't change.
   (Alternative stopping conditions are "if the change in the error is below a specified threshold" or "if the absolute change in any w_{ij} is below a given threshold.")

After initialization, FCM repeatedly computes the centroids of each cluster and the fuzzy pseudo-partition until the partition does not change. FCM is similar in structure to the K-means algorithm, which after initialization, alternates between a step that updates the centroids and a step that assigns each object to the closest centroid. Specifically, computing a fuzzy pseudo-partition is equivalent to the assignment step. As with K-means, FCM can be interpreted as attempting to minimize the sum of the squared error (SSE), although FCM is based on a fuzzy version of SSE. Indeed, K-means can be regarded as a special case of FCM and the behavior of the two algorithms is quite similar. The details of FCM are described below.

Computing SSE   The definition of the sum of the squared error (SSE) is modified as follows:

$$\mathrm{SSE}(C_1, C_2, \ldots, C_k) = \sum_{j=1}^{k} \sum_{i=1}^{m} w_{ij}^{p} \, dist(\mathbf{x}_i, \mathbf{c}_j)^2 \tag{9.1}$$

where $\mathbf{c}_j$ is the centroid of the jth cluster and p, which is the exponent that determines the influence of the weights, has a value between 1 and ∞. Note that this SSE is just a weighted version of the traditional K-means SSE given in Equation 8.1.

Initialization   Random initialization is often used. In particular, weights are chosen randomly, subject to the constraint that the weights associated with any object must sum to 1. As with K-means, random initialization is simple, but often results in a clustering that represents a local minimum in terms of the SSE. Section 8.2.1, which contains a discussion on choosing initial centroids for K-means, has considerable relevance for FCM as well.

Computing Centroids   The definition of the centroid given in Equation 9.2 can be derived by finding the centroid that minimizes the fuzzy SSE as given by Equation 9.1. (See the approach in Section 8.2.6.) For a cluster, C_j, the corresponding centroid, $\mathbf{c}_j$, is defined by the following equation:

$$c_j = \sum_{i=1}^{m} w_{ij}^{p} \mathbf{x}_i / \sum_{i=1}^{m} w_{ij}^{p} \tag{9.2}$$

The fuzzy centroid definition is similar to the traditional definition except that all points are considered (any point can belong to any cluster, at least somewhat) and the contribution of each point to the centroid is weighted by its membership degree. In the case of traditional crisp sets, where all w_{ij} are either 0 or 1, this definition reduces to the traditional definition of a centroid.

There are a few considerations when choosing the value of p. Choosing $p = 2$ simplifies the weight update formula—see Equation 9.4. However, if p

is chosen to be near 1, then fuzzy c-means behaves like traditional K-means. Going in the other direction, as p gets larger, all the cluster centroids approach the global centroid of all the data points. In other words, the partition becomes fuzzier as p increases.

Updating the Fuzzy Pseudo-partition Since the fuzzy pseudo-partition is defined by the weight, this step involves updating the weights w_{ij} associated with the ith point and j^{th} cluster. The weight update formula given in Equation 9.3 can be derived by minimizing the SSE of Equation 9.1 subject to the constraint that the weights sum to 1.

$$ w_{ij} = \left(1/dist(\mathbf{x}_i, \mathbf{c}_j)^2 \right)^{\frac{1}{p-1}} \Big/ \sum_{q=1}^{k} \left(1/dist(\mathbf{x}_i, \mathbf{c}_q)^2 \right)^{\frac{1}{p-1}} \qquad (9.3) $$

This formula may appear a bit mysterious. However, note that if $p = 2$, then we obtain Equation 9.4, which is somewhat simpler. We provide an intuitive explanation of Equation 9.4, which, with a slight modification, also applies to Equation 9.3.

$$ w_{ij} = 1/dist(\mathbf{x}_i, \mathbf{c}_j)^2 \Big/ \sum_{q=1}^{k} 1/dist(\mathbf{x}_i, \mathbf{c}_q)^2 \qquad (9.4) $$

Intuitively, the weight w_{ij}, which indicates the degree of membership of point $\mathbf{x}_i$ in cluster C_j, should be relatively high if $\mathbf{x}_i$ is close to centroid $\mathbf{c}_j$ (if $dist(\mathbf{x}_i, \mathbf{c}_j)$ is low) and relatively low if $\mathbf{x}_i$ is far from centroid $\mathbf{c}_j$ (if $dist(\mathbf{x}_i, \mathbf{c}_j)$ is high). If $w_{ij} = 1/dist(\mathbf{x}_i, \mathbf{c}_j)^2$, which is the numerator of Equation 9.4, then this will indeed be the case. However, the membership weights for a point will not sum to one unless they are normalized; i.e., divided by the sum of all the weights as in Equation 9.4. To summarize, the membership weight of a point in a cluster is just the reciprocal of the square of the distance between the point and the cluster centroid divided by the sum of all the membership weights of the point.

Now consider the impact of the exponent $1/(p-1)$ in Equation 9.3. If $p > 2$, then this exponent decreases the weight assigned to clusters that are close to the point. Indeed, as p goes to infinity, the exponent tends to 0 and weights tend to the value $1/k$. On the other hand, as p approaches 1, the exponent increases the membership weights of points to which the cluster is close. As p goes to 1, the membership weight goes to 1 for the closest cluster and to 0 for all the other clusters. This corresponds to K-means.

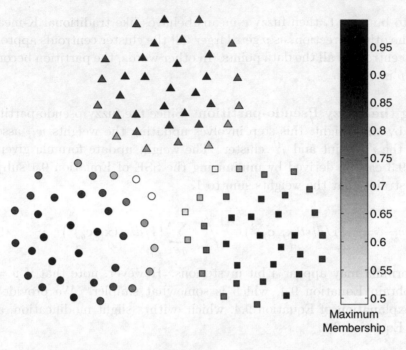

Figure 9.1. Fuzzy c-means clustering of a two-dimensional point set.

Example 9.1 (Fuzzy c-means on Three Circular Clusters). Figure 9.1 shows the result of applying fuzzy c-means to find three clusters for a two-dimensional data set of 100 points. Each point was assigned to the cluster in which it had the largest membership weight. The points belonging to each cluster are shown by different marker shapes, while the degree of membership in the cluster is shown by the shading. The darker the points, the stronger their membership in the cluster to which they have been assigned. The membership in a cluster is strongest toward the center of the cluster and weakest for those points that are between clusters.

Strengths and Limitations

A positive feature of FCM is that it produces a clustering that provides an indication of the degree to which any point belongs to any cluster. Otherwise, it has much the same strengths and weaknesses as K-means, although it is somewhat more computationally intensive.

9.2.2   Clustering Using Mixture Models

This section considers clustering based on statistical models. It is often convenient and effective to assume that data has been generated as a result of a statistical process and to describe the data by finding the statistical model that best fits the data, where the statistical model is described in terms of a distribution and a set of parameters for that distribution. At a high level, this process involves deciding on a statistical model for the data and estimating the parameters of that model from the data. This section describes a particular kind of statistical model, **mixture models**, which model the data by using a number of statistical distributions. Each distribution corresponds to a cluster and the parameters of each distribution provide a description of the corresponding cluster, typically in terms of its center and spread.

The discussion in this section proceeds as follows. After providing a description of mixture models, we consider how parameters can be estimated for statistical data models. We first describe how a procedure known as **maximum likelihood estimation (MLE)** can be used to estimate parameters for simple statistical models and then discuss how we can extend this approach for estimating the parameters of mixture models. Specifically, we describe the well-known **Expectation-Maximization (EM) algorithm**, which makes an initial guess for the parameters, and then iteratively improves these estimates. We present examples of how the EM algorithm can be used to cluster data by estimating the parameters of a mixture model and discuss its strengths and limitations.

A firm understanding of statistics and probability, as covered in Appendix C, is essential for understanding this section. Also, for convenience in the following discussion, we use the term probability to refer to both probability and probability density.

Mixture Models

Mixture models view the data as a set of observations from a mixture of different probability distributions. The probability distributions can be anything, but are often taken to be multivariate normal, since this type of distribution is well understood, mathematically easy to work with, and has been shown to produce good results in many instances. These types of distributions can model ellipsoidal clusters.

Conceptually, mixture models correspond to the following process of generating data. Given several distributions, usually of the same type, but with different parameters, randomly select one of these distributions and generate an object from it. Repeat the process m times, where m is the number of objects.

More formally, assume that there are K distributions and m objects, $\mathcal{X} = \{\mathbf{x}_1, \ldots, \mathbf{x}_m\}$. Let the jth distribution have parameters θ_j, and let Θ be the set of all parameters, i.e., $\Theta = \{\theta_1, \ldots, \theta_K\}$. Then, $prob(\mathbf{x}_i|\theta_j)$ is the probability of the ith object if it comes from the jth distribution. The probability that the jth distribution is chosen to generate an object is given by the weight w_j, $1 \leq j \leq K$, where these weights (probabilities) are subject to the constraint that they sum to one, i.e., $\sum_{j=1}^{K} w_j = 1$. Then, the probability of an object $\mathbf{x}$ is given by Equation 9.5.

$$prob(\mathbf{x}|\Theta) = \sum_{j=1}^{K} w_j p_j(\mathbf{x}|\theta_j) \tag{9.5}$$

If the objects are generated in an independent manner, then the probability of the entire set of objects is just the product of the probabilities of each individual $\mathbf{x}_i$.

$$prob(\mathcal{X}|\Theta) = \prod_{i=1}^{m} prob(\mathbf{x}_i|\Theta) = \prod_{i=1}^{m} \sum_{j=1}^{K} w_j p_j(\mathbf{x}_i|\theta_j) \tag{9.6}$$

For mixture models, each distribution describes a different group, i.e., a different cluster. By using statistical methods, we can estimate the parameters of these distributions from the data and thus describe these distributions (clusters). We can also identify which objects belong to which clusters. However, mixture modeling does not produce a crisp assignment of objects to clusters, but rather gives the probability with which a specific object belongs to a particular cluster.

Example 9.2 (Univariate Gaussian Mixture). We provide a concrete illustration of a mixture model in terms of Gaussian distributions. The probability density function for a one-dimensional Gaussian distribution at a point x is

$$prob(x_i|\Theta) = \frac{1}{\sqrt{2\pi}\sigma} e^{-\frac{(x-\mu)^2}{2\sigma^2}}. \tag{9.7}$$

The parameters of the Gaussian distribution are given by $\theta = (\mu, \sigma)$, where μ is the mean of the distribution and σ is the standard deviation. Assume that there are two Gaussian distributions, with a common standard deviation of 2 and means of -4 and 4, respectively. Also assume that each of the two

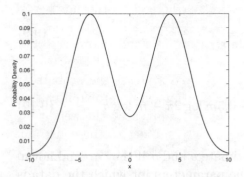

(a) Probability density function for the mixture model.

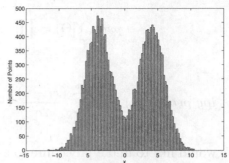

(b) 20,000 points generated from the mixture model.

Figure 9.2. Mixture model consisting of two normal distributions with means of -4 and 4, respectively. Both distributions have a standard deviation of 2.

distributions is selected with equal probability, i.e., $w_1 = w_2 = 0.5$. Then Equation 9.5 becomes the following:

$$prob(x|\Theta) = \frac{1}{2\sqrt{2\pi}} \, e^{-\frac{(x+4)^2}{8}} + \frac{1}{2\sqrt{2\pi}} \, e^{-\frac{(x-4)^2}{8}}. \qquad (9.8)$$

Figure 9.2(a) shows a plot of the probability density function of this mixture model, while Figure 9.2(b) shows the histogram for 20,000 points generated from this mixture model. ∎

Estimating Model Parameters Using Maximum Likelihood

Given a statistical model for the data, it is necessary to estimate the parameters of that model. A standard approach used for this task is maximum likelihood estimation, which we now explain.

To begin, consider a set of m points that are generated from a one-dimensional Gaussian distribution. Assuming that the points are generated independently, the probability of these points is just the product of their individual probabilities. (Again, we are dealing with probability densities, but to keep our terminology simple, we will refer to probabilities.) Using Equation 9.7, we can write this probability as shown in Equation 9.9. Since this probability would be a very small number, we typically will work with the log probability, as shown in Equation 9.10.

$$prob(\mathcal{X}|\Theta) = \prod_{i=1}^{m} \frac{1}{\sqrt{2\pi}\sigma}\, e^{-\frac{(x_i - u)^2}{2\sigma^2}} \qquad (9.9)$$

$$log\ prob(\mathcal{X}|\Theta) = -\sum_{i=1}^{m} \frac{(x_i - u)^2}{2\sigma^2} - 0.5m\log 2\pi - m\log\sigma \qquad (9.10)$$

We would like to find a procedure to estimate u and σ if they are unknown. One approach is to choose the values of the parameters for which the data is most probable (most likely). In other words, choose the μ and σ that maximize Equation 9.9. This approach is known in statistics as the **maximum likelihood principle**, and the process of applying this principle to estimate the parameters of a statistical distribution from the data is known as **maximum likelihood estimation (MLE)**.

The principle is called the maximum likelihood principle because, given a set of data, the probability of the data, regarded as a function of the parameters, is called a **likelihood function**. To illustrate, we rewrite Equation 9.9 as Equation 9.11 to emphasize that we view the statistical parameters μ and σ as our variables and that the data is regarded as a constant. For practical reasons, the log likelihood is more commonly used. The log likelihood function derived from the log probability of Equation 9.10 is shown in Equation 9.12. Note that the parameter values that maximize the log likelihood also maximize the likelihood since log is a monotonically increasing function.

$$likelihood(\Theta|\mathcal{X}) = L(\Theta|\mathcal{X}) = \prod_{i=1}^{m} \frac{1}{\sqrt{2\pi}\sigma}\, e^{-\frac{(x_i - \mu)^2}{2\sigma^2}} \qquad (9.11)$$

$$log\ likelihood(\Theta|\mathcal{X}) = \ell(\Theta|\mathcal{X}) = -\sum_{i=1}^{m} \frac{(x_i - \mu)^2}{2\sigma^2} - 0.5m\log 2\pi - m\log\sigma \qquad (9.12)$$

Example 9.3 (Maximum Likelihood Parameter Estimation). We provide a concrete illustration of the use of MLE for finding parameter values. Suppose that we have the set of 200 points whose histogram is shown in Figure 9.3(a). Figure 9.3(b) shows the maximum log likelihood plot for the 200 points under consideration. The values of the parameters for which the log probability is a maximum are $\mu = -4.1$ and $\sigma = 2.1$, which are close to the parameter values of the underlying Gaussian distribution, $\mu = -4.0$ and $\sigma = 2.0$. ∎

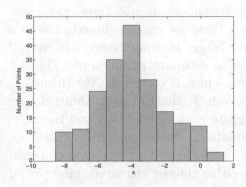

(a) Histogram of 200 points from a Gaussian distribution.

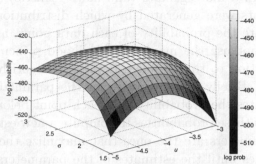

(b) Log likelihood plot of the 200 points for different values of the mean and standard deviation.

Figure 9.3. 200 points from a Gaussian distribution and their log probability for different parameter values.

Graphing the likelihood of the data for different values of the parameters is not practical, at least if there are more than two parameters. Thus, standard statistical procedure is to derive the maximum likelihood estimates of a statistical parameter by taking the derivative of likelihood function with respect to that parameter, setting the result equal to 0, and solving. In particular, for a Gaussian distribution, it can be shown that the mean and standard deviation of the sample points are the maximum likelihood estimates of the corresponding parameters of the underlying distribution. (See Exercise 9 on 648.) Indeed, for the 200 points considered in our example, the parameter values that maximized the log likelihood were precisely the mean and standard deviation of the 200 points, i.e., $u = -4.1$ and $\sigma = 2.1$.

Estimating Mixture Model Parameters Using Maximum Likelihood: The EM Algorithm

We can also use the maximum likelihood approach to estimate the model parameters for a mixture model. In the simplest case, we know which data objects come from which distributions, and the situation reduces to one of estimating the parameters of a single distribution given data from that distribution. For most common distributions, the maximum likelihood estimates of the parameters are calculated from simple formulas involving the data.

In a more general (and more realistic) situation, we do not know which points were generated by which distribution. Thus, we cannot directly calculate the probability of each data point, and hence, it would seem that we cannot use the maximum likelihood principle to estimate parameters. The solution to this problem is the EM algorithm, which is shown in Algorithm 9.2. Briefly, given a guess for the parameter values, the EM algorithm calculates the probability that each point belongs to each distribution and then uses these probabilities to compute a new estimate for the parameters. (These parameters are the ones that maximize the likelihood.) This iteration continues until the estimates of the parameters either do not change or change very little. Thus, we still employ maximum likelihood estimation, but via an iterative search.

Algorithm 9.2 EM algorithm.

1: Select an initial set of model parameters.

    (As with K-means, this can be done randomly or in a variety of ways.)

2: **repeat**

3:   **Expectation Step** For each object, calculate the probability that each object belongs to each distribution, i.e., calculate $prob(distribution\ j | \mathbf{x}_i, \Theta)$.

4:   **Maximization Step** Given the probabilities from the expectation step, find the new estimates of the parameters that maximize the expected likelihood.

5: **until** The parameters do not change.

    (Alternatively, stop if the change in the parameters is below a specified threshold.)

The EM algorithm is similar to the K-means algorithm given in Section 8.2.1. Indeed, the K-means algorithm for Euclidean data is a special case of the EM algorithm for spherical Gaussian distributions with equal covariance matrices, but different means. The expectation step corresponds to the K-means step of assigning each object to a cluster. Instead, each object is assigned to every cluster (distribution) with some probability. The maximization step corresponds to computing the cluster centroids. Instead, all the parameters of the distributions, as well as the weight parameters, are selected to maximize the likelihood. This process is often straightforward, as the parameters are typically computed using formulas derived from maximum likelihood estimation. For instance, for a single Gaussian distribution, the MLE estimate of the mean is the mean of the objects in the distribution. In the context of mixture models and the EM algorithm, the computation of the mean is modified to account for the fact that every object belongs to a distribution with a certain probability. This is illustrated further in the following example.

Example 9.4 (Simple Example of EM Algorithm). This example illustrates how EM operates when applied to the data in Figure 9.2. To keep the example as simple as possible, we assume that we know that the standard deviation of both distributions is 2.0 and that points were generated with equal probability from both distributions. We will refer to the left and right distributions as distributions 1 and 2, respectively.

We begin the EM algorithm by making initial guesses for μ_1 and μ_2, say, $\mu_1 = -2$ and $\mu_2 = 3$. Thus, the initial parameters, $\theta = (\mu, \sigma)$, for the two distributions are, respectively, $\theta_1 = (-2, 2)$ and $\theta_2 = (3, 2)$. The set of parameters for the entire mixture model is $\Theta = \{\theta_1, \theta_2\}$. For the expectation step of EM, we want to compute the probability that a point came from a particular distribution; i.e., we want to compute $prob(distribution\ 1|x_i, \Theta)$ and $prob(distribution\ 2|x_i, \Theta)$. These values can be expressed by the following equation, which is a straightforward application of Bayes rule (see Appendix C):

$$prob(distribution\ j|x_i, \theta) = \frac{0.5\ prob(x_i|\theta_j)}{0.5\ prob(x_i|\theta_1) + 0.5\ prob(x_i|\theta_2)}, \qquad (9.13)$$

where 0.5 is the probability (weight) of each distribution and j is 1 or 2.

For instance, assume one of the points is 0. Using the Gaussian density function given in Equation 9.7, we compute that $prob(0|\theta_1) = 0.12$ and $prob(0|\theta_2) = 0.06$. (Again, we are really computing probability densities.) Using these values and Equation 9.13, we find that $prob(distribution\ 1|0, \Theta) = 0.12/(0.12 + 0.06) = 0.66$ and $prob(distribution\ 2|0, \Theta) = 0.06/(0.12 + 0.06) = 0.33$. This means that the point 0 is twice as likely to belong to distribution 1 as distribution 2 based on the current assumptions for the parameter values.

After computing the cluster membership probabilities for all 20,000 points, we compute new estimates for μ_1 and μ_2 (using Equations 9.14 and 9.15) in the maximization step of the EM algorithm. Notice that the new estimate for the mean of a distribution is just a weighted average of the points, where the weights are the probabilities that the points belong to the distribution, i.e., the $prob(distribution\ j|x_i)$ values.

$$\mu_1 = \sum_{i=1}^{20,000} x_i \frac{prob(distribution\ 1|x_i, \Theta)}{\sum_{i=1}^{20,000} prob(distribution\ 1|x_i, \Theta)} \qquad (9.14)$$

Table 9.1. First few iterations of the EM algorithm for the simple example.

Iteration	μ_1	μ_2
0	-2.00	3.00
1	-3.74	4.10
2	-3.94	4.07
3	-3.97	4.04
4	-3.98	4.03
5	-3.98	4.03

$$\mu_2 = \sum_{i=1}^{20,000} x_i \frac{prob(distribution\ 2|x_i, \Theta)}{\sum_{i=1}^{20,000} prob(distribution\ 2|x_i, \Theta)} \tag{9.15}$$

We repeat these two steps until the estimates of μ_1 and μ_2 either don't change or change very little. Table 9.1 gives the first few iterations of the EM algorithm when it is applied to the set of 20,000 points. For this data, we know which distribution generated which point, so we can also compute the mean of the points from each distribution. The means are $\mu_1 = -3.98$ and $\mu_2 = 4.03$. ∎

Example 9.5 (The EM Algorithm on Sample Data Sets). We give three examples that illustrate the use of the EM algorithm to find clusters using mixture models. The first example is based on the data set used to illustrate the fuzzy c-means algorithm—see Figure 9.1. We modeled this data as a mixture of three two-dimensional Gaussian distributions with different means and identical covariance matrices. We then clustered the data using the EM algorithm. The results are shown in Figure 9.4. Each point was assigned to the cluster in which it had the largest membership weight. The points belonging to each cluster are shown by different marker shapes, while the degree of membership in the cluster is shown by the shading. Membership in a cluster is relatively weak for those points that are on the border of the two clusters, but strong elsewhere. It is interesting to compare the membership weights and probabilities of Figures 9.4 and 9.1. (See Exercise 11 on page 648.)

For our second example, we apply mixture model clustering to data that contains clusters with different densities. The data consists of two natural clusters, each with roughly 500 points. This data was created by combining two sets of Gaussian data, one with a center at $(-4,1)$ and a standard deviation of 2, and one with a center at $(0,0)$ and a standard deviation of 0.5. Figure 9.5 shows the clustering produced by the EM algorithm. Despite the differences in the density, the EM algorithm is quite successful at identifying the original clusters.

For our third example, we use mixture model clustering on a data set that K-means cannot properly handle. Figure 9.6(a) shows the clustering produced by a mixture model algorithm, while Figure 9.6(b) shows the K-means clustering of the same set of 1000 points. For mixture model clustering, each point has been assigned to the cluster for which it has the highest probability. In both figures, different markers are used to distinguish different clusters. Do not confuse the '+' and 'x' markers in Figure 9.6(a). ∎

Advantages and Limitations of Mixture Model Clustering Using the EM Algorithm

Finding clusters by modeling the data using mixture models and applying the EM algorithm to estimate the parameters of those models has a variety of advantages and disadvantages. On the negative side, the EM algorithm can be slow, it is not practical for models with large numbers of components, and it does not work well when clusters contain only a few data points or if the data points are nearly co-linear. There is also a problem in estimating the number of clusters or, more generally, in choosing the exact form of the model to use. This problem typically has been dealt with by applying a Bayesian approach, which, roughly speaking, gives the odds of one model versus another, based on an estimate derived from the data. Mixture models may also have difficulty with noise and outliers, although work has been done to deal with this problem.

On the positive side, mixture models are more general than K-means or fuzzy c-means because they can use distributions of various types. As a result, mixture models (based on Gaussian distributions) can find clusters of different sizes and elliptical shapes. Also, a model-based approach provides a disciplined way of eliminating some of the complexity associated with data. To see the patterns in data, it is often necessary to simplify the data, and fitting the data to a model is a good way to do that if the model is a good match for the data. Furthermore, it is easy to characterize the clusters produced, since they can be described by a small number of parameters. Finally, many sets of data are indeed the result of random processes, and thus should satisfy the statistical assumptions of these models.

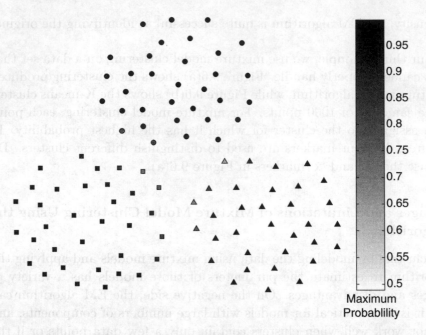

Figure 9.4. EM clustering of a two-dimensional point set with three clusters.

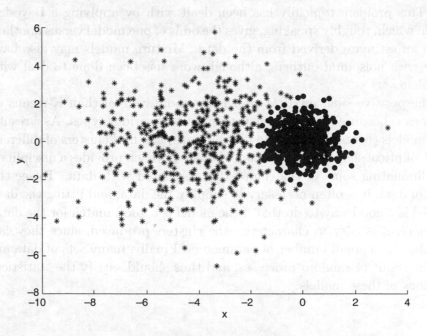

Figure 9.5. EM clustering of a two-dimensional point set with two clusters of differing density.

(a) Clusters produced by mixture model clustering.

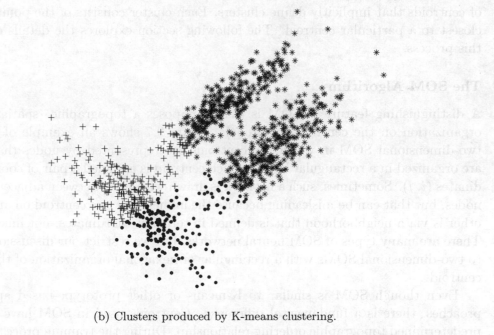

(b) Clusters produced by K-means clustering.

Figure 9.6. Mixture model and K-means clustering of a set of two-dimensional points.

9.2.3   Self-Organizing Maps (SOM)

The Kohonen Self-Organizing Feature Map (SOFM or SOM) is a clustering and data visualization technique based on a neural network viewpoint. Despite the neural network origins of SOM, it is more easily presented—at least in the context of this chapter—as a variation of prototype-based clustering. As with other types of centroid-based clustering, the goal of SOM is to find a set of centroids (**reference vectors** in SOM terminology) and to assign each object in the data set to the centroid that provides the best approximation of that object. In neural network terminology, there is one neuron associated with each centroid.

As with incremental K-means, data objects are processed one at a time and the closest centroid is updated. Unlike K-means, SOM imposes a topographic ordering on the centroids and nearby centroids are also updated. Furthermore, SOM does not keep track of the current cluster membership of an object, and, unlike K-means, if an object switches clusters, there is no explicit update of the old cluster centroid. Of course, the old cluster may well be in the neighborhood of the new cluster and thus may be updated for that reason. The processing of points continues until some predetermined limit is reached or the centroids are not changing very much. The final output of the SOM technique is a set of centroids that implicitly define clusters. Each cluster consists of the points closest to a particular centroid. The following section explores the details of this process.

The SOM Algorithm

A distinguishing feature of SOM is that it imposes a topographic (spatial) organization on the centroids (neurons). Figure 9.7 shows an example of a two-dimensional SOM in which the centroids are represented by nodes that are organized in a rectangular lattice. Each centroid is assigned a pair of coordinates (i, j). Sometimes, such a network is drawn with links between adjacent nodes, but that can be misleading because the influence of one centroid on another is via a neighborhood that is defined in terms of coordinates, not links. There are many types of SOM neural networks, but we restrict our discussion to two-dimensional SOMs with a rectangular or hexagonal organization of the centroids.

Even though SOM is similar to K-means or other prototype-based approaches, there is a fundamental difference. Centroids used in SOM have a predetermined topographic ordering relationship. During the training process, SOM uses each data point to update the closest centroid and centroids that are

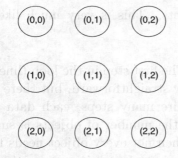

Figure 9.7. Two-dimensional 3-by-3 rectangular SOM neural network.

nearby in the topographic ordering. In this way, SOM produces an ordered set of centroids for any given data set. In other words, the centroids that are close to each other in the SOM grid are more closely related to each other than to the centroids that are farther away. Because of this constraint, the centroids of a two-dimensional SOM can be viewed as lying on a two-dimensional surface that tries to fit the n-dimensional data as well as possible. The SOM centroids can also be thought of as the result of a nonlinear regression with respect to the data points.

At a high level, clustering using the SOM technique consists of the steps described in Algorithm 9.3.

Algorithm 9.3 Basic SOM Algorithm.

1: Initialize the centroids.
2: **repeat**
3:    Select the next object.
4:    Determine the closest centroid to the object.
5:    Update this centroid and the centroids that are close, i.e., in a specified neighborhood.
6: **until** The centroids don't change much or a threshold is exceeded.
7: Assign each object to its closest centroid and return the centroids and clusters.

Initialization This step (line 1) can be performed in a number of ways. One approach is to choose each component of a centroid randomly from the range of values observed in the data for that component. While this approach works, it is not necessarily the best approach, especially for producing rapid convergence. Another approach is to randomly choose the initial centroids from the available data points. This is very much like randomly selecting centroids for K-means.

Selection of an Object   The first step in the loop (line 3) is the selection of the next object. This is fairly straightforward, but there are some difficulties. Since convergence may require many steps, each data object may be used multiple times, especially if the number of objects is small. However, if the number of objects is large, then not every object needs to be used. It is also possible to enhance the influence of certain groups of objects by increasing their frequency in the training set.

Assignment   The determination of the closest centroid (line 4) is also straightforward, although it requires the specification of a distance metric. The Euclidean distance metric is often used, as is the dot product metric. When using the dot product distance, the data vectors are typically normalized beforehand and the reference vectors are normalized at each step. In such cases, using the dot product metric is equivalent to using the cosine measure.

Update   The update step (line 5) is the most complicated. Let $\mathbf{m}_1, \ldots,$ $\mathbf{m}_k$ be the centroids. (For a rectangular grid, note that k is the product of the number of rows and the number of columns.) For time step t, let $\mathbf{p}(t)$ be the current object (point) and assume that the closest centroid to $\mathbf{p}(t)$ is $\mathbf{m}_j$. Then, for time $t + 1$, the jth centroid is updated by using the following equation. (We will see shortly that the update is really restricted to centroids whose neurons are in a small neighborhood of $\mathbf{m}_j$.)

$$\mathbf{m}_j(t+1) = \mathbf{m}_j(t) + h_j(t)(\mathbf{p}(t) - \mathbf{m}_j(t)) \tag{9.16}$$

Thus, at time t, a centroid $\mathbf{m}_j(t)$ is updated by adding a term, $h_j(t)\,(\mathbf{p}(t) - \mathbf{m}_j(t))$, which is proportional to the difference, $\mathbf{p}(t) - \mathbf{m}_j(t)$, between the centroid, $\mathbf{m}_j(t)$, and the current object, $\mathbf{p}(t)$. $h_j(t)$ determines the effect that the difference, $\mathbf{p}(t) - \mathbf{m}_j(t)$, will have and is chosen so that (1) it diminishes with time and (2) it enforces a neighborhood effect, i.e., the effect of an object is strongest on the centroids closest to the centroid $\mathbf{m}_j$. Here we are referring to the distance in the grid, not the distance in the data space. Typically, $h_j(t)$ is chosen to be one of the following two functions:

$$h_j(t) \;=\; \alpha(t)exp(-dist(\mathbf{r}_j, \mathbf{r}_k)^2/(2\sigma^2(t))) \qquad \text{(Gaussian function)}$$
$$h_j(t) \;=\; \alpha(t) \text{ if } dist(\mathbf{r}_j, \mathbf{r}_k) \leq threshold, \text{ 0 otherwise} \quad \text{(step function)}$$

These functions require more explanation. $\alpha(t)$ is a learning rate parameter, $0 < \alpha(t) < 1$, which decreases monotonically with time and controls the rate of convergence. $\mathbf{r}_k = (x_k, y_k)$ is the two-dimensional point that gives the grid coordinates of the kth centroid. $dist(\mathbf{r}_j, \mathbf{r}_k)$ is the Euclidean distance between the grid location of the two centroids, i.e., $\sqrt{(x_j - x_k)^2 + (y_j - y_k)^2}$. Consequently, for centroids whose grid locations are far from the grid location of centroid $\mathbf{m}_j$, the influence of object $\mathbf{p}(t)$ will be either greatly diminished or non-existent. Finally, note that σ is the typical Gaussian variance parameter and controls the width of the neighborhood, i.e., a small σ will yield a small neighborhood, while a large σ will yield a wide neighborhood. The threshold used for the step function also controls the neighborhood size.

Remember, it is the neighborhood updating technique that enforces a relationship (ordering) between centroids associated with neighboring neurons.

Termination Deciding when we are close enough to a stable set of centroids is an important issue. Ideally, iteration should continue until convergence occurs, that is, until the reference vectors either do not change or change very little. The rate of convergence will depend on a number of factors, such as the data and $\alpha(t)$. We will not discuss these issues further, except to mention that, in general, convergence can be slow and is not guaranteed.

Example 9.6 (Document Data). We present two examples. In the first case, we apply SOM with a 4-by-4 hexagonal grid to document data. We clustered 3204 newspaper articles from the *Los Angeles Times*, which come from 6 different sections: Entertainment, Financial, Foreign, Metro, National, and Sports. Figure 9.8 shows the SOM grid. We have used a hexagonal grid, which allows each centroid to have six immediate neighbors instead of four. Each SOM grid cell (cluster) has been labeled with the majority class label of the associated points. The clusters of each particular category form contiguous groups, and their position relative to other categories of clusters gives us additional information, e.g., that the Metro section contains stories related to all other sections. ∎

Example 9.7 (Two-Dimensional Points). In the second case, we use a rectangular SOM and a set of two-dimensional data points. Figure 9.9(a)

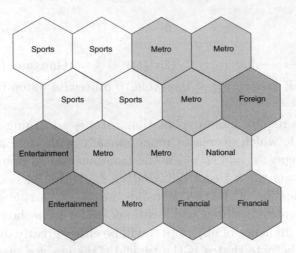

Figure 9.8. Visualization of the relationships between SOM cluster for *Los Angeles Times* document data set.

shows the points and the positions of the 36 reference vectors (shown as x's) produced by SOM. The points are arranged in a checkerboard pattern and are split into five classes: circles, triangles, squares, diamonds, and hexagons (stars). A 6-by-6 two-dimensional rectangular grid of centroids was used with random initialization. As Figure 9.9(a) shows, the centroids tend to distribute themselves to the dense areas. Figure 9.9(b) indicates the majority class of the points associated with that centroid. The clusters associated with triangle points are in one contiguous area, as are the centroids associated with the four other types of points. This is a result of the neighborhood constraints enforced by SOM. While there are the same number of points in each of the five groups, notice also that the centroids are not evenly distributed. This is partly due to the overall distribution of points and partly an artifact of putting each centroid in a single cluster. ∎

Applications

Once the SOM vectors are found, they can be used for many purposes other than clustering. For example, with a two-dimensional SOM, it is possible to associate various quantities with the grid points associated with each centroid (cluster) and to visualize the results via various types of plots. For example, plotting the number of points associated with each cluster yields a plot that reveals the distribution of points among clusters. A two-dimensional SOM is a non-linear projection of the original probability distribution function into two

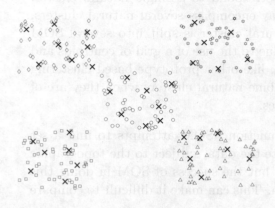

diamond	diamond	diamond	hexagon	hexagon	hexagon
diamond	diamond	diamond	circle	hexagon	hexagon
diamond	diamond	circle	circle	circle	hexagon
square	square	circle	circle	triangle	triangle
square	square	circle	circle	triangle	triangle
square	square	square	triangle	triangle	triangle

(a) Distribution of SOM reference vectors (**X**'s) for a two-dimensional point set.

(b) Classes of the SOM centroids.

Figure 9.9. SOM applied to two-dimensional data points.

dimensions. This projection attempts to preserve topological features; thus, using SOM to capture the structure of the data has been compared to the process of "pressing a flower."

Strengths and Limitations

SOM is a clustering technique that enforces neighborhood relationships on the resulting cluster centroids. Because of this, clusters that are neighbors are more related to one another than clusters that are not. Such relationships facilitate the interpretation and visualization of the clustering results. Indeed, this aspect of SOM has been exploited in many areas, such as visualizing Web documents or gene array data.

SOM also has a number of limitations, which are listed next. Some of the listed limitations are only valid if we consider SOM to be a standard clustering technique that aims to find the true clusters in the data, rather than a technique that uses clustering to help discover the structure of the data. Also, some of these limitations have been addressed either by extensions of SOM or by clustering algorithms inspired by SOM. (See the bibliographic notes.)

- The user must choose the settings of parameters, the neighborhood function, the grid type, and the number of centroids.

- A SOM cluster often does not correspond to a single natural cluster. In some cases, a SOM cluster may encompass several natural clusters, while in other cases a single natural cluster is split into several SOM clusters. This problem is partly due to the use of a grid of centroids and partly due to the fact that SOM, like other prototype-based clustering techniques, tends to split or combine natural clusters when they are of varying sizes, shapes, and densities.

- SOM lacks a specific objective function. SOM attempts to find a set of centroids that best approximate the data, subject to the topographic constraints among the centroids, but the success of SOM in doing this cannot be expressed by a function. This can make it difficult to compare different SOM clustering results.

- SOM is not guaranteed to converge, although, in practice, it typically does.

9.3   Density-Based Clustering

In Section 8.4, we considered DBSCAN, a simple, but effective algorithm for finding density-based clusters, i.e., dense regions of objects that are surrounded by low-density regions. This section examines additional density-based clustering techniques that address issues of efficiency, finding clusters in subspaces, and more accurately modeling density. First, we consider grid-based clustering, which breaks the data space into grid cells and then forms clusters from cells that are sufficiently dense. Such an approach can be efficient and effective, at least for low-dimensional data. Next, we consider subspace clustering, which looks for clusters (dense regions) in subsets of all dimensions. For a data space with n dimensions, potentially $2^n - 1$ subspaces need to be searched, and thus an efficient technique is needed to do this. CLIQUE is a grid-based clustering algorithm that provides an efficient approach to subspace clustering based on the observation that dense areas in a high-dimensional space imply the existence of dense areas in lower-dimensional space. Finally, we describe DENCLUE, a clustering technique that uses kernel density functions to model density as the sum of the influences of individual data objects. While DENCLUE is not fundamentally a grid-based technique, it does employ a grid-based approach to improve efficiency.

9.3.1 Grid-Based Clustering

A grid is an efficient way to organize a set of data, at least in low dimensions. The idea is to split the possible values of each attribute into a number of contiguous intervals, creating a set of grid cells. (We are assuming, for this discussion and the remainder of the section, that our attributes are ordinal, interval, or continuous.) Each object falls into a grid cell whose corresponding attribute intervals contain the values of the object. Objects can be assigned to grid cells in one pass through the data, and information about each cell, such as the number of points in the cell, can also be gathered at the same time.

There are a number of ways to perform clustering using a grid, but most approaches are based on density, at least in part, and thus, in this section, we will use grid-based clustering to mean density-based clustering using a grid. Algorithm 9.4 describes a basic approach to grid-based clustering. Various aspects of this approach are explored next.

Algorithm 9.4 Basic grid-based clustering algorithm.

1: Define a set of grid cells.
2: Assign objects to the appropriate cells and compute the density of each cell.
3: Eliminate cells having a density below a specified threshold, τ.
4: Form clusters from contiguous (adjacent) groups of dense cells.

Defining Grid Cells

This is a key step in the process, but also the least well defined, as there are many ways to split the possible values of each attribute into a number of contiguous intervals. For continuous attributes, one common approach is to split the values into equal width intervals. If this approach is applied to each attribute, then the resulting grid cells all have the same volume, and the density of a cell is conveniently defined as the number of points in the cell.

However, more sophisticated approaches can also be used. In particular, for continuous attributes any of the techniques that are commonly used to discretize attributes can be applied. (See Section 2.3.6.) In addition to the equal width approach already mentioned, this includes (1) breaking the values of an attribute into intervals so that each interval contains an equal number of points, i.e., equal frequency discretization, or (2) using clustering. Another approach, which is used by the subspace clustering algorithm MAFIA, initially breaks the set of values of an attribute into a large number of equal width intervals and then combines intervals of similar density.

Regardless of the approach taken, the definition of the grid has a strong impact on the clustering results. We will consider specific aspects of this later.

The Density of Grid Cells

A natural way to define the density of a grid cell (or a more generally shaped region) is as the number of points divided by the volume of the region. In other words, density is the number of points per amount of space, regardless of the dimensionality of that space. Specific, low-dimensional examples of density are the number of road signs per mile (one dimension), the number of eagles per square kilometer of habitat (two dimensions), and the number of molecules of a gas per cubic centimeter (three dimensions). As mentioned, however, a common approach is to use grid cells that have the same volume so that the number of points per cell is a direct measure of the cell's density.

Example 9.8 (Grid-Based Density). Figure 9.10 shows two sets of two-dimensional points divided into 49 cells using a 7-by-7 grid. The first set contains 200 points generated from a uniform distribution over a circle centered at (2, 3) of radius 2, while the second set has 100 points generated from a uniform distribution over a circle centered at (6, 3) of radius 1. The counts for the grid cells are shown in Table 9.2. Since the cells have equal volume (area), we can consider these values to be the densities of the cells. ∎

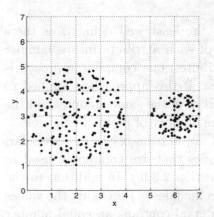

0	0	0	0	0	0	0
0	0	0	0	0	0	0
4	17	18	6	0	0	0
14	14	13	13	0	18	27
11	18	10	21	0	24	31
3	20	14	4	0	0	0
0	0	0	0	0	0	0

Figure 9.10. Grid-based density.   **Table 9.2.** Point counts for grid cells.

Forming Clusters from Dense Grid Cells

Forming clusters from adjacent groups of dense cells is relatively straightforward. (In Figure 9.10, for example, it is clear that there would be two clusters.) There are, however, some issues. We need to define what we mean by adjacent cells. For example, does a two-dimensional grid cell have 4 adjacent cells or 8? Also, we need an efficient technique to find the adjacent cells, particularly when only occupied cells are stored.

The clustering approach defined by Algorithm 9.4 has some limitations that could be addressed by making the algorithm slightly more sophisticated. For example, there are likely to be partially empty cells on the boundary of a cluster. Often, these cells are not dense. If so, they will be discarded and parts of a cluster will be lost. Figure 9.10 and Table 9.2 show that four parts of the larger cluster would be lost if the density threshold is 9. The clustering process could be modified to avoid discarding such cells, although this would require additional processing.

It is also possible to enhance basic grid-based clustering by using more than just density information. In many cases, the data has both spatial and non-spatial attributes. In other words, some of the attributes describe the location of objects in time or space, while other attributes describe other aspects of the objects. A common example is houses, which have both a location and a number of other characteristics, such as price or floor space in square feet. Because of spatial (or temporal) autocorrelation, objects in a particular cell often have similar values for their other attributes. In such cases, it is possible to filter the cells based on the statistical properties of one or more non-spatial attributes, e.g., average house price, and then form clusters based on the density of the remaining points.

Strengths and Limitations

On the positive side, grid-based clustering can be very efficient and effective. Given a partitioning of each attribute, a single pass through the data can determine the grid cell of every object and the count of every grid. Also, even though the number of potential grid cells can be high, grid cells need to be created only for non-empty cells. Thus, the time and space complexity of defining the grid, assigning each object to a cell, and computing the density of each cell is only $O(m)$, where m is the number of points. If adjacent, occupied cells can be efficiently accessed, for example, by using a search tree, then the entire clustering process will be highly efficient, e.g., with a time complexity of $O(m \log m)$. For this reason, the grid-based approach to density clustering forms the basis of a number of clustering algorithms, such as STING, GRIDCLUS, WaveCluster, Bang-Clustering, CLIQUE, and MAFIA.

On the negative side, grid-based clustering, like most density-based clustering schemes, is very dependent on the choice of the density threshold τ. If τ is too high, then clusters will be lost. If τ is too low, two clusters that should be separate may be joined. Furthermore, if there are clusters and noise of differing densities, then it may not be possible to find a single value of τ that works for all parts of the data space.

There are also a number of issues related to the grid-based approach. In Figure 9.10, for example, the rectangular grid cells do not accurately capture the density of the circular boundary areas. We could attempt to alleviate this problem by making the grid finer, but the number of points in the grid cells associated with a cluster would likely show more fluctuation since points in the cluster are not evenly distributed. Indeed, some grid cells, including those in the interior of the cluster, might even be empty. Another issue is that, depending on the placement or size of the cells, a group of points may appear in just one cell or be split between several different cells. The same group of points might be part of a cluster in the first case, but be discarded in the second. Finally, as dimensionality increases, the number of potential grid cells increases rapidly—exponentially in the number of dimensions. Even though it is not necessary to explicitly consider empty grid cells, it can easily happen that most grid cells contain a single object. In other words, grid-based clustering tends to work poorly for high-dimensional data.

9.3.2 Subspace Clustering

The clustering techniques considered until now found clusters by using all of the attributes. However, if only subsets of the features are considered, i.e., subspaces of the data, then the clusters that we find can be quite different from one subspace to another. There are two reasons that subspace clusters may be interesting. First, the data may be clustered with respect to a small set of attributes, but randomly distributed with respect to the remaining attributes. Second, there are cases in which different clusters exist in different sets of dimensions. Consider a data set that records the sales of various items at various times. (The times are the dimensions and the items are the objects.) Some items might show similar behavior (cluster together) for particular sets of months, e.g., summer, but different clusters would likely be characterized by different months (dimensions).

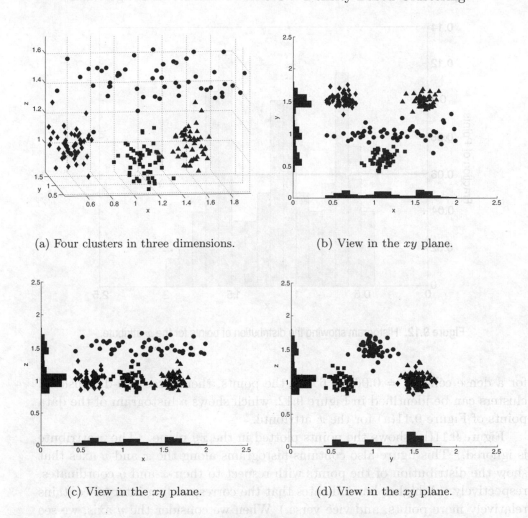

(a) Four clusters in three dimensions.

(b) View in the xy plane.

(c) View in the xy plane.

(d) View in the xy plane.

Figure 9.11. Example figures for subspace clustering.

Example 9.9 (Subspace Clusters). Figure 9.11(a) shows a set of points in three-dimensional space. There are three clusters of points in the full space, which are represented by squares, diamonds, and triangles. In addition, there is one set of points, represented by circles, that is not a cluster in three-dimensional space. Each dimension (attribute) of the example data set is split into a fixed number (η) of equal width intervals. There are $\eta = 20$ intervals, each of size 0.1. This partitions the data space into rectangular cells of equal volume, and thus, the density of each unit is the fraction of points it contains. Clusters are contiguous groups of dense cells. To illustrate, if the threshold

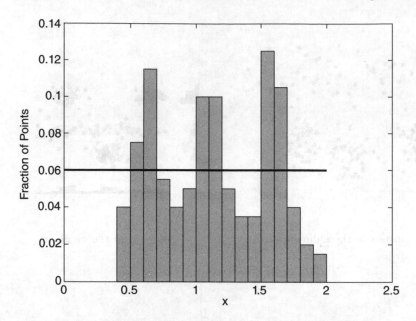

Figure 9.12. Histogram showing the distribution of points for the x attribute.

for a dense cell is $\xi = 0.06$, or 6% of the points, then three one-dimensional clusters can be identified in Figure 9.12, which shows a histogram of the data points of Figure 9.11(a) for the x attribute.

Figure 9.11(b) shows the points plotted in the xy plane. (The z attribute is ignored.) This figure also contains histograms along the x and y axes that show the distribution of the points with respect to their x and y coordinates, respectively. (A higher bar indicates that the corresponding interval contains relatively more points, and vice versa.) When we consider the y axis, we see three clusters. One is from the circle points that do not form a cluster in the full space, one consists of the square points, and one consists of the diamond and triangle points. There are also three clusters in the x dimension; they correspond to the three clusters—diamonds, triangles, and squares—in the full space. These points also form distinct clusters in the xy plane. Figure 9.11(c) shows the points plotted in the xz plane. There are two clusters, if we consider only the z attribute. One cluster corresponds to the points represented by circles, while the other consists of the diamond, triangle, and square points. These points also form distinct clusters in the xz plane. In Figure 9.11(d), there are three clusters when we consider both the y and z coordinates. One of these clusters consists of the circles; another consists of the points marked by squares. The diamonds and triangles form a single cluster in the yz plane.

These figures illustrate a couple of important facts. First, a set of points—the circles—may not form a cluster in the entire data space, but may form a cluster in a subspace. Second, clusters that exist in the full data space (or even a subspace) show up as clusters in lower-dimensional spaces. The first fact tells us that we may need to look in subsets of dimensions to find clusters, while the second fact tells us that many of the clusters we find in subspaces may only be "shadows" (projections) of higher-dimensional clusters. The goal is to find the clusters and the dimensions in which they exist, but we are typically not as interested in clusters that are projections of higher-dimensional clusters.

CLIQUE

CLIQUE (CLustering In QUEst) is a grid-based clustering algorithm that methodically finds subspace clusters. It is impractical to check each subspace for clusters since the number of such subspaces is exponential in the number of dimensions. Instead, CLIQUE relies on the following property:

Monotonicity property of density-based clusters If a set of points forms a density-based cluster in k dimensions (attributes), then the same set of points is also part of a density-based cluster in all possible subsets of those dimensions.

Consider a set of adjacent, k-dimensional cells that form a cluster; i.e., there is a collection of adjacent cells that have a density above the specified threshold ξ. A corresponding set of cells in $k-1$ dimensions can be found by omitting one of the k dimensions (attributes). The lower-dimensional cells are still adjacent, and each low-dimensional cell contains all points of the corresponding high-dimensional cell. It may contain additional points as well. Thus, a low-dimensional cell has a density greater than or equal to that of its corresponding high-dimensional cell. Consequently, the low-dimensional cells form a cluster; i.e., the points form a cluster with the reduced set of attributes.

Algorithm 9.5 gives a simplified version of the steps involved in CLIQUE. Conceptually, the CLIQUE algorithm is similar to the *Apriori* algorithm for finding frequent itemsets. See Chapter 6.

Strengths and Limitations of CLIQUE

The most useful feature of CLIQUE is that it provides an efficient technique for searching subspaces for clusters. Since this approach is based on the well-

---

Algorithm 9.5 CLIQUE.

1: Find all the dense areas in the one-dimensional spaces corresponding to each attribute. This is the set of dense one-dimensional cells.
2: $k \leftarrow 2$
3: **repeat**
4:    Generate all candidate dense k-dimensional cells from dense $(k-1)$-dimensional cells.
5:    Eliminate cells that have fewer than ξ points.
6:    $k \leftarrow k + 1$
7: **until** There are no candidate dense k-dimensional cells.
8: Find clusters by taking the union of all adjacent, high-density cells.
9: Summarize each cluster using a small set of inequalities that describe the attribute ranges of the cells in the cluster.

---

known *Apriori* principle from association analysis, its properties are well understood. Another useful feature is CLIQUE's ability to summarize the list of cells that comprises a cluster with a small set of inequalities.

Many limitations of CLIQUE are identical to the previously discussed limitations of other grid-based density schemes. Other limitations are similar to those of the *Apriori* algorithm. Specifically, just as frequent itemsets can share items, the clusters found by CLIQUE can share objects. Allowing clusters to overlap can greatly increase the number of clusters and make interpretation difficult. Another issue is that *Apriori* (and CLIQUE) potentially have exponential time complexity. In particular, CLIQUE will have difficulty if too many dense cells are generated at lower values of k. Raising the density threshold ξ can alleviate this problem. Still another potential limitation of CLIQUE is explored in Exercise 20 on page 650.

9.3.3   DENCLUE: A Kernel-Based Scheme for Density-Based Clustering

DENCLUE (DENsity CLUstEring) is a density-based clustering approach that models the overall density of a set of points as the sum of influence functions associated with each point. The resulting overall density function will have local peaks, i.e., local density maxima, and these local peaks can be used to define clusters in a natural way. Specifically, for each data point, a hill-climbing procedure finds the nearest peak associated with that point, and the set of all data points associated with a particular peak (called a **local density attractor**) becomes a cluster. However, if the density at a local peak is too low, then the points in the associated cluster are classified as noise

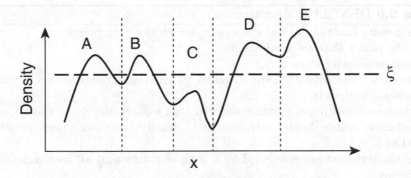

Figure 9.13. Illustration of DENCLUE density concepts in one dimension.

and discarded. Also, if a local peak can be connected to a second local peak by a path of data points, and the density at each point on the path is above the minimum density threshold, then the clusters associated with these local peaks are merged. Therefore, clusters of any shape can be discovered.

Example 9.10 (DENCLUE Density). We illustrate these concepts with Figure 9.13, which shows a possible density function for a one-dimensional data set. Points A–E are the peaks of this density function and represent local density attractors. The dotted vertical lines delineate local regions of influence for the local density attractors. Points in these regions will become center-defined clusters. The dashed horizontal line shows a density threshold, ξ. All points associated with a local density attractor that has a density less than ξ, such as those associated with C, will be discarded. All other clusters are kept. Note that this can include points whose density is less than ξ, as long as they are associated with local density attractors whose density is greater than ξ. Finally, clusters that are connected by a path of points with a density above ξ are combined. Clusters A and B would remain separate, while clusters D and E would be combined. ∎

The high-level details of the DENCLUE algorithm are summarized in Algorithm 9.6. Next, we explore various aspects of DENCLUE in more detail. First, we provide a brief overview of kernel density estimation and then present the grid-based approach that DENCLUE uses for approximating the density.

Kernel Density Estimation

DENCLUE is based on a well-developed area of statistics and pattern recognition that is known as **kernel density estimation**. The goal of this collection

---

Algorithm 9.6 DENCLUE algorithm.

1: Derive a density function for the space occupied by the data points.
2: Identify the points that are local maxima.
   (These are the density attractors.)
3: Associate each point with a density attractor by moving in the direction of maximum increase in density.
4: Define clusters consisting of points associated with a particular density attractor.
5: Discard clusters whose density attractor has a density less than a user-specified threshold of ξ.
6: Combine clusters that are connected by a path of points that all have a density of ξ or higher.

---

of techniques (and many other statistical techniques as well) is to describe the distribution of the data by a function. For kernel density estimation, the contribution of each point to the overall density function is expressed by an influence or **kernel function**. The overall density function is simply the sum of the influence functions associated with each point.

Typically, the influence or kernel function is symmetric (the same in all directions) and its value (contribution) decreases as the distance from the point increases. For example, for a particular point, $\mathbf{x}$, the Gaussian function, $K(y) = e^{-distance(\mathbf{x},\mathbf{y})^2/2\sigma^2}$, is often used as a kernel function. (σ is a parameter, which is analogous to the standard deviation) that governs how quickly the influence of a point drops off. Figure 9.14(a) shows what a Gaussian density function would look like for a single point in two dimensions, while Figures 9.14(c) and 9.14(d) show the overall density function produced by applying the Gaussian influence function to the set of points shown in Figure 9.14(b).

Implementation Issues

Computation of kernel density can be quite expensive, and DENCLUE uses a number of approximations to implement its basic approach efficiently. First, it explicitly computes density only at data points. However, this still would result in an $O(m^2)$ time complexity since the density at each point is a function of the density contributed by every point. To reduce the time complexity, DENCLUE uses a grid-based implementation to efficiently define neighborhoods and thus limit the number of points that need to be considered to define the density at a point. First, a preprocessing step creates a set of grid cells. Only occupied cells are created, and these cells and their related information can be efficiently accessed via a search tree. Then, when computing the density of a point and finding its nearest density attractor, DENCLUE considers only the points in

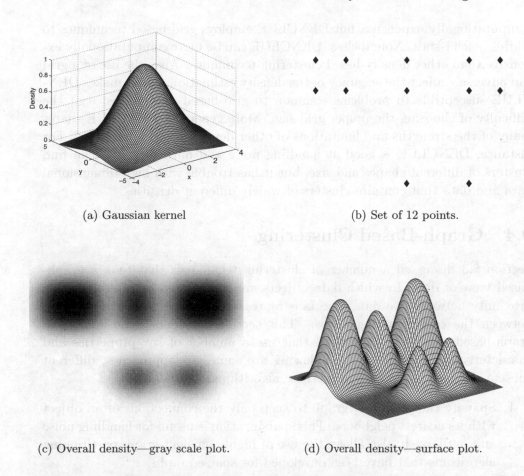

(a) Gaussian kernel

(b) Set of 12 points.

(c) Overall density—gray scale plot.

(d) Overall density—surface plot.

Figure 9.14. Example of the Gaussian influence (kernel) function and an overall density function.

the neighborhood; i.e., points in the same cell and in cells that are connected to the point's cell. While this approach can sacrifice some accuracy with respect to density estimation, computational complexity is greatly reduced.

Strengths and Limitations of DENCLUE

DENCLUE has a solid theoretical foundation because is based on kernel density functions and the notion of kernel density estimation, which is a well-developed area of statistics. For this reason, DENCLUE provides a more flexible and potentially more accurate way to compute density than other grid-based clustering techniques and DBSCAN. (DBSCAN is a special case of DENCLUE.) An approach based on kernel density functions is inherently computationally expensive, but DENCLUE employs grid-based techniques to address such issues. Nonetheless, DENCLUE can be more computationally expensive than other density-based clustering techniques. Also, the use of a grid can adversely affect the accuracy of the density estimation, and it makes DEN-CLUE susceptible to problems common to grid-based approaches; e.g., the difficulty of choosing the proper grid size. More generally, DENCLUE shares many of the strengths and limitations of other density-based approaches. For instance, DENCLUE is good at handling noise and outliers and it can find clusters of different shapes and size, but it has trouble with high-dimensional data and data that contains clusters of widely different densities.

9.4   Graph-Based Clustering

Section 8.3 discussed a number of clustering techniques that took a graph-based view of data, in which data objects are represented by nodes and the proximity between two data objects is represented by the weight of the edge between the corresponding nodes. This section considers some additional graph-based clustering algorithms that use a number of key properties and characteristics of graphs. The following are some key approaches, different subsets of which are employed by these algorithms.

1. Sparsify the proximity graph to keep only the connections of an object with its nearest neighbors. This sparsification is useful for handling noise and outliers. It also allows the use of highly efficient graph partitioning algorithms that have been developed for sparse graphs.

2. Define a similarity measure between two objects based on the number of nearest neighbors that they share. This approach, which is based on the observation that an object and its nearest neighbors usually belong to the same class, is useful for overcoming problems with high dimensionality and clusters of varying density.

3. Define core objects and build clusters around them. To do this for graph-based clustering, it is necessary to introduce a notion of density-based on a proximity graph or a sparsified proximity graph. As with DBSCAN, building clusters around core objects leads to a clustering technique that can find clusters of differing shapes and sizes.

4. Use the information in the proximity graph to provide a more sophisticated evaluation of whether two clusters should be merged. Specifically,

two clusters are merged only if the resulting cluster will have characteristics similar to the original two clusters.

We begin by discussing the sparsification of proximity graphs, providing two examples of techniques whose approach to clustering is based solely on this technique: MST, which is equivalent to the single link clustering algorithm, and Opossum. We then discuss Chameleon, a hierarchical clustering algorithm that uses a notion of self-similarity to determine if clusters should be merged. We next define Shared Nearest Neighbor (SNN) similarity, a new similarity measure, and introduce the Jarvis-Patrick clustering algorithm, which uses this similarity. Finally, we discuss how to define density and core objects based on SNN similarity and introduce an SNN density-based clustering algorithm, which can be viewed as DBSCAN with a new similarity measure.

9.4.1 Sparsification

The m by m proximity matrix for m data points can be represented as a dense graph in which each node is connected to all others and the weight of the edge between any pair of nodes reflects their pairwise proximity. Although every object has some level of similarity to every other object, for most data sets, objects are highly similar to a small number of objects and weakly similar to most other objects. This property can be used to sparsify the proximity graph (matrix), by setting many of these low-similarity (high-dissimilarity) values to 0 before beginning the actual clustering process. The sparsification may be performed, for example, by breaking all links that have a similarity (dissimilarity) below (above) a specified threshold or by keeping only links to the k nearest neighbors of point. This latter approach creates what is called a **k-nearest neighbor graph**.

Sparsification has several beneficial effects:

- **Data size is reduced.** The amount of data that needs to be processed to cluster the data is drastically reduced. Sparsification can often eliminate more than 99% of the entries in a proximity matrix. As a result, the size of problems that can be handled is increased.

- **Clustering may work better.** Sparsification techniques keep the connections to their nearest neighbors of an object while breaking the connections to more distant objects. This is in keeping with the **nearest neighbor principle** that the nearest neighbors of an object tend to belong to the same class (cluster) as the object itself. This reduces the impact of noise and outliers and sharpens the distinction between clusters.

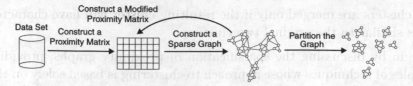

Figure 9.15. Ideal process of clustering using sparsification.

- **Graph partitioning algorithms can be used.** There has been a considerable amount of work on heuristic algorithms for finding min-cut partitionings of sparse graphs, especially in the areas of parallel computing and the design of integrated circuits. Sparsification of the proximity graph makes it possible to use graph partitioning algorithms for the clustering process. For example, Opossum and Chameleon use graph partitioning.

Sparsification of the proximity graph should be regarded as an initial step before the use of actual clustering algorithms. In theory, a perfect sparsification could leave the proximity matrix split into connected components corresponding to the desired clusters, but in practice, this rarely happens. It is easy for a single edge to link two clusters or for a single cluster to be split into several disconnected subclusters. Indeed, as we shall see when we discuss Jarvis-Patrick and SNN density-based clustering, the sparse proximity graph is often modified to yield a new proximity graph. This new proximity graph can again be sparsified. Clustering algorithms work with the proximity graph that is the result of all these preprocessing steps. This process is summarized in Figure 9.15.

9.4.2   Minimum Spanning Tree (MST) Clustering

In Section 8.3, where we described agglomerative hierarchical clustering techniques, we mentioned that divisive hierarchical clustering algorithms also exist. We saw an example of one such technique, bisecting K-means, in Section 8.2.3. Another divisive hierarchical technique, **MST**, starts with the minimum spanning tree of the proximity graph and can be viewed as an application of sparsification for finding clusters. We briefly describe this algorithm. Interestingly, this algorithm also produces the same clustering as single link agglomerative clustering. See Exercise 13 on page 648.

A **minimum spanning tree** of a graph is a subgraph that (1) has no cycles, i.e., is a tree, (2) contains all the nodes of the graph, and (3) has the minimum total edge weight of all possible spanning trees. The terminology,

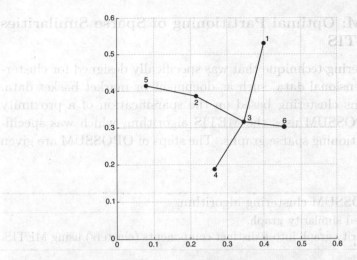

Figure 9.16. Minimum spanning tree for a set of six two-dimensional points.

minimum spanning tree, assumes that we are working only with dissimilarities or distances, and we will follow this convention. This is not a limitation, however, since we could convert similarities to dissimilarities or modify the notion of a minimum spanning tree to work with similarities. An example of a minimum spanning tree for some two-dimensional points is shown in Figure 9.16.

The MST divisive hierarchical algorithm is shown in Algorithm 9.7. The first step is to find the MST of the original dissimilarity graph. Note that a minimum spanning tree can be viewed as a special type of sparsified graph. Step 3 can also be viewed as graph sparsification. Hence, MST can be viewed as a clustering algorithm based on the sparsification of the dissimilarity graph.

Algorithm 9.7 MST divisive hierarchical clustering algorithm.

1: Compute a minimum spanning tree for the dissimilarity graph.
2: **repeat**
3:     Create a new cluster by breaking the link corresponding to the largest dissimilarity.
4: **until** Only singleton clusters remain.

9.4.3   OPOSSUM: Optimal Partitioning of Sparse Similarities Using METIS

OPOSSUM is a clustering technique that was specifically designed for clustering sparse, high dimensional data, such as document or market basket data. Like MST, it performs clustering based on the sparsification of a proximity graph. However, OPOSSUM uses the METIS algorithm, which was specifically created for partitioning sparse graphs. The steps of OPOSSUM are given in Algorithm 9.8.

Algorithm 9.8 OPOSSUM clustering algorithm.

1: Compute a sparsified similarity graph.
2: Partition the similarity graph into k distinct components (clusters) using METIS.

The similarity measures used are those appropriate for sparse, high dimensional data, such as the extended Jaccard measure or the cosine measure. The METIS graph partitioning program partitions a sparse graph into k distinct components, where k is a user-specified parameter, in order to (1) minimize the weight of the edges (the similarity) between components and (2) fulfill a balance constraint. OPOSSUM uses one of the following two balance constraints: (1) the number of objects in each cluster must be roughly the same, or (2) the sum of the attribute values must be roughly the same. The second constraint is useful when, for example, the attribute values represent the cost of an item.

Strengths and Weaknesses

OPOSSUM is simple and fast. It partitions the data into roughly equal-sized clusters, which, depending on the goal of the clustering, can be viewed as an advantage or a disadvantage. Because they are constrained to be of roughly equal size, clusters can be broken or combined. However, if OPOSSUM is used to generate a large number of clusters, then these clusters are typically relatively pure pieces of larger clusters. Indeed, OPOSSUM is similar to the initial step of the Chameleon clustering routine, which is discussed next.

9.4.4   Chameleon: Hierarchical Clustering with Dynamic Modeling

Agglomerative hierarchical clustering techniques operate by merging the two most similar clusters, where the definition of cluster similarity depends on

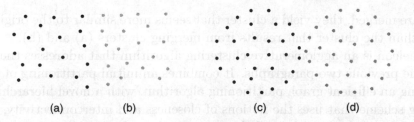

(a)   (b)   (c)   (d)

Figure 9.17. Situation in which closeness is not the appropriate merging criterion. ©1999, IEEE

the particular algorithm. Some agglomerative algorithms, such as group average, base their notion of similarity on the strength of the connections between the two clusters (e.g., the pairwise similarity of points in the two clusters), while other techniques, such as the single link method, use the closeness of the clusters (e.g., the minimum distance between points in different clusters) to measure cluster similarity. Although there are two basic approaches, using only one of these two approaches may lead to mistakes in merging clusters. Consider Figure 9.17, which shows four clusters. If we use the closeness of clusters (as measured by the closest two points in different clusters) as our merging criterion, then we would merge the two circular clusters, (c) and (d),which almost touch, instead of the rectangular clusters, (a) and (b), which are separated by a small gap. However, intuitively, we should have merged rectangular clusters, (a) and (b). Exercise 15 on page 649 asks for an example of a situation in which the strength of connections likewise leads to an unintuitive result.

Another problem is that most clustering techniques have a global (static) model of clusters. For instance, K-means assumes that the clusters will be globular, while DBSCAN defines clusters based on a single density threshold. Clustering schemes that use such a global model cannot handle cases in which cluster characteristics, such as size, shape, and density, vary widely between clusters. As an example of the importance of the local (dynamic) modeling of clusters, consider Figure 9.18. If we use the closeness of clusters to determine which pair of clusters should be merged, as would be the case if we used, for example, the single link clustering algorithm, then we would merge clusters (a) and (b). However, we have not taken into account the characteristics of each individual cluster. Specifically, we have ignored the density of the individual clusters. For clusters (a) and (b), which are relatively dense, the distance between the two clusters is significantly larger than the distance between a point and its nearest neighbors within the same cluster. This is not the case for clusters (c) and (d), which are relatively sparse. Indeed, when clusters (c) and (d) are merged, they yield a cluster that seems more similar to the original clusters than the cluster that results from merging clusters (a) and (b).

Chameleon is an agglomerative clustering algorithm that addresses the issues of the previous two paragraphs. It combines an initial partitioning of the data, using an efficient graph partitioning algorithm, with a novel hierarchical clustering scheme that uses the notions of closeness and interconnectivity, together with the local modeling of clusters. The key idea is that two clusters should be merged only if the resulting cluster is similar to the two original clusters. Self-similarity is described first, and then the remaining details of the Chameleon algorithm are presented.

Deciding Which Clusters to Merge

The agglomerative hierarchical clustering techniques considered in Section 8.3 repeatedly combine the two closest clusters and are principally distinguished from one another by the way they define cluster proximity. In contrast, Chameleon aims to merge the pair of clusters that results in a cluster that is most similar to the original pair of clusters, as measured by closeness and interconnectivity. Because this approach depends only on the pair of clusters and not on a global model, Chameleon can handle data that contains clusters with widely different characteristics.

Following are more detailed explanations of the properties of closeness and interconnectivity. To understand these properties, it is necessary to take a proximity graph viewpoint and to consider the number of the links and the strength of those links among points within a cluster and across clusters.

- **Relative Closeness (RC)** is the absolute closeness of two clusters normalized by the internal closeness of the clusters. Two clusters are combined only if the points in the resulting cluster are almost as close to each other as in each of the original clusters. Mathematically,

$$RC = \frac{\bar{S}_{EC}(C_i, C_j)}{\frac{m_i}{m_i + m_j} \bar{S}_{EC}(C_i) + \frac{m_j}{m_i + m_j} \bar{S}_{EC}(C_j)}, \qquad (9.17)$$

  where m_i and m_j are the sizes of clusters C_i and C_j, respectively, $\bar{S}_{EC}(C_i, C_j)$ is the average weight of the edges (of the k-nearest neighbor graph) that connect clusters C_i and C_j; $\bar{S}_{EC}(C_i)$ is the average weight of edges if we bisect cluster C_i; and $\bar{S}_{EC}(C_j)$ is the average weight of edges if we bisect cluster C_j. (*EC* stands for edge cut.) Figure 9.18 illustrates the notion of relative closeness. As discussed previously, while clusters

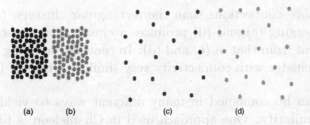

Figure 9.18. Illustration of the notion of relative closeness. ©1999, IEEE

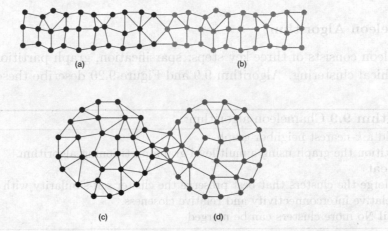

Figure 9.19. Illustration of the notion of relative interconnectedness. ©1999, IEEE

(a) and (b) are closer in absolute terms than clusters (c) and (d), this is not true if the nature of the clusters is taken into account.

- **Relative Interconnectivity (RI)** is the absolute interconnectivity of two clusters normalized by the internal connectivity of the clusters. Two clusters are combined if the points in the resulting cluster are almost as strongly connected as points in each of the original clusters. Mathematically,

$$RI = \frac{EC(C_i, C_j)}{\frac{1}{2}(EC(C_i) + EC(C_j))},\qquad (9.18)$$

where $EC(C_i, C_j)$ is the sum of the edges (of the k-nearest neighbor graph) that connect clusters C_i and C_j; $EC(C_i)$ is the minimum sum of the cut edges if we bisect cluster C_i; and $EC(C_j)$ is the minimum sum of the cut edges if we bisect cluster C_j. Figure 9.19 illustrates the notion of relative interconnectivity. The two circular clusters, (c) and (d), have more connections than the rectangular clusters, (a) and (b). However, merging (c) and (d) produces a cluster that has connectivity quite different from that of (c) and (d). In contrast, merging (a) and (b) produces a cluster with connectivity very similar to that of (a) and (b).

RI and RC can be combined in many different ways to yield an overall measure of self-similarity. One approach used in Chameleon is to merge the pair of clusters that maximizes $RI(C_i, C_j) * RC(C_i, C_j)^\alpha$, where α is a user-specified parameter that is typically greater than 1.

Chameleon Algorithm

Chameleon consists of three key steps: sparsification, graph partitioning, and hierarchical clustering. Algorithm 9.9 and Figure 9.20 describe these steps.

Algorithm 9.9 Chameleon algorithm.

1: Build a k-nearest neighbor graph.
2: Partition the graph using a multilevel graph partitioning algorithm.
3: **repeat**
4:    Merge the clusters that best preserve the cluster self-similarity with respect to relative interconnectivity and relative closeness.
5: **until** No more clusters can be merged.

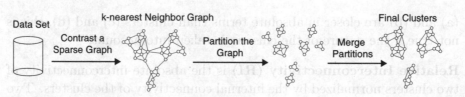

Figure 9.20. Overall process by which Chameleon performs clustering. ©1999, IEEE

Sparsification The first step in Chameleon is to generate a k-nearest neighbor graph. Conceptually, such a graph is derived from the proximity graph, and it contains links only between a point and its k nearest neighbors, i.e., the points to which it is closest. As mentioned, working with a sparsified proximity graph instead of the full proximity graph can significantly reduce the effects of noise and outliers and improve computational efficiency.

Graph Partitioning

Once a sparsified graph has been obtained, an efficient multilevel graph partitioning algorithm, such as METIS (see bibliographic notes) can be used to partition the data set. Chameleon starts with an all-inclusive graph (cluster) and then bisects the largest current subgraph (cluster) until no cluster has more than MIN_SIZE points, where MIN_SIZE is a user-specified parameter. This process results in a large number of roughly equally sized groups of well-connected vertices (highly similar data points). The goal is to ensure that each partition contains objects mostly from one true cluster.

Agglomerative Hierarchical Clustering As discussed previously, Chameleon merges clusters based on the notion of self-similarity. Chameleon can be parameterized to merge more than one pair of clusters in a single step and to stop before all objects have been merged into a single cluster.

Complexity Assume that m is the number of data points and p is the number of partitions. Performing an agglomerative hierarchical clustering of the p partitions obtained from the graph partitioning requires time $O(p^2 \log p)$. (See Section 8.3.1.) The amount of time required for partitioning the graph is $O(mp + m \log m)$. The time complexity of graph sparsification depends on how much time it takes to build the k-nearest neighbor graph. For low-dimensional data, this takes $O(m \log m)$ time if a k-d tree or a similar type of data structure is used. Unfortunately, such data structures only work well for low-dimensional data sets, and thus, for high-dimensional data sets, the time complexity of the sparsification becomes $O(m^2)$. Since only the k-nearest neighbor list needs to be stored, the space complexity is $O(km)$ plus the space required to store the data.

Example 9.11. Chameleon was applied to two data sets that clustering algorithms such as K-means and DBSCAN have difficulty clustering. The results of this clustering are shown in Figure 9.21. The clusters are identified by the shading of the points. In Figure 9.21(a), the two clusters are irregularly shaped and quite close to each other. Also, noise is present. In Figure 9.21(b), the two clusters are connected by a bridge, and again, noise is present. Nonetheless, Chameleon identifies what most people would identify as the natural clusters. Chameleon has specifically been shown to be very effective for clustering spatial data. Finally, notice that Chameleon does not discard noise points, as do other clustering schemes, but instead assigns them to the clusters. ∎

(a)   **(b)**

Figure 9.21. Chameleon applied to cluster a pair of two-dimensional sets of points. ©1999, IEEE

Strengths and Limitations

Chameleon can effectively cluster spatial data, even though noise and outliers
are present and the clusters are of different shapes, sizes, and density. Chameleon assumes that the groups of objects produced by the sparsification and
graph partitioning process are subclusters; i.e., that most of the points in a
partition belong to the same true cluster. If not, then agglomerative hierarchical clustering will only compound the errors since it can never separate
objects that have been wrongly put together. (See the discussion in Section
8.3.4.) Thus, Chameleon has problems when the partitioning process does not
produce subclusters, as is often the case for high-dimensional data.

9.4.5   Shared Nearest Neighbor Similarity

In some cases, clustering techniques that rely on standard approaches to similarity and density do not produce the desired clustering results. This section
examines the reasons for this and introduces an indirect approach to similarity
that is based on the following principle:

> If two points are similar to many of the same points, then they are
> similar to one another, even if a direct measurement of similarity
> does not indicate this.

We motivate the discussion by first explaining two problems that an SNN
version of similarity addresses: low similarity and differences in density.

Problems with Traditional Similarity in High-Dimensional Data

In high-dimensional spaces, it is not unusual for similarity to be low. Consider, for example, a set of documents such as a collection of newspaper articles

Table 9.3. Similarity among documents in different sections of a newspaper.

Section	Average Cosine Similarity
Entertainment	0.032
Financial	0.030
Foreign	0.030
Metro	0.021
National	0.027
Sports	0.036
All Sections	0.014

that come from a variety of sections of the newspaper: Entertainment, Financial, Foreign, Metro, National, and Sports. As explained in Chapter 2, these documents can be viewed as vectors in a high-dimensional space, where each component of the vector (attribute) records the number of times that each word in a vocabulary occurs in a document. The cosine similarity measure is often used to assess the similarity between documents. For this example, which comes from a collection of articles from the *Los Angeles Times*, Table 9.3 gives the average cosine similarity in each section and among the entire set of documents.

The similarity of each document to its most similar document (the first nearest neighbor) is better, 0.39 on average. However, a consequence of low similarity among objects of the same class is that their nearest neighbor is often not of the same class. In the collection of documents from which Table 9.3 was generated, about 20% of the documents have a nearest neighbor of a different class. In general, if direct similarity is low, then it becomes an unreliable guide for clustering objects, especially for agglomerative hierarchical clustering, where the closest points are put together and cannot be separated afterward. Nonetheless, it is still usually the case that a large majority of the nearest neighbors of an object belong to the same class; this fact can be used to define a proximity measure that is more suitable for clustering.

Problems with Differences in Density

Another problem relates to differences in densities between clusters. Figure 9.22 shows a pair of two-dimensional clusters of points with differing density. The lower density of the rightmost cluster is reflected in a lower average distance among the points. Even though the points in the less dense cluster form an equally valid cluster, typical clustering techniques will have more difficulty finding such clusters. Also, normal measures of cohesion, such as SSE, will indicate that these clusters are less cohesive. To illustrate with a real example,

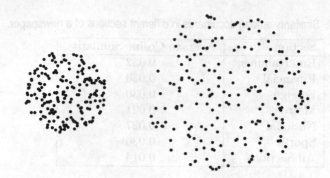

Figure 9.22. Two circular clusters of 200 uniformly distributed points.

the stars in a galaxy are no less real clusters of stellar objects than the planets in a solar system, even though the planets in a solar system are considerably closer to one another on average, than the stars in a galaxy.

SNN Similarity Computation

In both situations, the key idea is to take the context of points into account in defining the similarity measure. This idea can be made quantitative by using a **shared nearest neighbor** definition of similarity in the manner indicated by Algorithm 9.10. Essentially, the SNN similarity is the number of shared neighbors as long as the two objects are on each other's nearest neighbor lists. Note that the underlying proximity measure can be any meaningful similarity or dissimilarity measure.

Algorithm 9.10 Computing shared nearest neighbor similarity

1: Find the k-nearest neighbors of all points.
2: **if** two points, $\mathbf{x}$ and $\mathbf{y}$ are *not* among the k-nearest neighbors of each other **then**
3:     $similarity(\mathbf{x}, \mathbf{y}) \leftarrow 0$
4: **else**
5:     $similarity(\mathbf{x}, \mathbf{y}) \leftarrow$ number of shared neighbors
6: **end if**

The computation of SNN similarity is described by Algorithm 9.10 and graphically illustrated by Figure 9.23. Each of the two black points has eight nearest neighbors, including each other. Four of those nearest neighbors—the points in gray—are shared. Thus, the shared nearest neighbor similarity between the two points is 4.

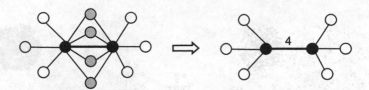

Figure 9.23. Computation of SNN similarity between two points.

The similarity graph of the SNN similarities among objects is called the **SNN similarity graph**. Since many pairs of objects will have an SNN similarity of 0, this is a very sparse graph.

SNN Similarity versus Direct Similarity

SNN similarity is useful because it addresses some of the problems that occur with direct similarity. First, since it takes into account the context of an object by using the number of shared nearest neighbors, SNN similarity handles the situation in which an object happens to be relatively close to another object, but belongs to a different class. In such cases, the objects typically do not share many near neighbors and their SNN similarity is low.

SNN similarity also addresses problems with clusters of varying density. In a low-density region, the objects are farther apart than objects in denser regions. However, the SNN similarity of a pair of points only depends on the number of nearest neighbors two objects share, not how far these neighbors are from each object. Thus, SNN similarity performs an automatic scaling with respect to the density of the points.

9.4.6 The Jarvis-Patrick Clustering Algorithm

Algorithm 9.11 expresses the Jarvis-Patrick clustering algorithm using the concepts of the last section. The JP clustering algorithm replaces the proximity between two points with the SNN similarity, which is calculated as described in Algorithm 9.10. A threshold is then used to sparsify this matrix of SNN similarities. In graph terms, an SNN similarity graph is created and sparsified. Clusters are simply the connected components of the SNN graph.

Algorithm 9.11 Jarvis-Patrick clustering algorithm.

1: Compute the SNN similarity graph.
2: Sparsify the SNN similarity graph by applying a similarity threshold.
3: Find the connected components (clusters) of the sparsified SNN similarity graph.

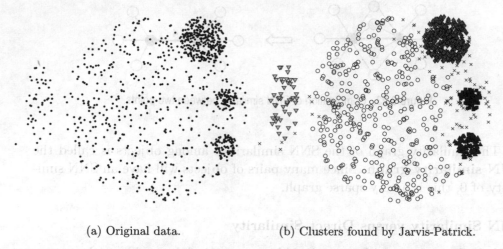

(a) Original data.   (b) Clusters found by Jarvis-Patrick.

Figure 9.24. Jarvis-Patrick clustering of a two-dimensional point set.

The storage requirements of the JP clustering algorithm are only $O(km)$, since it is not necessary to store the entire similarity matrix, even initially. The basic time complexity of JP clustering is $O(m^2)$, since the creation of the k-nearest neighbor list can require the computation of $O(m^2)$ proximities. However, for certain types of data, such as low-dimensional Euclidean data, special techniques, e.g., a k-d tree, can be used to more efficiently find the k-nearest neighbors without computing the entire similarity matrix. This can reduce the time complexity from $O(m^2)$ to $O(m \log m)$.

Example 9.12 (JP Clustering of a Two-Dimensional Data Set). We applied JP clustering to the "fish" data set shown in Figure 9.24(a) to find the clusters shown in Figure 9.24(b). The size of the nearest neighbor list was 20, and two points were placed in the same cluster if they shared at least 10 points. The different clusters are shown by the different markers and different shading. The points whose marker is an "x" were classified as noise by Jarvis-Patrick. They are mostly in the transition regions between clusters of different density. ∎

Strengths and Limitations

Because JP clustering is based on the notion of SNN similarity, it is good at dealing with noise and outliers and can handle clusters of different sizes, shapes, and densities. The algorithm works well for high-dimensional data and is particularly good at finding tight clusters of strongly related objects.

However, JP clustering defines a cluster as a connected component in the SNN similarity graph. Thus, whether a set of objects is split into two clusters or left as one may depend on a single link. Hence, JP clustering is somewhat brittle; i.e., it may split true clusters or join clusters that should be kept separate.

Another potential limitation is that not all objects are clustered. However, these objects can be added to existing clusters, and in some cases, there is no requirement for a complete clustering. JP clustering has a basic time complexity of $O(m^2)$, which is the time required to compute the nearest neighbor list for a set of objects in the general case. In certain cases, e.g., low-dimensional data, special techniques can be used to reduce the time complexity for finding nearest neighbors to $O(m \log m)$. Finally, as with other clustering algorithms, choosing the best values for the parameters can be challenging.

9.4.7   SNN Density

As discussed in the introduction to this chapter, traditional Euclidean density becomes meaningless in high dimensions. This is true whether we take a grid-based view, such as that used by CLIQUE, a center-based view, such as that used by DBSCAN, or a kernel-density estimation approach, such as that used by DENCLUE. It is possible to use the center-based definition of density with a similarity measure that works well for high dimensions, e.g., cosine or Jaccard, but as described in Section 9.4.5, such measures still have problems. However, since the SNN similarity measure reflects the local configuration of the points in the data space, it is relatively insensitive to variations in density and the dimensionality of the space, and is a promising candidate for a new measure of density.

This section explains how to define a concept of SNN density by using SNN similarity and following the DBSCAN approach described in Section 8.4. For clarity, the definitions of that section are repeated, with appropriate modification to account for the fact that we are using SNN similarity.

Core points. A point is a core point if the number of points within a given neighborhood around the point, as determined by SNN similarity and a supplied parameter *Eps* exceeds a certain threshold *MinPts*, which is also a supplied parameter.

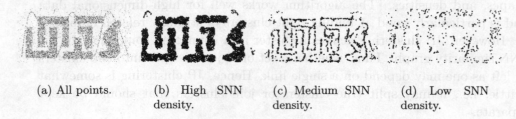

| (a) All points. | (b) High SNN density. | (c) Medium SNN density. | (d) Low SNN density. |

Figure 9.25. SNN density of two-dimensional points.

Border points. A border point is a point that is not a core point, i.e., there are not enough points in its neighborhood for it to be a core point, but it falls within the neighborhood of a core point.

Noise points. A noise point is any point that is neither a core point nor a border point.

SNN density measures the degree to which a point is surrounded by similar points (with respect to nearest neighbors). Thus, points in regions of high and low density will typically have relatively high SNN density, while points in regions where there is a transition from low to high density—points that are between clusters—will tend to have low SNN density. Such an approach may be better suited for data sets in which there are wide variations in density, but clusters of low density are still interesting.

Example 9.13 (Core, Border, and Noise Points). To make the preceding discussion of SNN density more concrete, we provide an example of how SNN density can be used to find core points and remove noise and outliers. There are 10,000 points in the 2D point data set shown in Figure 9.25(a). Figures 9.25(b–d) distinguish between these points based on their SNN density. Figure 9.25(b) shows the points with the highest SNN density, while Figure 9.25(c) shows points of intermediate SNN density, and Figure 9.25(d) shows figures of the lowest SNN density. From these figures, we see that the points that have high density (i.e., high connectivity in the SNN graph) are candidates for being representative or core points since they tend to be located well inside the cluster, while the points that have low connectivity are candidates for being noise points and outliers, as they are mostly in the regions surrounding the clusters. ∎

9.4.8 SNN Density-Based Clustering

The SNN density defined above can be combined with the DBSCAN algorithm to create a new clustering algorithm. This algorithm is similar to the JP clustering algorithm in that it starts with the SNN similarity graph. However, instead of using a threshold to sparsify the SNN similarity graph and then taking connected components as clusters, the SNN density-based clustering algorithm simply applies DBSCAN.

The SNN Density-based Clustering Algorithm

The steps of the SNN density-based clustering algorithm are shown in Algorithm 9.12.

Algorithm 9.12 SNN density-based clustering algorithm.

1: Compute the SNN similarity graph.
2: Apply DBSCAN with user-specified parameters for *Eps* and *MinPts*.

The algorithm automatically determines the number of clusters in the data. Note that not all the points are clustered. The points that are discarded include noise and outliers, as well as points that are not strongly connected to a group of points. SNN density-based clustering finds clusters in which the points are strongly related to one another. Depending on the application, we might want to discard many of the points. For example, SNN density-based clustering is good for finding topics in groups of documents.

Example 9.14 (SNN Density-based Clustering of Time Series). The SNN density-based clustering algorithm presented in this section is more flexible than Jarvis-Patrick clustering or DBSCAN. Unlike DBSCAN, it can be used for high-dimensional data and situations in which the clusters have different densities. Unlike Jarvis-Patrick, which performs a simple thresholding and then takes the connected components as clusters, SNN density-based clustering uses a less brittle approach that relies on the concepts of SNN density and core points.

To demonstrate the capabilities of SNN density-based clustering on high-dimensional data, we applied it to monthly time series data of atmospheric pressure at various points on the Earth. More specifically, the data consists of the average monthly sea-level pressure (SLP) for a period of 41 years at each point on a 2.5° longitude-latitude grid. The SNN density-based clustering algorithm found the clusters (gray regions) indicated in Figure 9.26. Note that these are clusters of time series of length 492 months, even though they are visualized as two-dimensional regions. The white areas are regions in which the pressure was not as uniform. The clusters near the poles are elongated because of the distortion of mapping a spherical surface to a rectangle.

Using SLP, Earth scientists have defined time series, called **climate indices**, that are useful for capturing the behavior of phenomena involving the Earth's climate. For example, anomalies in climate indices are related to abnormally low or high precipitation or temperature in various parts of the world. Some of the clusters found by SNN density-based clustering have a strong connection to some of the climate indices known to Earth scientists.

Figure 9.27 shows the SNN density structure of the data from which the clusters were extracted. The density has been normalized to be on a scale between 0 and 1. The density of a time series may seem like an unusual concept, but it measures the degree to which the time series and its nearest neighbors have the same nearest neighbors. Since each time series is associated with a location, it is possible to plot these densities on a two-dimensional plot. Because of temporal autocorrelation, these densities form meaningful patterns, e.g., it is possible to visually identify the clusters of Figure 9.27. ∎

Strengths and Limitations

The strengths and limitations of SNN density-based clustering are similar to those of JP clustering. However, the use of core points and SNN density adds considerable power and flexibility to this approach.

9.5   Scalable Clustering Algorithms

Even the best clustering algorithm is of little value if it takes an unacceptably long time to execute or requires too much memory. This section examines clustering techniques that place significant emphasis on scalability to the very large data sets that are becoming increasingly common. We start by discussing some general strategies for scalability, including approaches for reducing the number of proximity calculations, sampling the data, partitioning the data, and clustering a summarized representation of the data. We then discuss two specific examples of scalable clustering algorithms: CURE and BIRCH.

9.5.1   Scalability: General Issues and Approaches

The amount of storage required for many clustering algorithms is more than linear; e.g., with hierarchical clustering, memory requirements are usually

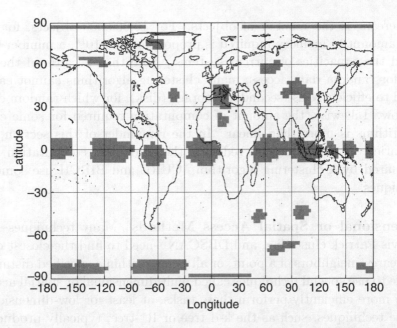

Figure 9.26. Clusters of pressure time series found using SNN density-based clustering.

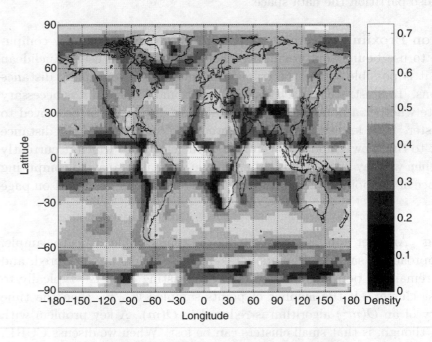

Figure 9.27. SNN density of pressure time series.

$O(m^2)$, where m is the number of objects. For 10,000,000 objects, for example, the amount of memory required is proportional to 10^{14}, a number still well beyond the capacities of current systems. Note that because of the requirement for random data access, many clustering algorithms cannot easily be modified to efficiently use secondary storage (disk), for which random data access is slow. Likewise, the amount of computation required for some clustering algorithms is more than linear. In the remainder of this section, we discuss a variety of techniques for reducing the amount of computation and storage required by a clustering algorithm. CURE and BIRCH use some of these techniques.

Multidimensional or Spatial Access Methods   Many techniques—K-means, Jarvis Patrick clustering, and DBSCAN—need to find the closest centroid, the nearest neighbors of a point, or all points within a specified distance. It is possible to use special techniques called multidimensional or spatial access methods to more efficiently perform these tasks, at least for low-dimensional data. These techniques, such as the k-d tree or R*-tree, typically produce a hierarchical partition of the data space that can be used to reduce the time required to find the nearest neighbors of a point. Note that grid-based clustering schemes also partition the data space.

Bounds on Proximities   Another approach to avoiding proximity computations is to use bounds on proximities. For instance, when using Euclidean distance, it is possible to use the triangle inequality to avoid many distance calculations. To illustrate, at each stage of traditional K-means, it is necessary to evaluate whether a point should stay in its current cluster or be moved to a new cluster. If we know the distance between the centroids and the distance of a point to the (newly updated) centroid of the cluster to which it currently belongs, then we may be able to use the triangle inequality to avoid computing the distance of the point to any of the other centroids. See Exercise 21 on page 650.

Sampling   Another approach to reducing the time complexity is to sample. In this approach, a sample of points is taken, these points are clustered, and then the remaining points are assigned to the existing clusters—typically to the closest cluster. If the number of points sampled is $\sqrt{m}$, then the time complexity of an $O(m^2)$ algorithm is reduced to $O(m)$. A key problem with sampling, though, is that small clusters can be lost. When we discuss CURE, we will provide a technique for investigating how frequently such problems occur.

Partitioning the Data Objects Another common approach to reducing time complexity is to use some efficient technique to partition the data into disjoint sets and then cluster these sets separately. The final set of clusters either is the union of these separate sets of clusters or is obtained by combining and/or refining the separate sets of clusters. We only discuss bisecting K-means (Section 8.2.3) in this section, although many other approaches based on partitioning are possible. One such approach will be described, when we describe CURE later on in this section.

If K-means is used to find K clusters, then the distance of each point to each cluster centroid is calculated at each iteration. When K is large, this can be very expensive. Bisecting K-means starts with the entire set of points and uses K-means to repeatedly bisect an existing cluster until we have obtained K clusters. At each step, the distance of points to two cluster centroids is computed. Except for the first step, in which the cluster being bisected consists of all the points, we only compute the distance of a subset of points to the two centroids being considered. Because of this fact, bisecting K-means can run significantly faster than regular K-means.

Summarization Another approach to clustering is to summarize the data, typically in a single pass, and then cluster the summarized data. In particular, the leader algorithm (see Exercise 12 on page 562) either puts a data object in the closest cluster (if that cluster is sufficiently close) or starts a new cluster that contains the current object. This algorithm is linear in the number of objects and can be used to summarize the data so that other clustering techniques can be used. The BIRCH algorithm uses a similar concept.

Parallel and Distributed Computation If it is not possible to take advantage of the techniques described earlier, or if these approaches do not yield the desired accuracy or reduction in computation time, then other approaches are needed. A highly effective approach is to distribute the computation among multiple processors.

9.5.2 BIRCH

BIRCH (Balanced Iterative Reducing and Clustering using Hierarchies) is a highly efficient clustering technique for data in Euclidean vector spaces, i.e., data for which averages make sense. BIRCH can efficiently cluster such data with one pass and can improve that clustering with additional passes. BIRCH can also deal effectively with outliers.

BIRCH is based on the notion of a Clustering Feature (CF) and a CF tree. The idea is that a cluster of data points (vectors) can be represented by a triple of numbers (N, LS, SS), where N is the number of points in the cluster, LS is the linear sum of the points, and SS is the sum of squares of the points. These are common statistical quantities that can be updated incrementally and that can be used to compute a number of important quantities, such as the centroid of a cluster and its variance (standard deviation). The variance is used as a measure of the diameter of a cluster.

These quantities can also be used to compute the distance between clusters. The simplest approach is to calculate an L_1 (city block) or L_2 (Euclidean) distance between centroids. We can also use the diameter (variance) of the merged cluster as a distance. A number of different distance measures for clusters are defined by BIRCH, but all can be computed using the summary statistics.

A CF tree is a height-balanced tree. Each interior node has entries of the form $[CF_i, child_i]$, where $child_i$ is a pointer to the ith child node. The space that each entry takes and the page size determine the number of entries in an interior node. The space of each entry is, in turn, determined by the number of attributes of each point.

Leaf nodes consist of a sequence of clustering features, CF_i, where each clustering feature represents a number of points that have been previously scanned. Leaf nodes are subject to the restriction that each leaf node must have a diameter that is less than a parameterized threshold, T. The space that each entry takes, together with the page size, determines the number of entries in a leaf.

By adjusting the threshold parameter T, the height of the tree can be controlled. T controls the fineness of the clustering, i.e., the extent to which the data in the original set of data is reduced. The goal is to keep the CF tree in main memory by adjusting the T parameter as necessary.

A CF tree is built as the data is scanned. As each data point is encountered, the CF tree is traversed, starting from the root and choosing the closest node at each level. When the closest leaf cluster for the current data point is finally identified, a test is performed to see if adding the data item to the candidate cluster will result in a new cluster with a diameter greater than the given threshold, T. If not, then the data point is added to the candidate cluster by updating the CF information. The cluster information for all nodes from the leaf to the root is also updated.

If the new cluster has a diameter greater than T, then a new entry is created if the leaf node is not full. Otherwise the leaf node must be split. The two entries (clusters) that are farthest apart are selected as seeds and the remaining entries are distributed to one of the two new leaf nodes, based on which leaf node contains the closest seed cluster. Once the leaf node has been split, the parent node is updated and split if necessary; i.e., if the parent node is full. This process may continue all the way to the root node.

BIRCH follows each split with a merge step. At the interior node where the split stops, the two closest entries are found. If these entries do not correspond to the two entries that just resulted from the split, then an attempt is made to merge these entries and their corresponding child nodes. This step is intended to increase space utilization and avoid problems with skewed data input order.

BIRCH also has a procedure for removing outliers. When the tree needs to be rebuilt because it has run out of memory, then outliers can optionally be written to disk. (An outlier is defined to be a node that has far fewer data points than average.) At certain points in the process, outliers are scanned to see if they can be absorbed back into the tree without causing the tree to grow in size. If so, they are reabsorbed. If not, they are deleted.

BIRCH consists of a number of phases beyond the initial creation of the CF tree. All the phases of BIRCH are described briefly in Algorithm 9.13.

9.5.3 CURE

CURE (Clustering Using REpresentatives) is a clustering algorithm that uses a variety of different techniques to create an approach that can handle large data sets, outliers, and clusters with non-spherical shapes and non-uniform sizes. CURE represents a cluster by using multiple representative points from the cluster. These points will, in theory, capture the geometry and shape of the cluster. The first representative point is chosen to be the point farthest from the center of the cluster, while the remaining points are chosen so that they are farthest from all the previously chosen points. In this way, the representative points are naturally relatively well distributed. The number of points chosen is a parameter, but it was found that a value of 10 or more worked well.

Once the representative points are chosen, they are shrunk toward the center by a factor, α. This helps moderate the effect of outliers, which are usually farther away from the center and thus, are shrunk more. For example, a representative point that was a distance of 10 units from the center would

---

Algorithm 9.13 BIRCH.

1: **Load the data into memory by creating a CF tree that summarizes the data.**

2: **Build a smaller CF tree if it is necessary for phase 3.** T is increased, and then the leaf node entries (clusters) are reinserted. Since T has increased, some clusters will be merged.

3: **Perform global clustering.** Different forms of global clustering (clustering that uses the pairwise distances between all the clusters) can be used. However, an agglomerative, hierarchical technique was selected. Because the clustering features store summary information that is important to certain kinds of clustering, the global clustering algorithm can be applied as if it were being applied to all the points in a cluster represented by the CF.

4: **Redistribute the data points using the centroids of clusters discovered in step 3, and thus, discover a new set of clusters.** This overcomes certain problems that can occur in the first phase of BIRCH. Because of page size constraints and the T parameter, points that should be in one cluster are sometimes split, and points that should be in different clusters are sometimes combined. Also, if the data set contains duplicate points, these points can sometimes be clustered differently, depending on the order in which they are encountered. By repeating this phase multiple times, the process converges to a locally optimum solution.

---

move by 3 units (for $\alpha = 0.7$), while a representative point at a distance of 1 unit would only move 0.3 units.

CURE uses an agglomerative hierarchical scheme to perform the actual clustering. The distance between two clusters is the minimum distance between any two representative points (after they are shrunk toward their respective centers). While this scheme is not exactly like any other hierarchical scheme that we have seen, it is equivalent to centroid-based hierarchical clustering if $\alpha = 0$, and roughly the same as single link hierarchical clustering if $\alpha = 1$. Notice that while a hierarchical clustering scheme is used, the goal of CURE is to find a given number of clusters as specified by the user.

CURE takes advantage of certain characteristics of the hierarchical clustering process to eliminate outliers at two different points in the clustering process. First, if a cluster is growing slowly, then this may mean that it consists mostly of outliers, since by definition, outliers are far from others and will not be merged with other points very often. In CURE, this first phase of outlier elimination typically occurs when the number of clusters is 1/3 the original number of points. The second phase of outlier elimination occurs when the number of clusters is on the order of K, the number of desired clusters. At this point, small clusters are again eliminated.

Since the worst-case complexity of CURE is $O(m^2 \log m)$, it cannot be applied directly to large data sets. For this reason, CURE uses two techniques to speed up the clustering process. The first technique takes a random sample and performs hierarchical clustering on the sampled data points. This is followed by a final pass that assigns each remaining point in the data set to one of the clusters by choosing the cluster with the closest representative point. We discuss CURE's sampling approach in more detail later.

In some cases, the sample required for clustering is still too large and a second additional technique is required. In this situation, CURE partitions the sample data and then clusters the points in each partition. This preclustering step is then followed by a clustering of the intermediate clusters and a final pass that assigns each point in the data set to one of the clusters. CURE's partitioning scheme is also discussed in more detail later.

Algorithm 9.14 summarizes CURE. Note that K is the desired number of clusters, m is the number of points, p is the number of partitions, and q is the desired reduction of points in a partition, i.e., the number of clusters in a partition is $\frac{m}{pq}$. Therefore, the total number of clusters is $\frac{m}{pq}$. For example, if $m = 10,000$, $p = 10$, and $q = 100$, then each partition contains $10,000/10 = 1000$ points, and there would be $1000/100 = 10$ clusters in each partition and $10,000/100 = 100$ clusters overall.

Algorithm 9.14 CURE.

1: **Draw a random sample from the data set.** The CURE paper is notable for explicitly deriving a formula for what the size of this sample should be in order to guarantee, with high probability, that all clusters are represented by a minimum number of points.
2: **Partition the sample into p equal-sized partitions.**
3: **Cluster the points in each partition into $\frac{m}{pq}$ clusters using CURE's hierarchical clustering algorithm to obtain a total of $\frac{m}{q}$ clusters.** Note that some outlier elimination occurs during this process.
4: **Use CURE's hierarchical clustering algorithm to cluster the $\frac{m}{q}$ clusters found in the previous step until only K clusters remain.**
5: **Eliminate outliers.** This is the second phase of outlier elimination.
6: **Assign all remaining data points to the nearest cluster to obtain a complete clustering.**

Sampling in CURE

A key issue in using sampling is whether the sample is representative, that is, whether it captures the characteristics of interest. For clustering, the issue is whether we can find the same clusters in the sample as in the entire set of objects. Ideally, we would like the sample to contain some objects for each cluster and for there to be a separate cluster in the sample for those objects that belong to separate clusters in the entire data set.

A more concrete and attainable goal is to guarantee (with a high probability) that we have at least some points from each cluster. The number of points required for such a sample varies from one data set to another and depends on the number of objects and the sizes of the clusters. The creators of CURE derived a bound for the sample size that would be needed to ensure (with high probability) that we obtain at least a certain number of points from a cluster. Using the notation of this book, this bound is given by the following theorem.

Theorem 9.1. *Let f be a fraction, $0 \leq f \leq 1$. For cluster C_i of size m_i, we will obtain at least $f * m_i$ objects from cluster C_i with a probability of $1 - \delta, 0 \leq \delta \leq 1$, if our sample size s is given by the following:*

$$s = fm + \frac{m}{m_i} * \log \frac{1}{\delta} + \frac{m}{m_i} \sqrt{\log \frac{1}{\delta}^2 + 2 * f * m_i * \log \frac{1}{\delta}}. \qquad (9.19)$$

where m is the number of objects.

While this expression may look intimidating, it is reasonably easy to use. Suppose that there are 100,000 objects and that the goal is to have an 80% chance of obtaining 10% of the objects in cluster C_i, which has a size of 1000. In this case, $f = 0.1$, $\delta = 0.2$, $m = 100,000$, $m_i = 1000$, and thus $s = 11,962$. If the goal is a 5% sample of C_i, which is 50 objects, then a sample size of 6440 will suffice.

Again, CURE uses sampling in the following way. First a sample is drawn, and then CURE is used to cluster this sample. After clusters have been found, each unclustered point is assigned to the closest cluster.

Partitioning

When sampling is not enough, CURE also uses a partitioning approach. The idea is to divide the points into p groups of size m/p and to use CURE to cluster each partition in order to reduce the number of objects by a factor of $q > 1$, where q can be roughly thought of as the average size of a cluster in a partition.

Overall, $\frac{m}{pq}$ clusters are produced. (Note that since CURE represents each cluster by a number of representative points, the reduction in the number of objects is not pq.) This preclustering step is then followed by a final clustering of the m/pq intermediate clusters to produce the desired number of clusters (K). Both clustering passes use CURE's hierarchical clustering algorithm and are followed by a final pass that assigns each point in the data set to one of the clusters.

The key issue is how p and q should be chosen. Algorithms such as CURE have a time complexity of $O(m^2)$ or higher, and furthermore, require that all the data be in main memory. We therefore want to choose p small enough so that an entire partition can be processed in main memory and in a 'reasonable' amount of time. At the current time, a typical desktop computer can perform a hierarchical clustering of a few thousand objects in a few seconds.

Another factor for choosing p, and also q, concerns the quality of the clustering. Specifically, the objective is to choose the values of p and q such that objects from the same underlying cluster end up in the same clusters eventually. To illustrate, suppose there are 1000 objects and a cluster of size 100. If we randomly generate 100 partitions, then each partition will, on average, have only one point from our cluster. These points will likely be put in clusters with points from other clusters or will be discarded as outliers. If we generate only 10 partitions of 100 objects, but q is 50, then the 10 points from each cluster (on average) will likely still be combined with points from other clusters, since there are only (on average) 10 points per cluster and we need to produce, for each partition, two clusters. To avoid this last problem, which concerns the proper choice of q, a suggested strategy is not to combine clusters if they are too dissimilar.

9.6 Which Clustering Algorithm?

A variety of factors need to be considered when deciding which type of clustering technique to use. Many, if not all, of these factors have been discussed to some extent in the current and previous chapters. Our goal in this section is to succinctly summarize these factors in a way that sheds some light on which clustering algorithm might be appropriate for a particular clustering task.

Type of Clustering One important factor in making sure that the type of clustering matches the intended use is the type of clustering produced by the algorithm. For some applications, such as creating a biological taxonomy, a hierarchy is preferred. In the case of clustering for summarization, a partitional clustering is typical. In yet other applications, both may prove useful.

Most clustering applications require a clustering of all (or almost all) of the objects. For instance, if clustering is used to organize a set of documents for browsing, then we would like most documents to belong to a group. However, if we wanted to find the strongest themes in a set of documents, then we might prefer to have a clustering scheme that produces only very cohesive clusters, even if many documents were left unclustered.

Finally, most applications of clustering assume that each object is assigned to one cluster (or one cluster on a level for hierarchical schemes). As we have seen, however, probabilistic and fuzzy schemes provide weights that indicate the degree or probability of membership in various clusters. Other techniques, such as DBSCAN and SNN density-based clustering, have the notion of core points, which strongly belong to one cluster. Such concepts may be useful in certain applications.

Type of Cluster   Another key aspect is whether the type of cluster matches the intended application. There are three commonly encountered types of clusters: prototype-, graph-, and density-based. Prototype-based clustering schemes, as well as some graph-based clustering schemes—complete link, centroid, and Ward's—tend to produce globular clusters in which each object is sufficiently close to the cluster's prototype or to the other objects in the cluster. If, for example, we want to summarize the data to reduce its size and we want to do so with the minimum amount of error, then one of these types of techniques would be most appropriate. In contrast, density-based clustering techniques, as well as some graph-based clustering techniques, such as single link, tend to produce clusters that are not globular and thus contain many objects that are not very similar to one another. If clustering is used to segment a geographical area into contiguous regions based on the type of land cover, then one of these techniques is more suitable than a prototype-based scheme such as K-means.

Characteristics of Clusters   Besides the general type of cluster, other cluster characteristics are important. If we want to find clusters in subspaces of the original data space, then we must choose an algorithm such as CLIQUE, which explicitly looks for such clusters. Similarly, if we are interested in enforcing spatial relationships between clusters, then SOM or some related approach would be appropriate. Also, clustering algorithms differ widely in their ability to handle clusters of varying shapes, sizes, and densities.

Characteristics of the Data Sets and Attributes As discussed in the introduction, the type of data set and attributes can dictate the type of algorithm to use. For instance, the K-means algorithm can only be used on data for which an appropriate proximity measure is available that allows meaningful computation of a cluster centroid. For other clustering techniques, such as many agglomerative hierarchical approaches, the underlying nature of the data sets and attributes is less important as long as a proximity matrix can be created.

Noise and Outliers Noise and outliers are particularly important aspects of the data. We have tried to indicate the effect of noise and outliers on the various clustering algorithms that we have discussed. In practice, however, it may be difficult to evaluate the amount of noise in the data set or the number of outliers. More than that, what is noise or an outlier to one person may be interesting to another person. For example, if we are using clustering to segment an area into regions of different population density, we do not want to use a density-based clustering technique, such as DBSCAN, that assumes that regions or points with density lower than a global threshold are noise or outliers. As another example, hierarchical clustering schemes, such as CURE, often discard clusters of points that are growing slowly since such groups tend to represent outliers. However, in some applications we may be most interested in relatively small clusters; e.g., in market segmentation, such groups might represent the most profitable customers.

Number of Data Objects We have considered how clustering is affected by the number of data objects in considerable detail in previous sections. We reiterate, however, that this factor often plays an important role in determining the type of clustering algorithm to be used. Suppose that we want to create a hierarchical clustering of a set of data, we are not interested in a complete hierarchy that extends all the way to individual objects, but only to the point at which we have split the data into a few hundred clusters. If the data is very large, we cannot directly apply an agglomerative hierarchical clustering technique. We could, however, use a divisive clustering technique, such as the minimum spanning tree (MST) algorithm, which is the divisive analog to single link, but this would only work if the data set is not too large. Bisecting K-means would also work for many data sets, but if the data set is large enough that it cannot be contained completely in memory, then this scheme also runs into problems. In this situation, a technique such as BIRCH, which does not require that all data be in main memory, becomes more useful.

Number of Attributes   We have also discussed the impact of dimensionality at some length. Again, the key point is to realize that an algorithm that works well in low or moderate dimensions may not work well in high dimensions. As in many other cases in which a clustering algorithm is inappropriately applied, the clustering algorithm may run and produce clusters, but the clusters may not represent the true structure of the data.

Cluster Description   One aspect of clustering techniques that is often overlooked is how the resulting clusters are described. Prototype clusters are succinctly described by a small set of cluster prototypes. In the case of mixture models, the clusters are described in terms of small sets of parameters, such as the mean vector and the covariance matrix. This is also a very compact and understandable representation. For SOM, it is typically possible to visualize the relationships between clusters in a two-dimensional plot, such as that of Figure 9.8. For graph- and density-based clustering approaches, however, clusters are typically described as sets of cluster members. Nonetheless, in CURE, clusters can be described by a (relatively) small set of representative points. Also, for grid-based clustering schemes, such as CLIQUE, more compact descriptions can be generated in terms of conditions on the attribute values that describe the grid cells in the cluster.

Algorithmic Considerations   There are also important aspects of algorithms that need to be considered. Is the algorithm non-deterministic or order-dependent? Does the algorithm automatically determine the number of clusters? Is there a technique for determining the values of various parameters? Many clustering algorithms try to solve the clustering problem by trying to optimize an objective function. Is the objective a good match for the application objective? If not, then even if the algorithm does a good job of finding a clustering that is optimal or close to optimal with respect to the objective function, the result is not meaningful. Also, most objective functions give preference to larger clusters at the expense of smaller clusters.

Summary   The task of choosing the proper clustering algorithm involves considering all of these issues, and domain-specific issues as well. There is no formula for determining the proper technique. Nonetheless, a general knowledge of the types of clustering techniques that are available and consideration of the issues mentioned above, together with a focus on the intended application, should allow a data analyst to make an informed decision on which clustering approach (or approaches) to try.

9.7   Bibliographic Notes

An extensive discussion of fuzzy clustering, including a description of fuzzy c-means and formal derivations of the formulas presented in Section 9.2.1, can be found in the book on fuzzy cluster analysis by Höppner et al. [441]. While not discussed in this chapter, AutoClass by Cheeseman et al. [424] is one of the earliest and most prominent mixture-model clustering programs. An introduction to mixture models can be found in the tutorial of Bilmes [420], the book by Mitchell [450] (which also describes how the K-means algorithm can be derived from a mixture model approach), and the article by Fraley and Raftery [429].

Besides data exploration, SOM and its supervised learning variant, Learning Vector Quantization (LVQ), have been used for many tasks: image segmentation, organization of document files, and speech processing. Our discussion of SOM was cast in the terminology of prototype-based clustering. The book on SOM by Kohonen et al. [447] contains an extensive introduction to SOM that emphasizes its neural network origins, as well as a discussion of some of its variations and applications. One important SOM-related clustering development is the Generative Topographic Map (GTM) algorithm by Bishop et al. [421], which uses the EM algorithm to find Gaussian models satisfying two-dimensional topographic constraints.

The description of Chameleon can be found in the paper by Karypis et al. [445]. Capabilities similar, although not identical to those of Chameleon have been implemented in the CLUTO clustering package by Karypis [425]. The METIS graph partitioning package by Karypis and Kumar [446] is used to perform graph partitioning in both programs, as well as in the OPOSSUM clustering algorithm by Strehl and Ghosh [459]. The notion of SNN similarity was introduced by Jarvis and Patrick [442]. A hierarchical clustering scheme based on a similar concept of mutual nearest neighbors was proposed by Gowda and Krishna [434]. Guha et al. [437] created ROCK, a hierarchical graph-based clustering algorithm for clustering transaction data, which among other interesting features, also uses a notion of similarity based on shared neighbors that closely resembles the SNN similarity developed by Jarvis and Patrick. A description of the SNN density-based clustering technique can be found in the publications of Ertöz et al. [426, 427]. SNN density-based clustering was used by Steinbach et al. [457] to find climate indices.

Examples of grid-based clustering algorithms are OptiGrid (Hinneburg and Keim [440]), the BANG clustering system (Schikuta and Erhart [455]), and WaveCluster (Sheikholeslami et al. [456]). The CLIQUE algorithm is described in the paper by Guha et al. [418]. MAFIA (Nagesh et al. [452]) is a modification of CLIQUE whose goal is improved efficiency. Kailing et al. [444] have developed SUBCLU (density-connected SUBspace CLUstering), a subspace clustering algorithm based on DBSCAN. The DENCLUE algorithm was proposed by Hinneburg and Keim [439].

Our discussion of scalability was strongly influenced by the article of Ghosh [432]. A wide-ranging discussion of specific techniques for clustering massive data sets can be found in the paper by Murtagh [451]. CURE is work by Guha et al. [436], while details of BIRCH are in the paper by Zhang et al. [460]. CLARANS (Ng and Han [453]) is an algorithm for scaling K-medoid clustering to larger databases. A discussion of scaling EM and K-means clustering to large data sets is provided by Bradley et al. [422, 423].

There are many aspects of clustering that we have not covered. Additional pointers are given in the books and surveys mentioned in the bibliographic notes of the previous chapter. Here, we mention four areas—omitting, unfortunately, many more. Clustering of transaction data (Ganti et al. [430], Gibson et al. [433], Han et al. [438], and Peters and Zaki [454]) is an important area, as transaction data is common and of commercial importance. Streaming data is also becoming increasingly common and important as communications and sensor networks become pervasive. Two introductions to clustering for data streams are given in articles by Barbará [419] and Guha et al. [435]. Conceptual clustering (Fisher and Langley [428], Jonyer et al. [443], Mishra et al. [449], Michalski and Stepp [448], Stepp and Michalski [458]), which uses more complicated definitions of clusters that often correspond better to human notions of a cluster, is an area of clustering whose potential has perhaps not been fully realized. Finally, there has been a great deal of clustering work for data compression in the area of vector quantization. The book by Gersho and Gray [431] is a standard text in this area.

Bibliography

[418] R. Agrawal, J. Gehrke, D. Gunopulos, and P. Raghavan. Automatic subspace clustering of high dimensional data for data mining applications. In *Proc. of 1998 ACM-SIGMOD Intl. Conf. on Management of Data*, pages 94–105, Seattle, Washington, June 1998. ACM Press.

[419] D. Barbará. Requirements for clustering data streams. *SIGKDD Explorations Newsletter*, 3(2):23–27, 2002.

[420] J. Bilmes. A Gentle Tutorial on the EM Algorithm and its Application to Parameter Estimation for Gaussian Mixture and Hidden Markov Models. Technical Report ICSI-TR-97-021, University of California at Berkeley, 1997.

[421] C. M. Bishop, M. Svensen, and C. K. I. Williams. GTM: A principled alternative to the self-organizing map. In C. von der Malsburg, W. von Seelen, J. C. Vorbruggen, and

B. Sendhoff, editors, *Artificial Neural Networks—ICANN96. Intl. Conf, Proc.*, pages 165–170. Springer-Verlag, Berlin, Germany, 1996.

[422] P. S. Bradley, U. M. Fayyad, and C. Reina. Scaling Clustering Algorithms to Large Databases. In *Proc. of the 4th Intl. Conf. on Knowledge Discovery and Data Mining*, pages 9–15, New York City, August 1998. AAAI Press.

[423] P. S. Bradley, U. M. Fayyad, and C. Reina. Scaling EM (Expectation Maximization) Clustering to Large Databases. Technical Report MSR-TR-98-35, Microsoft Research, October 1999.

[424] P. Cheeseman, J. Kelly, M. Self, J. Stutz, W. Taylor, and D. Freeman. AutoClass: a Bayesian classification system. In *Readings in knowledge acquisition and learning: automating the construction and improvement of expert systems*, pages 431–441. Morgan Kaufmann Publishers Inc., 1993.

[425] CLUTO 2.1.1: Software for Clustering High-Dimensional Datasets. /www.cs.umn.edu/~karypis, November 2003.

[426] L. Ertöz, M. Steinbach, and V. Kumar. A New Shared Nearest Neighbor Clustering Algorithm and its Applications. In *Workshop on Clustering High Dimensional Data and its Applications, Proc. of Text Mine'01, First SIAM Intl. Conf. on Data Mining*, Chicago, IL, USA, 2001.

[427] L. Ertöz, M. Steinbach, and V. Kumar. Finding Clusters of Different Sizes, Shapes, and Densities in Noisy, High Dimensional Data. In *Proc. of the 2003 SIAM Intl. Conf. on Data Mining*, San Francisco, May 2003. SIAM.

[428] D. Fisher and P. Langley. Conceptual clustering and its relation to numerical taxonomy. *Artificial Intelligence and Statistics*, pages 77–116, 1986.

[429] C. Fraley and A. E. Raftery. How Many Clusters? Which Clustering Method? Answers Via Model-Based Cluster Analysis. *The Computer Journal*, 41(8):578–588, 1998.

[430] V. Ganti, J. Gehrke, and R. Ramakrishnan. CACTUS–Clustering Categorical Data Using Summaries. In *Proc. of the 5th Intl. Conf. on Knowledge Discovery and Data Mining*, pages 73–83. ACM Press, 1999.

[431] A. Gersho and R. M. Gray. *Vector Quantization and Signal Compression*, volume 159 of *Kluwer International Series in Engineering and Computer Science*. Kluwer Academic Publishers, 1992.

[432] J. Ghosh. Scalable Clustering Methods for Data Mining. In N. Ye, editor, *Handbook of Data Mining*, pages 247–277. Lawrence Ealbaum Assoc, 2003.

[433] D. Gibson, J. M. Kleinberg, and P. Raghavan. Clustering Categorical Data: An Approach Based on Dynamical Systems. *VLDB Journal*, 8(3–4):222–236, 2000.

[434] K. C. Gowda and G. Krishna. Agglomerative Clustering Using the Concept of Mutual Nearest Neighborhood. *Pattern Recognition*, 10(2):105–112, 1978.

[435] S. Guha, A. Meyerson, N. Mishra, R. Motwani, and L. O'Callaghan. Clustering Data Streams: Theory and Practice. *IEEE Transactions on Knowledge and Data Engineering*, 15(3):515–528, May/June 2003.

[436] S. Guha, R. Rastogi, and K. Shim. CURE: An Efficient Clustering Algorithm for Large Databases. In *Proc. of 1998 ACM-SIGMOD Intl. Conf. on Management of Data*, pages 73–84. ACM Press, June 1998.

[437] S. Guha, R. Rastogi, and K. Shim. ROCK: A Robust Clustering Algorithm for Categorical Attributes. In *Proc. of the 15th Intl. Conf. on Data Engineering*, pages 512–521. IEEE Computer Society, March 1999.

[438] E.-H. Han, G. Karypis, V. Kumar, and B. Mobasher. Hypergraph Based Clustering in High-Dimensional Data Sets: A Summary of Results. *IEEE Data Eng. Bulletin*, 21 (1):15–22, 1998.

[439] A. Hinneburg and D. A. Keim. An Efficient Approach to Clustering in Large Multimedia Databases with Noise. In *Proc. of the 4th Intl. Conf. on Knowledge Discovery and Data Mining*, pages 58–65, New York City, August 1998. AAAI Press.

[440] A. Hinneburg and D. A. Keim. Optimal Grid-Clustering: Towards Breaking the Curse of Dimensionality in High-Dimensional Clustering. In *Proc. of the 25th VLDB Conf.*, pages 506–517, Edinburgh, Scotland, UK, September 1999. Morgan Kaufmann.

[441] F. Höppner, F. Klawonn, R. Kruse, and T. Runkler. *Fuzzy Cluster Analysis: Methods for Classification, Data Analysis and Image Recognition*. John Wiley & Sons, New York, July 2 1999.

[442] R. A. Jarvis and E. A. Patrick. Clustering Using a Similarity Measure Based on Shared Nearest Neighbors. *IEEE Transactions on Computers*, C-22(11):1025–1034, 1973.

[443] I. Jonyer, D. J. Cook, and L. B. Holder. Graph-based hierarchical conceptual clustering. *Journal of Machine Learning Research*, 2:19–43, 2002.

[444] K. Kailing, H.-P. Kriegel, and P. Kröger. Density-Connected Subspace Clustering for High-Dimensional Data. In *Proc. of the 2004 SIAM Intl. Conf. on Data Mining*, pages 428–439, Lake Buena Vista, Florida, April 2004. SIAM.

[445] G. Karypis, E.-H. Han, and V. Kumar. CHAMELEON: A Hierarchical Clustering Algorithm Using Dynamic Modeling. *IEEE Computer*, 32(8):68–75, August 1999.

[446] G. Karypis and V. Kumar. Multilevel k-way Partitioning Scheme for Irregular Graphs. *Journal of Parallel and Distributed Computing*, 48(1):96–129, 1998.

[447] T. Kohonen, T. S. Huang, and M. R. Schroeder. *Self-Organizing Maps*. Springer-Verlag, December 2000.

[448] R. S. Michalski and R. E. Stepp. Automated Construction of Classifications: Conceptual Clustering Versus Numerical Taxonomy. *IEEE Transactions on Pattern Analysis and Machine Intelligence*, 5(4):396–409, 1983.

[449] N. Mishra, D. Ron, and R. Swaminathan. A New Conceptual Clustering Framework. *Machine Learning Journal*, 56(1–3):115–151, July/August/September 2004.

[450] T. Mitchell. *Machine Learning*. McGraw-Hill, Boston, MA, 1997.

[451] F. Murtagh. Clustering massive data sets. In J. Abello, P. M. Pardalos, and M. G. C. Reisende, editors, *Handbook of Massive Data Sets*. Kluwer, 2000.

[452] H. Nagesh, S. Goil, and A. Choudhary. Parallel Algorithms for Clustering High-Dimensional Large-Scale Datasets. In R. L. Grossman, C. Kamath, P. Kegelmeyer, V. Kumar, and R. Namburu, editors, *Data Mining for Scientific and Engineering Applications*, pages 335–356. Kluwer Academic Publishers, Dordrecht, Netherlands, October 2001.

[453] R. T. Ng and J. Han. CLARANS: A Method for Clustering Objects for Spatial Data Mining. *IEEE Transactions on Knowledge and Data Engineering*, 14(5):1003–1016, 2002.

[454] M. Peters and M. J. Zaki. CLICKS: Clustering Categorical Data using K-partite Maximal Cliques. In *Proc. of the 21st Intl. Conf. on Data Engineering*, Tokyo, Japan, April 2005.

[455] E. Schikuta and M. Erhart. The BANG-Clustering System: Grid-Based Data Analysis. In *Advances in Intelligent Data Analysis, Reasoning about Data, Second Intl. Symposium, IDA-97, London*, volume 1280 of *Lecture Notes in Computer Science*, pages 513–524. Springer, August 1997.

[456] G. Sheikholeslami, S. Chatterjee, and A. Zhang. Wavecluster: A multi-resolution clustering approach for very large spatial databases. In *Proc. of the 24th VLDB Conf.*, pages 428–439, New York City, August 1998. Morgan Kaufmann.

[457] M. Steinbach, P.-N. Tan, V. Kumar, S. Klooster, and C. Potter. Discovery of climate indices using clustering. In *KDD '03: Proceedings of the ninth ACM SIGKDD international conference on Knowledge discovery and data mining*, pages 446–455, New York, NY, USA, 2003. ACM Press.

[458] R. E. Stepp and R. S. Michalski. Conceptual clustering of structured objects: A goal-oriented approach. *Artificial Intelligence*, 28(1):43–69, 1986.

[459] A. Strehl and J. Ghosh. A Scalable Approach to Balanced, High-dimensional Clustering of Market-Baskets. In *Proc. of the 7th Intl. Conf. on High Performance Computing (HiPC 2000)*, volume 1970 of *Lecture Notes in Computer Science*, pages 525–536, Bangalore, India, December 2000. Springer.

[460] T. Zhang, R. Ramakrishnan, and M. Livny. BIRCH: an efficient data clustering method for very large databases. In *Proc. of 1996 ACM-SIGMOD Intl. Conf. on Management of Data*, pages 103–114, Montreal, Quebec, Canada, June 1996. ACM Press.

9.8   Exercises

1. For sparse data, discuss why considering only the presence of non-zero values might give a more accurate view of the objects than considering the actual magnitudes of values. When would such an approach not be desirable?

2. Describe the change in the time complexity of K-means as the number of clusters to be found increases.

3. Consider a set of documents. Assume that all documents have been normalized to have unit length of 1. What is the "shape" of a cluster that consists of all documents whose cosine similarity to a centroid is greater than some specified constant? In other words, $\cos(d, c) \geq \delta$, where $0 < \delta \leq 1$.

4. Discuss the advantages and disadvantages of treating clustering as an optimization problem. Among other factors, consider efficiency, non-determinism, and whether an optimization-based approach captures all types of clusterings that are of interest.

5. What is the time and space complexity of fuzzy c-means? Of SOM? How do these complexities compare to those of K-means?

6. Traditional K-means has a number of limitations, such as sensitivity to outliers and difficulty in handling clusters of different sizes and densities, or with non-globular shapes. Comment on the ability of fuzzy c-means to handle these situations.

7. For the fuzzy c-means algorithm described in this book, the sum of the membership degree of any point over all clusters is 1. Instead, we could only require that the membership degree of a point in a cluster be between 0 and 1. What are the advantages and disadvantages of such an approach?

8. Explain the difference between likelihood and probability.

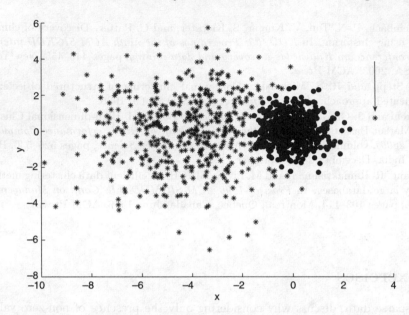

Figure 9.28. Data set for Exercise 12. EM clustering of a two-dimensional point set with two clusters of differing density.

9. Equation 9.12 gives the likelihood for a set of points from a Gaussian distribution as a function of the mean μ and the standard deviation σ. Show mathematically that the maximum likelihood estimate of μ and σ are the sample mean and the sample standard deviation, respectively.

10. We take a sample of adults and measure their heights. If we record the gender of each person, we can calculate the average height and the variance of the height, separately, for men and women. Suppose, however, that this information was not recorded. Would it be possible to still obtain this information? Explain.

11. Compare the membership weights and probabilities of Figures 9.1 and 9.4, which come, respectively, from applying fuzzy and EM clustering to the same set of data points. What differences do you detect, and how might you explain these differences?

12. Figure 9.28 shows a clustering of a two-dimensional point data set with two clusters: The leftmost cluster, whose points are marked by asterisks, is somewhat diffuse, while the rightmost cluster, whose points are marked by circles, is compact. To the right of the compact cluster, there is a single point (marked by an arrow) that belongs to the diffuse cluster, whose center is farther away than that of the compact cluster. Explain why this is possible with EM clustering, but not K-means clustering.

13. Show that the MST clustering technique of Section 9.4.2 produces the same clusters as single link. To avoid complications and special cases, assume that all the pairwise similarities are distinct.

14. One way to sparsify a proximity matrix is the following: For each object (row in the matrix), set all entries to 0 except for those corresponding to the objects k-nearest neighbors. However, the sparsified proximity matrix is typically not symmetric.

    (a) If object a is among the k-nearest neighbors of object b, why is b not guaranteed to be among the k-nearest neighbors of a?

    (b) Suggest at least two approaches that could be used to make the sparsified proximity matrix symmetric.

15. Give an example of a set of clusters in which merging based on the closeness of clusters leads to a more natural set of clusters than merging based on the strength of connection (interconnectedness) of clusters.

16. Table 9.4 lists the two nearest neighbors of four points.

Table 9.4. Two nearest neighbors of four points.

Point	First Neighbor	Second Neighbor
1	4	3
2	3	4
3	4	2
4	3	1

Calculate the SNN similarity between each pair of points using the definition of SNN similarity defined in Algorithm 9.10.

17. For the definition of SNN similarity provided by Algorithm 9.10, the calculation of SNN distance does not take into account the position of shared neighbors in the two nearest neighbor lists. In other words, it might be desirable to give higher similarity to two points that share the same nearest neighbors in the same or roughly the same order.

    (a) Describe how you might modify the definition of SNN similarity to give higher similarity to points whose shared neighbors are in roughly the same order.

    (b) Discuss the advantages and disadvantages of such a modification.

18. Name at least one situation in which you would *not* want to use clustering based on SNN similarity or density.

19. Grid-clustering techniques are different from other clustering techniques in that they partition space instead of sets of points.

(a) How does this affect such techniques in terms of the description of the resulting clusters and the types of clusters that can be found?

(b) What kind of cluster can be found with grid-based clusters that cannot be found by other types of clustering approaches? (Hint: See Exercise 20 in Chapter 8, page 564.)

20. In CLIQUE, the threshold used to find cluster density remains constant, even as the number of dimensions increases. This is a potential problem since density drops as dimensionality increases; i.e., to find clusters in higher dimensions the threshold has to be set at a level that may well result in the merging of low-dimensional clusters. Comment on whether you feel this is truly a problem and, if so, how you might modify CLIQUE to address this problem.

21. Given a set of points in Euclidean space, which are being clustered using the K-means algorithm with Euclidean distance, the triangle inequality can be used in the assignment step to avoid calculating all the distances of each point to each cluster centroid. Provide a general discussion of how this might work.

22. Instead of using the formula derived in CURE—see Equation 9.19—we could run a Monte Carlo simulation to directly estimate the probability that a sample of size s would contain at least a certain fraction of the points from a cluster. Using a Monte Carlo simulation compute the probability that a sample of size s contains 50% of the elements of a cluster of size 100, where the total number of points is 1000, and where s can take the values 100, 200, or 500.

10

Anomaly Detection

In anomaly detection, the goal is to find objects that are different from most other objects. Often, anomalous objects are known as **outliers**, since, on a scatter plot of the data, they lie far away from other data points. Anomaly detection is also known as **deviation detection**, because anomalous objects have attribute values that deviate significantly from the expected or typical attribute values, or as **exception mining**, because anomalies are exceptional in some sense. In this chapter, we will mostly use the terms *anomaly* or *outlier*.

There are a variety of anomaly detection approaches from several areas, including statistics, machine learning, and data mining. All try to capture the idea that an anomalous data object is unusual or in some way inconsistent with other objects. Although unusual objects or events are, by definition, relatively rare, this does not mean that they do not occur frequently in absolute terms. For example, an event that is "one in a thousand" can occur millions of times when billions of events are considered.

In the natural world, human society, or the domain of data sets, most events and objects are, by definition, commonplace or ordinary. However, we have a keen awareness of the possibility of objects that are unusual or extraordinary. This includes exceptionally dry or rainy seasons, famous athletes, or an attribute value that is much smaller or larger than all others. Our interest in anomalous events and objects stems from the fact that they are often of unusual importance: A drought threatens crops, an athlete's exceptional skill may lead to victory, and anomalous values in experimental results may indicate either a problem with the experiment or a new phenomenon to be investigated.

The following examples illustrate applications for which anomalies are of considerable interest.

From Chapter 10 of *Introduction to Data Mining*, First Edition. Pang-Ning Tan, Michael Steinbach, Vipin Kumar. Copyright © 2006 by Pearson Education, Inc. All rights reserved.

- **Fraud Detection.** The purchasing behavior of someone who steals a credit card is probably different from that of the original owner. Credit card companies attempt to detect a theft by looking for buying patterns that characterize theft or by noticing a change from typical behavior. Similar approaches are used for other types of fraud.

- **Intrusion Detection.** Unfortunately, attacks on computer systems and computer networks are commonplace. While some of these attacks, such as those designed to disable or overwhelm computers and networks, are obvious, other attacks, such as those designed to secretly gather information, are difficult to detect. Many of these intrusions can only be detected by monitoring systems and networks for unusual behavior.

- **Ecosystem Disturbances.** In the natural world, there are atypical events that can have a significant effect on human beings. Examples include hurricanes, floods, droughts, heat waves, and fires. The goal is often to predict the likelihood of these events and the causes of them.

- **Public Health.** In many countries, hospitals and medical clinics report various statistics to national organizations for further analysis. For example, if all children in a city are vaccinated for a particular disease, e.g., measles, then the occurrence of a few cases scattered across various hospitals in a city is an anomalous event that may indicate a problem with the vaccination programs in the city.

- **Medicine.** For a particular patient, unusual symptoms or test results may indicate potential health problems. However, whether a particular test result is anomalous may depend on other characteristics of the patient, such as age and sex. Furthermore, the categorization of a result as anomalous or not incurs a cost—unneeded additional tests if a patient is healthy and potential harm to the patient if a condition is left undiagnosed and untreated.

Although much of the recent interest in anomaly detection has been driven by applications in which anomalies are the focus, historically, anomaly detection (and removal) has been viewed as a technique for improving the analysis of typical data objects. For instance, a relatively small number of outliers can distort the mean and standard deviation of a set of values or alter the set of clusters produced by a clustering algorithm. Therefore, anomaly detection (and removal) is often a part of data preprocessing.

In this chapter, we will focus on anomaly detection. After a few preliminaries, we provide a detailed discussion of some important approaches to anomaly detection, illustrating them with examples of specific techniques.

10.1 Preliminaries

Before embarking on a discussion of specific anomaly detection algorithms, we provide some additional background. Specifically, we (1) explore the causes of anomalies, (2) consider various anomaly detection approaches, (3) draw distinctions among approaches based on whether they use class label information, and (4) describe issues common to anomaly detection techniques.

10.1.1 Causes of Anomalies

The following are some common causes of anomalies: data from different classes, natural variation, and data measurement or collection errors.

Data from Different Classes An object may be different from other objects, i.e., anomalous, because it is of a different type or class. To illustrate, someone committing credit card fraud belongs to a different class of credit card users than those people who use credit cards legitimately. Most of the examples presented at the beginning of the chapter, namely, fraud, intrusion, outbreaks of disease, and abnormal test results, are examples of anomalies that represent a different class of objects. Such anomalies are often of considerable interest and are the focus of anomaly detection in the field of data mining.

The idea that anomalous objects come from a different source (class) than most of the data objects is stated in the often-quoted definition of an outlier by the statistician Douglas Hawkins.

Definition 10.1 (Hawkins' Definition of an Outlier). An outlier is an observation that differs so much from other observations as to arouse suspicion that it was generated by a different mechanism.

Natural Variation Many data sets can be modeled by statistical distributions, such as a normal (Gaussian) distribution, where the probability of a data object decreases rapidly as the distance of the object from the center of the distribution increases. In other words, most of the objects are near a center (average object) and the likelihood that an object differs significantly from this average object is small. For example, an exceptionally tall person is not anomalous in the sense of being from a separate class of objects, but only in the sense of having an extreme value for a characteristic (height) possessed by all the objects. Anomalies that represent extreme or unlikely variations are often interesting.

Data Measurement and Collection Errors   Errors in the data collection or measurement process are another source of anomalies. For example, a measurement may be recorded incorrectly because of human error, a problem with the measuring device, or the presence of noise. The goal is to eliminate such anomalies, since they provide no interesting information but only reduce the quality of the data and the subsequent data analysis. Indeed, the removal of this type of anomaly is the focus of data preprocessing, specifically data cleaning.

Summary   An anomaly may be a result of the causes given above or of other causes that we did not consider. Indeed, the anomalies in a data set may have several sources, and the underlying cause of any particular anomaly is often unknown. In practice, anomaly detection techniques focus on finding objects that differ substantially from most other objects, and the techniques themselves are not affected by the source of an anomaly. Thus, the underlying cause of the anomaly is only important with respect to the intended application.

10.1.2   Approaches to Anomaly Detection

Here, we provide a high-level description of some anomaly detection techniques and their associated definitions of an anomaly. There is some overlap between these techniques, and relationships among them are explored further in Exercise 1 on page 680.

Model-Based Techniques   Many anomaly detection techniques first build a model of the data. Anomalies are objects that do not fit the model very well. For example, a model of the distribution of the data can be created by using the data to estimate the parameters of a probability distribution. An object does not fit the model very well; i.e., it is an anomaly, if it is not very likely under the distribution. If the model is a set of clusters, then an anomaly is an object that does not strongly belong to any cluster. When a regression model is used, an anomaly is an object that is relatively far from its predicted value.

Because anomalous and normal objects can be viewed as defining two distinct classes, classification techniques can be used for building models of these two classes. Of course, classification techniques can only be used if class labels are available for some of the objects so that a training set can be constructed. Also, anomalies are relatively rare, and this needs to be taken into account when choosing both a classification technique and the measures to be used for evaluation. (See Section 5.7.)

In some cases, it is difficult to build a model; e.g., because the statistical distribution of the data is unknown or no training data is available. In these situations, techniques that do not require a model, such as those described below, can be used.

Proximity-Based Techniques It is often possible to define a proximity measure between objects, and a number of anomaly detection approaches are based on proximities. Anomalous objects are those that are distant from most of the other objects. Many of the techniques in this area are based on distances and are referred to as **distance-based outlier detection techniques**. When the data can be displayed as a two- or three-dimensional scatter plot, distance-based outliers can be detected visually, by looking for points that are separated from most other points.

Density-Based Techniques Estimates of the density of objects are relatively straightforward to compute, especially if a proximity measure between objects is available. Objects that are in regions of low density are relatively distant from their neighbors, and can be considered anomalous. A more sophisticated approach accommodates the fact that data sets can have regions of widely differing densities, and classifies a point as an outlier only if it has a local density significantly less than that of most of its neighbors.

10.1.3 The Use of Class Labels

There are three basic approaches to anomaly detection: unsupervised, supervised, and semi-supervised. The major distinction is the degree to which class labels (anomaly or normal) are available for at least some of the data.

Supervised anomaly detection Techniques for supervised anomaly detection require the existence of a training set with both anomalous and normal objects. (Note that there may be more than one normal or anomalous class.) As mentioned previously, classification techniques that address the so-called rare class problem are particularly relevant because anomalies are relatively rare with respect to normal objects. See Section 5.7.

Unsupervised anomaly detection In many practical situations, class labels are not available. In such cases, the objective is to assign a score (or a label) to each instance that reflects the degree to which the instance is anomalous. Note that the presence of many anomalies that are similar to each other can cause them all to be labeled normal or have a low outlier score. Thus, for unsupervised anomaly detection to be successful, anomalies must be distinct from one another, as well as normal objects.

Semi-supervised anomaly detection Sometimes training data contains labeled normal data, but has no information about the anomalous objects. In the semi-supervised setting, the objective is to find an anomaly label or score for a set of given objects by using the information from labeled normal objects. Note that in this case, the presence of many related outliers in the set of objects to be scored does not impact the outlier evaluation. However, in many practical situations, it can be difficult to find a small set of representative normal objects.

All anomaly detection schemes described in this chapter can be used in supervised or unsupervised mode. Supervised schemes are essentially the same as classification schemes for rare classes discussed in Section 5.7.

10.1.4 Issues

There are a variety of important issues that need to be addressed when dealing with anomalies.

Number of Attributes Used to Define an Anomaly The question of whether an object is anomalous based on a single attribute is a question of whether the object's value for that attribute is anomalous. However, since an object may have many attributes, it may have anomalous values for some attributes, but ordinary values for other attributes. Furthermore, an object may be anomalous even if none of its attribute values are individually anomalous. For example, it is common to have people who are two feet tall (children) or are 300 pounds in weight, but uncommon to have a two-foot tall person who weighs 300 pounds. A general definition of an anomaly must specify how the values of multiple attributes are used to determine whether or not an object is an anomaly. This is a particularly important issue when the dimensionality of the data is high.

Global versus Local Perspective An object may seem unusual with respect to all objects, but not with respect to objects in its local neighborhood. For example, a person whose height is 6 feet 5 inches is unusually tall with respect to the general population, but not with respect to professional basketball players.

Degree to Which a Point Is an Anomaly The assessment of whether an object is an anomaly is reported by some techniques in a binary fashion: An object is either an anomaly or it is not. Frequently, this does not reflect the underlying reality that some objects are more extreme anomalies than others. Hence, it is desirable to have some assessment of the degree to which an object is anomalous. This assessment is known as the **anomaly** or **outlier score**.

Identifying One Anomaly at a Time versus Many Anomalies at Once In some techniques, anomalies are removed one at a time; i.e., the most anomalous instance is identified and removed and then the process repeats. For other techniques, a collection of anomalies is identified together. Techniques that attempt to identify one anomaly at a time are often subject to a problem known as **masking**, where the presence of several anomalies masks the presence of all. On the other hand, techniques that detect multiple outliers at once can experience **swamping**, where normal objects are classified as outliers. In model-based approaches, these effects can happen because the anomalies distort the data model.

Evaluation If class labels are available to identify anomalies and normal data, then the effectiveness of an anomaly detection scheme can be evaluated by using measures of classification performance discussed in Section 5.7. But since the anomalous class is usually much smaller than the normal class, measures such as precision, recall, and false positive rate are more appropriate than accuracy. If class labels are not available, then evaluation is difficult. However, for model-based approaches, the effectiveness of outlier detection can be judged with respect to the improvement in the model once anomalies are eliminated.

Efficiency There are significant differences in the computational cost of various anomaly detection schemes. Classification-based schemes can require significant resources to create the classification model, but are usually inexpensive to apply. Likewise, statistical approaches create a statistical model and can then categorize an object in constant time. Proximity-based approaches naturally have a time complexity of $O(m^2)$, where m is the number of objects, because the information they require can usually only be obtained by computing the proximity matrix. This time complexity can be reduced in specific cases, such as low-dimensional data, by the use of special data structure and algorithms. The time complexity of other approaches is considered in Exercise 6 on page 681.

Road Map

The next four sections describe several major categories of anomaly detection approaches: statistical, proximity-based, density-based, and cluster-based. One or more specific techniques are considered within each of these categories. In these sections, we will follow common practice and use the term outlier instead of anomaly.

10.2 Statistical Approaches

Statistical approaches are model-based approaches; i.e., a model is created for the data, and objects are evaluated with respect to how well they fit the model. Most statistical approaches to outlier detection are based on building a probability distribution model and considering how likely objects are under that model. This idea is expressed by Definition 10.2.

Definition 10.2 (Probabilistic Definition of an Outlier). An outlier is an object that has a low probability with respect to a probability distribution model of the data.

A probability distribution model is created from the data by estimating the parameters of a user-specified distribution. If the data is assumed to have a Gaussian distribution, then the mean and standard deviation of the underlying distribution can be estimated by computing the mean and standard deviation of the data. The probability of each object under the distribution can then be estimated.

A wide variety of statistical tests based on Definition 10.2 have been devised to detect outliers, or **discordant observations**, as they are often called in the statistical literature. Many of these discordancy tests are highly specialized and assume a level of statistical knowledge beyond the scope of this text. Thus, we illustrate the basic ideas with a few examples and refer the reader to the bibliographic notes for further pointers.

Issues

Among the important issues facing this approach to outlier detection are the following:

Identifying the specific distribution of a data set. While many types of data can be described by a small number of common distributions, such as Gaussian, Poisson, or binomial, data sets with non-standard distributions are relatively common. Of course, if the wrong model is chosen, then an object can be erroneously identified as an outlier. For example, the data may be modeled as coming from a Gaussian distribution, but may actually come from a distribution that has a higher probability (than the Gaussian distribution) of having values far from the mean. Statistical distributions with this type of behavior are common in practice and are known as **heavy-tailed distributions**.

The number of attributes used. Most statistical outlier detection techniques apply to a single attribute, but some techniques have been defined for multivariate data.

Mixtures of distributions. The data can be modeled as a mixture of distributions, and outlier detection schemes can be developed based on such models. Although potentially more powerful, such models are more complicated, both to understand and to use. For example, the distributions need to be identified before objects can be classified as outliers. See the discussion of mixture models and the EM algorithm in Section 9.2.2.

10.2.1 Detecting Outliers in a Univariate Normal Distribution

The Gaussian (normal) distribution is one of the most frequently used distributions in statistics, and we will use it to describe a simple approach to statistical outlier detection. This distribution has two parameters, μ and σ, which are the mean and standard deviation, respectively, and is represented using the notation $N(\mu, \sigma)$. Figure 10.1 shows the density function of $N(0, 1)$.

There is little chance that an object (value) from a $N(0, 1)$ distribution will occur in the tails of the distribution. For instance, there is only a probability of 0.0027 that an object lies beyond the central area between ± 3 standard deviations. More generally, if c is a constant and x is the attribute value of an object, then the probability that $|x| \geq c$ decreases rapidly as c increases. Let $\alpha = prob(|x| \geq c)$. Table 10.1 shows some sample values for c and the

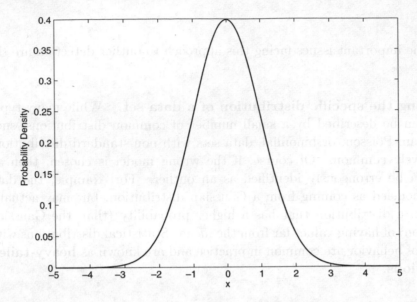

Figure 10.1. Probability density function of a Gaussian distribution with a mean of 0 and a standard deviation of 1.

corresponding values for α when the distribution is $N(0,1)$. Note that a value that is more than 4 standard deviations from the mean is a one-in-ten-thousand occurrence.

Table 10.1. Sample pairs (c, α), $\alpha = prob(|x| \geq c)$ for a Gaussian distribution with mean 0 and standard deviation 1.

c	α for $N(0,1)$
1.00	0.3173
1.50	0.1336
2.00	0.0455
2.50	0.0124
3.00	0.0027
3.50	0.0005
4.00	0.0001

Because a value's distance c from the center of the $N(0,1)$ distribution is directly related to the value's probability, it can be used as the basis of a test for whether an object (value) is an outlier as indicated in Definition 10.3.

Definition 10.3 (Outlier for a Single *N(0,1)* Gaussian Attribute). An object with attribute value x from a Gaussian distribution with mean of 0 and standard deviation 1 is an outlier if

$$|x| \geq c, \tag{10.1}$$

where c is a constant chosen so that $prob(|x|) \geq c = \alpha$.

To use this definition it is necessary to specify a value for α. From the viewpoint that unusual values (objects) indicate a value from a different distribution, α indicates the probability that we mistakenly classify a value from the given distribution as an outlier. From the viewpoint that an outlier is a rare value of a $N(0,1)$ distribution, α specifies the degree of rareness.

If the distribution of an attribute of interest (for the normal objects) has a Gaussian distribution with mean μ and a standard deviation σ, i.e., a $N(\mu, \sigma)$ distribution, then to use Definition 10.3, we need to transform the attribute x to a new attribute z, which has a $N(0,1)$ distribution. In particular, the approach is to set $z = (x - \mu)/\sigma$. (z is typically called a z score.) However, μ and σ are typically unknown and are estimated using the sample mean $\overline{x}$ and sample standard deviation s_x. In practice, this works well when the number of observations is large. However, we note that the distribution of z is not actually $N(0,1)$. A more sophisticated statistical procedure (Grubbs' test) is explored in Exercise 7 on page 681.

10.2.2   Outliers in a Multivariate Normal Distribution

For multivariate Gaussian observations, we would like to take an approach similar to that given for a univariate Gaussian distribution. In particular, we would like to classify points as outliers if they have low probability with respect to the estimated distribution of the data. Furthermore, we would like to be able to judge this with a simple test, for example, the distance of a point from the center of the distribution.

However, because of the correlation between the different variables (attributes), a multivariate normal distribution is not symmetrical with respect to its center. Figure 10.2 shows the probability density of a two-dimensional multivariate Gaussian distribution with mean of (0,0) and a covariance matrix of

$$\Sigma = \begin{pmatrix} 1.00 & 0.75 \\ 0.75 & 3.00 \end{pmatrix}.$$

If we are to use a simple threshold for whether an object is an outlier, then we will need a distance measure that takes the shape of the data distribution into account. The Mahalanobis distance is such a distance. See Equation 2.14 on page 81. The Mahalanobis distance between a point $\mathbf{x}$ and the mean of the data $\overline{\mathbf{x}}$ is shown in Equation 10.2.

$$mahalanobis(\mathbf{x}, \overline{\mathbf{x}}) = (\mathbf{x} - \overline{\mathbf{x}})\mathbf{S}^{-1}(\mathbf{x} - \overline{\mathbf{x}})^T, \tag{10.2}$$

where $\mathbf{S}$ is the covariance matrix of the data.

It is easy to show that the Mahalanobis distance of a point to the mean of the underlying distribution is directly related to the probability of the point. In particular, the Mahalanobis distance is equal to the log of the probability density of the point plus a constant. See Exercise 9 on page 682.

Example 10.1 (Outliers in a Multivariate Normal Distribution). Figure 10.3 shows the Mahalanobis distance (from the mean of the distribution) for points in a two-dimensional data set. The points A $(-4, 4)$ and B $(5, 5)$ are outliers that were added to the data set, and their Mahalanobis distance is indicated in the figure. The other 2000 points of the data set were randomly generated using the distribution used for Figure 10.2.

Both A and B have large Mahalanobis distances. However, even though A is closer to the center (the large black x at (0,0)) as measured by Euclidean distance, it is farther away than B in terms of the Mahalanobis distance because the Mahalanobis distance takes the shape of the distribution into account. In particular, point B has a Euclidean distance of $5\sqrt{2}$ and a Mahalanobis distance of 24, while the point A has a Euclidean distance of $4\sqrt{2}$ and a Mahalanobis distance of 35. ∎

10.2.3 A Mixture Model Approach for Anomaly Detection

This section presents an anomaly detection technique that uses a mixture model approach. In clustering (see Section 9.2.2), the mixture model approach assumes that the data comes from a mixture of probability distributions and that each cluster can be identified with one of these distributions. Similarly, for anomaly detection, the data is modeled as a mixture of two distributions, one for ordinary data and one for outliers.

For both clustering and anomaly detection, the goal is to estimate the parameters of the distributions in order to maximize the overall likelihood (probability) of the data. In clustering, the EM algorithm is used to estimate the parameters of each probability distribution. However, the anomaly detection technique presented here uses a simpler approach. Initially, all the

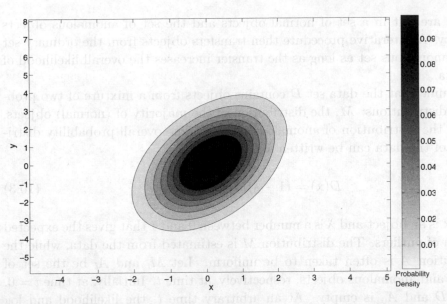

Figure 10.2. Probability density of points for the Gaussian distribution used to generate the points of Figure 10.3.

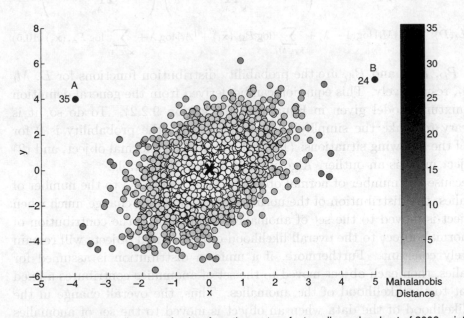

Figure 10.3. Mahalanobis distance of points from the center of a two-dimensional set of 2002 points.

objects are put in a set of normal objects and the set of anomalous objects is empty. An iterative procedure then transfers objects from the ordinary set to the anomalous set as long as the transfer increases the overall likelihood of the data.

Assume that the data set D contains objects from a mixture of two probability distributions: M, the distribution of the majority of (normal) objects, and A, the distribution of anomalous objects. The overall probability distribution of the data can be written as

$$D(\mathbf{x}) = (1 - \lambda)M(\mathbf{x}) + \lambda A(\mathbf{x}). \tag{10.3}$$

where $\mathbf{x}$ is an object and λ is a number between 0 and 1 that gives the expected fraction of outliers. The distribution M is estimated from the data, while the distribution A is often taken to be uniform. Let M_t and A_t be the set of normal and anomalous objects, respectively, at time t. Initially, at time $t = 0$, $M_0 = D$ and A_0 is empty. At an arbitrary time t, the likelihood and log likelihood of the entire data set D are given by the following two equations, respectively:

$$L_t(D) = \prod_{\mathbf{x}_i \in D} P_D(\mathbf{x}_i) = \left((1 - \lambda)^{|M_t|} \prod_{\mathbf{x}_i \in M_t} P_{M_t}(\mathbf{x}_i) \right) \left(\lambda^{|A_t|} \prod_{\mathbf{x}_i \in A_t} P_{A_t}(\mathbf{x}_i) \right) \tag{10.4}$$

$$LL_t(D) = |M_t| \log(1 - \lambda) + \sum_{\mathbf{x}_i \in M_t} \log P_{M_t}(\mathbf{x}_i) + |A_t| \log \lambda + \sum_{\mathbf{x}_i \in A_t} \log P_{A_t}(\mathbf{x}_i) \tag{10.5}$$

where P_D, P_{M_t}, and P_{A_t} are the probability distribution functions for D, M_t and A_t, respectively. This equation can be derived from the general definition of a mixture model given in Equation 9.6 (Section 9.2.2). To do so, it is necessary to make the simplifying assumption that the probability is 0 for both of the following situations: (1) an object in A is a normal object, and (2) an object in M is an outlier. Algorithm 10.1 gives the details.

Because the number of normal objects is large compared to the number of anomalies, the distribution of the normal objects may not change much when an object is moved to the set of anomalies. In that case, the contribution of each normal object to the overall likelihood of the normal objects will remain relatively constant. Furthermore, if a uniform distribution is assumed for anomalies, then each object moved to the set of anomalies contributes a fixed amount to the likelihood of the anomalies. Thus, the overall change in the total likelihood of the data when an object is moved to the set of anomalies is roughly equal to the probability of the object under a uniform distribution

---

Algorithm 10.1 Likelihood-based outlier detection.

1: Initialization: At time $t = 0$, let M_t contain all the objects, while A_t is empty. Let $LL_t(D) = LL(M_t) + LL(A_t)$ be the log likelihood of all the data.
2: **for** each point $\mathbf{x}$ that belongs to M_t **do**
3:    Move $\mathbf{x}$ from M_t to A_t to produce the new data sets A_{t+1} and M_{t+1}.
4:    Compute the new log likelihood of D, $LL_{t+1}(D) = LL(M_{t+1}) + LL(A_{t+1})$
5:    Compute the difference, $\Delta = LL_t(D) - LL_{t+1}(D)$
6:    **if** $\Delta > c$, where c is some threshold **then**
7:        $\mathbf{x}$ is classified as an anomaly, i.e., M_{t+1} and A_{t+1} are left unchanged and become the current normal and anomaly sets.
8:    **end if**
9: **end for**

(weighted by λ) minus the probability of the object under the distribution of the normal data points (weighted by $1 - \lambda$). Consequently, the set of anomalies will tend to consist of those objects that have significantly higher probability under a uniform distribution rather than under the distribution of the normal objects.

In the situation just discussed, the approach described by Algorithm 10.1 is roughly equivalent to classifying objects with a low probability under the distribution of normal objects as outliers. For example, when applied to the points in Figure 10.3, this technique would classify points A and B (and other points far from the mean) as outliers. However, if the distribution of the normal objects changes significantly as anomalies are removed or the distribution of the anomalies can be modeled in a more sophisticated manner, then the results produced by this approach will be different than the results of simply classifying low-probability objects as outliers. Also, this approach can work even when the distribution of objects is multimodal.

10.2.4   Strengths and Weaknesses

Statistical approaches to outlier detection have a firm foundation and build on standard statistical techniques, such as estimating the parameters of a distribution. When there is sufficient knowledge of the data and the type of test that should be applied these tests can be very effective. There are a wide variety of statistical outliers tests for single attributes. Fewer options are available for multivariate data, and these tests can perform poorly for high-dimensional data.

10.3   Proximity-Based Outlier Detection

Although there are several variations on the idea of proximity-based anomaly detection, the basic notion is straightforward. An object is an anomaly if it is distant from most points. This approach is more general and more easily applied than statistical approaches, since it is easier to determine a meaningful proximity measure for a data set than to determine its statistical distribution.

One of the simplest ways to measure whether an object is distant from most points is to use the distance to the k-nearest neighbor. This is captured by Definition 10.4. The lowest value of the outlier score is 0, while the highest value is the maximum possible value of the distance function—usually infinity.

Definition 10.4 (Distance to k-Nearest Neighbor). The outlier score of an object is given by the distance to its k-nearest neighbor.

Figure 10.4 shows a set of two-dimensional points. The shading of each point indicates its outlier score using a value of $k = 5$. Note that outlying point C has been correctly assigned a high outlier score.

The outlier score can be highly sensitive to the value of k. If k is too small, e.g., 1, then a small number of nearby outliers can cause a low outlier score. For example, Figure 10.5 shows a set of two-dimensional points in which another point is close to C. The shading reflects the outlier score using a value of $k = 1$. Note that both C and its neighbor have a low outlier score. If k is too large, then it is possible for all objects in a cluster that has fewer objects than k to become outliers. For example, Figure 10.6 shows a two-dimensional data set that has a natural cluster of size 5 in addition to a larger cluster of size 30. For $k = 5$, the outlier score of all points in the smaller cluster is very high. To make the scheme more robust to the choice of k, Definition 10.4 can be modified to use the average of the distances to the first k-nearest neighbors.

10.3.1   Strengths and Weaknesses

The distance-based outlier detection scheme described above, and other related schemes, are simple. However, proximity-based approaches typically take $O(m^2)$ time. For large data sets this can be too expensive, although specialized algorithms can be used to improve performance in the case of low-dimensional data. Also, the approach is sensitive to the choice of parameters. Furthermore, it cannot handle data sets with regions of widely differing densities because it uses global thresholds that cannot take into account such density variations.

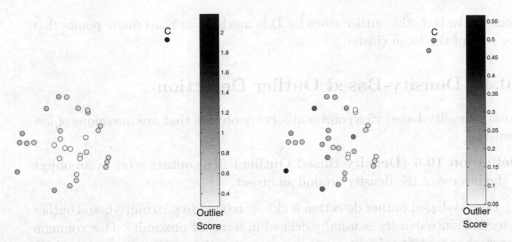

Figure 10.4. Outlier score based on the distance to fifth nearest neighbor.

Figure 10.5. Outlier score based on the distance to the first nearest neighbor. Nearby outliers have low outlier scores.

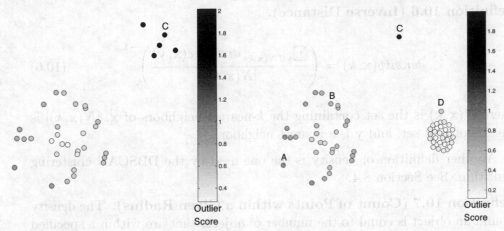

Figure 10.6. Outlier score based on distance to the fifth nearest neighbor. A small cluster becomes an outlier.

Figure 10.7. Outlier score based on the distance to the fifth nearest neighbor. Clusters of differing density.

To illustrate this, consider the set of two-dimensional points in Figure 10.7. This figure has one rather loose cluster of points, another dense cluster of points, and two points, C and D, that are quite far from these two clusters. Assigning the outlier score to points according to Definition 10.4 for $k = 5$, correctly identifies point C to be an outlier, but shows a low outlier score for point D. In fact, the outlier score for D is much lower than many points that are part of the loose cluster.

10.4   Density-Based Outlier Detection

From a density-based viewpoint, outliers are objects that are in regions of low density.

Definition 10.5 (Density-Based Outlier). The outlier score of an object is the inverse of the density around an object.

Density-based outlier detection is closely related to proximity-based outlier detection since density is usually defined in terms of proximity. One common approach is to define density as the reciprocal of the average distance to the k nearest neighbors. If this distance is small, the density is high, and vice versa. This is captured by Definition 10.6.

Definition 10.6 (Inverse Distance).

$$density(\mathbf{x}, k) = \left(\frac{\sum_{\mathbf{y} \in N(\mathbf{x},k)} distance(\mathbf{x}, \mathbf{y})}{|N(\mathbf{x}, k)|} \right)^{-1} \tag{10.6}$$

where $N(\mathbf{x}, k)$ is the set containing the k-nearest neighbors of $\mathbf{x}$, $|N(\mathbf{x}, k)|$ is the size of that set, and $\mathbf{y}$ is a nearest neighbor.

Another definition of density is the one used by the DBSCAN clustering algorithm. See Section 8.4.

Definition 10.7 (Count of Points within a Given Radius). The density around an object is equal to the number of objects that are within a specified distance d of the object.

The parameter d needs to be chosen carefully. If d is too small, then many normal points may have low density and thus a high outlier score. If d is chosen to be large, then many outliers may have densities (and outlier scores) that are similar to normal points.

Detecting outliers using any of the definitions of density has similar characteristics and limitations to those of the proximity-based outlier schemes discussed in Section 10.3. In particular, they cannot identify outliers correctly when the data contains regions of differing densities. (See Figure 10.7.) To correctly identify outliers in such data sets, we need a notion of density that is relative to the neighborhood of the object. For example, point D in Figure

10.7 has a higher absolute density, according to Definitions 10.6 and 10.7, than point A, but its density is lower relative to its nearest neighbors.

There are many ways to define the relative density of an object. One method that is used by the SNN density-based clustering algorithm is discussed in Section 9.4.8. Another method is to compute the relative density as the ratio of the density of a point $\mathbf{x}$ and the average density of its nearest neighbors $\mathbf{y}$ as follows:

$$average\ relative\ density(\mathbf{x}, k) = \frac{density(\mathbf{x}, k)}{\sum_{\mathbf{y} \in N(\mathbf{x},k)} density(y, k)/|N(\mathbf{x}, k)|}. \quad (10.7)$$

10.4.1   Detection of Outliers Using Relative Density

In this section, we describe a technique that is based on the notion of relative density. This technique, which is a simplified version of the Local Outlier Factor (LOF) technique (see bibliographic notes), is described in Algorithm 10.2. The details of the algorithm are examined in more detail below, but in summary, it works as follows. We calculate the outlier score for each object for a specified number of neighbors (k) by first computing the density of an object $density(\mathbf{x}, k)$ based on its nearest neighbors. The average density of the neighbors of a point is then calculated and used to compute the average relative density of the point as indicated in Equation 10.7. This quantity provides an indication of whether $\mathbf{x}$ is in a denser or sparser region of the neighborhood than its neighbors and is taken as the outlier score of $\mathbf{x}$.

Algorithm 10.2 Relative density outlier score algorithm.

1: {k is the number of nearest neighbors}
2: **for all** objects $\mathbf{x}$ **do**
3:     Determine $N(\mathbf{x}, k)$, the k-nearest neighbors of $\mathbf{x}$.
4:     Determine $density(\mathbf{x}, k)$, the density of $\mathbf{x}$ using its nearest neighbors, i.e., the objects in $N(\mathbf{x}, k)$.
5: **end for**
6: **for all** objects $\mathbf{x}$ **do**
7:     Set the *outlier score*$(\mathbf{x}, k) = average\ relative\ density(\mathbf{x}, k)$ from Equation 10.7.
8: **end for**

Example 10.2 (Relative Density Outlier Detection). We illustrate the performance of the relative density outlier detection method by using the example data set shown in Figure 10.7. Here, $k = 10$. The outlier scores for

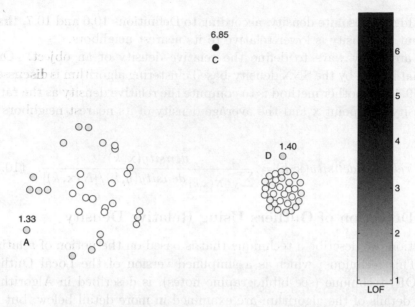

Figure 10.8. Relative density (LOF) outlier scores for two-dimensional points of Figure 10.7.

these points are shown in Figure 10.8. The shading of each point is determined by its score; i.e., points with a high score are darker. We have labeled points A, C, and D, which have the largest outlier scores, with these values. Respectively, these points are the most extreme outlier, the most extreme point with respect to the compact set of points, and the most extreme point in the loose set of points. ∎

10.4.2 Strengths and Weaknesses

Outlier detection based on relative density gives a quantitative measure of the degree to which an object is an outlier and can work well even if data has regions of differing density. Like distance-based approaches, these approaches naturally have $O(m^2)$ time complexity (where m is the number of objects), although this can be reduced to $O(m \log m)$ for low-dimensional data by using special data structures. Parameter selection can also be difficult, although the standard LOF algorithm addresses this by looking at a variety of values for k and then taking the maximum outlier scores. However, the upper and lower bounds of these values still need to be chosen.

10.5   Clustering-Based Techniques

Cluster analysis finds groups of strongly related objects, while anomaly detection finds objects that are not strongly related to other objects. It should not be surprising, then, that clustering can be used for outlier detection. In this section, we will discuss several such techniques.

One approach to using clustering for outlier detection is to discard small clusters that are far from other clusters. This approach can be used with any clustering technique, but requires thresholds for the minimum cluster size and the distance between a small cluster and other clusters. Often, the process is simplified by discarding all clusters smaller than a minimum size. This scheme is highly sensitive to the number of clusters chosen. Also, it is hard to attach an outlier score to objects using this scheme. Note that considering groups of objects as outliers extends the notion of outliers from individual objects to groups of objects, but does not change anything essential.

A more systematic approach is to first cluster all objects and then assess the degree to which an object belongs to any cluster. For prototype-based clustering, the distance of an object to its cluster center can be used to measure the degree to which the object belongs to a cluster. More generally, for clustering techniques that are based on an objective function, we can use the objective function to assess how well an object belongs to any cluster. In particular, if the elimination of an object results in a substantial improvement in the objective, then we would classify the object as an outlier. To illustrate, for K-means, eliminating an object that is far from the center of its associated cluster can substantially improve the sum of the squared error (SSE) of the cluster. In summary, clustering creates a model of the data and anomalies distort that model. This idea is captured in Definition 10.8.

Definition 10.8 (Clustering-Based Outlier). An object is a cluster-based outlier if the object does not strongly belong to any cluster.

When used with clustering schemes that have an objective function, this definition is a special case of the definition of a model-based anomaly. Although Definition 10.8 is more natural for prototype-based schemes or schemes that have an objective function, it can also encompass density- and connectivity-based clustering approaches to outlier detection. In particular, for density-based clustering, an object does not strongly belong to any cluster if its density is too low, while for connectivity-based clustering, an object does not strongly belong to any cluster if it is not strongly connected.

Below, we will discuss issues that need to be addressed by any technique for clustering-based outlier detection. Our discussion will focus on prototype-based clustering techniques, such as K-means.

10.5.1 Assessing the Extent to Which an Object Belongs to a Cluster

For prototype-based clusters, there are several ways to assess the extent to which an object belongs to a cluster. One method is to measure the distance of the object to the cluster prototype and take this as the outlier score of the object. However, if the clusters are of differing densities, then we can construct an outlier score that measures the relative distance of an object from the cluster prototype with respect to the distances of the other objects in the cluster. Another possibility, provided that the clusters can be accurately modeled in terms of Gaussian distributions, is to use the Mahalanobis distance.

For clustering techniques that have an objective function, we can assign an outlier score to an object that reflects the improvement in the objective function when that object is eliminated. However, assessing the degree to which a point is an outlier based on the objective function can be computationally intensive. For that reason, the distance-based approaches of the previous paragraph are often preferred.

Example 10.3 (Clustering-Based Example). This example is based on the set of points shown in Figure 10.7. Prototype-based clustering uses the K-means algorithm, and the outlier score of a point is computed in two ways: (1) by the point's distance from its closest centroid, and (2) by the point's relative distance from its closest centroid, where the relative distance is the ratio of the point's distance from the centroid to the median distance of all points in the cluster from the centroid. The latter approach is used to adjust for the large difference in density between the compact and loose clusters.

The resulting outlier scores are shown in Figures 10.9 and 10.10. As before, the outlier score, measured in this case by the distance or relative distance, is indicated by the shading. We use two clusters in each case. The approach based on raw distance has problems with the differing densities of the clusters, e.g., D is not considered an outlier. For the approach based on relative distances, the points that have previously been identified as outliers using LOF (A, C, and D) also show up as outliers here. ∎

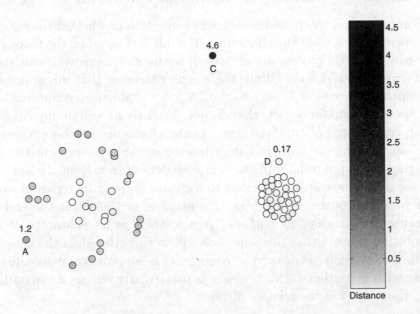

Figure 10.9. Distance of points from closest centroid.

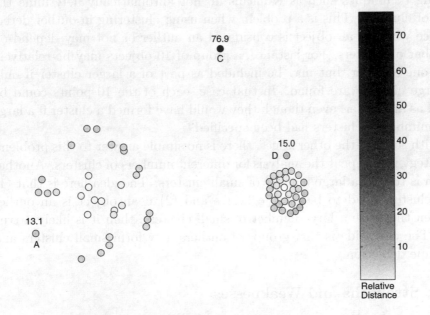

Figure 10.10. Relative distance of points from closest centroid.

10.5.2   Impact of Outliers on the Initial Clustering

If outliers are detected by clustering, there is a question of whether the results are valid since outliers affect the clustering. To address this issue, the following approach can be used: objects are clustered, outliers are removed, and then the objects are clustered again. While there is no guarantee that this approach will yield optimal results, it is easy to use. A more sophisticated approach is to have a special group for objects that do not currently fit well in any cluster. This group represents potential outliers. As the clustering process proceeds, clusters change. Objects that no longer belong strongly to any cluster are added to the set of potential outliers, while objects currently in the set are tested to see if they now strongly belong to a cluster and can be removed from the set of potential outliers. The objects remaining in the set at the end of the clustering are classified as outliers. Again, there is no guarantee of an optimal solution or even that this approach will work better than the simpler one described previously. For example, a cluster of noise points may look like a real cluster with no outliers. This problem is particularly serious if the outlier score is computed using the relative distance.

10.5.3   The Number of Clusters to Use

Clustering techniques such as K-means do not automatically determine the number of clusters. This is a problem when using clustering in outlier detection, since whether an object is considered an outlier or not may depend on the number of clusters. For instance, a group of 10 objects may be relatively close to one another, but may be included as part of a larger cluster if only a few large clusters are found. In that case, each of the 10 points could be regarded as an outlier, even though they would have formed a cluster if a large enough number of clusters had been specified.

As with some of the other issues, there is no simple answer to this problem. One strategy is to repeat the analysis for different numbers of clusters. Another approach is to find a large number of small clusters. The idea here is that (1) smaller clusters tend to be more cohesive and (2) if an object is an outlier even when there are a large number of small clusters, then it is likely a true outlier. The downside is that groups of outliers may form small clusters and thus escape detection.

10.5.4   Strengths and Weaknesses

Some clustering techniques, such as K-means, have linear or near-linear time and space complexity and thus, an outlier detection technique based on such algorithms can be highly efficient. Also, the definition of a cluster is often complementary to that of an outlier and thus, it is usually possible to find both clusters and outliers at the same time. On the negative side, the set of outliers produced and their scores can be heavily dependent upon the number of clusters used as well as the presence of outliers in the data. For example, clusters produced by prototype-based algorithms can be distorted by the presence of outliers. The quality of outliers produced by a clustering algorithm is heavily impacted by the quality of clusters produced by the algorithm. As discussed in Chapters 8 and 9, each clustering algorithm is suitable only for a certain type of data; hence the clustering algorithm needs to be chosen carefully.

10.6 Bibliographic Notes

Anomaly detection has a long history, particularly in statistics, where it is known as outlier detection. Relevant books on the topic are those of Barnett and Lewis [464], Hawkins [483], and Rousseeuw and Leroy [513]. The article by Beckman and Cook [466] provides a general overview of how statisticians look at the subject of outlier detection and provides a history of the subject dating back to comments by Bernoulli in 1777. Also see the related articles [467, 484]. Another general article on outlier detection is the one by Barnett [463]. Articles on finding outliers in multivariate data include those by Davies and Gather [474], Gnanadesikan and Kettenring [480], Rocke and Woodruff [511], Rousseeuw and van Zomerenand [515], and Scott [516]. Rosner [512] provides a discussion of finding multiple outliers at the same time.

An extensive survey of outlier detection methods is provided by Hodge and Austin [486]. Markou and Singh [506, 507] give a two-part review of techniques for novelty detection that covers statistical and neural network techniques, respectively. Grubbs' procedure for detecting outliers was originally described in [481]. The mixture model outlier approach discussed in Section 10.2.3 is from Eskin [476]. The notion of a distance-based outlier and the fact that this definition can include many statistical definitions of an outlier was described by Knorr et al. [496–498]. The LOF technique (Breunig et al. [468, 469]) grew out of DBSCAN. Ramaswamy et al. [510] propose a distance-based outlier detection procedure that gives each object an outlier score based on the distance of its k-nearest neighbor. Efficiency is achieved by partitioning the data using the first phase of BIRCH (Section 9.5.2). Chaudhary et al. [470] use k-d trees to improve the efficiency of outlier detection, while Bay and Schwabacher [465] use randomization and pruning to improve performance. Aggarwal and Yu [462] use projection to address outlier detection for high-dimensional data, while Shyu et al. [518] use an approach based on principal components. A theoretical discussion of outlier removal in high-dimensional space can be found in the paper by Dunagan and Vempala [475]. The use of information measures in anomaly detection is described by Lee and Xiang [504], while an approach based on the χ^2 measure is given by Ye and Chen [520].

Many different types of classification techniques can be used for anomaly detection. A discussion of approaches in the area of neural networks can be found in papers by Hawkins et al. [485], Ghosh and Schwartzbard [479], and Sykacek [519]. Recent work on rare class detection includes the work of Joshi et al. [490–494]. The rare class problem is also sometimes referred to as the imbalanced data set problem. Of relevance are an AAAI workshop (Japkowicz [488]), an ICML workshop (Chawla et al. [471]), and a special issue of SIGKDD Explorations (Chawla et al. [472]).

Clustering and anomaly detection have a long relationship. In Chapters 8 and 9, we considered techniques, such as BIRCH, CURE, DENCLUE, DB-SCAN, and SNN density-based clustering, which specifically include techniques for handling anomalies. Statistical approaches that discuss this relationship are described in papers by Scott [516] and Hardin and Rocke [482].

In this chapter, we have focused on basic anomaly detection schemes. We have not considered schemes that take into account the spatial or temporal nature of the data. Shekhar et al. [517] provide a detailed discussion of the problem of spatial outliers and present a unified approach to spatial outlier detection. The issue of outliers in time series was first considered in a statistically rigorous way by Fox [478]. Muirhead [508] provides a discussion of different types of outliers in time series. Abraham and Chuang [461] propose a Bayesian approach to outliers in time series, while Chen and Liu [473] consider different types of outliers in time series and propose a technique to detect them and obtain good estimates of time series parameters. Work on finding deviant or surprising patterns in time series databases has been performed by Jagadish et al. [487] and Keogh et al. [495]. Outlier detection based on geometric ideas, such as the depth of convex hulls, has been explored in papers by Johnson et al. [489], Liu et al. [505], and Rousseeuw et al. [514].

An important application area for anomaly detection is intrusion detection. Surveys of the applications of data mining to intrusion detection are given by Lee and Stolfo [502] and Lazarevic et al. [501]. In a different paper, Lazarevic et al. [500] provide a comparison of anomaly detection routines specific to network intrusion. A framework for using data mining techniques for intrusion detection is provided by Lee et al. [503]. Clustering-based approaches in the area of intrusion detection include work by Eskin et al. [477], Lane and Brodley [499], and Portnoy et al. [509].

Bibliography

[461] B. Abraham and A. Chuang. Outlier Detection and Time Series Modeling. *Technometrics*, 31(2):241–248, May 1989.

[462] C. C. Aggarwal and P. S. Yu. Outlier detection for high dimensional data. In *Proc. of 2001 ACM-SIGMOD Intl. Conf. on Management of Data*, pages 37–46. ACM Press, 2001.

[463] V. Barnett. The Study of Outliers: Purpose and Model. *Applied Statistics*, 27(3): 242–250, 1978.

[464] V. Barnett and T. Lewis. *Outliers in Statistical Data*. Wiley Series in Probability and Statistics. John Wiley & Sons, 3rd edition, April 1994.

[465] S. D. Bay and M. Schwabacher. Mining distance-based outliers in near linear time with randomization and a simple pruning rule. In *Proc. of the 9th Intl. Conf. on Knowledge Discovery and Data Mining*, pages 29–38. ACM Press, 2003.

[466] R. J. Beckman and R. D. Cook. 'Outlier.........s'. *Technometrics*, 25(2):119–149, May 1983.

[467] R. J. Beckman and R. D. Cook. ['Outlier.........s']: Response. *Technometrics*, 25(2): 161–163, May 1983.

[468] M. M. Breunig, H.-P. Kriegel, R. T. Ng, and J. Sander. OPTICS-OF: Identifying Local Outliers. In *Proceedings of the Third European Conference on Principles of Data Mining and Knowledge Discovery*, pages 262–270. Springer-Verlag, 1999.

[469] M. M. Breunig, H.-P. Kriegel, R. T. Ng, and J. Sander. LOF: Identifying density-based local outliers. In *Proc. of 2000 ACM-SIGMOD Intl. Conf. on Management of Data*, pages 93–104. ACM Press, 2000.

[470] A. Chaudhary, A. S. Szalay, and A. W. Moore. Very fast outlier detection in large multidimensional data sets. In *Proc. ACM SIGMOD Workshop on Research Issues in Data Mining and Knowledge Discovery (DMKD)*, 2002.

[471] N. V. Chawla, N. Japkowicz, and A. Kolcz, editors. *Workshop on Learning from Imbalanced Data Sets II, 20th Intl. Conf. on Machine Learning*, 2000. AAAI Press.

[472] N. V. Chawla, N. Japkowicz, and A. Kolcz, editors. *SIGKDD Explorations Newsletter, Special issue on learning from imbalanced datasets*, volume 6(1), June 2004. ACM Press.

[473] C. Chen and L.-M. Liu. Joint Estimation of Model Parameters and Outlier Effects in Time Series. *Journal of the American Statistical Association*, 88(421):284–297, March 1993.

[474] L. Davies and U. Gather. The Identification of Multiple Outliers. *Journal of the American Statistical Association*, 88(423):782–792, September 1993.

[475] J. Dunagan and S. Vempala. Optimal outlier removal in high-dimensional spaces. *Journal of Computer and System Sciences, Special Issue on STOC 2001*, 68(2):335–373, March 2004.

[476] E. Eskin. Anomaly Detection over Noisy Data using Learned Probability Distributions. In *Proc. of the 17th Intl. Conf. on Machine Learning*, pages 255–262, 2000.

[477] E. Eskin, A. Arnold, M. Prerau, L. Portnoy, and S. J. Stolfo. A geometric framework for unsupervised anomaly detection. In *Applications of Data Mining in Computer Security*, pages 78–100. Kluwer Academics, 2002.

[478] A. J. Fox. Outliers in Time Series. *Journal of the Royal Statistical Society. Series B (Methodological)*, 34(3):350–363, 1972.

[479] A. Ghosh and A. Schwartzbard. A Study in Using Neural Networks for Anomaly and Misuse Detection. In *8th USENIX Security Symposium*, August 1999.

[480] R. Gnanadesikan and J. R. Kettenring. Robust Estimates, Residuals, and Outlier Detection with Multiresponse Data. *Biometrics*, 28(1):81–124, March 1972.

[481] F. Grubbs. Procedures for Testing Outlying Observations. *Annal of Mathematical Statistics*, 21(1):27–58, March 1950.

[482] J. Hardin and D. M. Rocke. Outlier Detection in the Multiple Cluster Setting using the Minimum Covariance Determinant Estimator. *Computational Statistics and Data Analysis*, 44:625–638, 2004.

[483] D. M. Hawkins. *Identification of Outliers*. Monographs on Applied Probability and Statistics. Chapman & Hall, May 1980.

[484] D. M. Hawkins. '[Outlier..........s]': Discussion. *Technometrics*, 25(2):155–156, May 1983.

[485] S. Hawkins, H. He, G. J. Williams, and R. A. Baxter. Outlier Detection Using Replicator Neural Networks. In *DaWaK 2000: Proc. of the 4th Intnl. Conf. on Data Warehousing and Knowledge Discovery*, pages 170–180. Springer-Verlag, 2002.

[486] V. J. Hodge and J. Austin. A Survey of Outlier Detection Methodologies. *Artificial Intelligence Review*, 22:85–126, 2004.

[487] H. V. Jagadish, N. Koudas, and S. Muthukrishnan. Mining Deviants in a Time Series Database. In *Proc. of the 25th VLDB Conf.*, pages 102–113, 1999.

[488] N. Japkowicz, editor. *Workshop on Learning from Imbalanced Data Sets I, Seventeenth National Conference on Artificial Intelligence, Published as Technical Report WS-00-05*, 2000. AAAI Press.

[489] T. Johnson, I. Kwok, and R. T. Ng. Fast Computation of 2-Dimensional Depth Contours. In *KDD98*, pages 224–228, 1998.

[490] M. V. Joshi. On Evaluating Performance of Classifiers for Rare Classes. In *Proc. of the 2002 IEEE Intl. Conf. on Data Mining*, pages 641–644, 2002.

[491] M. V. Joshi, R. C. Agarwal, and V. Kumar. Mining needle in a haystack: Classifying rare classes via two-phase rule induction. In *Proc. of 2001 ACM-SIGMOD Intl. Conf. on Management of Data*, pages 91–102. ACM Press, 2001.

[492] M. V. Joshi, R. C. Agarwal, and V. Kumar. Predicting rare classes: can boosting make any weak learner strong? In *Proc. of 2002 ACM-SIGMOD Intl. Conf. on Management of Data*, pages 297–306. ACM Press, 2002.

[493] M. V. Joshi, R. C. Agarwal, and V. Kumar. Predicting Rare Classes: Comparing Two-Phase Rule Induction to Cost-Sensitive Boosting. In *Proc. of the 6th European Conf. of Principles and Practice of Knowledge Discovery in Databases*, pages 237–249. Springer-Verlag, 2002.

[494] M. V. Joshi, V. Kumar, and R. C. Agarwal. Evaluating Boosting Algorithms to Classify Rare Classes: Comparison and Improvements. In *Proc. of the 2001 IEEE Intl. Conf. on Data Mining*, pages 257–264, 2001.

[495] E. Keogh, S. Lonardi, and B. Chiu. Finding Surprising Patterns in a Time Series Database in Linear Time and Space. In *Proc. of the 8th Intl. Conf. on Knowledge Discovery and Data Mining*, Edmonton, Alberta, Canada, July 2002.

[496] E. M. Knorr and R. T. Ng. A Unified Notion of Outliers: Properties and Computation. In *Proc. of the 3rd Intl. Conf. on Knowledge Discovery and Data Mining*, pages 219–222, 1997.

[497] E. M. Knorr and R. T. Ng. Algorithms for Mining Distance-Based Outliers in Large Datasets. In *Proc. of the 24th VLDB Conf.*, pages 392–403, 24–27 1998.

[498] E. M. Knorr, R. T. Ng, and V. Tucakov. Distance-based outliers: algorithms and applications. *The VLDB Journal*, 8(3-4):237–253, 2000.

[499] T. Lane and C. E. Brodley. An Application of Machine Learning to Anomaly Detection. In *Proc. 20th NIST-NCSC National Information Systems Security Conf.*, pages 366–380, 1997.

[500] A. Lazarevic, L. Ertöz, V. Kumar, A. Ozgur, and J. Srivastava. A Comparative Study of Anomaly Detection Schemes in Network Intrusion Detection. In *Proc. of the 2003 SIAM Intl. Conf. on Data Mining*, 2003.

[501] A. Lazarevic, V. Kumar, and J. Srivastava. Intrusion Detection: A Survey. In *Managing Cyber Threats: Issues, Approaches and Challenges*, pages 19–80. Kluwer Academic Publisher, 2005.

[502] W. Lee and S. J. Stolfo. Data Mining Approaches for Intrusion Detection. In *7th USENIX Security Symposium*, pages 26–29, January 1998.

[503] W. Lee, S. J. Stolfo, and K. W. Mok. A Data Mining Framework for Building Intrusion Detection Models. In *IEEE Symposium on Security and Privacy*, pages 120–132, 1999.

[504] W. Lee and D. Xiang. Information-theoretic measures for anomaly detection. In *Proc. of the 2001 IEEE Symposium on Security and Privacy*, pages 130–143, May 2001.

[505] R. Y. Liu, J. M. Parelius, and K. Singh. Multivariate analysis by data depth: descriptive statistics, graphics and inference. *Annals of Statistics*, 27(3):783–858, 1999.

[506] M. Markou and S. Singh. Novelty detection: A review–part 1: Statistical approaches. *Signal Processing*, 83(12):2481–2497, 2003.

[507] M. Markou and S. Singh. Novelty detection: A review–part 2: Neural network based approaches. *Signal Processing*, 83(12):2499–2521, 2003.

[508] C. R. Muirhead. Distinguishing Outlier Types in Time Series. *Journal of the Royal Statistical Society. Series B (Methodological)*, 48(1):39–47, 1986.

[509] L. Portnoy, E. Eskin, and S. J. Stolfo. Intrusion detection with unlabeled data using clustering. In *In ACM Workshop on Data Mining Applied to Security*, 2001.

[510] S. Ramaswamy, R. Rastogi, and K. Shim. Efficient algorithms for mining outliers from large data sets. In *Proc. of 2000 ACM-SIGMOD Intl. Conf. on Management of Data*, pages 427–438. ACM Press, 2000.

[511] D. M. Rocke and D. L. Woodruff. Identification of Outliers in Multivariate Data. *Journal of the American Statistical Association*, 91(435):1047–1061, September 1996.

[512] B. Rosner. On the Detection of Many Outliers. *Technometrics*, 17(3):221–227, 1975.

[513] P. J. Rousseeuw and A. M. Leroy. *Robust Regression and Outlier Detection*. Wiley Series in Probability and Statistics. John Wiley & Sons, September 2003.

[514] P. J. Rousseeuw, I. Ruts, and J. W. Tukey. The Bagplot: A Bivariate Boxplot. *The American Statistician*, 53(4):382–387, November 1999.

[515] P. J. Rousseeuw and B. C. van Zomeren. Unmasking Multivariate Outliers and Leverage Points. *Journal of the American Statistical Association*, 85(411):633–639, September 1990.

[516] D. W. Scott. Partial Mixture Estimation and Outlier Detection in Data and Regression. In M. Hubert, G. Pison, A. Struyf, and S. V. Aelst, editors, *Theory and Applications of Recent Robust Methods*, Statistics for Industry and Technology. Birkhauser, 2003.

[517] S. Shekhar, C.-T. Lu, and P. Zhang. A Unified Approach to Detecting Spatial Outliers. *GeoInformatica*, 7(2):139–166, June 2003.

[518] M.-L. Shyu, S.-C. Chen, K. Sarinnapakorn, and L. Chang. A Novel Anomaly Detection Scheme Based on Principal Component Classifier. In *Proc. of the 2003 IEEE Intl. Conf. on Data Mining*, pages 353–365, 2003.

[519] P. Sykacek. Equivalent error bars for neural network classifiers trained by bayesian inference. In *Proc. of the European Symposium on Artificial Neural Networks*, pages 121–126, 1997.

[520] N. Ye and Q. Chen. Chi-square Statistical Profiling for Anomaly Detection. In *Proc. of the 2000 IEEE Workshop on Information Assurance and Security*, pages 187–193, June 2000.

10.7   Exercises

1. Compare and contrast the different techniques for anomaly detection that were presented in Section 10.1.2. In particular, try to identify circumstances in which the definitions of anomalies used in the different techniques might be equivalent or situations in which one might make sense, but another would not. Be sure to consider different types of data.

2. Consider the following definition of an anomaly: An anomaly is an object that is unusually influential in the creation of a data model.

   (a) Compare this definition to that of the standard model-based definition of an anomaly.

   (b) For what sizes of data sets (small, medium, or large) is this definition appropriate?

3. In one approach to anomaly detection, objects are represented as points in a multidimensional space, and the points are grouped into successive shells, where each shell represents a layer around a grouping of points, such as a convex hull. An object is an anomaly if it lies in one of the outer shells.

   (a) To which of the definitions of an anomaly in Section 10.1.2 is this definition most closely related?

   (b) Name two problems with this definition of an anomaly.

4. Association analysis can be used to find anomalies as follows. Find strong association patterns, which involve some minimum number of objects. Anomalies are those objects that do not belong to any such patterns. To make this more concrete, we note that the hyperclique association pattern discussed in Section 6.8 is particularly suitable for such an approach. Specifically, given a user-selected h-confidence level, maximal hyperclique patterns of objects are found. All objects that do not appear in a maximal hyperclique pattern of at least size three are classified as outliers.

   (a) Does this technique fall into any of the categories discussed in this chapter? If so, which one?

   (b) Name one potential strength and one potential weakness of this approach.

5. Discuss techniques for combining multiple anomaly detection techniques to improve the identification of anomalous objects. Consider both supervised and unsupervised cases.

6. Describe the potential time complexity of anomaly detection approaches based on the following approaches: model-based using clustering, proximity-based, and density. No knowledge of specific techniques is required. Rather, focus on the basic computational requirements of each approach, such as the time required to compute the density of each object.

7. The Grubbs' test, which is described by Algorithm 10.3, is a more statistically sophisticated procedure for detecting outliers than that of Definition 10.3. It is iterative and also takes into account the fact that the z-score does not have a normal distribution. This algorithm computes the z-score of each value based on the sample mean and standard deviation of the current set of values. The value with the largest magnitude z-score is discarded if its z-score is larger than g_c, the critical value of the test for an outlier at significance level α. This process is repeated until no objects are eliminated. Note that the sample mean, standard deviation, and g_c are updated at each iteration.

Algorithm 10.3 Grubbs' approach for outlier elimination.

1: Input the values and α

   $\{m$ is the number of values, α is a parameter, and t_c is a value chosen so that $\alpha = prob(x \geq t_c)$ for a t distribution with $m - 2$ degrees of freedom.$\}$

2: **repeat**

3:    Compute the sample mean ($\overline{x}$) and standard deviation (s_x).

4:    Compute a value g_c so that $prob(|z| \geq g_c) = \alpha$.

     (In terms of t_c and m, $g_c = \frac{m-1}{\sqrt{m}} \sqrt{\frac{t_c^2}{m-2+t_c^2}}$.)

5:    Compute the z-score of each value, i.e., $z = (x - \overline{x})/s_x$.

6:    Let $g = \max |z|$, i.e., find the z-score of largest magnitude and call it g.

7:    **if** $g > g_c$ **then**

8:      Eliminate the value corresponding to g.

9:      $m \leftarrow m - 1$

10:   **end if**

11: **until** No objects are eliminated.

   (a) What is the limit of the value $\frac{m-1}{\sqrt{m}} \sqrt{\frac{t_c^2}{m-2+t_c^2}}$ used for Grubbs' test as m approaches infinity? Use a significance level of 0.05.

(b) Describe, in words, the meaning of the previous result.

8. Many statistical tests for outliers were developed in an environment in which a few hundred observations was a large data set. We explore the limitations of such approaches.

   (a) For a set of 1,000,000 values, how likely are we to have outliers according to the test that says a value is an outlier if it is more than three standard deviations from the average? (Assume a normal distribution.)

   (b) Does the approach that states an outlier is an object of unusually low probability need to be adjusted when dealing with large data sets? If so, how?

9. The probability density of a point $\mathbf{x}$ with respect to a multivariate normal distribution having a mean μ and covariance matrix Σ is given by the equation

$$prob(\mathbf{x}) = \frac{1}{(\sqrt{2\pi})^m |\Sigma|^{1/2}} \, e^{-\frac{(\mathbf{x}-\mu)\Sigma^{-1}(\mathbf{x}-\mu)}{2}}. \qquad (10.8)$$

Using the sample mean $\overline{\mathbf{x}}$ and covariance matrix $\mathbf{S}$ as estimates of the mean μ and covariance matrix Σ, respectively, show that the $\log prob(\mathbf{x})$ is equal to the Mahalanobis distance between a data point $\mathbf{x}$ and the sample mean $\overline{\mathbf{x}}$ plus a constant that does not depend on $\mathbf{x}$.

10. Compare the following two measures of the extent to which an object belongs to a cluster: (1) distance of an object from the centroid of its closest cluster and (2) the silhouette coefficient described in Section 8.5.2.

11. Consider the (relative distance) K-means scheme for outlier detection described in Section 10.5 and the accompanying figure, Figure 10.10.

    (a) The points at the bottom of the compact cluster shown in Figure 10.10 have a somewhat higher outlier score than those points at the top of the compact cluster. Why?

    (b) Suppose that we choose the number of clusters to be much larger, e.g., 10. Would the proposed technique still be effective in finding the most extreme outlier at the top of the figure? Why or why not?

    (c) The use of relative distance adjusts for differences in density. Give an example of where such an approach might lead to the wrong conclusion.

12. If the probability that a normal object is classified as an anomaly is 0.01 and the probability that an anomalous object is classified as anomalous is 0.99, then

what is the false alarm rate and detection rate if 99% of the objects are normal? (Use the definitions given below.)

$$\text{detection rate} \ = \ \frac{\text{number of anomalies detected}}{\text{total number of anomalies}} \quad (10.9)$$

$$\text{false alarm rate} \ = \ \frac{\text{number of false anomalies}}{\text{number of objects classified as anomalies}} \quad (10.10)$$

13. When a comprehensive training set is available, a supervised anomaly detection technique can typically outperform an unsupervised anomaly technique when performance is evaluated using measures such as the detection and false alarm rate. However, in some cases, such as fraud detection, new types of anomalies are always developing. Performance can be evaluated according to the detection and false alarm rates, because it is usually possible to determine upon investigation whether an object (transaction) is anomalous. Discuss the relative merits of supervised and unsupervised anomaly detection under such conditions.

14. Consider a group of documents that has been selected from a much larger set of diverse documents so that the selected documents are as dissimilar from one another as possible. If we consider documents that are not highly related (connected, similar) to one another as being anomalous, then all of the documents that we have selected might be classified as anomalies. Is it possible for a data set to consist only of anomalous objects or is this an abuse of the terminology?

15. Consider a set of points, where most points are in regions of low density, but a few points are in regions of high density. If we define an anomaly as a point in a region of low density, then most points will be classified as anomalies. Is this an appropriate use of the density-based definition of an anomaly or should the definition be modified in some way?

16. Consider a set of points that are uniformly distributed on the interval [0,1]. Is the statistical notion of an outlier as an infrequently observed value meaningful for this data?

17. An analyst applies an anomaly detection algorithm to a data set and finds a set of anomalies. Being curious, the analyst then applies the anomaly detection algorithm to the set of anomalies.

    (a) Discuss the behavior of each of the anomaly detection techniques described in this chapter. (If possible, try this for real data sets and algorithms.)

    (b) What do you think the behavior of an anomaly detection algorithm should be when applied to a set of anomalous objects?

Dimensionality Reduction

This appendix considers various techniques for dimensionality reduction. The goal is to expose the reader to the issues involved and to describe some of the more common approaches. We begin with a discussion of Principal Components Analysis (PCA) and Singular Value Decomposition (SVD). These methods are described in some detail since they are among the most commonly used approaches and we can build on the discussion of linear algebra in Appendix A. However, there are many other approaches that are also employed for dimensionality reduction, and thus, we provide a quick overview of several other techniques. We conclude with a short review of important issues.

B.1 PCA and SVD

PCA and SVD are two closely related techniques. For PCA, the mean of the data is removed, while for SVD, it is not. These techniques have been widely used for decades in a number of fields. In the following discussion, we will assume that the reader is familiar with linear algebra at the level presented in Appendix A.

B.1.1 Principal Components Analysis (PCA)

The goal of PCA is to find a new set of dimensions (attributes) that better captures the variability of the data. More specifically, the first dimension is chosen to capture as much of the variability as possible. The second dimension is orthogonal to the first, and, subject to that constraint, captures as much of the remaining variability as possible, and so on.

Appendix B   Dimensionality Reduction

PCA has several appealing characteristics. First, it tends to identify the strongest patterns in the data. Hence, PCA can be used as a pattern-finding technique. Second, often most of the variability of the data can be captured by a small fraction of the total set of dimensions. As a result, dimensionality reduction using PCA can result in relatively low-dimensional data and it may be possible to apply techniques that don't work well with high-dimensional data. Third, since the noise in the data is (hopefully) weaker than the patterns, dimensionality reduction can eliminate much of the noise. This is beneficial both for data mining and other data analysis algorithms.

We briefly describe the mathematical basis of PCA and then present an example.

Mathematical Details

Statisticians summarize the variability of a collection of multivariate data; i.e., data that has multiple continuous attributes, by computing the covariance matrix $\mathbf{S}$ of the data.

Definition B.1. Given an m by n data matrix $\mathbf{D}$, whose m rows are data objects and whose n columns are attributes, the covariance matrix of $\mathbf{D}$ is the matrix $\mathbf{S}$, which has entries s_{ij} defined as

$$s_{ij} = covariance(\mathbf{d}_{*i}, \mathbf{d}_{*j}). \qquad (\text{B.1})$$

In words, s_{ij} is the covariance of the ith and j^{th} attributes (columns) of the data.

The covariance of two attributes is defined in Appendix C, and is a measure of how strongly the attributes vary together. If $i = j$, i.e., the attributes are the same, then the covariance is the variance of the attribute. If the data matrix $\mathbf{D}$ is preprocessed so that the mean of each attribute is 0, then $\mathbf{S} = \mathbf{D}^T\mathbf{D}$.

A goal of PCA is to find a transformation of the data that satisfies the following properties:

1. Each pair of new attributes has 0 covariance (for distinct attributes).

2. The attributes are ordered with respect to how much of the variance of the data each attribute captures.

3. The first attribute captures as much of the variance of the data as possible.

4. Subject to the orthogonality requirement, each successive attribute captures as much of the remaining variance as possible.

A transformation of the data that has these properties can be obtained by using eigenvalue analysis of the covariance matrix. Let $\lambda_1, \ldots, \lambda_n$ be the eigenvalues of $\mathbf{S}$. The eigenvalues are all non-negative and can be ordered such that $\lambda_1 \geq \lambda_2 \geq \ldots \lambda_{m-1} \geq \lambda_m$. (Covariance matrices are examples of what are called **positive semidefinite matrices**, which, among other properties, have non-negative eigenvalues.) Let $\mathbf{U} = [\mathbf{u}_1, \ldots, \mathbf{u}_n]$ be the matrix of eigenvectors of $\mathbf{S}$. These eigenvectors are ordered so that the ith eigenvector corresponds to the ith largest eigenvalue. Finally, assume that data matrix $\mathbf{D}$ has been preprocessed so that the mean of each attribute (column) is 0. We can make the following statements.

- The data matrix $\mathbf{D}' = \mathbf{DU}$ is the set of transformed data that satisfies the conditions posed above.

- Each new attribute is a linear combination of the original attributes. Specifically, the weights of the linear combination for the ith attribute are the components of the ith eigenvector. This follows from the fact that the jth column of $\mathbf{D}'$ is given by $\mathbf{Du}_j$ and the definition of matrix-vector multiplication given in Equation A.12.

- The variance of the ith new attribute is λ_i.

- The sum of the variance of the original attributes is equal to the sum of the variance of the new attributes.

- The new attributes are called **principal components**; i.e., the first new attribute is the first principal component, the second new attribute is the second principal component, and so on.

The eigenvector associated with the largest eigenvalue indicates the direction in which the data has the most variance. In other words, if all of the data vectors are projected onto the line defined by this vector, the resulting values would have the maximum variance with respect to all possible directions. The eigenvector associated with the second largest eigenvalue is the direction (orthogonal to that of the first eigenvector) in which the data has the largest remaining variance.

The eigenvectors of $\mathbf{S}$ define a new set of axes. Indeed, PCA can be viewed as a rotation of the original coordinate axes to a new set of axes that are aligned with the variability in the data. The total variability of the data is preserved, but the new attributes are now uncorrelated.

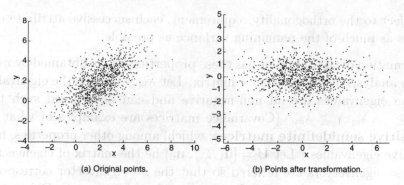

(a) Original points.   (b) Points after transformation.

Figure B.1. Using PCA to transform the data.

Example B.1 (Two-Dimensional Data). We illustrate the use of PCA for aligning the axes in the directions of the maximum variability of the data. Figure B.1 shows a set of 1000 two-dimensional data points, before and after a PCA transformation. The total variance for the original set of points is the sum of the variance of the x and y attributes, which is equal to $2.84 + 2.95 = 5.79$. After transformation, the variance is $4.81 + 0.98 = 5.79$. ■

Example B.2 (Iris Data). This example uses the Iris data set to demonstrate the use of PCA for dimensionality reduction. This data set contains 150 data objects (flowers); there are 50 flowers from each of three different Iris species: Setosa, Versicolour, and Virginica. Each flower is described by four attributes: sepal length, sepal width, petal length, and petal width. See Chapter 3 for more details.

Figure B.2(a) shows a plot of the fraction of the overall variance accounted for by each eigenvalue (principal component) of the covariance matrix. This type of plot is known as a **scree plot** and is useful for determining how many principal components need to be kept to capture most of the variability of the data. For the Iris data, the first principal component accounts for most of the variation (92.5%), the second for only 5.3%, and the last two components for just 2.2%. Thus, keeping only the first two principal components preserves most of the variability in the data set. Figure B.2(b) shows a scatter plot of the Iris data based on the first two principal components. Note that the Setosa flowers are well separated from the Versicolour and Virginica flowers. The latter two sets of flowers, while much closer to each other, are still relatively well separated.

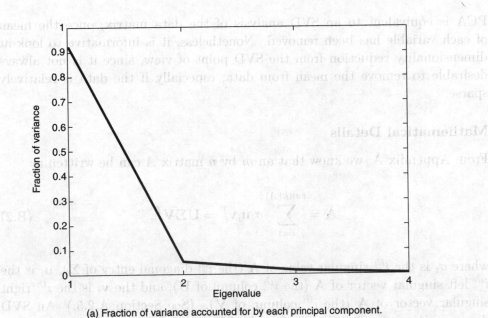

(a) Fraction of variance accounted for by each principal component.

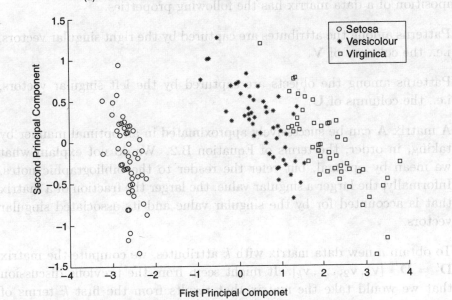

(b) Plot of first two principal components of Iris data.

Figure B.2. PCA applied to the Iris data set.

B.1.2   SVD

PCA is equivalent to an SVD analysis of the data matrix, once the mean of each variable has been removed. Nonetheless, it is informative to look at dimensionality reduction from the SVD point of view, since it is not always desirable to remove the mean from data, especially if the data is relatively sparse.

Mathematical Details

From Appendix A, we know that an m by n matrix A can be written as

$$\mathbf{A} = \sum_{i=1}^{rank(A)} \sigma_i \mathbf{u}_i \mathbf{v}_i^T = \mathbf{U\Sigma V}^T. \tag{B.2}$$

where σ_i is the ith singular value of $\mathbf{A}$ (the ith diagonal entry of $\mathbf{\Sigma}$), $\mathbf{u}_i$ is the ith left singular vector of $\mathbf{A}$ (the ith column of $\mathbf{U}$), and the $\mathbf{v}_i$ is the ith right singular vector of $\mathbf{A}$ (the ith column of $\mathbf{V}$). (See Section A.2.5.) An SVD decomposition of a data matrix has the following properties.

- Patterns among the attributes are captured by the right singular vectors, i.e., the columns of $\mathbf{V}$.

- Patterns among the objects are captured by the left singular vectors, i.e., the columns of $\mathbf{U}$.

- A matrix $\mathbf{A}$ can be successively approximated in an optimal manner by taking, in order, the terms of Equation B.2. We do not explain what we mean by optimal, but refer the reader to the bibliographic notes. Informally, the larger a singular value, the larger the fraction of a matrix that is accounted for by the singular value and its associated singular vectors.

- To obtain a new data matrix with k attributes, we compute the matrix $\mathbf{D'} = \mathbf{D} * [\mathbf{v}_1, \mathbf{v}_2, \ldots, \mathbf{v}_k]$. It might seem from the previous discussion that we would take the matrix that results from the first k terms of Equation A.12. However, while the resulting matrix is of rank k, it still has n columns (attributes).

Example B.3 (Document Data). SVD decomposition can be used to analyze document data. The data for this example consists of 3204 newspaper articles from the *Los Angeles Times*. These articles come from 6 different sections: Entertainment, Financial, Foreign, Metro, National, and Sports. The data matrix is a document-term matrix, where each row represents a document and each column is a term (word). The value of the ij^{th} entry is the number of times the jth term occurs in the ith document. The data was processed using standard techniques to remove common words, to adjust for the different frequencies with which terms appear, and to adjust for the different lengths of documents. (See Section 2.3.7 for more details.)

An SVD analysis of the data was performed to find the first 100 singular values and vectors. (For many data sets, it is too expensive to find a full SVD or PCA decomposition and often pointless since relatively few of the singular values or eigenvalues are required to capture the structure of the matrix.) The largest singular value is associated with common terms that are frequent, but not eliminated by the preprocessing. (It can happen that the strongest patterns represent noise or uninteresting patterns.)

However, the patterns associated with other singular values were more interesting. For example, the following are the top 10 terms (words) associated with the strongest components in the second right singular vector:

```
game, score, lead, team, play, rebound, season, coach, league,
goal
```

These are all terms associated with sports. Not surprisingly, the documents associated with the strongest components of the second left singular vector are predominantly from the Sports section.

The top 10 terms associated with the strongest components in the third right singular vector are the following:

```
earn, million, quarter, bank, rose, billion, stock, company,
corporation, revenue
```

These are all financial terms, and, not surprisingly, the documents associated with the strongest components in the third left singular vector are predominantly from the Financial section.

We reduced the dimensionality of the data using the second and third singular vectors, i.e., $\mathbf{D}' = \mathbf{D} * [\mathbf{v}_2, \mathbf{v}_3]$. In other words, all documents were expressed in terms of two attributes, one relating to Sports and one relating to Finance. A scatter plot of documents is given by Figure B.3. For clarity, non-Sports, non-Financial documents have been eliminated. The Sports documents are shown in a lighter shade of gray, while the Financial documents are a darker gray. The two different categories of documents are well separated for

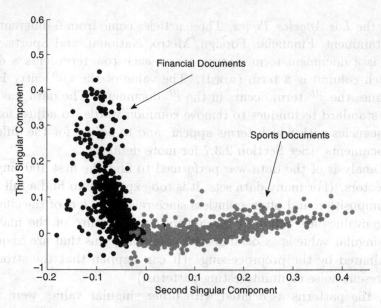

Figure B.3. Plot of Sports and Financial documents from the *LA Times* using the second and third singular values.

the most part. Indeed, the Sports documents do not vary much with respect to the Financial variable (component 3) and the Financial documents do not vary much with respect to the Sports variable (component 2).

B.2   Other Dimensionality Reduction Techniques

In this section, we review a few other dimensionality reduction techniques. These techniques will be discussed more briefly, with a focus on their general motivation and approach.

B.2.1   Factor Analysis

For PCA and SVD, the new attributes that are produced are linear combinations of the original variables. With factor analysis, the goal is to express the original variables as linear combinations of a small number of **hidden** or **latent attributes**. The motivation is based on the following observation. Often there are characteristics of data objects that are hard to measure directly, but that seem to be related to measurable characteristics. One common example is intelligence and performance on various types of IQ tests. Another common example is the connection between performance in various athletic events and an athlete's speed and strength. If a small number of attributes can be found that group and summarize the original attributes, then we will have achieved both a reduction in dimensionality and an increase in our understanding of the data.

The motivation for factor analysis is sometimes also explained in terms of the covariance or correlation matrix of the data. Suppose that a group of attributes are not very highly correlated to other attributes, but are strongly correlated to one another, perhaps because they measure the same underlying quantity. In this case, it would seem desirable to develop techniques that could find a single underlying attribute that summarizes each such group.

For example, consider a data set that records the performance of a group of athletes in the ten separate events that comprise the decathlon. We might find that athletes tend to show the same performance in all events that emphasize speed; i.e., slow athletes are consistently slow and fast athletes are consistently fast. Likewise, we might find that an athlete's behavior in an event that requires strength indicates how he or she will perform in another event that emphasizes strength. Hence, we might hypothesize that an athlete's performance in any given event is really determined by the nature of the event and two underlying factors: speed and strength. Factor analysis attempts to discover such relationships.

More formally, let $\mathbf{f}_1, \mathbf{f}_2, \ldots, \mathbf{f}_p$ be the **latent factors**, i.e., the underlying or hidden attributes. Note that these are the new attributes and have a value for each object. If the original data matrix is $\mathbf{D}$, an m by n matrix, then the new data matrix is $\mathbf{F} = [\mathbf{f}_1, \mathbf{f}_2, \ldots, \mathbf{f}_p]$, which is an m by p matrix. (Note that $\mathbf{f}_{*j} = \mathbf{f}_j$.) The ij^{th} entry of $\mathbf{F}$ is f_{ij}, the jth component of $\mathbf{f}_i$.

Assume that the mean of each attribute is 0. If $\mathbf{d}_{i*}$ is the ith row of the original data matrix $\mathbf{D}$, then $\mathbf{f}_{i*}$ is the corresponding row of the new data matrix, $\mathbf{F}$. The standard factor analysis model assumes the following relationship between the old and new data objects:

$$\mathbf{d}_{i*}^T = \mathbf{\Lambda}\mathbf{f}_{i*}^T + \boldsymbol{\epsilon} \tag{B.3}$$

or equivalently by

$$d_{ij} = \lambda_{j1}f_{i1} + \lambda_{j2}f_{i2}, \ldots, \lambda_{jp}f_{ip} + \epsilon_i. \tag{B.4}$$

$\mathbf{\Lambda}$, which has entries λ_{kl}, is an n by p matrix of **factor loadings** that indicate, for each of the original attributes, how the original value depends on the latent factors, i.e., the new attributes. To illustrate, in the decathlon example, there would be two latent factors: speed and strength. These correspond to columns of **F**. Each athlete would be represented by a row of **F** with entries recording the athlete's speed and strength. Each column of **D** would correspond to one of the ten events of the decathlon, while each row again corresponds to an athlete. The ij^{th} entry of **D** is the performance of the ith athlete in the jth event. **Λ** would be a 10 by 2 matrix. If the first column of **D** records the performance of the athletes on the 100-meter dash, then the performance of athlete i in the 100-meter dash is written as $d_{i1} = \lambda_{11}f_{i1} + \lambda_{12}f_{i2}$, where f_{i1} is a value indicating the speed of athlete i and f_{i2} is a value indicating the strength of athlete i. λ_{11} and λ_{12} indicate how an athlete's speed and strength, respectively, should be weighted to predict an athlete's performance in the 100 meter dash. We would expect that λ_{11} would be relatively large compared to λ_{12}. Note that these weights are the same across all objects (athletes).

Since all latent factors are involved in the determination of the value of any original attribute, they are known as **common factors**. ϵ is an error term that accounts for the portion of the attributes that is not accounted for by the common factors, and hence, the components of ϵ are known as the **specific factors**.

Example B.4 (Factor Analysis of Iris Data). This example is based on the Iris data set. For this data, only a single factor could be found. The flowers in the Iris data set are organized so that the first 50 flowers are of species Setosa, the second 50 are Versicolour, and the last 50 are Virginica. This single factor (attribute) is plotted against flower as shown in Figure B.4. This factor seems to capture the distinction among the three species.

B.2.2   Locally Linear Embedding (LLE)

LLE is a technique for dimensionality reduction based on the idea of analyzing overlapping local neighborhoods in order to determine the local structure. The LLE algorithm is given below.

Algorithm B.1 LLE algorithm.

1: Find the nearest neighbors of each data point.
2: Express each point $\mathbf{x}_i$ as a linear combination of the other points, i.e., $\mathbf{x}_i = \sum_j w_{ij}\mathbf{x}_j$, where $\sum_j w_{ij} = 1$ and $w_{ij} = 0$ if $\mathbf{x}_j$ is not a near neighbor of $\mathbf{x}_i$.
3: Find the coordinates of each point in lower-dimensional space of specified dimension p by using the weights found in step 2.

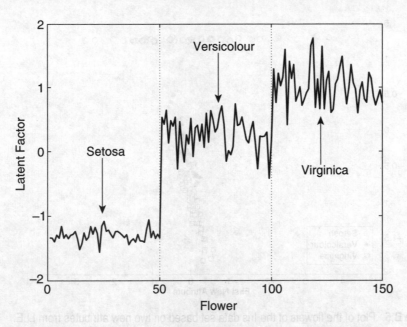

Figure B.4. Plot of the flower of the Iris data set versus the single latent factor.

In step 2, the weight matrix $\mathbf{W}$, whose entries are w_{ij}, is found by minimizing the squared approximation error as measured by the following equation. W can be found by solving a least squares problem. (Such problems were discussed in Appendix A.)

$$error(\mathbf{W}) = \sum_i \left(\mathbf{x}_i - \sum_j w_{ij}\mathbf{x}_j \right)^2 \tag{B.5}$$

Step 3 performs the actual dimensionality reduction. Given the weight matrix and a number of dimensions, p, specified by the user, the algorithm constructs a "neighborhood preserving embedding" of the data into the lower-dimensional space. If $\mathbf{y}_i$ is the vector in the lower-dimensional space that corresponds to $\mathbf{x}_i$ and $\mathbf{Y}$ is the new data matrix whose i^{th} row is $\mathbf{y}_i$, then this can be accomplished by finding a $\mathbf{Y}$ that minimizes the following equation.

$$error(\mathbf{Y}) = \sum_i \left(\mathbf{y}_i - \sum_j w_{ij}\mathbf{y}_j \right)^2 \tag{B.6}$$

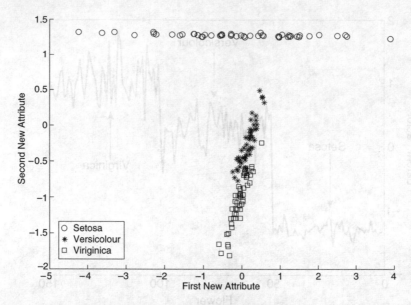

Figure B.5. Plot of the flowers of the Iris data set based on two new attributes from LLE.

Example B.5. the use of LLE for dimensionality reduction is illustrated using the Iris data set. Specifically, the data was projected to two dimensions. A neighborhood of 30 points was used. A scatter plot of the projected data is shown in Figure B.5. The data can also be projected to one dimension. In that case, it looks much like Figure B.4.

B.2.3 Multidimensional Scaling, FastMap, and ISOMAP

Multidimensional scaling is a technique that is often used for dimensionality reduction. A number of variations of this technique have been proposed, but the general strategy of these techniques is the same: Find a projection of the data to a lower-dimensional space that preserves pairwise distances as well as possible, as measured by an objective function. Because of this strategy, MDS starts from a dissimilarity matrix, and thus, can be used even for data that does not originally have a vector space representation, e.g., strings.

Standard MDS Techniques

We begin by describing the classical MDS approach for projecting data to a p-dimensional space. Assume that we are given a distance matrix $\mathbf{D}$, where the entry d_{ij} is the distance between the ith and j^{th} objects. Let d'_{ij} be the distance between the objects after they have been transformed. Classical MDS tries to assign each object to a p-dimensional point such that a quantity called **stress** is minimized, where stress is defined as

$$stress = \sqrt{\frac{\sum_{ij} \left(d'_{ij} - d_{ij}\right)^2}{\sum_{ij} d_{ij}^2}}. \tag{B.7}$$

The classical version of MDS is an example of **metric MDS** techniques, which assume that the dissimilarities are continuous variables (interval or ration). **Non-metric MDS** techniques assume that the data is categorical (at best ordinal). We will not discuss the details of these algorithms, except to say that the typical approach is to initially assign objects to p-dimensional points in some manner and then try to modify the points to reduce the stress.

When classical MDS or some of the other standard variants of MDS are applied to the Iris data set, they yield almost the same results as shown in Figure B.2. Indeed, classical MDS for Euclidean distance is equivalent to PCA.

FastMap

A recent development in the area of MDS is the algorithm FastMap. It has the same goal as other MDS techniques, but has two important differences.

- It is faster—linear complexity.

- It can operate incrementally.

The FastMap algorithm identifies a pair of objects and then computes the distance of each remaining object in this direction. This can be accomplished using only pairwise distances by employing certain facts of geometry, namely, the law of cosines. This distance is taken as the value of the first attribute. The objects are then projected onto an $(n-1)$-dimensional subspace. Again, this can be performed using only pairwise distances. The process is then repeated.

The FastMap algorithm is initially applied to an entire data set. However, if we keep track of the pairs of objects that are chosen at each step, then we can incrementally apply FastMap to a new object. The only information needed is the distance of the new object to the selected pairs.

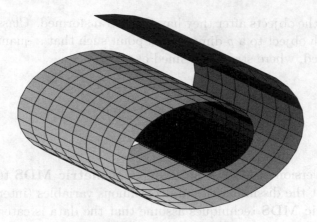

Figure B.6. Plot of Swiss roll data set.

ISOMAP

MDS and PCA are not good at dimensionality reduction when the points have a complicated, non-linear relationship to one another. (An exceptions is kernel PCA—see bibliographic notes.) ISOMAP, which is an extension of traditional MDS, was developed to handle such data sets. An example of the type of data set that it can handle is given in Figure B.6, which shows a plot of the "Swiss roll" surface. A data set with this structure constitutes a two-dimensional set of data in a three-dimensional space, but one that cannot be successfully handled by PCA or MDS. However, ISOMAP can successfully analyze this data set.

Algorithm B.2 outlines the basic ISOMAP algorithm. Nearest neighbors

---

Algorithm B.2 ISOMAP Algorithm.

1: Find the nearest neighbors of each data point and create a weighted graph by connecting a point to its nearest neighbors. The nodes are the data points and the weights of the links are the distances between points.
2: Redefine the distances between points to be the length of the shortest path between the two points in the neighborhood graph.
3: Apply classical MDS to the new distance matrix.

---

can be defined, either by taking the k-nearest points, where k is a parameter, or by taking all points within a specified radius of the point. The purpose of step 2 is to compute the geodesic distance; i.e., the distance between two points that stays on the surface, rather than the Euclidean distance. As an

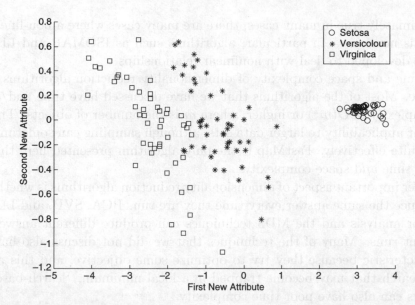

Figure B.7. Plot of the flower of the Iris data set based on two new attributes from ISOMAP.

example, the Euclidean distance between two cities on opposite sides of the Earth is the length of a line segment that passes through the Earth, while the geodesic distance between two cities is the length of the shortest arc on the surface of the Earth.

Example B.6. ISODATA was used to project the Iris data into two dimensions. See Figure B.7. The result is similar to previous techniques.

B.2.4   Common Issues

As with other data analysis techniques, we can distinguish between different dimensionality techniques in a number of areas. One key issue is the quality of the result: Can a technique produce a reasonably faithful representation of the data in a lower-dimensional space? Does this representation capture the characteristics of the data that are important to the intended application (e.g., clusters), while eliminating aspects that are irrelevant or even detrimental (e.g., noise)?

To a large extent, the answer depends on the kind of data and data distributions that can be analyzed by the dimensionality reduction approach. Techniques such as PCA, SVD, and factor analysis assume that there is a linear relationship between the old and new sets of attributes. Although this may be approximately true in many cases, there are many cases where a non-linear approach is necessary. In particular, algorithms such as ISOMAP and LLE have been developed to deal with nonlinear relationships.

The time and space complexity of dimensionality reduction algorithms is a key issue. Most of the algorithms that we have discussed have time and/or space complexity of $O(m^2)$ or higher, where m is the number of objects. This limits their applicability to larger data sets, although sampling can sometimes be used quite effectively. FastMap is the only algorithm presented here that has linear time and space complexity.

Another important aspect of dimensionality reduction algorithms is whether they produce the same answer every time they are run. PCA, SVD, and LLE do. Factor analysis and the MDS techniques can produce different answers on different runs. Many of the techniques that we did not discuss also have this characteristic because they try to optimize some objective, and this requires a search that may become trapped in a local minimum. Search-based approaches can also have poor time complexity.

Finally, a key issue is determining the number of dimensions for the dimensionality reduction. The techniques that we have considered can typically perform a dimensionality reduction to almost any number of dimensions. The goodness of the reduction is typically measured by some quantity that can be plotted, as in a scree plot. In some cases, this curve provides a clear indication of the intrinsic dimensionality. In many other situations, a choice needs to be made between a smaller number of dimensions and a larger approximation error, and a smaller approximation error and more dimensions.

B.3   Bibliographic Notes

Dimensionality reduction is a broad topic, and the relevant references are scattered across many fields. A comprehensive discussion of PCA can be found in the book by Jolliffe [531], while an introduction to SVD is given by Demmel [527] and other linear algebra texts. Kernel PCA is described by Schölkopf et al. [534]. Many books on multivariate statistical analysis, such as that by Anderson [524], also include discussions on PCA, as well as factor analysis. More details on MDS can be found in the book by Kruskal and Wish [532]. The FastMap algorithm was proposed by Faloutsos and Lin [529]. The papers for LLE (Roweis and Saul [535]) and ISOMAP (Tenenbaum et al. [533]) appeared in the same issue of *Science*. MATLAB code for the ISOMAP and LLE algorithms is available on the Web. Other articles that may be of interest include those by M. Belkin and P. Niyogi [525], Donoho and Grimes [528], and Ye et al. [536, 537]

There are many other techniques that are often used for dimensionality reduction or are strongly related to it. These areas include principal curves and surfaces, non-linear PCA (including neural network approaches), vector quantization, random projections, Independent Components Analysis (ICA), Self-Organizing Maps (SOM), projection pursuit, regression-based approaches, genetic algorithms, and optimization-based approaches such as simulated or deterministic annealing. Descriptions of these areas and additional references can be found in two surveys on dimensionality reduction by Fodor [530] and Carreira-Perpinan [526]. SOM is discussed in Section 9.2.3.

Bibliography

[524] T. W. Anderson. *An Introduction to Multivariate Statistical Analysis*. Wiley, 2nd edition, July 2003.

[525] M. Belkin and P. Niyogi. Laplacian eigenmaps for dimensionality reduction and data representation. Technical Report TR 2002-01, Department of Computer Science and Statistics, University of Chicago, January 2002.

[526] M. A. Carreira-Perpinan. A Review of Dimension Reduction Techniques. Technical Report CS–96–09, Dept. of Computer Science, University of Sheffield, January 1997.

[527] J. W. Demmel. *Applied Numerical Linear Algebra*. SIAM Press, September 1997.

[528] D. L. Donoho and C. Grimes. Hessian eigenmaps: Locally linear embedding techniques for high-dimensional data. *PNAS*, 100(10):5591–5596, 2003.

[529] C. Faloutsos and K.-I. Lin. FastMap: A Fast Algorithm for Indexing, Data-Mining and Visualization of Traditional and Multimedia Datasets. In *Proc. of the 1995 ACM SIGMOD Intl. Conf. on Management of Data*, pages 163–174, San Jose, California, June 1995.

[530] I. K. Fodor. A survey of dimension reduction techniques. Technical Report UCRL-ID-148494, LLNL, June 2002.

[531] I. T. Jolliffe. *Principal Component Analysis*. Springer-Verlag, 2nd edition, October 2002.

[532] J. B. Kruskal and M. Wish. *Multidimensional Scaling*. SAGE Publications, January 1978.

[533] S. T. Roweis and L. K. Saul. Nonlinear Dimensionality Reduction by Locally Linear Embedding. *Science*, 290(5500):2323–2326, 2000.

[534] B. Schölkopf, A. J. Smola, and K.-R. Müller. Nonlinear Component Analysis as a Kernel Eigenvalue Problem. *Neural Computation*, 10(5):1299–1319, 1998.

[535] J. B. Tenenbaum, V. d. Silva, and J. C. Langford. A Global Geometric Framework for Nonlinear Dimensionality Reduction. *Science*, 290(5500):2319–2323, 2000.

[536] J. Ye, R. Janardan, and Q. Li. GPCA: an efficient dimension reduction scheme for image compression and retrieval. In *Proc. of the 10th Intl. Conf. on Knowledge Discovery and Data Mining*, pages 354–363, Seattle, Washington, August 2004. ACM.

[537] J. Ye, Q. Li, H. Xiong, H. Park, R. Janardan, and V. Kumar. IDR/QR: an incremental dimension reduction algorithm via QR decomposition. In *Proc. of the 10th Intl. Conf. on Knowledge Discovery and Data Mining*, pages 364–373, Seattle, Washington, 2004. ACM.

Regression

Regression is a predictive modeling technique where the target variable to be estimated is continuous. Examples of applications of regression include predicting a stock market index using other economic indicators, forecasting the amount of precipitation in a region based on characteristics of the jet stream, projecting the total sales of a company based on the amount spent for advertising, and estimating the age of a fossil according to the amount of carbon-14 left in the organic material.

D.1 Preliminaries

Let D denote a data set that contains N observations,

$$D = \{(\mathbf{x}_i, y_i) \mid i = 1, 2, \ldots, N\}.$$

Each $\mathbf{x}_i$ corresponds to the set of attributes of the ith observation (also known as the **explanatory variables**) and y_i corresponds to the **target** (or response) **variable**. The explanatory attributes of a regression task can be either discrete or continuous.

Definition D.1 (Regression). Regression is the task of learning a **target function** f that maps each attribute set $\mathbf{x}$ into a continuous-valued output y.

The goal of regression is to find a target function that can fit the input data with minimum error. The **error function** for a regression task can be

From Appendix D of *Introduction to Data Mining*, First Edition. Pang-Ning Tan, Michael Steinbach, Vipin Kumar. Copyright © 2006 by Pearson Education, Inc. All rights reserved.

expressed in terms of the sum of absolute or squared error:

$$\text{Absolute Error} \;=\; \sum_i |y_i - f(\mathbf{x}_i)| \qquad (D.1)$$

$$\text{Squared Error} \;=\; \sum_i (y_i - f(\mathbf{x}_i))^2 \qquad (D.2)$$

D.2   Simple Linear Regression

Consider the physiological data shown in Figure D.1. The data corresponds to measurements of heat flux and skin temperature of a person during sleep. Suppose we are interested in predicting the skin temperature of a person based on the heat flux measurements generated by a heat sensor. The two-dimensional scatter plot shows that there is a strong linear relationship between the two variables.

Heat Flux	Skin Temperature	Heat Flux	Skin Temperature	Heat Flux	Skin Temperature
10.858	31.002	6.3221	31.581	4.3917	32.221
10.617	31.021	6.0325	31.618	4.2951	32.259
10.183	31.058	5.7429	31.674	4.2469	32.296
9.7003	31.095	5.5016	31.712	4.0056	32.334
9.652	31.133	5.2603	31.768	3.716	32.391
10.086	31.188	5.1638	31.825	3.523	32.448
9.459	31.226	5.0673	31.862	3.4265	32.505
8.3972	31.263	4.9708	31.919	3.3782	32.543
7.6251	31.319	4.8743	31.975	3.4265	32.6
7.1907	31.356	4.7777	32.013	3.3782	32.657
7.046	31.412	4.7295	32.07	3.3299	32.696
6.9494	31.468	4.633	32.126	3.3299	32.753
6.7081	31.524	4.4882	32.164	3.4265	32.791

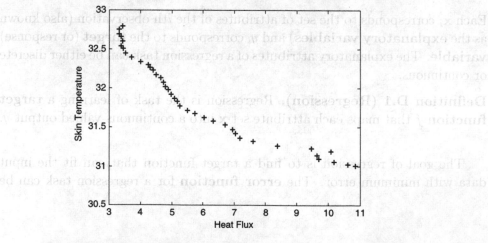

Figure D.1. Measurements of heat flux and skin temperature of a person.

D.2.1 Least Square Method

Suppose we wish to fit the following linear model to the observed data:

$$f(x) = \omega_1 x + \omega_0, \tag{D.3}$$

where ω_0 and ω_1 are parameters of the model and are called the **regression coefficients**. A standard approach for doing this is to apply the **method of least squares**, which attempts to find the parameters (ω_0, ω_1) that minimize the sum of the squared error

$$SSE = \sum_{i=1}^{N} [y_i - f(x_i)]^2 = \sum_{i=1}^{N} [y_i - \omega_1 x - \omega_0]^2, \tag{D.4}$$

which is also known as the **residual sum of squares**.

This optimization problem can be solved by taking the partial derivative of E with respect to ω_0 and ω_1, setting them to zero, and solving the corresponding system of linear equations.

$$\frac{\partial E}{\partial \omega_0} = -2 \sum_{i=1}^{N} [y_i - \omega_1 x_i - \omega_0] = 0$$

$$\frac{\partial E}{\partial \omega_1} = -2 \sum_{i=1}^{N} [y_i - \omega_1 x_i - \omega_0] x_i = 0 \tag{D.5}$$

These equations can be summarized by the following matrix equation, which is also known as the **normal equation**:

$$\begin{pmatrix} N & \sum_i x_i \\ \sum_i x_i & \sum_i x_i^2 \end{pmatrix} \begin{pmatrix} \omega_0 \\ \omega_1 \end{pmatrix} = \begin{pmatrix} \sum_i y_i \\ \sum_i x_i y_i \end{pmatrix}. \tag{D.6}$$

Since $\sum_i x_i = 229.9$, $\sum_i x_i^2 = 1569.2$, $\sum_i y_i = 1242.9$, and $\sum_i x_i y_i = 7279.7$, the normal equations can be solved to obtain the following estimates for the parameters.

$$\begin{pmatrix} \hat{\omega}_0 \\ \hat{\omega}_1 \end{pmatrix} = \begin{pmatrix} 39 & 229.9 \\ 229.9 & 1569.2 \end{pmatrix}^{-1} \begin{pmatrix} 1242.9 \\ 7279.7 \end{pmatrix}$$

$$= \begin{pmatrix} 0.1881 & -0.0276 \\ -0.0276 & 0.0047 \end{pmatrix} \begin{pmatrix} 1242.9 \\ 7279.7 \end{pmatrix}$$

$$= \begin{pmatrix} 33.1699 \\ -0.2208 \end{pmatrix}$$

Thus, the linear model that best fits the data in terms of minimizing the SSE is

$$f(x) = 33.17 - 0.22x.$$

Figure D.2 shows the line corresponding to this model.

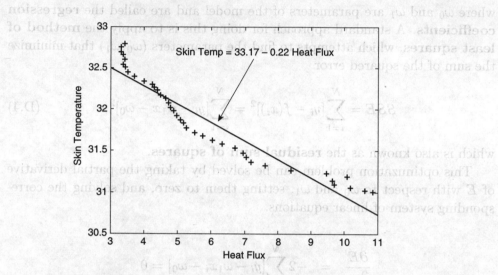

Figure D.2. A linear model that fits the data given in Figure D.1.

We can show that the general solution to the normal equations given in D.6 can be expressed as follow:

$$\hat{\omega}_0 = \overline{y} - \hat{\omega}_1 \overline{x}$$
$$\hat{\omega}_1 = \frac{\sigma_{xy}}{\sigma_{xx}} \tag{D.7}$$

where $\overline{x} = \sum_i x_i / N$, $\overline{y} = \sum_i y_i / N$, and

$$\sigma_{xy} = \sum_i (x_i - \overline{x})(y_i - \overline{y}) \tag{D.8}$$

$$\sigma_{xx} = \sum_i (x_i - \overline{x})^2 \tag{D.9}$$

$$\sigma_{yy} = \sum_i (y_i - \overline{y})^2 \tag{D.10}$$

Thus, linear model that results in the minimum squared error is given by

$$f(x) = \bar{y} + \frac{\sigma_{xy}}{\sigma_{xx}}[x - \bar{x}]. \tag{D.11}$$

In summary, the least squares method is a systematic approach to fit a linear model to the response variable y by minimizing the squared error between the true and estimated value of y. Although the model is relatively simple, it seems to provide a reasonably accurate approximation because a linear model is the first-order Taylor series approximation for any function with continuous derivatives.

D.2.2 Analyzing Regression Errors

Some data sets may contain errors in their measurements of $\mathbf{x}$ and y. In addition, there may exist confounding factors that affect the response variable y, but are not included in the model specification. Because of this, the response variable y in regression tasks can be non-deterministic, i.e., it may produce a different value even though the same attribute set $\mathbf{x}$ is provided.

We can model this type of situation using a probabilistic approach, where y is treated as a random variable:

$$\begin{aligned} y &= f(\mathbf{x}) + [y - f(\mathbf{x})] \\ &= f(\mathbf{x}) + \epsilon. \end{aligned} \tag{D.12}$$

Both measurement errors and errors in model specification have been absorbed into a random noise term, ϵ. The random noise present in data is typically assumed to be independent and follow a certain probability distribution.

For example, if the random noise comes from a normal distribution with zero mean and variance σ^2, then

$$P(\epsilon|\mathbf{x}, \Omega) = \frac{1}{\sqrt{2\pi\sigma^2}} \exp^{-\frac{[y - f(\mathbf{x}, \Omega)]^2}{2\sigma^2}} \tag{D.13}$$

$$\log[P(\epsilon|\mathbf{x}, \Omega)] = -\frac{1}{2}(y - f(\mathbf{x}, \Omega))^2 + \text{constant} \tag{D.14}$$

This analysis shows that minimizing the SSE, $[y - f(\mathbf{x}, \Omega)]^2$, implicitly assumes that the random noise follows a normal distribution. Furthermore, it can be shown that the constant model, $f(\mathbf{x}, \Omega) = c$, that best minimizes this type of error is the mean, i.e., $c = \bar{y}$.

Appendix D   Regression

Another typical probability model for noise uses the Laplacian distribution:

$$P(\epsilon|\mathbf{x}, \Omega) = c \exp^{-c|y - f(\mathbf{x}, \Omega)|} \tag{D.15}$$

$$\log[P(\epsilon|\mathbf{x}, \Omega)] = -c|y - f(\mathbf{x}, \Omega)| + \text{constant} \tag{D.16}$$

This suggests that minimizing the absolute error $|y - f(\mathbf{x}, \Omega)|$ implicitly assumes that the random noise follows a Laplacian distribution. The best constant model for this case corresponds to $f(\mathbf{x}, \Omega) = \tilde{y}$, the median value of y.

Besides the SSE given in Equation D.4, we can also define two other types of errors:

$$SST = \sum_i (y_i - \overline{y})^2 \tag{D.17}$$

$$SSM = \sum_i (f(x_i) - \overline{y})^2 \tag{D.18}$$

where SST is known as the total sum of squares and SSM is known as the regression sum of squares. SST represents the prediction error when the average value $\overline{y}$ is used as an estimate for the response variable. SSM, on the other hand, represents the amount of error in the regression model. The relationship among SST, SSE, and SSM is derived as follows:

$$
\begin{aligned}
SSE &= \sum_i [y_i - \overline{y} + \overline{y} - f(x_i)]^2 \\
&= \sum_i [y_i - \overline{y}]^2 + \sum_i [f(x_i) - \overline{y}]^2 + 2 \sum_i (y_i - \overline{y})(\overline{y} - f(x_i)) \\
&= \sum_i [y_i - \overline{y}]^2 + \sum_i [f(x_i) - \overline{y}]^2 - 2 \sum_i (y_i - \overline{y})\omega_1(x_i - \overline{x}) \\
&= \sum_i [y_i - \overline{y}]^2 + \sum_i [f(x_i) - \overline{y}]^2 - 2 \sum_i \omega_1^2(x_i - \overline{x})^2 \\
&= \sum_i [y_i - \overline{y}]^2 - \sum_i [f(x_i) - \overline{y}]^2 \\
&= SST - SSM \tag{D.19}
\end{aligned}
$$

where we have applied the following relationships:

$$\overline{y} - f(x_i) = -\omega_1(x_i - \overline{x})$$

$$\sum_i [y_i - \overline{y}][x_i - \overline{x}] = \sigma_{xy} = \omega_1 \sigma_{xx} = \omega_1 \sum_i [x_i - \overline{x}]^2.$$

Thus, we can write $SST = SSE + SSM$.

D.2.3 Analyzing Goodness of Fit

One way to measure the goodness of the fit is by computing the following measure:

$$R^2 = \frac{SSM}{SST} = \frac{\sum_i [f(x_i) - \bar{y}]^2}{\sum_i [y_i - \bar{y}]^2} \qquad (D.20)$$

The R^2 (or *coefficient of determination*) for a regression model may range between 0 and 1. Its value is close to 1 if most of the variability observed in the response variable can be explained by the regression model.

R^2 is also related to the correlation coefficient, r, which measures the strength of the linear relationship between the explanatory and response variables

$$r = \frac{\sigma_{xy}}{\sqrt{\sigma_{xx}\sigma_{xy}}}. \qquad (D.21)$$

From Equations D.9, D.10, and D.11, we can write

$$
\begin{aligned}
R^2 &= \frac{\sum_i [f(x_i) - \bar{y}]^2}{\sum_i [y_i - \bar{y}]^2} \\
&= \frac{\sum_i [\frac{\sigma_{xy}}{\sigma_{xx}}(x_i - \bar{x})]^2}{\sigma_{yy}} \\
&= \frac{\sigma_{xy}^2}{\sigma_{xx}^2 \sigma_{yy}} \sum_i (x_i - \bar{x})^2 \\
&= \frac{\sigma_{xy}^2}{\sigma_{xx}^2 \sigma_{yy}} \sigma_{xx} \\
&= \frac{\sigma_{xy}^2}{\sigma_{xx}\sigma_{yy}}. \qquad (D.22)
\end{aligned}
$$

The above analysis shows that the correlation coefficient is equivalent to the square root of the coefficient of determination (except for its sign, which depends on the direction of the relationship, whether positive or negative).

It is worth noting that R^2 increases as we add more explanatory variables into the model. One way to correct for the number of explanatory variables added to the model is by using the following adjusted R^2 measure:

$$\text{Adjusted } R^2 = 1 - \left(\frac{N-1}{N-d}\right)(1 - R^2), \qquad (D.23)$$

where N is the number of data points and $d+1$ is the number of parameters of the regression model.

D.3   Multivariate Linear Regression

The normal equations can be written in a more compact form using the following matrix notation. Let $\mathbf{X} = (\mathbf{1}\ \mathbf{x})$, where $\mathbf{1} = (1, 1, 1, \ldots)^T$ and $\mathbf{x} = (x_1, x_2, \ldots, x_N)^T$. Then, we can show that

$$\mathbf{X}^T\mathbf{X} = \begin{pmatrix} \mathbf{1}^T\mathbf{1} & \mathbf{1}^T\mathbf{x} \\ \mathbf{x}^T\mathbf{1} & \mathbf{x}^T\mathbf{x} \end{pmatrix} = \begin{pmatrix} N & \sum_i x_i \\ \sum_i x_i & \sum_i x_i^2 \end{pmatrix}, \tag{D.24}$$

which is equivalent to the left-hand side matrix of the normal equation. Similarly, if $\mathbf{y} = (y_1, y_2, \ldots, y_N)^T$, we can show that

$$\begin{pmatrix} \mathbf{1} & \mathbf{x} \end{pmatrix}^T \mathbf{y} = \begin{pmatrix} \mathbf{1}^T\mathbf{y} \\ \mathbf{x}^T\mathbf{y} \end{pmatrix} = \begin{pmatrix} \sum_i y_i \\ \sum_i x_i y_i \end{pmatrix}, \tag{D.25}$$

which is equivalent to the right-hand side matrix of the normal equation. Substituting Equations D.24 and D.25 into Equation D.6 we obtain the following equation:

$$\mathbf{X}^T\mathbf{X}\Omega = \mathbf{X}^T\mathbf{y}, \tag{D.26}$$

where $\Omega = (\omega_0, \omega_1)^T$. We can solve for the parameters in Ω can as follows:

$$\Omega = (\mathbf{X}^T\mathbf{X})^{-1}\mathbf{X}^T\mathbf{y}, \tag{D.27}$$

The above notation is useful because it allows us to extend the linear regression method to the multivariate case. More specifically, if the attribute set consists of d explanatory attributes $(x_1, x_2, \ldots, x_d)$, $\mathbf{X}$ becomes an $N \times d$ **design matrix**:

$$\mathbf{X} = \begin{pmatrix} 1 & x_{11} & x_{12} & \ldots & x_{1d} \\ 1 & x_{21} & x_{22} & \ldots & x_{2d} \\ \ldots & \ldots & \ldots & \ldots & \ldots \\ 1 & x_{N1} & x_{N2} & \ldots & x_{Nd} \end{pmatrix}, \tag{D.28}$$

while $\Omega = (\omega_0, \omega_1, \ldots, \omega_{d-1})^T$ is a d-dimensional vector. The parameters can be computed by solving the matrix equation given in Equation D.26.

D.4   Alternative Least-Square Regression Methods

The least squares method can also be used to find other types of regression models that minimize the SSE. More specifically, if the regression model is

$$y = f(\mathbf{x}, \Omega) + \epsilon \tag{D.29}$$

$$= \omega_0 + \sum_i \omega_i g_i(\mathbf{x}) + \epsilon, \tag{D.30}$$

and the random noise is normally distributed, then we can apply the same methodology as before to determine the parameter vector Ω. The g_i's can be any type of basis functions, including polynomial, kernel, and other nonlinear functions.

For example, suppose $\mathbf{x}$ is a two-dimensional feature vector and the regression model is a polynomial function of degree 2

$$f(x_1, x_2, \Omega) = \omega_0 + \omega_1 x_1 + \omega_2 x_2 + \omega_3 x_1 x_2 + \omega_4 x_1^2 + \omega_5 x_2^2. \tag{D.31}$$

If we create the following design matrix:

$$\mathbf{X} = \begin{pmatrix} 1 & x_{11} & x_{12} & x_{11}x_{12} & x_{11}^2 & x_{22}^2 \\ 1 & x_{21} & x_{22} & x_{21}x_{22} & x_{21}^2 & x_{22}^2 \\ \dots & \dots & \dots & \dots & \dots & \dots \\ 1 & x_{N1} & x_{N2} & x_{N1}x_{N2} & x_{N1}^2 & x_{N2}^2 \end{pmatrix}, \tag{D.32}$$

where x_{ij} is the jth attribute of the ith observation, then the regression problem becomes equivalent to solving Equation D.26. The least-square solution to the parameter vector Ω is given by Equation D.27. By choosing the appropriate design matrix, we can extend this method to any type of basis functions.

D.4   Alternative Least-Square Regression Methods

The least-square method can also be used to find other types of regression models that minimize the SSE. More specifically, if the regression model is

$$\hat{y} = f(x, M) + \tag{D.29}$$

$$= \left[\sum_i \omega_i f_i(x) \right] + \tag{D.8}$$

and the random noise is normally distributed, then we can apply the same methodology as before to determine the parameter vector θ. The $f_i(x)$ can be any type of basis functions, including polynomial, radial, and other nonlinear functions.

For example, suppose x is a two-dimensional feature vector and the regression model is a polynomial function of degree 2:

$$f(x_1, x_2, \Omega) = \omega_1 + \omega_2 x_1 + \omega_3 x_2 + \omega_4 x_1 x_2 + \omega_5 x_1^2 + \omega_6 x_2^2 \tag{D.31}$$

If we create the following design matrix:

$$X = \begin{pmatrix} 1 & x_{11} & x_{12} & x_{11}x_{12} & x_{11}^2 & x_{12}^2 \\ 1 & x_{21} & x_{22} & x_{21}x_{22} & x_{21}^2 & x_{22}^2 \\ & & & \vdots & & \\ 1 & x_{N1} & x_{N2} & x_{N1}x_{N2} & x_{N1}^2 & x_{N2}^2 \end{pmatrix} \tag{D.32}$$

where x_{ij} is the jth attribute of the ith observation, then the regression problem becomes equivalent to solving Equation D.20. The least-square solution for the parameter vector Ω is given by Equation D.27. By choosing the appropriate design matrix, we can extend this method to any type of basis functions.

E

Optimization

Optimization is a methodology for finding the maximum or minimum value of a function. It is an important topic in data mining because there are many data mining tasks that can be cast as optimization problems. For example, the K-means clustering algorithm described in Section 8.2.1 seeks to find a set of clusters that minimizes the sum of the squared error (SSE). Similarly, the method of least squares presented in Section D.2.1 is designed to learn the regression coefficients that minimize the SSE of the model. This section presents a brief overview of the various techniques used to solve optimization problems.

E.1 Unconstrained Optimization

Suppose $f(x)$ is a univariate function with continuous first-order and second-order derivatives. In an unconstrained optimization problem, the task is to locate the solution x^* that maximizes or minimizes $f(x)$ without imposing any constraints on x^*. The solution x^*, which is known as a **stationary point**, can be found by taking the first derivative of f and setting it to zero:

$$\frac{df}{dx}\bigg|_{x=x^*} = 0.$$

$f(x^*)$ can take a maximum or minimum value depending on the second-order derivative of the function:

- x^* is a maximum stationary point if $\frac{d^2f}{dx^2} < 0$ at $x = x^*$.

- x^* is a minimum stationary point if $\frac{d^2f}{dx^2} > 0$ at $x = x^*$.

- x^* is a point of inflection when $\frac{d^2 f}{dx^2} = 0$ at $x = x^*$.

Figure E.1 illustrates an example of a function that contains all three stationary points (maximum, minimum, and point of inflection).

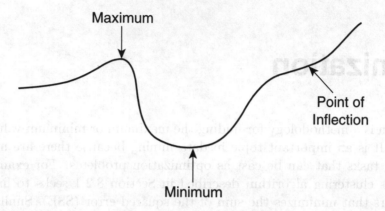

Figure E.1. Stationary points of a function.

This definition can be extended to a multivariate function, $f(x_1, x_2, \ldots, x_d)$, where the condition for finding a stationary point $\mathbf{x}^* = [x_1^*, x_2^*, \ldots, x_d^*]^T$ is

$$\left. \frac{\partial f}{\partial x_i} \right|_{x_i = x_i^*} = 0, \ \forall i = 1, 2, \ldots, d. \tag{E.1}$$

However, unlike univariate functions, it is more difficult to determine whether $\mathbf{x}^*$ corresponds to a maximum or minimum stationary point. The difficulty arises because we need to consider the partial derivatives $\frac{\partial^2 f}{dx_i dx_j}$ for all possible pairs of i and j. The complete set of second-order partial derivatives is given by the Hessian matrix

$$\mathbf{H}(\mathbf{x}) = \begin{bmatrix} \frac{\partial^2 f}{\partial x_1 \partial x_1} & \frac{\partial^2 f}{\partial x_1 \partial x_2} & \cdots & \frac{\partial^2 f}{\partial x_1 \partial x_d} \\ \frac{\partial^2 f}{\partial x_2 \partial x_1} & \frac{\partial^2 f}{\partial x_2 \partial x_2} & \cdots & \frac{\partial^2 f}{\partial x_2 \partial x_d} \\ \cdots & \cdots & & \cdots \\ \frac{\partial^2 f}{\partial x_d \partial x_1} & \frac{\partial^2 f}{\partial x_d \partial x_2} & \cdots & \frac{\partial^2 f}{\partial x_d \partial x_d} \end{bmatrix}. \tag{E.2}$$

- A Hessian matrix $\mathbf{H}$ is positive definite if and only if $\mathbf{x}^T \mathbf{H} \mathbf{x} > 0$ for any non-zero vector $\mathbf{x}$. If $\mathbf{H}(\mathbf{x}^*)$ is positive definite, then $\mathbf{x}^*$ is a minimum stationary point.

- A Hessian is negative definite if and only if $\mathbf{x}^T\mathbf{H}\mathbf{x} < 0$ for any non-zero vector $\mathbf{x}$. If $\mathbf{H}(\mathbf{x}^*)$ is negative definite, then $\mathbf{x}^*$ is a maximum stationary point.

- A Hessian is indefinite if $\mathbf{x}^T\mathbf{H}\mathbf{x}$ is positive for some value of $\mathbf{x}$ and negative for others. A stationary point with indefinite Hessian is a **saddle point**, which can have a minimum value in one direction, and a maximum value in another.

Example E.1. Suppose $f(x, y) = 3x^2 + 2y^3 - 2xy$. Figure E.2 shows a plot of this function. The conditions for finding the stationary points of this function are

$$\frac{\partial f}{\partial x} = 6x - 2y = 0$$
$$\frac{\partial f}{\partial y} = 6y^2 - 2x = 0 \qquad\qquad (E.3)$$

whose solutions are $x^* = y^* = 0$ or $x^* = 1/27$, $y^* = 1/9$.

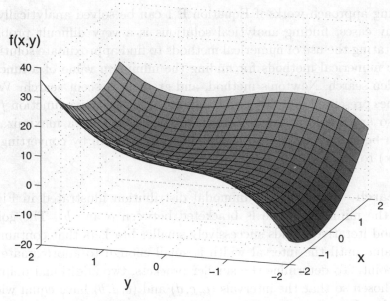

Figure E.2. Plot for the function $f(x, y) = 3x^2 + 2y^3 - 2xy$.

The Hessian of f is

$$\mathbf{H}(x, y) = \begin{bmatrix} 6 & -2 \\ -2 & 12y \end{bmatrix}.$$

At $x = y = 0$,

$$\mathbf{H}(0, 0) = \begin{bmatrix} 6 & -2 \\ -2 & 0 \end{bmatrix}.$$

Since $[x\ y]\ H(0,0)\ [x\ y]^T = 6x^2 - 4xy = 2x(3x - 2y)$, which can be either positive or negative, the Hessian is indefinite and $(0, 0)$ is a saddle point.

At $x = 1/27$, $y = 1/9$,

$$\mathbf{H}(1/27, 1/9) = \begin{bmatrix} 6 & -2 \\ -2 & 12/9 \end{bmatrix}.$$

Since $[x\ y]\ \mathbf{H}(1/27, 1/9)\ [x\ y]^T = 4x^2 - 2xy + 4y^2/3 = 4(x - y/4)^2 + 13y^2/4 > 0$ for non-zero x and y, the Hessian is positive definite. Therefore, $(1/27, 1/9)$ is a minimum stationary point. The minimum value of f is -0.0014.   ∎

E.1.1   Numerical Methods

The preceding approach works if Equation E.1 can be solved analytically for $\mathbf{x}^*$. In many cases, finding analytical solutions is a very difficult problem, thus necessitating the use of numerical methods to find approximate solutions. Some of the numerical methods for finding the minimum value of a function include golden search, Newton's method, and gradient descent search. While the techniques presented here are used to minimize the objective function $f(\mathbf{x})$, they are also applicable to maximization problems because a maximization problem can be easily turned into a minimization problem by converting the function $f(\mathbf{x})$ to $-f(\mathbf{x})$.

Golden Search   Consider the unimodal distribution illustrated in Figure E.3, where the minimum value is bracketed between a and b. The golden search method iteratively finds successively smaller brackets that contain the minimum value until the interval width is small enough to approximate the stationary point. To determine the smaller brackets, two additional points, c and d, are chosen so that the intervals (a, c, d) and (c, d, b) have equal width. Let $c - a = b - d = \alpha(b - a)$ and $d - c = \beta \times (b - a)$. Therefore,

$$1 = \frac{(b - d) + (d - c) + (c - a)}{b - a} = \alpha + \beta + \alpha,$$

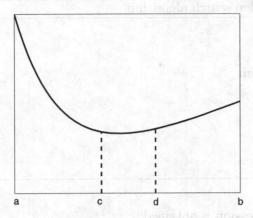

Figure E.3. Example of a unimodal function.

or equivalently,

$$\beta = 1 - 2\alpha. \tag{E.4}$$

The widths are also chosen to obey the following condition so that a recursive procedure can be applied:

$$\frac{d - c}{b - c} = \frac{c - a}{b - a},$$

or equivalently,

$$\frac{\beta}{1 - \alpha} = \alpha. \tag{E.5}$$

Together, Equations E.4 and E.5 can be solved to yield $\alpha = 0.382$ and $\beta = 0.236$. By comparing $f(c)$ with $f(d)$, it is possible to detect whether the minimum value occurs in the interval (a, c, d) or (c, d, b). The interval that contains the minimum value is then recursively partitioned until the interval width is small enough to approximate the minimum value, as shown in Algorithm E.1.

The golden search method makes no assumption about the function, other than it must be continuous and unimodal within the initial bracket $[a, b]$. It converges linearly to the solution for the minimum value.

Newton's Method   Newton's method is based on using a quadratic approximation to the function $f(x)$. By using a Taylor series expansion of f around

Appendix E Optimization

Algorithm E.1 Golden search algorithm.

1: $c = a + 0.382(b - a)$.
2: **while** $b - a > \epsilon$ **do**
3:    $d = b - 0.382(b - a)$.
4:    **if** $f(d) > f(c)$ **then**
5:      $b = d$.
6:    **else**
7:      $a = c, c = d$.
8:    **end if**
9: **end while**
10: **return** c.

---

x_0, the following expression is obtained:

$$f(x) \approx f(x_0) + (x - x_0)f'(x_0) + \frac{(x - x_0)^2}{2}f''(x_0). \qquad (E.6)$$

Taking the derivative of the function with respect to x and setting it to zero leads to the following equation:

$$
\begin{aligned}
f'(x) &= f'(x_0) + (x - x_0)f''(x_0) = 0 \\
x &= x_0 - \frac{f'(x_0)}{f''(x_0)}.
\end{aligned}
\qquad (E.7)
$$

Equation E.7 can be used to update x until it converges to the location of the minimum value. It can be shown that Newton's method has quadratic convergence, although it may fail to converge in some cases, especially when the initial point x_0 is located far away from the minimum point. A summary of this method is given in Algorithm E.2

Algorithm E.2 Newton's method.

1: Let x_0 be the initial point.
2: **while** $|f'(x_0)| > \epsilon$ **do**
3:    $x = x_0 - \frac{f'(x_0)}{f''(x_0)}$.
4:    $x_0 = x$.
5: **end while**
6: **return** x.

Newton's method can be extended to multivariate data by replacing the first order derivative $f'(x)$ with the gradient operator $\nabla f(\mathbf{x})$ and the second order derivative $f''(x)$ with the Hessian matrix $\mathbf{H}$:

$$\mathbf{x} = \mathbf{x} - \mathbf{H}^{-1}\nabla f(\mathbf{x}).$$

However, instead of computing the inverse of the Hessian matrix, it is easier to solve the following equation:

$$\mathbf{Hz} = -\nabla f(\mathbf{x})$$

to obtain the vector $\mathbf{z}$. The iterative formula for finding the stationary point is modified to $\mathbf{x} = \mathbf{x} + \mathbf{z}$.

Gradient Descent Method   Newton's method is one of several incremental methods to progressively locate the stationary point of a function using the following update formula:

$$\mathbf{x} = \mathbf{x} + \lambda g(\mathbf{x})), \tag{E.8}$$

The function $g(\mathbf{x})$ determines the direction in which the search should proceed and λ determines the step size.

The gradient descent method assumes that the function $f(\mathbf{x})$ is differentiable and computes the stationary point as follows:

$$\mathbf{x} = \mathbf{x} - \lambda \nabla f(\mathbf{x}), \tag{E.9}$$

In this method, the location of $\mathbf{x}$ is updated in the direction of the steepest descent, which means that $\mathbf{x}$ is moved towards the decreasing value of f. Section 5.4.2 described how the gradient descent method can be used to learn the weight parameters of an artificial neural network. A summary of this method is given in Algorithm E.3. Notice that the algorithm looks very similar to Algorithm E.2, except for the update formula.

Algorithm E.3 Gradient descent method.

1: Let $\mathbf{x}_0$ be the initial point.
2: **while** $\|\nabla f(\mathbf{x}_0)\| > \epsilon$ **do**
3:    $x = x_0 - \lambda \nabla f(\mathbf{x}).$
4:    $x_0 = x.$
5: **end while**
6: **return** x.

E.2   Constrained Optimization

This section examines how to solve an optimization problem when the variables are subjected to various types of constraints.

E.2.1   Equality Constraints

Consider the problem of finding the minimum value of $f(x_1, x_2, \ldots, x_d)$ subjected to equality constraints of the form

$$g_i(\mathbf{x}) = 0, \ i = 1, 2, \ldots, p.$$

A method known as Lagrange multipliers can be used to solve the constrained optimization problem. This method involves the following steps:

1. Define the Lagrangian, $L(\mathbf{x}, \lambda) = f(\mathbf{x}) + \sum_{i=1}^{p} \lambda_i g_i(\mathbf{x})$, where λ_i is a dummy variable called the **Lagrange multiplier**.

2. Set the first-order derivatives of the Lagrangian with respect to $\mathbf{x}$ and the Lagrange multipliers to zero,

$$\frac{\partial L}{\partial x_i} = 0, \ \forall i = 1, 2, \ldots, d$$

and

$$\frac{\partial L}{\partial \lambda_i} = 0, \ \forall i = 1, 2, \ldots, p.$$

3. Solve the $(d + p)$ equations in step 2 to obtain the stationary point $\mathbf{x}^*$ and the corresponding values for λ_i's.

The following example illustrates how the Lagrange multiplier method works.

Example E.2. Let $f(x, y) = x + 2y$. Suppose we want to minimize the function $f(x, y)$ subject to the constraint $x^2 + y^2 - 4 = 0$. The Lagrange multiplier method can be used to solve this constrained optimization problem in the following way.

First, we introduce the Lagrangian

$$L(x, y, \lambda) = x + 2y + \lambda(x^2 + y^2 - 4),$$

where λ is the Lagrange multiplier. To determine its minimum value, we need to differentiate the Lagrangian with respect to its parameters:

$$\frac{\partial L}{\partial x} = 1 + 2\lambda x = 0 \tag{E.10}$$

$$\frac{\partial L}{\partial y} = 2 + 2\lambda y = 0 \tag{E.11}$$

$$\frac{\partial L}{\partial \lambda} = x^2 + y^2 - 4 = 0$$

Solving these equations yields $\lambda = \pm\sqrt{5}/4$, $x = \mp 2/\sqrt{5}$, and $y = \mp 4/\sqrt{5}$. When $\lambda = \sqrt{5}/4$, $f(-2/\sqrt{5}, -4/\sqrt{5}) = -10/\sqrt{5}$. Similarly, when $\lambda = -\sqrt{5}/4$, $f(2/\sqrt{5}, 4/\sqrt{5}) = 10/\sqrt{5}$. Thus, the function $f(x, y)$ has its minimum value at $x = -2/\sqrt{5}$ and $y = -4/\sqrt{5}$. ∎

E.2.2 Inequality Constraints

Consider the problem of finding the minimum value of $f(x_1, x_2, \ldots, x_d)$ subjected to inequality constraints of the form

$$h_i(\mathbf{x}) \leq 0, \ i = 1, 2, \ldots, q.$$

The method for solving this problem is quite similar to the Lagrange method described above. However, the inequality constraints impose additional conditions to the optimization problem. Specifically, the optimization problem stated above leads to the following Lagrangian

$$L = f(\mathbf{x}) + \sum_{i=1}^{q} \lambda_i h_i(\mathbf{x}), \tag{E.12}$$

and constraints known as the Karush-Kuhn-Tucker (KKT) conditions:

$$\frac{\partial L}{\partial x_i} = 0, \ \forall i = 1, 2, \ldots, d \tag{E.13}$$

$$h_i(\mathbf{x}) \leq 0, \ \forall i = 1, 2, \ldots, q \tag{E.14}$$

$$\lambda_i \geq 0, \ \forall i = 1, 2, \ldots, q \tag{E.15}$$

$$\lambda_i h_i(\mathbf{x}) = 0, \ \forall i = 1, 2, \ldots, q. \tag{E.16}$$

Notice that the Lagrange multipliers are no longer unbounded in the presence of inequality constraints.

Example E.3. Suppose we want to minimize the function $f(x,y) = (x - 1)^2 + (y - 3)^2$ subject to the following constraints:

$$x + y \leq 2, \quad \text{and} \quad y \geq x.$$

The Lagrangian for this problem is $L = (x - 1)^2 + (y - 3)^2 + \lambda_1(x + y - 2) + \lambda_2(x - y)$ subjected to the following KKT constraints:

$$\frac{\partial L}{\partial x} = 2(x - 1) + \lambda_1 + \lambda_2 = 0 \tag{E.17}$$

$$\frac{\partial L}{\partial y} = 2(y - 3) + \lambda_1 - \lambda_2 = 0 \tag{E.18}$$

$$\lambda_1(x + y - 2) = 0 \tag{E.19}$$

$$\lambda_2(x - y) = 0 \tag{E.20}$$

$$\lambda_1 \geq 0, \ \lambda_2 \geq 0, \ x + y \leq 2, \ y \geq x \tag{E.21}$$

To solve the above equations, we need to examine all the possible cases of Equations E.19 and E.20.

Case 1: $\lambda_1 = 0$, $\lambda_2 = 0$. In this case, we obtain the following equations:

$$2(x - 1) = 0 \quad \text{and} \quad 2(y - 3) = 0,$$

whose solution is given by $x = 1$ and $y = 3$. Since $x + y = 4$, this is not a feasible solution because it violates the constraint $x + y \leq 2$.

Case 2: $\lambda_1 = 0$, $\lambda_2 \neq 0$. In this case, we obtain the following equations:

$$x - y = 0, \ 2(x - 1) + \lambda_2 = 0, \ 2(y - 3) - \lambda_2 = 0,$$

whose solution is given by $x = 2$, $y = 2$, and $\lambda_2 = -2$, which is not a feasible solution because it violates the conditions $\lambda_2 \geq 0$ and $x + y \leq 2$.

Case 3: $\lambda_1 \neq 0$, $\lambda_2 = 0$. In this case, we obtain the following equations:

$$x + y - 2 = 0, \ 2(x - 1) + \lambda_1 = 0, \ -2(x + 1) + \lambda_1 = 0,$$

whose solution is given by $x = 0$, $y = 2$, and $\lambda_1 = 2$, which is a feasible solution.

Case 4: $\lambda_1 \neq 0$, $\lambda_2 \neq 0$. In this case, we obtain the following equations:

$$x + y - 2 = 0,\ x - y = 0,\ 2(x-1) + \lambda_1 + \lambda_2 = 0,\ 2(y-3) + \lambda_1 - \lambda_2 = 0,$$

whose solution is $x = 1$, $y = 1$, $\lambda_1 = 2$, and $\lambda_2 = -2$, which is not a feasible solution.

Therefore, the solution for this problem is $x = 0$ and $y = 2$.   ∎

Solving the KKT conditions can be quite a laborious task especially if the number of constraining inequalities is large. In such cases, finding a closed-form solution is no longer possible and it is necessary to use numerical techniques such as linear and quadratic programming.

Copyright Permissions

Some figures and part of the text of Chapter 9 originally appeared in the article "Finding Clusters of Different Sizes, Shapes, and Densities in Noisy, High Dimensional Data," Levent Ertöz, Michael Steinbach, and Vipin Kumar, *Proceedings of the Third SIAM International Conference on Data Mining*, San Francisco, CA, May 1–3, 2003, SIAM. ©2003, SIAM. The material is reprinted here by permission of the publisher, SIAM.

Some figures and part of the text of Chapter 7 appeared in the article "Selecting the Right Objective Measure for Association Analysis," Pang-Ning Tan, Vipin Kumar, and Jaideep Srivastava, *Information Systems*, 29(4), 293-313, 2004, Elsevier. ©2004, Elsevier. The material is reprinted here by permission of the publisher, Elsevier.

Some of the figures and text of Chapters 9 appeared in the article "Discovery of Climate Indices Using Clustering," Michael Steinbach, Pang-Ning Tan, Vipin Kumar, Steven Klooster, and Christopher Potter, *KDD '03: Proceedings of the Ninth ACM SIGKDD International Conference on Knowledge Discovery and Data Mining*, 446–455, Washington, DC, August 2003, ACM. ©2003, ACM, INC. The material is reprinted here by permission of the publisher, ACM. DOI = http://doi.acm.org/10.1145/956750.956801

Some of the figures (1-7,13) and text of Chapter 8 originally appeared in the chapter "The Challenge of Clustering High-Dimensional Data," Levent Ertoz, Michael Steinbach, and Vipin Kumar in *New Directions in Statistical Physics, Econophysics, Bioinformatics, and Pattern Recognition*, 273–312, Editor, Luc Wille, Springer, ISBN 3-540-43182-9. ©2004, Springer-Verlag. The material is reprinted here by permission of the publisher, Springer-Verlag.

Some of the figures and text of Chapter 9 originally appeared in the article "Chameleon: Hierarchical Clustering Using Dynamic Modeling," by Geogre Karypis, Eui-Hong (Sam) Han, and Vipin Kumar, IEEE Computer, Volume 32(8), 68-75, August, 1999, IEEE. ©1999, IEEE. The material is reprinted here by permission of the publisher, IEEE.

Page references followed by "f" indicate illustrated figures or photographs; followed by "t" indicates a table.

729